D1222274

HISTORICAL GEOLOGY

A Late Cretaceous Scene in Wyoming. In the foreground the greatest of carnivorous dinosaurs, *Tyrannosaurus rex;* right, a duck-bill dinosaur, *Trachydon;* below, the armored dinosaur, *Ankylosaurus;* in the sky the great pterosaur, *Pteranodon.* The flowering plants include magnolia, dogwood, and laurel.

GEOLOGY

SECOND EDITION

CARL O. DUNBAR

Professor Emeritus of Paleontology and Stratigraphy

Yale University

NEW YORK • JOHN WILEY & SONS, INC.

Sixth Printing, March, 1963

Library of Congress Catalog Card Number: 60-5598
Printed in the United States of America

PREFACE

Geology is still a rapidly growing science, and in many respects it has been stimulated in recent years by the epoch-making discoveries in atomic physics. In the single decade since publication of the first edition of *Historical Geology,* for example, more has been learned than was previously known about the use of radioactive isotopes in the dating of ancient rocks. Dating of late Pleistocene objects by radiocarbon was just beginning when the first edition was in press. Since the age of Precambrian rocks in many parts of the world have been determined, it is now evident that attempts at their classification on more than a regional basis is not yet feasable, and such terms as Archeozoic and Proterozoic eras are no longer useful. In the meantime advances in both geochemistry and astronomy have produced revolutionary changes in conceptions of the origin and cosmic history of the Earth. Growing knowledge and more mature deliberation have helped also to clarify the geologic history of mankind.

In attempting to bring the subject up to date, I have maintained the general organization of the first edition, but several of the chapters have been completely rewritten and most of the text has been recast in order to include new information and to make a more effective presentation. Discussion of the cosmic history of the Earth has been shifted to the Prologue as Chapter 4, preceding the chapter on evolution, which is introduced by a brief epitome of current speculation on the origin of life on Earth.

Once again I am deeply indebted to my colleagues with whom problems have been discussed: to Karl Waagé for help at many points, especially in the Mesozoic chapters; to Joseph Gregory for information about recent discoveries in vertebrate paleontology; to Horace Winchell for Figures 10 and 11; and to Karl Turekian for help with Chapters 2 and 4 in which geochemistry plays an important role. Since neither of these gentlemen has seen the manuscript in its final form, however, I alone must bear the entire responsibility for any errors or shortcomings. Richard Foster Flint's recent volume, *Glacial and Pleistocene Geology,* has been an indispensable source of information for Chapter 18, and A. S. Romer's *Vertebrate Paleontology* has been an equally important sourcebook for data on the history of vertebrate animals. For problems of correlation the *Correlation Charts* prepared by the Committee on Stratigraphy of the National Research Council have been freely used.

It is a pleasure to express my thanks to correspondents who have supplied information and illustrations for the book. Dr. Lauge Koch advised me, in advance of publication, about the new discoveries of the Devonian tetrapods in East Greenland, and, at his suggestion, Dr. Erik Jarvik rushed to me a copy of his fine paper and with permission to reproduce the illustrations in Figure 162; Professor A. C. Blanc of the University of Rome sent me data about the Neanderthal remains of Grotto San Felice at Monte Circeo and a picture of the fine skull reproduced as Figure 388; Dr. V. A. Orlov of the Academy of Sciences in Moscow kindly sent me original copy for Figures 230 and 231; Sir Wilbert Le Gros Clark of London has permitted me to reproduce figures from his fine volume, *The Fossil Evidence for Human Evolution;* Dr. Thomas Hendricks supplied information concerning the age of the Stanley and Jackfork formations in Arkansas and Oklahoma; Dr. Russell K. Grater sent me the fine photograph reproduced as Figure 28; Dr. A. R. Palmer supplied photographs of the amazing insect reproduced in Figure 23; and Professor Sherwood D. Tuttle wrote me numerous thoughtful suggestions as to the contents of the book and, among other things, stimulated me to include the discussion of the origin of life.

Many of the illustrations are new, and they come from many sources, each of which is gratefully acknowledged in the figure legends. The new format of the book has made it possible to use larger illustrations than in the previous edition. Special thanks go to Time and Life, Inc., for permission to reproduce portions of the mural, *The Age of Mammals,* which was painted by Rudolph F. Zallinger, under my supervision, for Life's *The World We Live In,* and for Figure 390, which is from Life's *Epic of Man.*

My cordial thanks go also to Rudolph F. Zallinger for the beautiful etching of the Beresovka mammoth which introduces Chapter 3, and to Shirley Glaser who retouched a number of the photographs and made several of the drawings, including the figures of Plate 18. I am again indebted to Percy A. Morris who made all the photographs of fossils used from the collections of Yale's Peabody Museum. All the line drawings and diagrams are mine.

CARL O. DUNBAR

New Haven, Connecticut
October, 1959

PREFACE to the first edition

The history of the Earth is a *drama* in which the actors are all real, and the stage is the whole wide world. The student must sense the action and feel the essence of high adventure in the *march of time* as shifting scenes unfold and living actors cross the stage. This viewpoint has controlled both the selection and the treatment of subject matter in this volume. No effort has been spared in preparing the illustrations to make the story vivid, and no extraneous material has been allowed to break its continuity, from the fiery birth of the planet to the unfolding of our modern world. The *prologue* is intended to set the stage and to insure understanding of the principles used in interpreting the Earth's history.

The *Appendix* was prepared for students who enroll in geology without previous training in biology. For such beginners the history of life on the Earth can have little meaning until they have learned something of the structure and relationships of at least the major groups of animals and plants. For several years Yale students have been required to study the material embraced in the Appendix as an outside assignment during the first weeks of the course. Upon beginning the study of the Paleozoic Era, each is required to pass a sight test showing that he can recognize the major groups of animals and plants. This treatment has been eminently satisfactory.

The subject matter of historical geology is inherently diversified, involving as it does certain aspects of astronomy, anthropology, and biology, as well as geology. The danger exists, therefore, that the beginner will feel bewildered by the mass of unfamiliar facts drawn from such widely different fields and, in the welter of details, will lose sight of the grand conceptions. For this reason we have tried to group all details about great principles. Believing it to be more important for the student to learn *how* a geologist thinks about the Earth than *what* he thinks about any particular detail, we have taken pains to emphasize principles of interpretation rather than to catalogue facts about the history of the Earth, appealing thus to understanding rather than to memory.

Stratified rocks with their entombed fossils form a manuscript in stone and are the source of much of our knowledge of the past history of the world. It must be confessed, however, that stratigraphic descriptions are dull and detailed unless related to the physical history they record. The late Ordovician formations in New York State, for example, might appear to have no more than purely local interest; but, when they are viewed as parts of a piedmont and coastal plain that was growing westward into an inland sea while the eastern border of the continent was rising into mountains, they take on significance. Therefore, in treating of each period of geologic history, we have tried at the outset to help the student visualize the physical geography of the time and understand the major physical changes our continent was undergoing. The panels of paleogeographic maps were designed as an aid to this end.

To avoid the monotony inherent in the systematic account of period after period, emphasis is varied from chapter to chapter. In the discussion of the Cambrian, for example, considerable space is devoted to paleogeography and to the bases for subdividing the rocks into series and formations; in the Ordovician chapter, the Taconian orogeny is discussed at length because it illustrates the principles used in recognizing and dating all later orogenic disturbances. In this way, general principles of interpretation are developed one after another in the early chapters, leaving room in later ones for greater detail. This we believe to be fitting, since human interest in the rocks and the fossils increases as we approach the modern world.

The facts of historical geology are drawn from many sources, and most of them are common knowledge. We have made no attempt to give credit for such general information except to cite works on subjects that are controversial and others so new that they may not be generally known to teachers of geology. Such references bear exponents in the text, referring to numbered citations at the end of the chapter.

This volume is a successor to, and an outgrowth of, the *Textbook of Historical Geology* by Schuchert and Dunbar. It preserves the same point of view and the same general organization except for the introductory chapters which are arranged so as to bring the geologic time scale near the front. The text of the previous work has been largely recast to take account of advances in knowledge or to make a more effective presentation. Special care has been given to the illustrations, many of which are new. The "bleed cuts" will speak for themselves.

In the preparation of this volume friendly assistance has been received from many sources. It is not possible to mention them all specifically, but my thanks are none the less real. Among those to whom I am most particularly indebted are my colleagues, Chester R. Longwell, Richard F. Flint, Adolph Knopf, Joseph T. Gregory, and John Rodgers, whom I have consulted on various problems in their several fields; G. Edward Lewis of the United States Geological Survey, who helped with the chapter on Mammals; Cornelius Osgood, chairman of the Department of Anthropology at Yale, who read and criticized the chapter on Man as it stood in the previous volume by Schuchert and Dunbar; W. W. Rubey, with whom I discussed plans for the book during the memorable days we spent aboard the U.S.S. *Panamint* on the way to Bikini. Others too numerous to mention have written to offer suggestions or to reply to inquiries about specific details. It is a pleasure to acknowledge all this friendly help, but, since none of those mentioned has read the manuscript in its final form, the writer alone must assume the responsibility for any shortcomings or mistakes.

The illustrations are from many sources, all of which are gratefully acknowledged in the credit lines attached to individual figures. The frontispiece and Figs. 192, 226, 232, and 262 are portions of a great mural in Peabody Museum, painted by Rudolph Zallinger under the direction of the scientific staff. My cordial thanks go also to other members of the museum staff: particularly, to Shirley P. Glaser, who drew several of the new text figures; to Percy A. Morris, who made nearly all the photographs of fossils in the museum; to Sally H. Donahue, for her faithful help in the long and tedious preparation of the manuscript; and to Clara M. LeVene, for her indispensable aid in the final editing of the work and the preparation of the index.

To Charles Schuchert my obligation is unbounded. At his feet I learned much of what appears here as my own. His association was a constant stimulus, and his memory is an abiding inspiration.

CARL O. DUNBAR

New Haven, Connecticut
October, 1948

CONTENTS

PART I

PART I

PROLOGUE

Figure I. A manuscript in stone. Wall of the Grand Canyon from Sublime Point on the north rim. Here the layers of bedded rock form a manuscript in stone more than a mile thick, recording more than 100,000,000 years of Earth's history. (Joseph Muench)

Chapter 1. Records in Stone

And some rin up hill and down dale
knapping the chucky stanes to pieces
wi' hammers, like sae many
road makers run daft. They say
it is to see how the world was made.
SIR WALTER SCOTT

THE LAYERS OF STRATIFIED ROCK ARE TABLETS of stone bearing a record, in code, of the long history of our world and of the dynasties of living creatures that preceded the advent of man (Fig. 1). To break that code and discover its secrets is a challenge that stirs the imagination. Some of its characters are now well understood and many of the larger features of Earth's history are clear, but there is still much to learn as we discover how better to interpret the more subtle meanings of the record. We may begin by examining some of the general principles of interpretation.

EVIDENCE OF ANCIENT LANDS AND SEAS

Plotting the Ancient Seaways. If North America were depressed 600 feet, the Mississippi Valley would be a great inland sea, the present Coastal Plain a shallow sea floor, and Florida a submarine bank (Fig. 2). Over these submerged areas sediment would spread, burying sea shells, sharks' teeth, and occasional bones of porpoises and whales, while beach gravel and barnacles and oyster banks would accumulate along the shore zone.

If later the continent were uplifted, the sea would of course disappear, but these marine deposits would form a telltale record of the submergence, and by plotting them on a map we could restore more or less accurately the limits of the vanished seaways; Figure 2 depicts such an hypothetical submergence of North America. Figure 3 shows its actual counterpart in Malaysia, which was long a part of the Asiatic mainland but in recent geologic time has been submerged about 200 feet, flooding the lower parts to form the Sunda Shelf. Drowned valleys of the streams that once

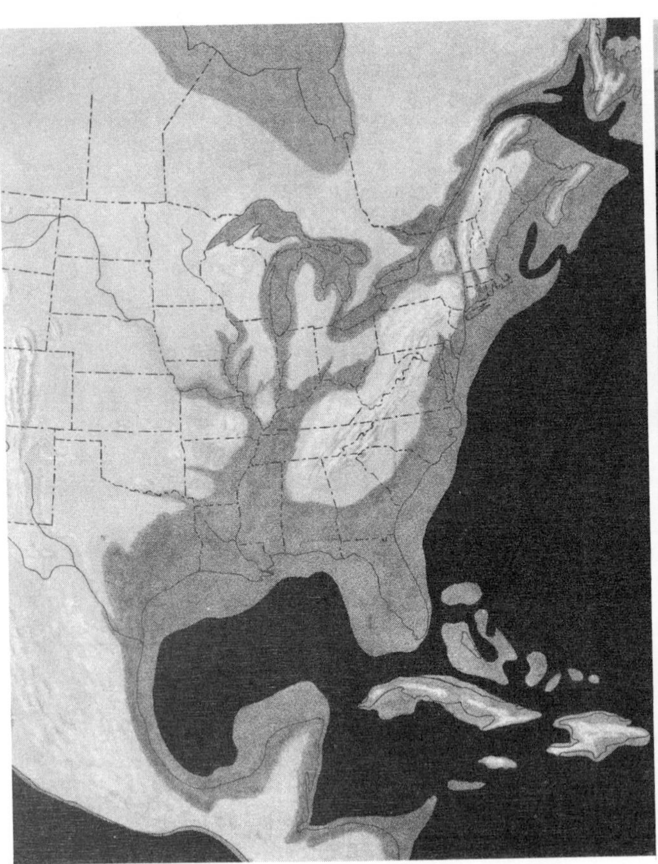

Figure 2. Southeastern part of North America as it would appear if depressed 600 feet. Shallow sea shaded; deep sea black.

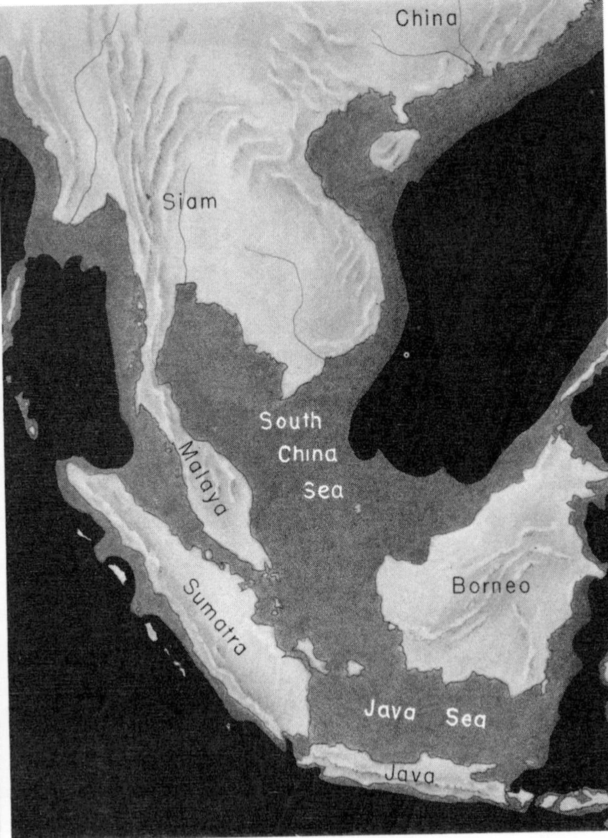

Figure 3. Malaysia, a portion of southeast Asia as it exists today, having been partly submerged within the near geologic past. (Adapted from Van Riel.)

crossed these lowlands can still be traced on the sea floor. The large animals of Borneo, Sumatra, and Java migrated from Asia across this intervening lowland before it was drowned.

Submergences of North America as great as this have occurred many times in the past, and the outlines of land and sea have thus varied widely from age to age.

Restoring Lost Lands. Layers of sediment spread over a land surface commonly bear evidence of the terrestrial environment in the form of mudcracks, footprints, or skeletons of land animals, remains of land plants, or coal. Fossil animals and plants may even indicate the approximate altitude and the climate under which the beds were deposited. A striking example occurs in Kashmir Valley high in the Himalayas, where at an elevation of 10,600 feet, plant-bearing deposits have yielded a tropical fig and a species of laurel that still inhabits India but lives only below an altitude of 6,000 feet and in localities of subtropical climate.[1] It is clear that the region was much lower and warmer when these plant beds were formed.

Since a land mass is constantly exposed to erosion, the sediments that accumulate on its surface are eventually reworked and carried into the sea, except where they have been downwarped or downfaulted below sealevel. Even marine strata, however, may throw much light on the position and character of the land from which they were derived. During transport, the sediment is size-graded, the coarsest material always coming to rest first, while progressively finer detritus is carried farther and farther. Hence, if a mass of strata grades from fine in one direction to coarser in another, it is evident that the ultimate source lay in the direction of increasing coarseness. Plotting of such data for the beds of a given age may indicate the approximate position and extent of the lands; and where a mass of strata shows changes from marine to non-marine, the approximate shoreline of the time may be drawn.

In most of the late geologic formations the application of these criteria is obvious, for they point to sources in land masses that are still supplying sediment. When applied to many of the ancient formations, however, they indicate highlands that no longer exist, and in some instances the results are surprising. The San Onofre conglomerate of California, for example, increases in coarseness toward the west, indicating a source of its boulders in highlands beyond the present shoreline. This is confirmed by the presence of boulders of peculiar types of metamorphic rock that are unknown on the mainland but crop out on Catalina Island, some 40 miles off shore. The inference is that the islands west of southern California are remnants of a larger land mass that stood high while the San Onofre conglomerate was forming, and has since foundered.

Of course, high relief and heavy rainfall result in rapid erosion and relatively coarse detritus; lowlands, on the contrary, supply only fine mud or minerals in solution, and warm moist climate leads to thorough chemical decay. Critical study of the sediments may therefore indicate not merely the position of land masses but also their relative height and the type of climate that prevailed during long-past geologic ages.

Vestiges of Mountains. The growth and decay of a mountain range are recorded in the rocks long after the mountains themselves have disappeared. The nature of the evidence is indicated in Figure 4. Block *A* represents the region before disturbance, formed of flat-lying bedded rocks with a lowland at the right and shallow sea at the left. Uplift is under way in block *B*, and the strata at the right are being buckled into low folds. Streams are beginning to intrench themselves and the old mantle of fine and well-decayed sediment is being stripped off and transported to the sea, to be spread again as layers of marine mud. Thus far there is but little sand and gravel because the streams still have a low gradient. Block *C* represents a later stage after strong folding and faulting have produced rugged relief in the mountain region, and rapid erosion is loading the stream with sand and gravel as well as mud. Upon reaching the shore zone the overloaded streams now tend to build an aggraded coastal plain extended locally into deltas. Meanwhile, the uplift in the mountain region is counterbalanced by sinking of a near-by geosyncline (*left*), and here the sediment derived from the mountains comes to rest, the gravel and coarse sand near shore and the finer sand and mud farther out. Block *D* shows a later stage after the region of uplift has been peneplaned. The mountains have now vanished, and sluggish streams meander across a lowland, carrying only the finest sediment.

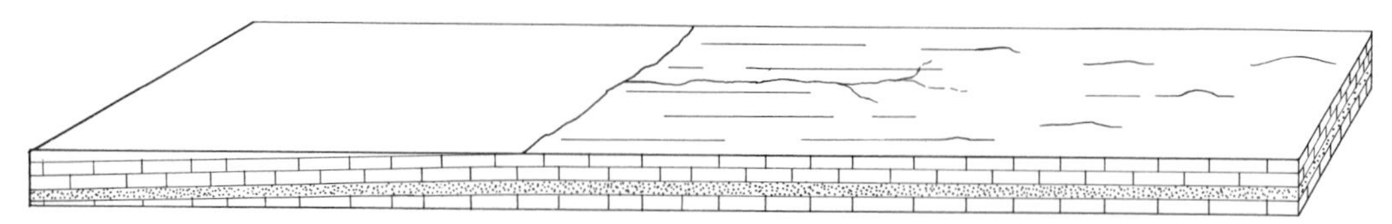

A. *Region of flat-lying rocks before uplift begins*

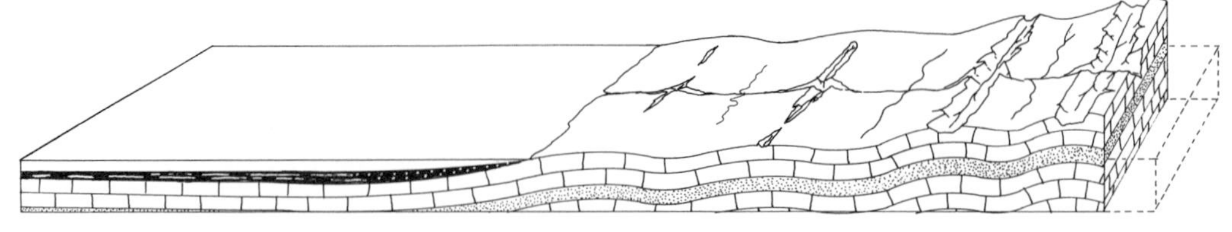

B. *Early stage of uplift with low folds; erosion beginning*

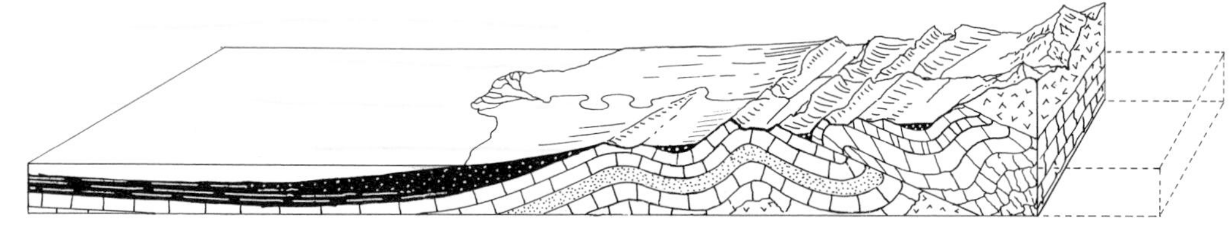

C. *Maximum uplift; rapid erosion supplying coarse sediment*

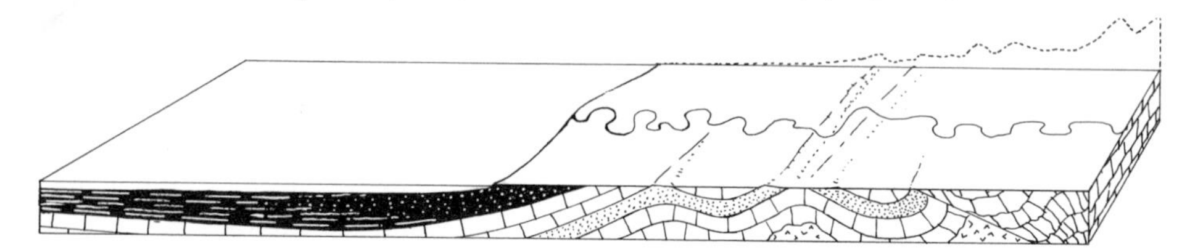

D. *Peneplaned surface after mountins are eroded away*

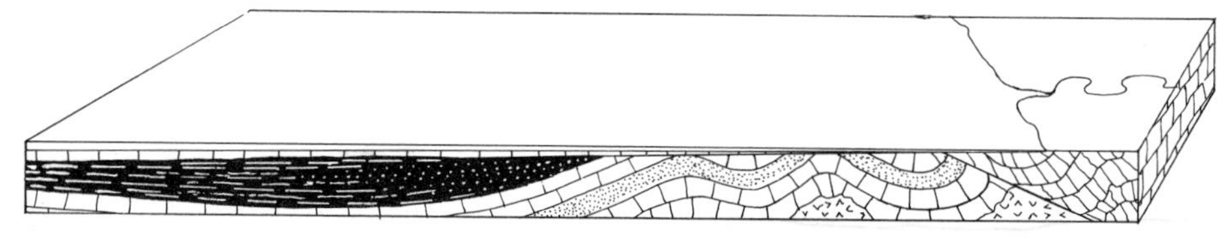

E. *Later submergence buries the roots of the mountains*

Figure 4. Five stages in the rise and decay of a mountain range. Sediments eroded from the rising range and deposited in the adjacent geosyncline are shown in black. Length of section, some tens of miles.

The cycle is complete in block *E* as the region is again submerged, and shallow sea creeps in over the site of the vanished highlands to bury the roots of the mountains with layers of fine mud.

At the surface all traces of the mountains are now gone; but underground there are records of two sorts, one where the mountains stood and another where their debris accumulated. If the region is uplifted and dissected at some later date, these records will be brought to light. In the area of disturbance a profound unconformity will separate the postorogenic strata from the buried roots of the mountains, whose truncated folds and faults may indicate the nature of the disturbance

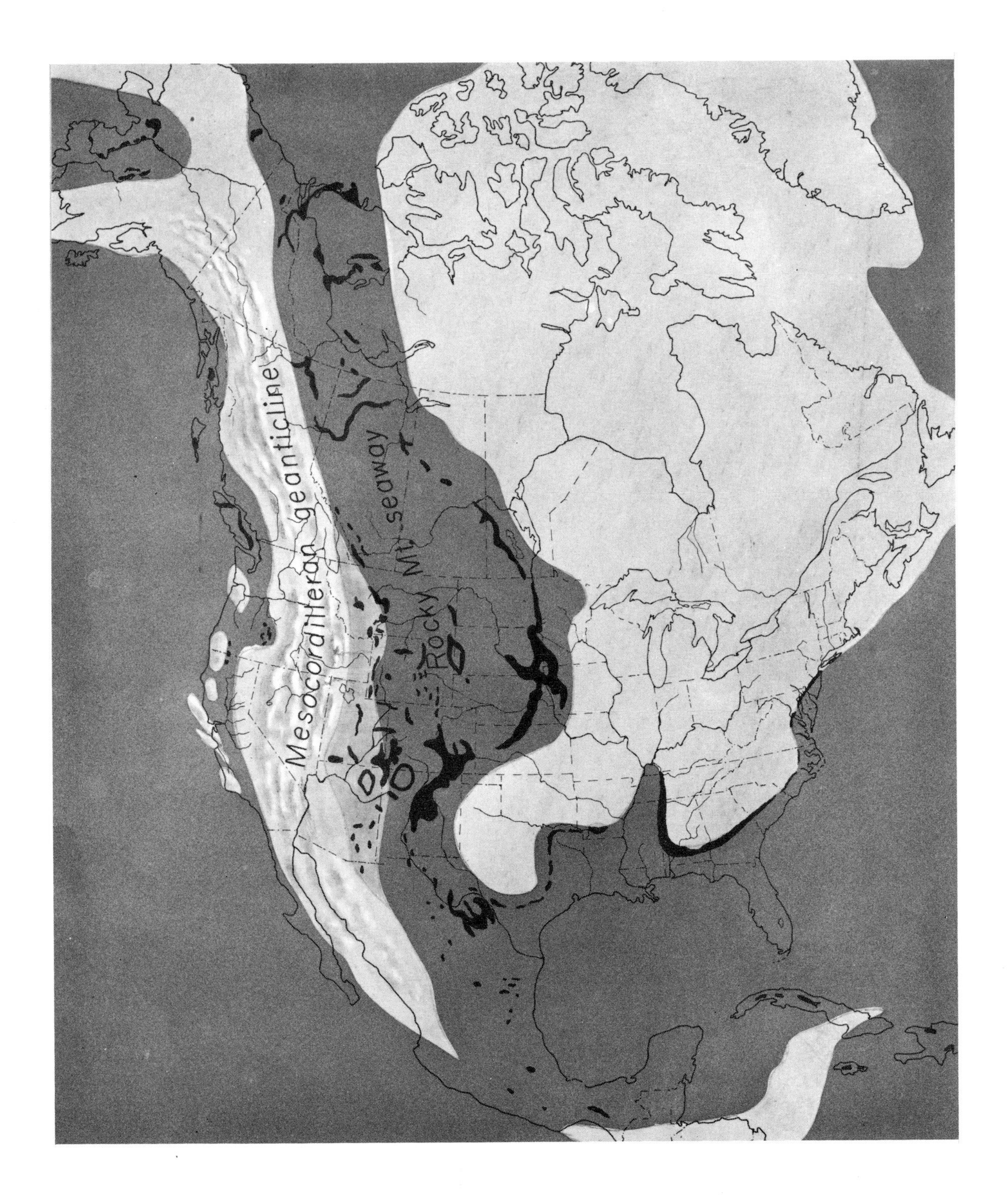

Figure 5. Paleogeographic map of North America as it was in mid-Cretaceous time. Present outcrops of Cretaceous rocks of this date are shown in solid black. Seaways darkly shaded; low coastal plain west of the Rocky Mountain seaway in lighter shading.

and something of the size of individual folds and fault blocks. In block *E* of our hypothetical case, for example, it is evident that the folds were open to the left of a major thrust and that to the right of it they were more severely mashed and deformed. It would be quite simple in such a case to count the major folds, restore the missing parts, and determine their approximate dimensions. The date of the disturbance is clearly later than the youngest strata involved in the deformation, and earlier than the beds next above the unconformity.

A complementary record is found in the area of deposition at the left (*black*). Insofar as the debris of the destroyed mountain range accumulated here, the volume of the detrital sediment bears a definite relation to the size and height of the range. Fossils in these deposits will record the geologic date at which uplift and erosion were taking place, and obviously the coarsest part of the sedimentary record will correspond in time with the most rapid erosion and the greatest relief in the uplifted area. In the region of deposition the growth of the range is reflected in increasing coarseness and ever wider spread of the sands and gravels, and its decline is betrayed by a return to deposits of finer and finer grain. Hence, if the region of deposition were available for study, it would still be possible to infer much about the position and size of the uplift and to date it in geologic time even if the site of the ancient mountains remained covered, or was repeatedly disturbed until the early record was obscured.

To apply this reasoning to a specific case, consider the sedimentary deposits of Late Cretaceous date* which are plotted in Figure 5. They clearly record a vast interior sea that extended from the Gulf of Mexico to the Arctic Ocean. In the eastern part these formations are of fine-grained shale with some interbedded chalky limestone; but toward the west they thicken and coarsen, including along the western margin vast deposits of sandstone with local conglomerates. Clearly the source of this material was chiefly to the west, and it must have been a highland of considerable ruggedness. Furthermore, as we approach the western margin, the rocks contain land plants and dinosaur bones, and locally have much interbedded coal. This must represent a swampy coastal lowland between the mountains and the sea. To supply the enormous volume of these detrital deposits to the Rocky Mountain geosyncline (estimated at more than 850,000,000 cubic miles) must have required the erosion of an average thickness of nearly 5 miles of rock from the source area.[2] It is evident, therefore, that this western land mass was either continuously or intermittently rising, and remained mountainous and rugged during the long span of Late Cretaceous time.

*The geologic time chart on page 15 shows the time relation of this period of Earth's history.

By the application of such principles we can restore the major geographic features of North America as they existed a hundred million years ago—a continent separated by a vast strait into two land masses, the eastern broad and low, the western narrow and mountainous.

The reconstruction of ancient lands and seas is the science of **paleogeography** (Gr. *palaios*, ancient + geography), and the inferred restorations (for example, Fig. 5) are **paleogeographic maps.**

THE GEOLOGIC TIME SCALE

History is a narrative of events that have succeeded one another in time, with an interpretation of their causes and interrelations. In this respect geologic and human history have much in common.

The story of civilization, for example, is based upon records from many parts of the world built into a composite whole. No single country, nor even a continent, could supply the necessary data, because the locus of important events that make history has shifted from time to time as one great civilization succeeded another. From ancient cultures of the Euphrates Valley, the center of interest shifted progressively to Egypt, to Greece, to Rome, and finally to Western Europe and the Americas. Basic to the story is **chronology**—a time scale divided into periods and ages in which events can be assigned their proper dates, permitting an analysis of causes and effects. Thus we recognize the three major divisions of ancient, medieval, and modern history, each further subdivided into ages on the basis of dynasties or cultural changes.

The geologic time scale (Fig. 8, page 15) covers the whole span of Earth's history and is divided into units large and small, whereby events can likewise be related in proper sequence. The record on which it is based comprises the rocks (especially the sedimentary rocks) that form the Earth's crust.

As important parts of the record were discovered, first in western Europe and then elsewhere, they have been pieced together in the form of a **geologic column**, a composite columnar section in which the rocks of one age are superposed upon those of the next older. It is important, then, to understand how the composite record comprised in the geologic column was built up. The principles involved are discussed in the following paragraphs.

Superposition. Since sedimentary rocks originate as loose sediment spread layer upon layer, it is evident that in any normal section the oldest bed is at the bottom, and each in turn is younger than the one on which it rests. Therefore, in a general study of a region of relatively simple structure, the sequence of beds, and of formations, can readily be ascertained. This simple and self-evident principle is the **Law of Superposition.**

In disturbed areas, of course, the normal succession may be locally inverted, as in the lower limb of an overturned fold, or it may be interrupted, or duplicated, by faults; but such abnormalities will betray themselves in evidences of disturbance and in an unnatural sequence of fossils (next paragraph).

Faunal Succession. Most sedimentary rocks include fossil remains of the animals and plants that lived while they were accumulating. The **assemblage** of animal species living together at a given time and place constitutes a **fauna**; the corresponding assemblage of plants is a **flora.** Thus the animals that now inhabit a region constitute a modern fauna, and the assemblage recorded by fossils in a bed of stratified rock constitutes an older fauna that lived while the rock was forming.

Just before 1800 William Smith, studying the Jurassic rocks of England, discovered that each formation has a distinct fauna, unlike those above or below. He also saw that the characteristic fauna of any formation can be found in outcrop after outcrop as it is traced across the countryside, and so the characteristic fossils serve as a **guide** or **index** to distinct formations which he could recognize in any outcrop, without the necessity of careful tracing. Vast experience, accumulated since the days of Smith, has shown that this is a principle of general application—the faunas and floras of each age in Earth's history are unique, and permit us to recognize contemporaneous deposits, even in widely separated regions, and so to piece together scattered fragments of the record and place them in proper sequence.

William Smith did not know why each formation possesses a distinct fauna; his inference was based solely on study of a region of richly fossiliferous rocks where the strata dip gently and the order of superposition is self-evident. We now know, of course, that different kinds of animals and plants have succeeded one another in time because **life has continuously evolved;** and inasmuch as organic evolution is world wide in its operation, only rocks formed during the same age could bear identical faunas.

Where the structure of the rocks is simple, the succession of faunas that occupied the region from age to age can be determined by studying the fossils of successive formations.

When this succession has been confirmed by wide experience in many regions of undisturbed strata, we may be confident that different forms of life succeeded one another in this order in time on the Earth. The appearance of trilobites and dinosaurs and three-toed horses is not fortuitous and irregular; each lived only at a certain time in geologic history, and each is found fossil only in a certain part of the geologic column. The relative time of existence of a vast number of kinds of animals and plants has now been established, and their place in the geologic column has been confirmed by the cooperation of geologists the world over. This is not a theory derived a priori, but a discovery painfully and tediously worked out by the systematic study of the faunas of rock formations carefully located in the geologic column. It is an important natural law that **fossil faunas and floras succeed one another in a definite and determinable order.**

Correlation of the Fragments of the Record. The matching of strata or formations from outcrop to outcrop (or from well to well underground) to determine their mutual relations and degree of equivalence in age is known as **correlation.** It is an important step in working out the geologic history, because no single area contains a record of all geologic time, and if it did, the section would be so thick that its base would be buried beyond our reach; but deposition has always been going on in one place or another, and we need only discover and correlate enough of the scattered fragments to build up a composite record of all geologic time. For more than a hundred years the geologists of all countries have been cooperating in this endeavor, and the total thickness of the stratified rocks now recognized would exceed 500,000 feet (95 miles) if all the beds were directly superposed.

Some of the criteria used in correlation are illustrated by Figure 6. The left block (*A*) represents the formations exposed near the mouth of the Grand Canyon, and the right one (*B*) a corresponding section at Bright Angel Trail about 100 miles farther east. A general view of these formations may be seen in Figure 220 (p. 258).

At Bright Angel Trail ten formations of stratified rock are recognized, and in the western section there are also ten. When we attempt to correlate one with the other, it appears that No. 10 at Bright Angel Trail is the same as No. 10 at the mouth of the canyon, because (1) it holds the same relative position at the rim of the canyon; (2) it presents the same lithologic appearance (being a buff-weathering, cherty limestone); (3) it agrees in thickness; and (4) it yields the same kinds of marine fossils which in each section are limited to this unit. If more proof were needed, (5) we could follow the rim of the canyon and trace the formation from one section into the other. This is the Kaibab limestone that rims the Grand Canyon from end to end.

In the same way, No. 5 of the eastern section can

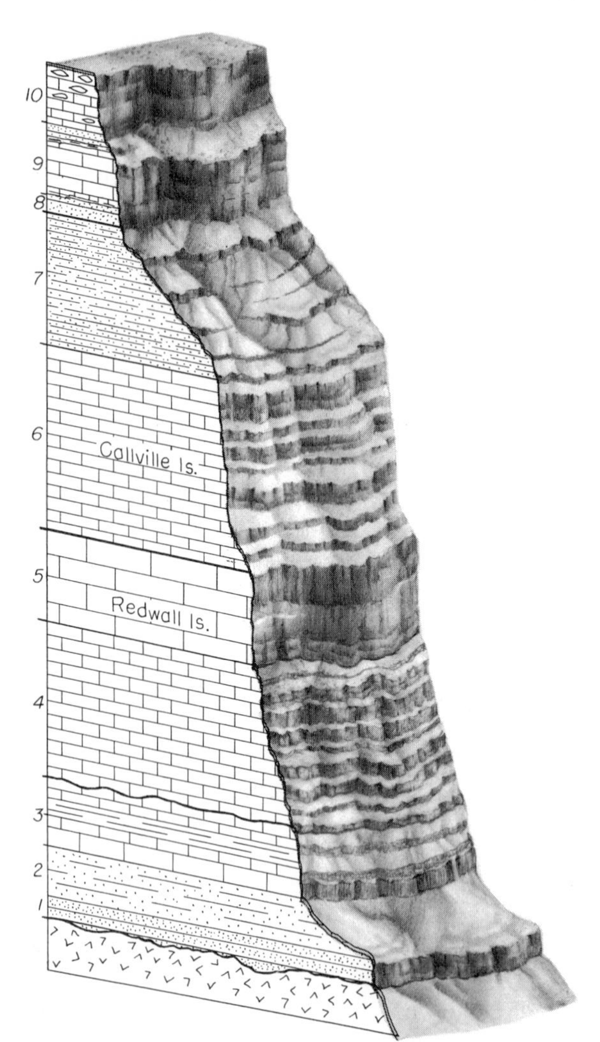

Figure 6*A*. Block of the canyon wall and section of formations exposed near the mouth of the Grand Canyon of the Colorado River; recognized formations numbered 1 to 10.

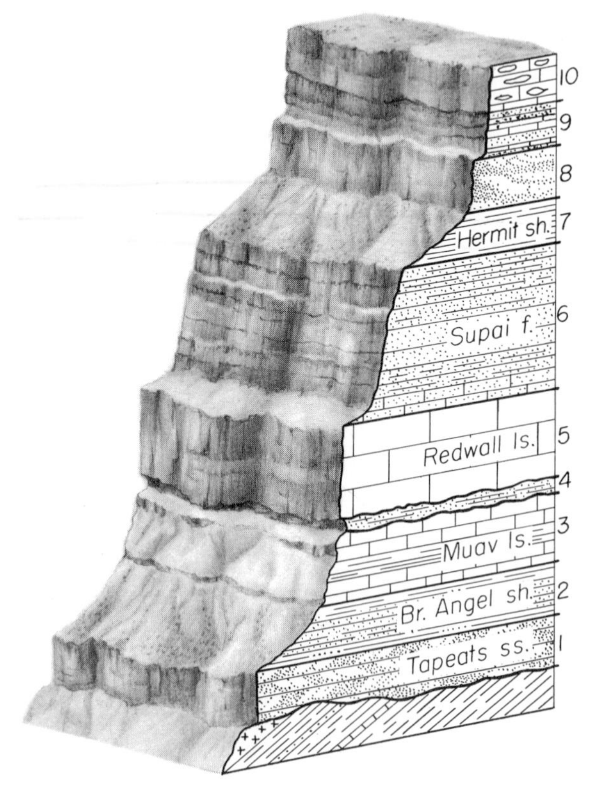

Figure 6*B*. Block and section exposed near Bright Angel Trail about 100 miles east of the block shown in part *A*, and at the same scale.

be correlated with No. 5 of the west. It is the cliff-forming Redwall limestone that maintains the same lithologic character and approximately the same thickness for a distance of more than 100 miles (Fig. 220, p. 258). Furthermore, it has distinctive fossils, and it crops out in a bold cliff and forms a bench that can be followed continuously along the canyon wall.

This gives us two tie-points or **key horizons** for correlating the distant sections. The intervening formations, however, present more difficulty. In the eastern section No. 6 is a bright red sandstone and sandy siltstone with fossil plants and footprints of land animals; No. 6 of the western section is a light gray limestone bearing marine fossils. The two seem to hold the same relative position in the sections, just above the Redwall limestone, but they are totally different in lithology, are unequal in thickness, and have no fossils in common, the one bearing only marine shells and the other only remains of land life. It is evident that both are limited in age to some part of the time between the deposition of the Redwall and the Kaibab limestones, but several alternatives must be considered: (1) the Callville limestone may be the older, thinning eastward to disappear short of Bright Angel Trail, either because (*a*) it was never deposited there, or (*b*) it was eroded away before deposition of the Supai formation; or (2) the Supai formation may be the older, thinning westward for either of the reasons suggested above; or (3) they may be equivalent in age, having formed under different environments; or (4) they may be equivalent in part, with one representing more time than the other. Most of the criteria used to correlate the Kaibab or the Redwall limestone cannot be applied here, for the Callville and Supai formations are dissimilar in lithology, are unequal in thickness, and have no fossils in common. But the Callville can be traced eastward along the walls of the Grand Canyon, and the upper part of it is found to change laterally, as the limestone beds first become sandy, then reddish, and finally alternate with layers of red siltstone and sandstone (Fig. 222, p. 260). In short, it grades laterally into the Supai formation and the two formations **intertongue;** they must therefore have been laid down at the same time. The intertonguing of these formations, one marine and the other non-marine, indicates that the shore fluctuated back and forth across a wide belt during deposition. Fossils, however, indicate that the lower part of the Callville limestone is older than any part of the Supai; hence this part of the Callville formation probably never extended as far east as Bright Angel Trail. More field work actually is needed to confirm this belief.

Still another basis for correlating the Callville limestone and the Supai redbeds might have been used, even if the Grand Canyon had not revealed the lateral gradation and intertonguing of one into the other. The fossil plants of the Supai might indicate the same position in the geologic column as the marine fossils of the upper part of the Callville. This would be true if in some other region—say, New Mexico or Kansas—there were an alternation of marine and non-marine beds carrying the Supai flora and the Callville fauna. Indeed, correlation of two sections in this manner through a third is common practice.

Similar problems are presented by formation No. 4, which, although it holds the same relative position in each section, between the Muav and the Redwall limestones, differs in lithology and thickness and in faunal content in the two sections.

To recapitulate, it may be noted that formations in separate outcrops may be correlated because of (1) lithologic similarity, (2) similar thickness, (3) similar position in a sequence of formations some of which are known to be equivalent, (4) continuous tracing between outcrops, (5) lateral gradation and intertonguing of one into the other when the formations are lithologically dissimilar, (6) identical faunas, or (7) fossils that are dissimilar (for example, marine versus non-marine) but are known to occur together elsewhere and therefore to indicate the same age. These are some, but not all, of the means by which strata of the same ages are correlated from place to place. Commonly not all of them can be applied to a given situation; the more that can be used, the more secure the correlation.

Units Nos. 1 and 2 of these sections present an interesting problem. No. 1, the Tapeats sandstone, is unfossiliferous and probably non-marine. It can be followed in continuous outcrop from one section to the other and is clearly a lithologic unit. Unit No. 2, the Bright Angel shale, is marine, and it bears two very distinctive zones of fossils, a lower one of Lower Cambrian age and an upper one of Middle Cambrian age. When traced along the canyon walls however, these fossil zones are

Figure 7. Diagrammatic profile across an ocean basin and parts of adjacent continents, vertical scale greatly exaggerated. Line *a* represents sealevel; line *b* the level of the edge of the continental shelf; and line c the level of average depth of the ocean floor.

found not to parallel the lithologic boundaries. Clearly two of our criteria for correlation disagree. Lateral tracing would suggest that the Tapeats is all of one age; but the fossils clearly suggest that in the western reaches of the Grand Canyon the Tapeats sandstone and nearly all of the Bright Angel shale are Lower Cambrian but that both rise in the section toward the east and, at Bright Angel Trail, nearly all of the Bright Angel shale is of Middle Cambrian age. The explanation is that the sea gradually encroached on this region from the west, sand being spread as a low coastal plains deposit before the advancing shoreline whereas the mud was carried into the sea, and that the sea did not reach the vicinity of Bright Angel Trail until about the end of Early Cambrian time. In this case the formation boundaries cross time lines. This is not an unusual situation, but the evidence is uncommonly clear in this section.

SUBDIVISION OF THE RECORD

Although time flows continuously, both human and geologic history are punctuated by important events that justify the recognition of distinct ages. Indeed, if we are to describe and discuss the vast record embraced in 500,000 feet of strata, it must be subdivided into convenient units, both large and small; and it is highly desirable that the subdivisions should have a natural basis, applicable the world over, so that work in different countries will fit into a common framework. Thus far, however, geologists are divided into two schools, one convinced that there is a natural physical basis for the larger subdivisions (however imperfect), and the other believing that the subdivisions are man-made and arbitrary, albeit useful and necessary. We will examine these opposed views in turn.

Theory of a Natural Basis for Subdivision. Those who believe there is a natural, physical basis for the major subdivisions of the geologic column reason as follows:

1. If deposition of sediment should cease everywhere for a time, a natural break or **hiatus** in the stratigraphic record would be world wide. Even if the sites of deposition merely shifted off the continental masses into regions now covered by the sea, an effective hiatus would appear since we are directly concerned only with the exposed part of the record.
2. At long intervals the Earth's crust has undergone major readjustments that produced broad uplift of the continental masses and deepened the ocean basins.
3. The margins of the continents drop off steeply to the ocean floor which has an average depth of more than 12,000 feet (Fig. 7); and the oceans at present are slightly more than brimful, spilling over the continental shelves to form shallow marginal seas, and in a few places spreading far inland to form **epeiric** seas like the Baltic (Gr. *epeiros*, the mainland). Recoverable sedimentary deposits have formed only in such shallow seas or on the land, those of the ocean basins being forever lost to us.
4. If at any time broad crustal warping has deepened and enlarged the ocean basins this should have drawn off the marine waters leaving the continents exposed to widespread erosion.
5. If relative stability for a long time followed such an event, sealevel would slowly rise as each unit of sediment carried to the sea displaced an equal volume of water; or if portions of the ocean floor were upwarped, the sealevel would rise and flood the lower parts of the continents to produce another segment of the record.

6. Inasmuch as the oceans are freely connected, the rise or fall of sealevel would be eustatic, affecting all the continents at once. Insofar as this is true, it would produce subdivisions of the stratigraphic record at once natural and universal.

But experience shows clearly that the problem is not so simple. We have assumed, thus far, that the continental masses stood firm during the postulated rise and fall of sealevel; but there is abundant evidence that during late geologic time extensive warping of the continents has caused parts of the coastal belts to rise and others to be drowned, while farther inland mountains are rising locally and structural basins are still subsiding. It is altogether probable that this has been the history of the past.

Therefore, even if extensive eustatic changes of sealevel have occurred at times in the past, the breaks could hardly be universal or uniform in magnitude. If local warping within the continents was out of phase with the rise and fall of sealevel, deposition may have continued locally even while most of the continent was undergoing erosion.

Theory of Arbitrary Subdivision. The irregularity of movement in the continental masses has led many geologists to believe there are no major breaks in the record affecting all the continents at once. This school argues that the crust is continually adjusting itself, rising here and sinking there, so that no major eustatic changes in sealevel occur. They argue also that since the oceans vastly exceed the continents in area it would require a rise or fall of some thousands of feet over a large area of the ocean floor to produce a eustatic change of a few hundred feet in sealevel. On the assumption that there are, therefore, no major, world-wide breaks in the stratigraphic record, this school argues that the several geologic systems have a natural basis only where first defined, and their boundaries must be recognized in other parts of the world only by correlation with their type regions.

Conclusion. It is not yet possible to settle this controversy for two main reasons: (1) the stratigraphic record is still very incompletely known in large parts of the world, and (2) we do not yet know the basic causes of diastrophism. Space will not permit a review of the arguments pro and con. It may be noted in passing, however, that the continents are now nearly emergent as compared with much of the geologic past when vast epeiric seas covered millions of square miles (e.g., Fig. 5). We are at the culmination of a retreat that has been general during the last fifty million years or so. At the same time the submerged sea mounts and the coral atolls of the mid-Pacific indicate that a vast area of that ocean floor has slowly subsided by an amount of several thousands of feet—a subsidence vast enough to account for the lowered sealevel. A similarly widespread emergence of all the continents occurred toward the end of the Paleozoic Era, and another preceded that era. These breaks are so general that they are recognized the world over. If this be admitted, perhaps there are other breaks less widespread yet important enough to afford a natural, even though imperfect, basis for subdivision. In any event, however, all are agreed that the subdivisions smaller than systems are essentially provincial.

Biologic Basis of Subdivision. Since life on the Earth has been continuously evolving, the faunas and floras preserved as fossils provide a basis for chronology; but if the record were complete they might show gradual change and yet afford no basis for subdivision of the record.

The changes have not been gradual however. At certain times, as at the end of each era, extinctions of dominant groups of organisms have occurred within a relatively short span of time and other groups have rapidly expanded to take their place. To a lesser extent this is true of the ends of the several periods of geologic time. This suggests that the progress of evolution has been strongly influenced by physical changes on the Earth. Uplift and continental emergence have radically altered the general environment, changing the course of ocean currents, interfering with atmospheric circulation, and modifying the climate. Moreover, the restriction of the shallow seas to the very margins of the continents has caused migrations and crowding amongst the marine animals while placing the land life under stress climates. Such physical changes must have accelerated the evolutionary changes in some groups and led to vast extinctions in others. Such times of rapid change appear to coincide generally with the major physical breaks in the record. In any event, they aid greatly in recognizing the major subdivisions of Earth history.

GROUPING AND NAMING OF UNITS

Two Eons of Time. One of the greatest milestones in geologic history marks the beginning of the Cambrian Period when abundant fossils made their appearance (Fig. 8, p. 15). Although life was certainly present long before, fossils are so rare and obscure in the older rocks as to be of little use in correlation, and only physical criteria can be applied in working out the earlier history of the Earth. Since the beginning of Cambrian time, however, abundant fossils provide a continuing record of life and at the same time serve to date the rocks the world over and permit a broad synthesis of geologic history. Because of the contrast in the life record, these greatest divisions of geologic time have been named the **Cryptozoic Eon** (Gr. *kryptos*, hidden + *zoon*, life) and the **Phanerozoic Eon** (Gr. *phaneros*, visible or evident + *zoon*, life), respectively.

Eras of Phanerozoic Time. Three major subdivisions of Phanerozoic time based on the dominant and characteristic forms of life, are termed **eras**. These are as follows:

3. **The Cenozoic Era** (Gr. *kainos*, recent + *zoon*, life) dominated by such familiar animals as the mammals and by modern plants.
2. **The Mesozoic Era** (Gr. *mesos*, medieval + *zoon*, life), dominated by extinct reptiles such as dinosaurs and pterosaurs.
1. **The Paleozoic Era** (Gr. *palaeos*, ancient + *zoon*, life), dominated by extinct groups, chiefly invertebrates, such as trilobites and graptolites and tetracorals.

The Cryptozoic Eon was much longer than the Phanerozoic and undoubtedly included several great eras of time, but, in the absence of fossils they cannot be defined on any world-wide basis, and attempts at major subdivision are thus far unsuccessful, as explained in Chapter 6.

Periods of Time and Systems of Rocks. The major subdivisions of each era are termed **periods** of time and the rocks formed during a period constitute a **system**. Each system is based upon a region where it was first defined and where it is a natural rock unit, separated from the rocks below and above by a major structural break or by general differences in lithology and life record indicating an important change in regimen. Most of the systems were defined in Western Europe during the early part of the nineteenth century and were then considered to be natural subdivisions that could be recognized the world over. Those who believe that great diastropic changes affected the Earth at such times (p. 12) seek to adjust the boundaries where necessary to fit the most widespread breaks in other regions. On the other hand, those who believe such major changes are provincial or local, argue that the limits originally defined must be accepted and rocks in all other parts of the world must be judged to belong to a particular system on the basis of correlation by fossils.

A system of rocks is generally named for the region in which it was defined, and the corresponding period of time bears the same name. Thus the **Cambrian System** was named for Cambria, the Roman name for Wales, though it includes rocks of equivalent age in all parts of the world. The **Permian System**, likewise, was named for the province of Perm in Russia, and the **Permian Period** embraces the time during which these rocks were formed. In a few instances the system was named for some lithologic peculiarity in its type region. Thus, for example, the **Cretaceous System** was so named because of the prominence of chalk (L. *creta*, chalk) and the **Carboniferous System** for the abundance of coal in its type region (L. *carbo*, coal + *ferere*, to bear).

Epochs of Time and Series of Rocks. Lesser and more local breaks subdivide the systems into **series** of rock and the periods into corresponding **epochs** of time. Some of the systems are subdivided into two, others into three, four, or five series. These are commonly given geographic names. For example, the Ordovician System in North America is divided into **Canadian**, **Champlainian**, and **Cincinnatian** series. The last was named for fine exposures about Cincinnati, Ohio, but includes all rocks of equivalent age wherever they can be identified, that is, all rocks formed during the Cincinnatian Epoch.

It is commonly not feasible to identify these minor subdivisions in widely separated regions, so

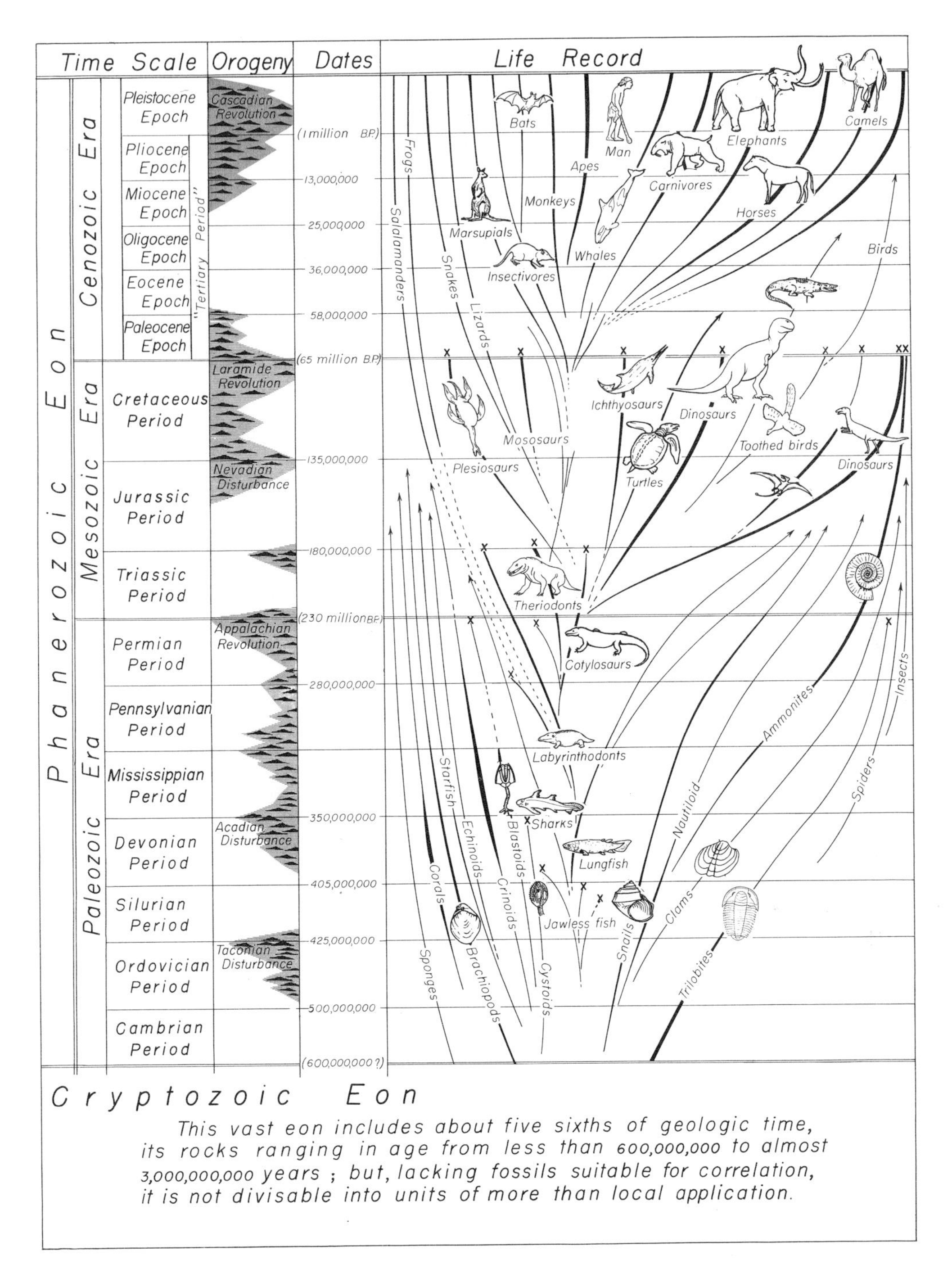

Figure 8. The geologic time scale and important dates and events in the history of North America. Space allotted to different time units is not to uniform scale. Shading to indicate times of chief orogeny is purely symbolical. Pre-Jurassic orogenies were chiefly in the Appalachian region, whereas later ones were chiefly in the West. Note that each orogenic movement was of great duration and that some part of the continent was undergoing mountain-making throughout most of geologic history. Note also that all the major groups of invertebrate animals were well represented in the Paleozoic Era; that reptiles appeared late in this era but dominated the Mesozoic Era, at the close of which the chief reptilian stocks died out; and that mammals dominated the Cenozoic Era. A cross at the ends of a line indicates extinction; a dart indicates that the group persisted to the present. Dates are chiefly after Faul (1960) and Kulp (1961).

a distinct set of series and epochs is recognized in each isolated continent.

Geographic names are generally used for the series and epochs but in systems in which three series are recognized, they are commonly referred to merely as **Lower, Middle,** and **Upper,** without the use of a geographic name. The corresponding epochs are then **Early, Middle,** and **Late.** These words are capitalized when used in this technical sense for a definite stratigraphic or time unit, but are not capitalized when used in a more general or indefinite sense. Thus, the *Lower Cambrian* rocks were formed during *Early Cambrian* time, but cephalopods first appeared in *late Cambrian* time.

Ages of Time and Stages of Rocks. Rocks of a series may be further subdivided into **stages** and the corresponding time units into **ages.**

Formations. The fundamental stratigraphic unit used in mapping and description is the **formation.** It is a **lithologic unit** (for example, limestone, dolostone, sandstone, siltstone, or shale, or an intimate interbedding of different lithologic types) that can be distinguished at sight from underlying and overlying masses of strata. Several typical formations are shown in the walls of the Grand Canyon (Fig. 6).

The formation is named for a locality where it is first defined and is typically displayed. The **St. Louis limestone,** for example, was named at St. Louis, Missouri, and the **Kaibab limestone** in the Kaibab Plateau of Arizona. When the formation consists of a single kind of rock, the lithology is indicated in the name, for example, **Dakota sandstone** and **Bighorn dolostone;** but if it consists of interbedded types, the lithology cannot be thus simply expressed and it is merely designated a formation, for example, **Supai formation** (which consists of interbedded sandstone, siltstone, and shale). The place name is merely a qualifying adjective indicating *which* limestone or sandstone or formation is meant, and it must not be used alone. Thus one writes, "The *Redwall limestone* forms bold cliffs," not "The *Redwall* forms bold cliffs."

A formation may vary considerably in age from place to place as shown in Figures 278 and 281 (pp. 327 and 330). In the former it is evident that deposition of the Selma chalk began in western Alabama while the Coffee sand was forming farther west, but deposition of chalk gradually spread westward. Still later the McNairy sand and the Ripley shale spread farther and farther eastward, restricting the area of chalk deposition. As a result, the top (and the base) of each of these formations varies in age along the Gulf Coast. This is not an exceptional circumstance, but a very normal relation. Since a formation thus commonly varies in age from place to place, it is not feasible to recognize a corresponding time unit.

Groups of Formations. Two or more formations sharing some distinctive lithologic peculiarity may be embraced in a **group.** A good example is the **Glen Canyon group** of massive, cliff-forming sandstones in the Colorado Plateau. Another is the **Newark group** of redbeds that occupy the fault troughs of Triassic date in the Appalachian region. Inasmuch as a group is based upon lithologic peculiarities, it is essentially a local unit, and its upper and lower limits may vary in age from place to place. For these reasons the group, like the formation, has no corresponding time unit. Such purely lithogenetic units as the formation and the group are written in lower case to distinguish them from time units (periods, eras, and ages) and time-stratigraphic units (systems, series, and stages) which are capitalized. Thus we write, "The *St. Louis limestone* is a part of the *Mississippian System* and was formed during the *Mississippian Period.*"

REFERENCES

1. Puri, G. S., 1947, The occurrence of a tropical fig (*Ficus cunia Buch-Ham.*) in the Karewa beds at Liddarmarg, Pir Panjal range, Kashmir, with remarks on the sub-tropical forests of the Kashmir valley during the Pleistocene. *Indian Bot. Soc., Jour.*, vol. 26, no. 3, pp. 131–135.

———, 1948, A preliminary note on the Pleistocene flora of the Karewa formations of Kashmir. *Quart. Jour. Geol., Min., and Metal Soc. of India,* vol. 20, no. 2, pp. 61–66.

2. Gilluly, James, 1949, Distribution of mountain building in time. *Geol. Soc. Amer., Bull.*, vol. 60, pp. 571–573.

Evidence of radioactivity in the black mineral Samarskite from Mitchell County, North Carolina. Left, normal photograph of a slice of the mineral; right, photograph from a negative exposed while enclosed in its opaque cover upon which the specimen had been placed. It was in similar manner that Becquerel, in 1896, accidentally discovered radioactivity.

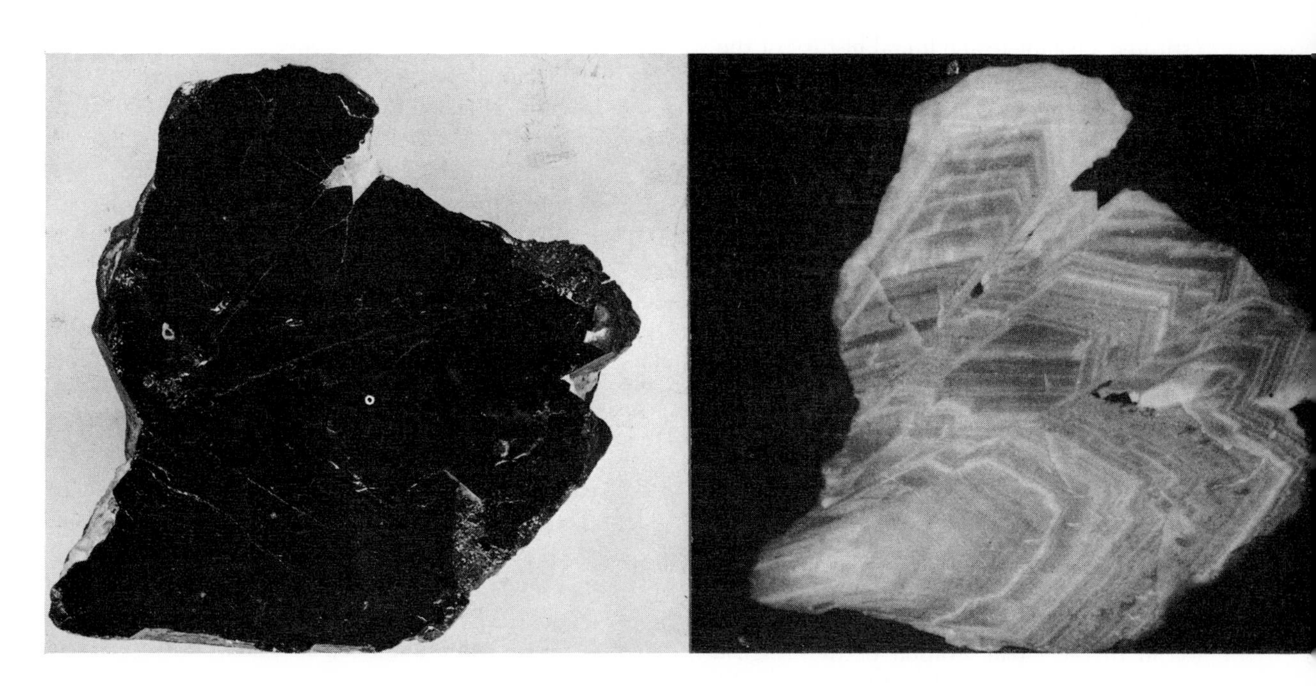

Chapter 2. The Scale of Geologic Time

The poor world is almost six thousand years old.

AS YOU LIKE IT, ACT IV, SCENE 1

EARLY SPECULATION

PHILOSOPHERS HAVE SPECULATED ON THE AGE of the Earth since time immemorial, and their beliefs have ranged from that of the Brahmins of India who regarded the world as eternal, to the conviction, widely held for a time in the Christian world, that Creation occurred only about 6,000 years ago.

The latter belief, which was current in western Europe during the Middle Ages, sprang from the assumption that the Old Testament Scriptures constituted a complete and literal history of the world. It was given added authority about the middle of the seventeenth century by certain Anglican churchmen. Perhaps the first of these was John Lightfoot, a distinguished Greek scholar and Vice Chancellor of Cambridge University, who, in 1642, deduced that the moment of Creation was "9:00 o'clock in the morning on September seventeenth."[1] He did not at this time indicate the year of Creation, but in a later chapter of the same work, in 1644, he stated that it was 3928 B.C. On the basis of similar reasoning, Archbishop Ussher, Primate of Ireland, in 1658, wrote:[2]

> In the beginning God created Heaven and Earth, Gen. I, V. 1., which beginning of time, according to our Chronologie, fell upon the entrance of night preceding the twentythird day of Octob. in the year of the Julian Calendar, 710 [i.e., 4004 B.C.]

And in the Great Edition of the English Bible, published in 1701, Bishop Lloyd inserted the date 4004 B.C. as a marginal commentary.[3] This was repeated in many later editions of the Authorized English Version of the Bible and thus was incorporated into the dogma of the Christian Church. Thereafter for more than a century it was considered heretical to assume more than 6,000 years for the formation of the Earth and all its features.

Geology grew up under this influence and, during its early years supernatural explanations were invoked for many natural phenomena. The glacial drift so widely spread over western Europe, for example, was attributed to the Biblical Flood; deep river gorges were believed to be clefts in the rocks produced by earthquakes, and mountains were believed to have arisen with tumultuous violence.

The uprooting of such fantastic beliefs began with the Scottish geologist, James Hutton, whose *Theory of the Earth*, published in 1785, maintained that **the present is the key to the past** and that, given sufficient time, processes now at work could account for all the geologic features of the Globe. This philosophy, which came to be known as the **doctrine of uniformitarianism** demands an immensity of time; it has now gained universal acceptance among intelligent and informed people.

SCIENTIFIC APPROACH

Early attempts to determine the length of geologic time on a scientific basis also fell wide of the mark, not because of poor logic but because not enough critical information was yet available. It was as though scientists had attempted to launch an earth satellite when gunpowder was the most powerful propellant known.

One of the first attempts was based on the rate at which sediment is transported to basins of deposition. Indeed this method had been forseen by the Greek historian Herodotus about 450 B.C., when he observed the annual overflow of the Nile spreading a thin layer of sediment over its valley. He realized that the Nile Delta has grown by such annual increments of river-borne muds, and concluded that its building must have required many thousands of years. This was confirmed in 1854, when the foundation of the colossal statue of Ramses II at Memphis was discovered beneath 9 feet of river-laid deposits (Fig. 9). Since the statue is known to be about 3,200 years old, the rate of deposition at this place has averaged about 3½ inches per century. At this rate, burnt brick found some 40 feet below the surface at Memphis indicates that humans inhabited the region about 13,500 years ago. Yet these deposits are only a surface veneer of the great delta built by the Nile.

There are other local deposits for which the rate of deposition can be determined. The postglacial varved clays, for example, show summer and winter layers, which, like the growth rings in trees, are seasonal additions. Some of the older sedimentary formations likewise appear to be seasonally layered, notably the banded anhydrites of the Permian in West Texas (Fig. 219, p. 258) and the Green River Lake beds of the Eocene in Wyoming. On this basis Bradley estimated that 2,600 feet of the Green River shales required 6,500,000 years to accumulate.

Figure 9. The colossal statue of Ramses II at Memphis. This illustration by Bonomi in 1847 shows the statue as it lay face down, having fallen from its buried pedestal. About five years later, excavations were made to discover the thickness of river-laid sediment about its base. The Pyramids of Gizeh are seen in the distance at the left and the Nile River is near the horizon at the right. Two observers, one standing and one sitting, indicate the size of the statue.

But it was also hoped that by measuring the mass of all the sedimentary rocks of the Earth's crust, and the increment of sediment transported annually to the sea, it could be calculated how long erosion has been going on. Unfortunately, we have no assurance that the present rate of sedimentation is an average for all geologic time and, moreover, the mass of the sedimentary rocks formed since the beginning cannot be even approximately determined; in large part the deposits formed during one geologic age have been destroyed by erosion and redeposited in another. To an unknown degree, also, these rocks have been altered beyond recognition by metamorphism. The rate of sedimentation therefore can provide no valid measure of the length of geologic time, even though it clearly indicates that the Earth is very ancient.

An early attempt by Joly[4] to estimate the age of the Earth was based on the amount of salt in the ocean. It assumed: (1) that the primitive oceans were not salty, (2) that the NaC1 produced by weathering of the Earth's crust is carried to the sea where nearly all of it remains in solution, and (3) that the present rate of addition of salt is an average for all geologic time. Since the salinity is nearly uniform throughout the oceans, the total amount of salt now held in solution can be estimated with only a small percentage of error; and, by setting gauges at the mouths of major streams, an approximate measure of the annual increment of salt now being added could be estimated. When these calculations were first attempted, in 1899, a figure of approximately 100,000,000 years was indicated, and for a time this appeared to be a reasonable estimate of the length of geologic time; but further consideration showed that drastic revisions would be required. In the first place we do not know that the primeval oceans were not salty. In the second, much of the salt now being carried to the sea is not derived directly from the weathering of the primary rocks but is leached from sedimentary rocks where it was stored during previous erosion cycles. Moreover, some 14,000,000 tons is mined annually and thus artificially returned to the streams. All such salt has been previously removed from the sea and makes no permanent addition. Furthermore, we have no assurance that the present rate of erosion is an average for geologic time. In short, there are so many uncertain quantities involved that oceanic salt offers no promise of a reliable age determination.

In a series of papers between 1862 and 1897 the distinguished physicist, Lord Kelvin, attempted to determine the length of geologic time on physical principles and arrived at the final conclusion that the Earth is between 20 and 40 million years old. His reasoning was based on the assumption, however, that the Earth has been gradually cooling down from an original molten condition from which all its interior heat is inherited. The discovery of radioactivity in 1895 swept away the basis of his calculations.

DISCOVERY OF RADIOACTIVE CHRONOMETERS

A valid means of measuring geologic time was achieved only after the discovery of radioactivity about the turn of the present century. This now enables us to determine the age, *in years,* of many individual rock masses, and thus will make it possible to transform the *geologic* time scale (Fig. 8) into an *absolute* time scale.

The accidental discovery of the radioactivity of uranium by Becquerel in 1895 (Fig. 10) was followed by intensive studies of this newly disclosed property of matter, and the understanding that has since emerged may be briefly summarized as follows:

The atom consists of a small nucleus surrounded by a much larger swarm or cloud of electrons. The nucleus consists of protons, each of which carries a positive charge, and neutrons, which are without charge. Each electron carries a negative charge. All the elements are built of these three basic units—protons, neutrons, and electrons—and the differences among the elements is determined only

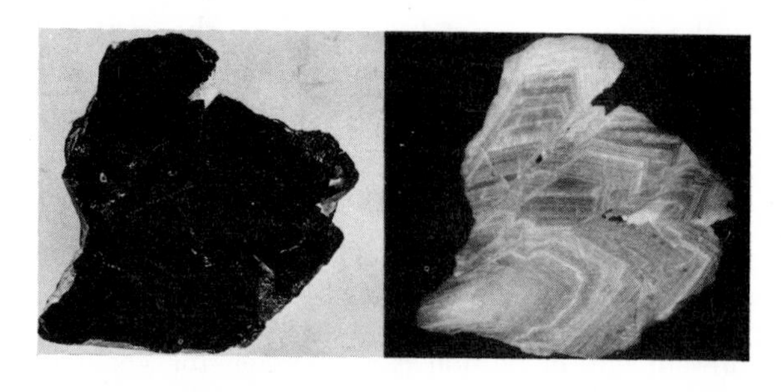

Figure 10 and chapter opening. Evidence of radioactivity in the black mineral Samarskite from Mitchell County, North Carolina. Left, normal photograph of a slice of the mineral; right, photograph from a negative exposed while enclosed in its opaque cover upon which the specimen had been placed. It was in similar manner that Becquerel, in 1896, accidentally discovered radioactivity.

by their number and arrangement. All the atoms of an element have a constant and unique number of protons. This is the *atomic number* of the element and determines its position in the periodic table.

The mass of the proton is the same in all the elements and is considered unity in the scale of mass. A neutron has almost the same mass as a proton, but that of the electron is negligible. The mass, or *atomic weight,* of an atom is then the sum of the masses of all its protons and neutrons. The simplest of all the elements is hydrogen which has only one proton. Its atomic number is therefore 1 and its mass 1. Common carbon, on the other hand, has 6 protons and 6 neutrons, its atomic number being 6 and its atomic weight 12. At the other extreme stand the heavy elements such as common uranium which has 92 protons and 146 neutrons. Its atomic number is 92 and its atomic weight 238.

It has been found, however, that many of the elements occur in two or more varieties distinguished by differences in the number of neutrons. One variety of carbon, for instance, has 6 neutrons, another 7, and a third 8. The atomic weights are respectively 12, 13, and 14, and they are distinguished as carbon^{12}, carbon^{13}, and carbon^{14} (C^{12}, C^{13}, C^{14}). Such varieties, distinguished by differences in the number of neutrons, are *isotopes.* As another example, uranium, with 92 protons, has one isotope (U^{235}) with 143 neutrons and another (U^{238}) with 146 neutrons. In spite of such differences in atomic weight, the several isotopes having the same number of protons belong to the same element since their chemical characteristics are determined not by the neutrons but by the nature of the electron cloud, which in turn is a function of the number of protons in the nucleus.

Certain isotopes of some of the elements are not quite stable, and, in these, transformations occur from time to time within the atoms that eventually reduce them to a stable state. During this process particles are discharged from the nucleus of the atom with high energy. These emitted particles produce the phenomenon known as *radioactivity.*

Uranium is one of the unstable elements, and, in its radioactive disintegration to lead, three main types of radiation may be distinguished. These are: (1) *gamma rays* (similar to X-rays but generally more energetic), (2) *alpha particles* (each consisting of 2 protons and 2 neutrons), and (3) *beta particles* (high energy electrons).

Upon its emission an alpha particle, being positively charged, immediately seizes a pair of electrons and thus becomes an atom of helium.

The loss of an alpha particle reduces both the atomic number and the atomic weight of the parent atom and transforms it into a different element. Thus, for example, discharge of one alpha particle from an atom of uranium transforms it into an atom of "ionium" (an isotope of thorium), and the loss of another alpha particle transforms it into an atom of radium. Thus, by a series of steps of emission of alpha particles, beta particles, and electrons an atom of uranium is eventually transformed into an atom of lead, which is stable. Thus the Alchemist's dream of transforming one element into another is actually realized!

One other type of alteration may take place within the atom: (1) Capture of an electron (which is negatively charged) by a proton (which is positively charged) will neutralize its charge and transform it into a neutron. This decreases the atomic number by one without changing the atomic weight. (2) Discharge of a beta particle converts a neutron into a proton. This increases the atomic number.

The rate and mode of radioactive disintegration are definite and unique for each unstable isotope. The rate is commonly expressed by the term *half life,* which is simply the length of time that is required for any given quantity of the material to be diminished by half. The following table[5] indicates the type of basic information now used in geochronometry. In this table α indicates an alpha particle and β a beta particle, and the half-life is expressed in billions of years.

Dating by the Uranium/Lead Ratio

In 1907 the American chemist, Boltwood, observed that uranium and thorium minerals such as uraninite, pitchblende, and samarskite (Fig. 10) invariably contain both lead and helium. He therefore concluded that these are the stable end products of the radioactive disintegration of uranium and thorium, and suggested that, the rate of disintegration being known, the length of time since the mineral crystallized could be calculated from the lead/uranium and lead/thorium ratios. For instance, using a simplified version of the radioactive disintegration data given above (and recognizing that U^{238} is presently about 140 times more abundant than its isotope U^{235}), we calculate that 1 gram of uranium will give annually 1/7,600,000,000 gram of lead. At this rate U grams of uranium will yield $U/7{,}600{,}000{,}000$ grams of lead in one year, and in t years it will yield $t \times U/7{,}600{,}000{,}000$ grams of lead. Then, the lead (Pb) produced by a given mass of uranium (U) in a certain number of years may be expressed thus:

$$Pb = \frac{tU}{7{,}600{,}000{,}000}$$

whence,

$$t = \frac{Pb}{U} \times 7{,}600{,}000{,}000$$

For example, crystals of uraninite (a complex silicate of uranium) from Branchville, Connecticut (Fig. 11), show a lead/uranium ratio of 0.050. Solving the equation,

$$t = 0.050 \times 7{,}600{,}000{,}000 = 380{,}000{,}000 \text{ years.}$$

This result is acceptable insofar as the assumptions, explicit and implicit, are valid. It soon became evident, however, that such simple calculations gave only approximately correct results, since when several dates from a single rock mass were determined it frequently turned out that they were not consistent. One of the difficulties lay in the assumption that at the time of crystallization no lead had been incorporated in the mineral. If lead

Parent, Element—Isotope	Daughter, Element—Isotope	Disintegration, Mode	Half Life, Billion Years
uranium—U^{238}	lead—Pb^{206}	$8\alpha + 6\beta$	4.51
uranium—U^{235}	lead—Pb^{207}	$7\alpha + 4\beta$	0.71
thorium—Th^{232}	lead—Pb^{208}	$6\alpha + 4\beta$	13.9
rubidium—Rb^{87}	strontium—Sr^{87}	β	50.0
potassium—K^{40}	argon—A^{40}	electron capture	12.4

Figure 11. Granite from Branchville, Connecticut. The small dark crystals (X) are *uraninite;* the lighter matrix is feldspar. The corrected ratio of lead to uranium in the uraninite indicates that this rock is 350,000,000 years old.

had been so incorporated the calculated age would be too great. Another source of error lay in the assumption that no lead had been added from underground solutions after crystallization.

As a result of pioneer work by A. O. Nier on precision mass spectrometry, it is now possible to determine the actual amounts of each of the lead isotopes. Then independent age determinations can be calculated from the three ratios, U^{235}/Pb^{207}, U^{238}/Pb^{206}, and Th^{232}/Pb^{208}. If there had been loss of lead by solution, the different isotopes would have gone into solution in equal amounts (since they behave alike chemically) and the calculated ages would disagree, since the three forms of lead were generated at different rates; but if they agree there can have been no loss and the calculated age has a very high degree of reliability.

It is even possible to determine whether any lead was incorporated at the time of crystallization or has been added since by ground water. It is known, for example, that common lead such as might be carried in solution, is a mixture of 4 isotopes in approximately the following proportions: 1 percent Pb^{204} (which is not radiogenic), 26 percent Pb^{206}, 21 percent Pb^{207}, and 52 percent Pb^{208}. Once the amount of Pb^{204} has been determined by mass spectrometry, the proper amounts of each of the other isotopes can be deducted before age calculations are made.

Independent age determinations may also be made from the lead/uranium ratios in the common accessory mineral zircon ($ZrSiO_4$). The advantages of this method are twofold: (1) zircons are ubiquitous in igneous rocks whereas uraninite is generally restricted to pegmatite dikes; (2) zircons are less subject than common uranium minerals to chemical changes during geological vicisitudes.

Dating by the Lead/Alpha-Particle Ratio

A simple method, first proposed in 1952[6], is based on the lead/alpha-particle ratio in zircon. Since the transformation of an atom of uranium (or of thorium) into an atom of lead involves the discharge of 8 alpha particles, the rate of discharge of alpha particles from a given mass of zircon gives a measure of the rate at which lead is being formed, since we know experimentally the rate at which the radioactive parents (uranium and thorium) disintegrate.

In practice, an age determination is made as follows. A fresh sample of zircon-bearing igneous rock is selected and crushed so that the grains separate and can be segregated and freed of matrix and fragments of other minerals. A small sample (about 60 milligrams) of pure zircon is thus secured for investigation. The lead content of the sample, in parts per million is then determined by mass spectroscopy, and the number of alpha particles emitted per hour is determined by a special type of Geiger counter. The age of the rock is then calculated from the formula

$$A = \frac{\text{Pb} \times k}{\alpha}$$

where A is the age in millions of years, Pb is the amount of lead in parts per million, k is a constant representing the rate at which alpha particles are emitted from the parent radioactive substances (uranium and thorium), and α is the observed count of alpha particles per milligrams of the sample per hour. If all the radiation is due to uranium, k equals 2,632, but if it is all due to thorium k equals 2,013, and if both uranium and thorium are present in equal amounts k equals 2,485. The proportions of uranium and thorium are determined spectroscopically and, whatever the ratio may be, the value of k is then readily calculated.

Because of its relative simplicity and the speed with which these measurements can be made, this method is currently being extensively used. Its proponents believe that there is little likelihood of lead having been incorporated in the zircon crystals when they formed, or of lead being added from underground solutions, because the lead atom, being about 50 percent larger than the zirconium atom, could not fit readily into the tightly packed space lattice, and because lead, being bivalent whereas zirconium is tetravalent, would require a complex and improbable double bonding. These claims are now denied by some of the specialists who express considerable doubt as to the reliability of dates based on the lead/alpha-particle ratio.

Ages Based on the Potassium/Argon Ratio

Potassium is one of the common elements found in rocks. One of its isotopes, K^{40}, is radioactive and can be used in geochronometry. There are two paths by which it can disintegrate: (1) By emission of a beta particle it is transformed into calcium^{40}; and (2) by electron capture it is transformed into argon^{40}. The latter mode is of the greater importance in geology not only because of its use in geochronometry but also because it explains the source of the great abundance of argon^{40} in the atmosphere (1 percent by volume).

Since argon is a gas, it tends to leak out of most minerals, especially the feldspars. Therefore when independent age determinations are made from the potassium/argon ratios in feldspars and in micas from the same igneous rock, the feldspars give ages far younger than the micas give. On the other hand, where this method has been applied to rock masses that have been independently dated by lead/uranium ratios, the age derived from the micas agrees well with that from the lead/uranium ratios. For this reason it appears that argon cannot escape from the space lattice of the micas, and only they are now used in measuring the K/A ratio.

Dating Based on the Rubidium/Strontium Ratio

The last common method for dating rocks is based on the ratio of rubidium^{87} to strontium^{87}.

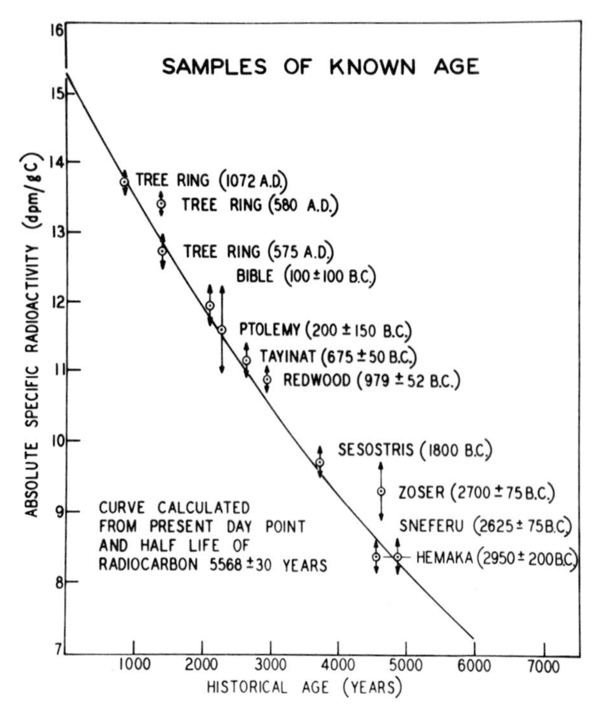

Figure 12. Predicted versus observed radioactivities of objects of known dates. The curve represents the theoretical decline of radioactivity in time. Each dot represents the observed radioactivity and the calculated age of a named object. Where the dots fall upon or near the curve the agreement is good. If such a dot be projected vertically to the baseline it will be found that the calculated age agrees closely with the known age. Reproduced from *Radiocarbon Dating* (University of Chicago Press) with the permission of the author, Dr. W. F. Libby.

Since this isotope of strontium tends to follow the rather abundant common strontium in its chemical associations, caution must be used to select minerals with a low content of common strontium or to make proper corrections for common strontium in a manner similar to that used for making corrections for lead.

The minerals commonly used are those rich in potassium since rubidium, being also an alkali metal, will tend to be associated with potassium in crystallization whereas strontium is discriminated against. Two micas, lepidolite and biotite, are the minerals commonly used.

It is now known that some of the rocks in the Earth's crust are almost 3,000,000,000 years old, that a good record of life, beginning with the Cambrian Period, takes us back some 600,000,000 years, and that human existence began some hundreds of thousands of years ago.

Ages exceeding 2,000,000,000 years have been determined for the oldest rocks in Manitoba, in the Kola Peninsula of Russia, and in South Africa.[7]

Radiocarbon Dating

The radioactive elements discussed above, having immensely long life periods, serve well to date the ancient rocks, but their disintegration is so slow that changes within a few million years fall within the limits of experimental error. For rocks less than ten or fifteen million years old we need radioactive isotopes of much shorter life periods, and, unfortunately, no suitable ones for most of this span are yet known; but for the last fifty thousand years or so, a radioactive isotope of carbon, C^{14}, is almost ideal. It was first discovered in nature by Dr. W. F. Libby, former chief of the United States Atomic Energy Commission, who by 1949 had developed the techniques of radiocarbon dating.[8] Its contributions to late Pleistocene history and to archeology are already spectacular.

Radiocarbon is formed in the outer atmosphere by the bombardment of cosmic rays which transform some of the atoms of nitrogen (N^{14}) into a radioactive isotope of carbon (C^{14}). The latter readily unites with oxygen to form CO_2 and is then rapidly mixed with the normal CO_2 in the atmosphere. The radiocarbon is slightly unstable, however, and is gradually transformed back into nitrogen. This takes place at such a rate that half of any given quantity of C^{14} will disappear in 5,568 years, and half the remainder will be gone in another 5,568 years, etc. Since radioactive carbon is constantly being formed in the upper atmosphere and constantly disappearing by transformation back into nitrogen, the ratio of radioactive CO_2 to normal CO_2 in the atmosphere must long since have reached a steady state, so that the ratio of radiocarbon (C^{14}) to normal carbon (C^{12}) is constant.

When used by plants, the two forms of carbon are built into their tissues in exactly this ratio, and when assimilated into animal tissue the ratio is also unchanged. Once locked in, however, the radiocarbon slowly reverts to nitrogen and the ratio of C^{14} to C^{12} gradually decreases. This ratio is then a measure of the time that has elapsed since the organism lived. If, for example, the ratio is one-half that in the atmosphere, then the organism lived about 5,568 years ago, and if it is one-fourth, the organism lived about 11,136 years ago. After about 30,000 years the amount of C^{14} remaining is so small as to be difficult to measure, and the probable error of age determination rises appreciably.

The reliability of radiocarbon dating can be objectively tested by applying it to the great trees in which growth rings record the last 3,000 to 4,000 years, and to archeologic objects that are independently dated. The high degree of correlation is indicated by Figure 12.

CALIBRATING THE GEOLOGIC TIME SCALE

The geologic time scale, based on the sequence of the stratified rocks, shows the *relative* antiquity of geologic events but not their *absolute* ages. If, however, we can establish enough dates, up and down the column, by radioactive criteria, it can be transformed into an *absolute* time scale. A beginning has been made, and we can confidently expect that with the next few decades the column will be well dated. Thus far, however, only a few absolute dates can be closely tied to the geologic record. The best of these are indicated in Figure 8.

New discoveries and refinements in measurement have served to discredit some of the dates given in the previous printings of this volume and to increase the span of Paleozoic time[11, 12]. Both K/A and U/Pb ratios in the Chattanooga shale, for example, agree in dating the base of the Mississippian as approximately 350,000,000 years old. This is supported by granites in Maine that cut Lower Devonian formations and are unconformably overlain by Mississippian rocks in which the K/A and Rb/Sr ratios agree well in indicating a date of about 360,000,000 years. Likewise a granite in Scotland that intruded Middle Silurian rocks and was exposed in Early Devonian time gives a date of about 400,000,000 years. Volcanic ash beds in the Middle Ordovician of Alabama and Eastern Tennessee have yielded Rb/Sr, U238/Pb206, and U235/Pb207 ratios that agree well in indicating an age of about 445,000,000 years. A post-Cambrian granite in Nova Scotia is found to be about 490,000,000 years old. These and many other recent datings indicate a time scale as revised in Figure 8.

In most instances radioactive minerals are found in pegmatites or granites that commonly can be only approximately dated geologically. A hypothetical case (Fig. 13) will illustrate the problem. Suppose that uranium minerals are found at locality X in pegmatite dikes related to a large granitic intrusion that deformed a roof of Cretaceous formations (K). In the surrounding region Cenozoic strata (O) unconformably overlie the deformed Cretaceous rocks but are not cut by the pegmatites. The minerals in the dikes give an absolute age, let us say, of 60,000,000 years. Obviously the dikes are younger than the intruded Cretaceous formations and older than the overlapping Cenozoic

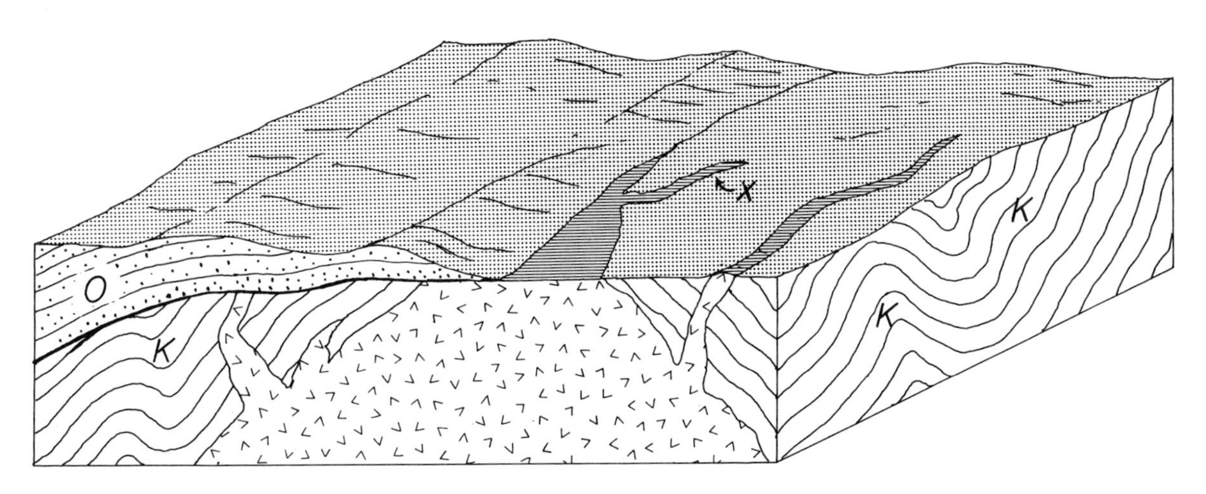

Figure 13. Block diagram to illustrate the problem of determining the *geologic* age of a radioactive mineral.

overlapping Cenozoic formations. But how closely can we locate this date in geologic time?

Suppose further that the highest Cretaceous rocks in the deformed area are dated by ammonites as Late (but not latest) Cretaceous; and that the lowest of the overlying Tertiary rocks are dated by plants or by vertebrate fossils as Early Oligocene. Then, clearly, the date of sixty million years B.P. (before the present) falls somewhere within the span of latest Cretaceous, Paleocene, or Eocene time. Such a wide span, however, leaves us with a very inexact geologic date for the emplacement of the pegmatites. On general principles we can narrow the possibilities considerably. We know, for example, that granite and pegmatite dikes form only at great depths where a magma cools slowly. A considerable thickness of the enclosing rock must therefore have been removed by erosion after intrusion and before the deposition of the Cenozoic cover. This probably involved the whole of the Eocene Epoch and we conclude that the granitic intrusion occurred very late in Cretaceous time or during the Paleocene Epoch. Geo logically speaking this was near the close of the Mesozoic Era, but from the data cited it could have been exactly at its close or some millions of years later, possibly near the close of Paleocene time.

The important date of the Mesozoic-Cenozoic boundary presents problems of this sort. The pitchblende deposit at Central City, in the Front Range of the Rockies in Colorado, has yielded reliable dates of approximately 60,000,000 years. The pitchblende veins are genetically related to a porphyry stock that cuts through a great thrust plate that has affected the Paleocene rocks in this area but not the true Eocene. This would seem to date the close of the Paleocene Epoch rather closely. But if so, what is the date of the beginning of the epoch which is the Mesozoic-Cenozoic boundary? Thus far we have no radioactive data at that horizon and can make only a rough estimate of the length of Paleocene time based on the relative thickness of Paleocene rocks as compared to those formed later, and on the relative amount of vertebrate evolution as shown by the fossils. The present best guess is about five million years, and on this basis the end of the Mesozoic Era is tentatively set at about 65,000,000 B.P.

The mineral glauconite occurs widely in sedimentary rocks from Cambrian to Recent, and commonly contains radioactive materials. If these could be used safely many points in the geologic time scale could be closely dated, but unfortunately they have given erratic and conflicting results. The trouble seems to be that the individual grains of glauconite were formed on the sea floor by alteration of ferromagnesian sand grains (such as mica flakes) derived from divers older rocks. In these, radioactive lead already present when the grains were deposited is added to that formed subsequently.

We may close this chapter with the conclusion that the Earth is at least 3,000,000,000 years old, that the beginning of the Paleozoic Era (with the first abundant fossils) was some 600,000,000 years ago, the beginning of the Mesozoic Era (Age of the Great Reptiles) about 230,000,000 years ago, and that of the Age of Mammals approximately 65,000,000 years ago, and that Man has existed on Earth for some hundreds of thousands of years.

> To grasp what these figures mean, [Mahoney[10] has written] we may imagine ourselves walking down the avenue of time into the past and covering a thousand years at each pace. The first step takes up back to William the Conqueror, the second to the beginning of the Christian era, the third to Helen of Troy, the fourth to Abraham, and the seventh to the earliest traditional history of Babylon and Egypt; . . . 130 paces takes us to Heidelberg man, and about ¼ mile to the oldest undoubted stone implements of Europe. And should we decide to continue our journey until we meet the most ancient fossil organisms, the journey would exceed 250 miles.

REFERENCES

1. Lightfoot, John, 1642, *A few and new observations on the Booke of Genesis. Most of them certaine, the rest probable, all harmlesse, strange, and rarely heard of before.* Printed by T. Badger, London.

In this publication (p. 3) the time is stated to be "nine of the clocke in the morning" but the day of the year is not given; but in a later chapter, "The Harmony of the Four Gospels" (1644), he deduces that the date was September 17.

2. Ussher, James, 1658, *Annals of the World.* London, at the sign of the Ship in St. Pauls Church-yard, Fleet Street.

3. *Oxford Cyclopedic Concordance,* Oxford University Press, London, p. 54. (I am indebted to Mr. George Bedigian for this reference.)

4. Joly, John, 1901, An estimate of the geological age of the earth. *Smithsonian Institution, Ann. Report for 1899,* pp. 247–288.

5. Tilton, G. R., and G. L. Davis, 1959, Geochronology. In *Researches in Geochemistry*, Philip H. Abelson, ed. John Wiley and Sons, New York, pp. 190–216.

6. Larsen, E. S., Jr., N. B. Keevil, and H. C. Harrison, 1952, Method for determining the age of igneous rocks using the accessory minerals. *Geol. Soc. Amer., Bull.*, vol. 63, pp. 1045–1052.

7. Knopf, Adolph, 1955, Bathyliths in time. *Geol. Soc. Amer., Special Paper 62*, pp. 685–702.

8. Libby, W. F., 1952, *Radiocarbon Dating*, University of Chicago Press, Chicago. ———, 1954, Radiocarbon dating. *Endeavor*, vol. 13, no. 49, pp. 5–16.

9. Carroll, Dorothy, 1959, Zircon from a bentonite bed in Martinsburg shale (Ordovician) at Fishers Hill, Virginia. *Geol. Soc. Amer., Bull.*, vol. 70, pp. 223–224.

10. Mahoney, D. J., 1943, The problem of antiquity of man in Australia. *Mem. Nat. Museum of Melbourne*, no. 13, p. 7.

11. Faul, Henry, 1960, Geologic Time Scale. *Geol. Soc. Amer., Bull.* vol. 71, pp. 637–644.

12. Kulp, J. Lawrence, 1961, Geologic Time Scale. *Science*, vol. 133, pp. 1105–1114.

Figure 14. The Beresovka mammoth mortally wounded by falling into a crevasse in the ice in Siberia some thousands of years ago. (Etching by Rudolf F. Zallinger.)

Chapter 3. *The Living Record of the Dead*

Race after race resigned their fleeting breath—
The rocks alone their curious annals save.

T. A. CONRAD

Earth's Cold-Storage Locker. In August, 1900, a Russian hunter, following a wounded deer along the valley of Beresovka River in eastern Siberia, came upon the head of an elephant sticking out of the frozen ground (Fig. 15). He chopped off a tusk, which he later sold to a Cossack through whom the news reached St. Petersburg that another frozen mammoth had been found. An expedition organized by the National Academy of Sciences to collect the specimen reached the locality in September, 1901, after a journey of some 3,000 miles, and after the back of the animal had been exposed to the warmth of two summers and part of the flesh had been gnawed away by wild animals. Excavation soon revealed, however, that the buried portion was still intact, and on one of the limbs the flesh was "dark red in color and looked as fresh as well-frozen beef or horse meat." Indeed, scraps of it were eagerly devoured by the collectors' dog team.

The animal had died in the position shown in Figure 14. Broken bones (several ribs, a hip, and a shoulder blade), as well as much clotted blood in the chest, and unswallowed food in its jaws, suggest a sudden and violent death; and the wall of ice beside it indicated that the animal had fallen into a crevasse and died struggling to extricate itself.

The presence of this elephant 60 miles within the Arctic Circle, and more than 2,000 miles north of the present range of living elephants, was no more surprising than its anatomical peculiarities. Unlike all living elephants it bore a thick coat of reddish-brown wool interspersed with long black contour hair. Its head was narrow, and had a distinctive high-crowned profile. It was, in short, a Woolly Mammoth belonging to a species that ranged widely over the northern parts of Eurasia and North America during the last great Ice Age, and was as well adapted as the reindeer to the frigid climate of the time.

Most of the Beresovka specimen is on display in

Figure 15. Frozen carcass of the Beresovka mammoth after partial excavation. (After Herz.)

Figure 16. Drawing of the woolly mammoth by prehistoric man on the wall of a cave at Combarelles, France, and modern restoration of the same by Charles R. Knight, based on this and the Beresovka specimen.

the Zoological Museum at the University in Leningrad, but pieces of the dried flesh, clotted blood, and woolly skin were presented to the United States Government and are now on display in the U.S. National Museum.

A similar frozen carcass, dead for more than 30,000 years,[13] was found in the Lena River delta in 1799 and was collected in 1806. The woolly mammoth has been extinct so long that no allusions to it appear in the legends of any living people, yet an unmistakable picture of it was left by prehistoric man on the walls of a cavern at Combarelles, France (Fig. 16). Beside the two nearly complete frozen carcasses described above, some fifty others, less complete, have been found in Siberia and in Alaska, preserved since prehistoric times in Nature's cold-storage locker. A similarly preserved extinct bison in Alaska is known from radiocarbon dating to have died 28,000 years ago.[1]

Images in Stone. Less spectacular but no less real are the bones and shells of animals, and the remains of plants, entombed in solid rock in many parts of the world. They are the remains of creatures that lived and died and were buried in sediment that later solidified into rock. The ancients observed such "images in stone" and speculated on their meaning. The Romans called them **fossils**, because they were objects dug up (Lat. *fossilis*, from *fodere*, to dig), and we have borrowed that name. The study of fossils is the science of **paleontology** (Gr. *palaios*, ancient + *onta*, existing things + *logos*, a discourse).

The Nature of Fossils. The term fossil was for a time applied to a wide range of "curios" found in the rocks, both organic and mineral; but it is now correctly used only for the remains of once-living things naturally preserved from the geologic past. Some degree of antiquity is thus implied, but since the present grades insensibly into the past, no sharp date line has been established. One geologic wag has proposed that "if the remains stink they belong to zoology, but if not, to paleontology." While making a point, this is hardly an acceptable criterion of antiquity! In general, organic remains in modern sediment are excluded, even though deeply buried, whereas identical objects in older deposits are accepted as fossils.

Extinction is not a criterion, since many of the existing species were already present millions of years ago and are preserved as fossils in Cenozoic rocks while, on the other hand, some species have become extinct within historic time. A good example is the Dodo, a giant flightless pigeon, that lived on Mauritius Islands in the Indian Ocean until 1681 when the last survivors were killed by white settlers. Remains of this bird now preserved in the British Museum are not fossils, first, because they were artificially preserved and, second, because they are not ancient. Nevertheless if remains of the Dodo were found in the Cenozoic rocks of the Islands they would be considered fossils.

Although coal and petroleum are derived from organic matter they are not considered to be fossil since they do not show organic structures. Not uncommonly, however, coal includes bits and

Figure 17. A skeleton in the rock. This complete skeleton of an extinct ground-sloth was discovered in the bank of a small arroyo in the Pampas formation in Argentina by the Marshall Field Expedition of 1927, and is now displayed in the Chicago Museum of Natural History exactly as it lay in the rock. Length about 8 feet. (Chicago Museum of Natural History.)

pieces of petrified wood or the imprints of leaves, and these are recognized as fossils *within* the coal.

Although the word fossil, as a noun, is correctly applied only to the remains or traces of once-living creatures, it is commonly used as an adjective in a figurative sense for inorganic phenomena preserved in the rocks. Thus, for example, we speak of fossil mudcracks, fossil rain prints, fossil soils, fossil dunes, or even of fossil fuels.

With similar poetic licence we sometimes speak of a species of existing animal or plant as a "living fossil," implying that it belongs to the remote geologic past but has somehow managed to survive. For example, when the coelocanth fish, *Latimeria*, was caught off the central east coast of Africa in 1939 it was hailed as a living fossil since it belongs to a tribe of lungfish that had its heyday in the Devonian Period and is not known in post-Mesozoic rocks.

TYPES OF FOSSILIZATION

Actual Preservation. The preservation of flesh and other soft tissues is possible only where bacterial action and decay have been almost miraculously inhibited. Cold storage in the Arctic ice is one means of such preservation. Oil seeps have also, in a few instances, afforded sufficiently antiseptic conditions. A remarkably complete carcass of the woolly rhinoceros was excavated from the muck of an oil seep in the district of Sarunia, Poland, in 1930, and a similar specimen from another oil seep is preserved in the museum at Lemberg, Poland, where the skeleton and the mounted skin stand side by side. The woolly rhinoceros was a contemporary of the woolly mammoth and, like the latter, was adapted to arctic conditions and has also been found preserved in ice.

Although soft tissues are rarely preserved and occur almost exclusively in late Pleistocene deposits, the hard parts such as bone, shells, or woody tissue, have commonly been preserved with little change since Cretaceous time. Logs embedded in Cretaceous clays or in Eocene lignites, for example, have suffered slight discoloration but still retain the woody structure and burn readily. Marine shells in some of the late Cretaceous forma-

Figure 18. A fossil fish (*Seriola*) related to the living pompano, from the Eocene beds at Monte Bolca, Italy. (Yale Peabody Museum.)

tions likewise show little alteration, retaining the original microstructure and, rarely, even the color pattern in spite of a hundred million years or so of antiquity.

Petrifaction. In the older rocks, the hard parts alone are usually preserved, and these commonly appear to be turned to stone, as indeed they are. Such fossils are said to be **petrified** (Lat. *petra*, stone + *facere*, to make). The change from the original condition is accomplished in one of the following ways:

1. By permineralization. If the original structure is porous, as bones or many kinds of shells, mineral matter may be added from the underground water to fill up all the voids without altering the original substances. This makes the object heavier, more compact, and more stonelike, at the same time protecting it from the air or solutions that would dissolve and destroy it. Such fossils are said to be **permineralized.** Petrified bones are commonly of this category (Figs. 17 and 18).

2. By replacement. The original substance may, however, be dissolved and **replaced** by mineral matter of a different sort. Wood is commonly preserved in this way, the woody tissue being replaced by silica. As a rule, the change is so gradual and so delicate that the cell walls and all the microscopic structures of the wood are preserved, even after the organic matter is gone, and the log is literally turned to stone (Fig. 19). The fossil forests of the Yellowstone and of Arizona provide striking and familiar illustrations. Such replacements of wood by either silica or calcium carbonate are known as far back as the Devonian Period.

On the other hand, the substitution may result in the loss of all internal structure while preserving the gross form of the organic object, as, for example, a coral or shell replaced by quartz, calcium carbonate, dolomite, etc. Such a fossil is a false replica or **pseudomorph**, showing only the external form (Fig. 22).

Where calcareous shells are embedded in limestone, some subtle chemical difference between the shells and the matrix commonly causes the shells to be replaced by silica while the surrounding stone is unaltered. In the weathering of such rocks the fossils are freed and may be collected as siliceous pseudomorphs on the surface. It is also possible to free them artificially by dissolving pieces of the limestone in hydrochloric, acetic, or formic acid (Fig. 22).

Calcareous nodules from a Miocene lake deposit near Yermo, California have thus yielded amazingly preserved insects and spiders in which all chitinous structures have been replaced by silica.[2] Freed by the use of formic acid, they reveal such delicate structures as the internal trachaea, the muscles, the heart, the alimentary canal, and genetalia (Fig. 23).

3. By distillation. The volatile elements of organic material may be distilled away, leaving a residue of carbon to record the form of the object. Leaves are generally preserved in this way, and the beautiful "carbon copies" of fern leaves in the shale above some of the coal beds give a vivid picture of the ancient plants (Fig. 20). More rarely animal tissue is recorded in this way, as in the Lower Jurassic ichthyosaurs of Germany whose skeletons, preserved in dark shale, are surrounded by a film of carbon showing the outline of the fleshy body and even of the fins and tail flukes (Fig. 21). At one famous locality in British Columbia, Middle Cambrian black shales have yielded an amazing array of soft-bodied invertebrate animals thus preserved as mere carbon films on the bedding planes (Pl. 3).

Molds, Casts, and Imprints. Shells or other organic structures embedded in rock may later be dissolved by percolating ground water, leaving an open space that preserves the form of the object. This hole is a **natural mold.** By pressing into it a plastic substance such as dental wax, we may obtain an artificial *cast* or replica of the original (Fig. 24). Percolating subsurface water has in many instances filled such holes with some other mineral substance, usually quartz, thus producing **natural casts.** The terminology applied to fossils follows that of foundry practice, the **cast** being the replica of the original, its counterpart being the **mold.** Hollow objects may have, besides the external mold, an internal mold or **core.** The molds of thin objects like leaves are commonly spoken of as **imprints** (Fig. 25 and 263, p. 308). The pattern of the

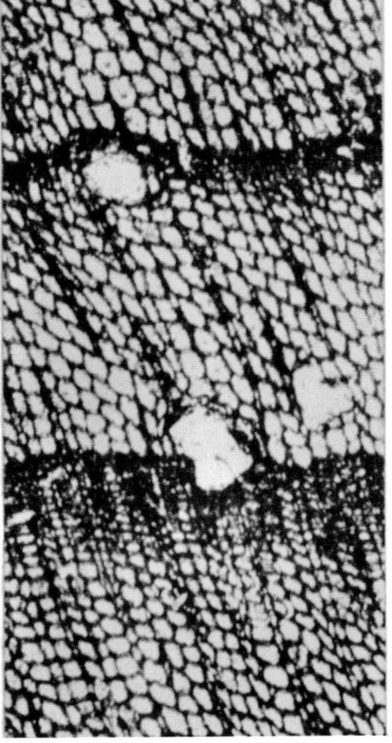

Figure 19. Petrified wood from the Fossil Forest of the Yellowstone National Park. Left, a piece of the petrified wood, slightly enlarged, showing the growth rings and medullary rays; right, a thin section cut from the end of this piece, enlarged about 12 times to show the cells in parts of 3 growth rings. Photographs not retouched. (Yale Peabody Museum.)

Figure 20. Fossil fern leaves preserved as a carbonaceous film in shales in the Coal Measures of Germany. (Yale Peabody Museum.)

scales in the skin of some dinosaurs is thus well shown by impressions in the matrix, although no other trace of the skin is preserved (Fig. 288, p. 338).

Among the most remarkable natural molds are those of insects and spiders preserved in amber in the Oligocene beds along the Baltic coast of Germany (Fig. 26). Amber is the dried and hardened residue of the resins exuded by evergreen trees such as the white fir. The insects and spiders were entangled while it was still soft and have since been entombed for more than 20 million years. For the most part the organic tissues have dried and almost disappeared, though rarely dried muscles and even the viscera can be recognized; but the sharp hollow molds in the transparent amber retain the shape of the insects with extraordinary faithfulness.

Footprints and Trails. (Fig. 27). The tracks left by a living animal are considered fossils, and they supplement the other remains in interesting ways. From the tracks we can tell whether an animal was bipedal or quadrapedal, whether it moved by running, leaping, or sprawling, and whether it was agile or ponderous. Thus, we know that although the bipedal dinosaurs were shaped much like a kangaroo they nevertheless ran like an ostrich. Tracks alone give us some of the earliest records of land vertebrates, and in some formations tracks alone prove that animals were once abundant where no skeletal remains are preserved. (See Fig. 237, p. 277.)

Coprolites. Fossil excrement constitutes another class of fossils, known as **coprolites.** These often contain undigested hard parts of animals or plants that were devoured. Wherever associated with skeletal remains in such a way that their source can be recognized, coprolites are of special significance for the light they throw on the food and feeding habits of the animal in question. For example, the dried dung found with fossil ground-sloths gives the only proof we have of the type of vegetation preferred by that race of extinct monsters (Fig. 28).

CONDITIONS FAVORING PRESERVATION

The buffalo carcasses strewn over the plains in uncounted numbers two generations ago have left hardly a present trace. The flesh was devoured soon after death by vultures or wolves and even the bones have crumbled to dust. This suggests that special conditions are required for preservation. Two such conditions are paramount.

Possession of Hard Parts. Animals or plants with hard parts have an overwhelming advantage in the chance of preservation. Leaves are commonly preserved as imprints or as carbonized films, but flesh decays so readily that preservation is rarely possible. Bones and shells and wood, on the contrary, form most of the fossil record. It is not surprising that many groups of soft-bodied animals such as worms and jellyfish have left almost no geologic record; the rare instances in which they were preserved, as in the Mid-Cambrian black shale of Mount Wapta (p. 122), serve only to emphasize what a wealth of animal life existed in the ancient seas that is virtually unrecorded.

Quick Burial. A carcass left exposed after death is almost sure to be torn apart or devoured by carnivores or other scavengers, and if it escapes these larger enemies, bacteria insure the decay of all but the hard parts, and even they crumble to dust after a few years if exposed to the weather. If buried under moist sediment or standing water, however, weathering is prevented, decay is greatly reduced, and scavengers cannot disturb the remains. For

Figure 21. Fossil ichthyosaur, a marine reptile from the Lower Jurassic shales of Holzmaden, Germany. The skeleton is permineralized, the flesh reduced to a film of carbon. The species ranges from 8 to 10 feet long. (American Museum of Natural History.)

Figure 22. Silicified shells etched from limestone. At the right, a block of cherty limestone of mid-Ordovician age from Lake St. John, Quebec; at the left, below, a piece of the same rock partly etched away by HCl; at the left, above, shells of snails and a small clam freed from the matrix. These shells are pseudomorphs in SiO_2. (Yale Peabody Museum.)

these reasons burial soon after death is the most important condition favoring preservation. This may occur in nature in several ways.

Animals drowned by **floods** are commonly swept along the channel to be buried in sand or mud, and where many individuals are killed in a single flood they are likely to be concentrated in favored deeps or areas of slack water. This probably accounts for the extraordinary concentration of fossil skeletons in some ancient channel deposits (Fig. 29).

Bogs and deposits of quicksand or of asphalt form natural death traps in which animals commonly mire and are quickly covered. The peat bogs that formed in the northern states after the last Pleistocene ice sheet melted away must have been a particular hazard to the elephants that still roamed this country, for isolated skeletons of mastodons and mamoths have been found in the peat at many places. Perhaps the most remarkable deposit of Pleistocene vertebrate fossils is that of Big Bone "Lick," a bog deposit about 20 miles south of Cincinnati from which more than 100 mastodons have been recovered along with skeletons of bison, moose, reindeer, and the wild horse. This locality was known to Thomas Jefferson, who sponsored extensive excavation and, during his presidency, reserved a room in the Presidential Mansion as a museum for the fossils he had secured.

In 1943 an artesian spring deposit of Pliocene date was discovered in Meade County, Kansas, containing a large fauna of mammals that had either been trapped by quicksand or were mired in the bog around the spring.[3] The fauna includes elephants, giant camels, wild horses, wolves, and great cats.

In 1942 a locality was discovered in the Pleistocene beds of San Pedro Valley, Arizona, where mastodons had mired in the marsh about a salt lake, their limb bones still remaining upright in the deposit.[4]

In several parts of the world natural **petroleum seeps** have formed traps as the more volatile constituents evaporated away leaving pools of sticky asphalt. The way in which they work is illustrated by an incident that occurred at Mount Pleasant, Michigan, in 1939, when four small boys ventured onto a pool of such asphalt discharged as waste from a coke plant.[5] After a few steps the first boy began to sink slowly. When two companions rushed to his aid they, too, were soon trapped like flies on sticky paper. The fourth lad, fortunately, ran for help and the others were rescued, but by the time help arrived the first boy was submerged up to his neck and the other two were waist-deep. The whole incident had transpired within about half an hour!

An amazing deposit of extinct fossil mammals trapped in this way occurs at Rancho La Brea in Los Angeles (Fig. 30). It was the scene of extensive oil seeps since at least early Pleistocene time, and animals coming to the seeps for water or attempting to cross patches of asphalt were trapped, like the Michigan boys. Their struggles and death cries attracted carnivores and scavengers which in turn became trapped. Bones of these victims have been recovered by the hundreds of thousands as the asphalt is being excavated for use. No flesh has been found here, but in similar oil seeps in Poland almost entire carcasses of the extinct woolly rhinoceros have been recovered.

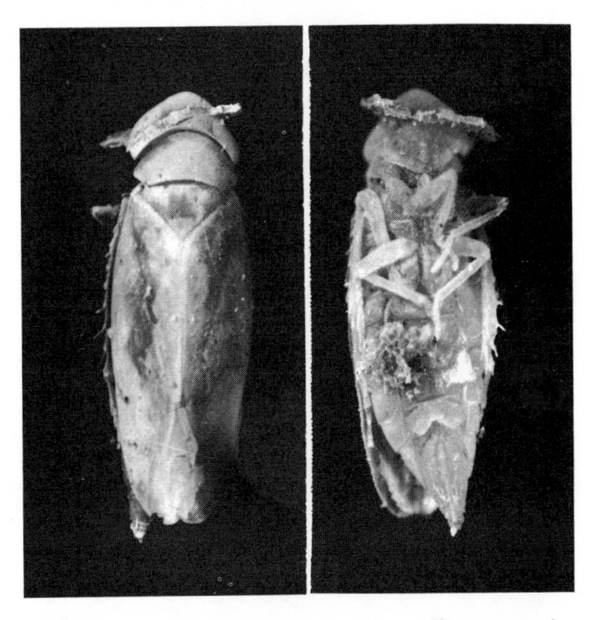

Figure 23. A leaf-hopper preserved as a siliceous pseudomorph and freed by formic acid from a calcareous nodule found in a lake deposit of Miocene date near Yermo, California. The specimen is only 3.3 mm. long. (Unretouched photograph by N. W. Shupe. U.S. Geological Survey, courtesy of A. R. Palmer.)

Caves and underground caverns are another source of fine fossils. They are often used as lairs by carnivores which drag their prey in to devour the flesh and leave the bones. Here the remains are largely

Figure 24. Left, natural mold of a brachiopod shell in sandstone; right, artificial cast from the same in plasticene. (Yale Peabody Museum.)

Figure 25. Imprint of a fern leaf in a concretion of Pennsylvanian age from Mazon Creek, Illinois. (Yale Peabody Museum.)

protected from the weather and, not uncommonly, they are soon covered by a limy deposit precipitated from dripping water. Some sink holes have served as traps into which animals have fallen. One such, near Cumberland, Maryland, has yielded the bones of 46 species of vertebrate animals, including wolves, bears, mastodons, tapirs, wild horses, deer, and antelope.[6]

The cave shown in Figure 28, is floored with deposits more than 20 feet deep in which skeletons of ground-sloths occur along with bones of the mountain lion, an extinct horse, mountain sheep and numerous other creatures.[7] This cave is so dry that decay is inhibited, and considerable portions of the skin and hair of the extinct ground-sloths have been recovered.

During the Ice Age primitive man took shelter in caves of this sort in various parts of Eurasia, tossing the refuse outside the entrance to accumulate, layer upon layer, through the centuries of occupation. Such deposits include the bones of the animals he used for food along with discarded or broken implements and ornaments. At the same time primitive man commonly buried his dead in the caves where they would be safe from scavenging wild beasts. Such caves provide the most important records of prehistoric peoples and their culture (Fig. 381, p. 442).

Falls of volcanic ash (Fig. 31) commonly kill and bury, as the tragic fate of Pompeii reminds us. Many fine fossil deposits in the Cenozoic rocks of western United States are in volcanic ash, like those of the John Day Basin in Oregon and Lake Florissant in Colorado. Flows of lava sometimes overwhelm timber, charring the tree trunks and

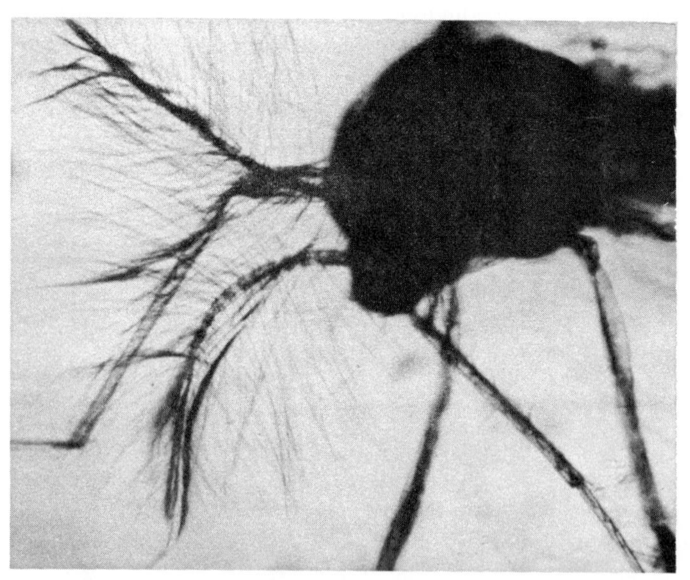

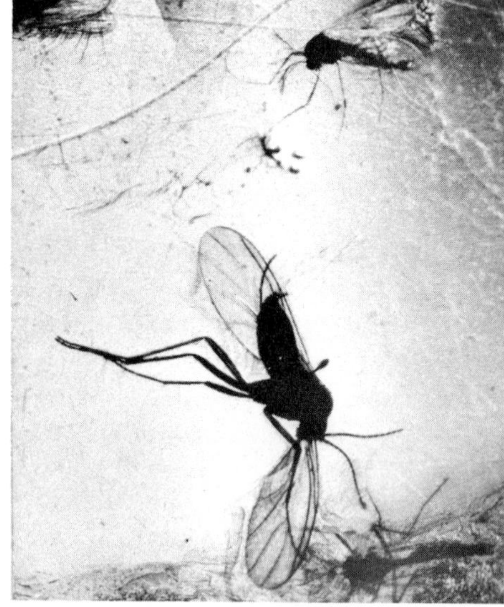

Figure 26. Insects preserved in amber. Right, two tiny specimens enlarged about 7 times; left, the smaller (upper) specimen, enlarged about 70 times, showing the microscopic filaments on its antennae. From the Oligocene beds of the Baltic coast of Germany. (Yale Peabody Museum.)

then solidifying before actually burning the wood; tuff and volcanic breccia also overwhelm and cover trees. In this way the magnificent fossil forests of Yellowstone were buried. Figure 32 shows a remarkable instance where fern leaves left an imprint on a thin flow of lava. In this unusual case the leaves were probably green and wet and the flow was very thin, so that the lava hardened before the leaves were burned. A cavity observed in the base of a lava flow in the Grand Coulee, Washington, in 1935 proved to be a natural mold of the body of an extinct twin-horned rhinoceros![8] The animal evidently had been killed and enveloped in the lava, which chilled and hardened before burning the flesh.

In deserts and along the seashore, **wind-blown sands** may overwhelm the living or bury the dead. Dry sands are not a good medium for fossilization, since oxygen can penetrate to great depths and solution after rainfalls is very active. Hence fossils are rare in desert deposits. Nevertheless the nests of dinosaur eggs found in Mongolia (Fig. 290, p. 340) were apparently preserved in this way by drifting sands.

Water-borne sediments are so much more widely distributed than all other kinds, that they include the great majority of all fossils. Flooded streams drown and bury their victims in the shifting channel sands or in the muds of the valley floor (Fig.33). Whether these objects are drift logs or leaves or animal bodies, the result is the same; they are buried in low places where the ground is generally moist, if not permanently water-covered, and where rapidly accumulating sediment gives them ever deeper and more permanent burial.

The shallow sea floor is the ulitmate repository of most of the sediment, and it is largely covered with such loose material in or upon which the teaming bottom life dwells. Most of the shells are soon covered by the sediment moved during storms. For this reason, **the sea bottom is the greatest region for the preservation of fossils,** and marine formations are rarely unfossiliferous.

Figure 27. Dinosaur footprints. Tracks of the three-toed dinosaur on a layer of Lower Cretaceous limestone near Glen Rose, Texas.

Occurrence of Fossils. It is hardly necessary to state that fossils never occur in plutonic rocks and are not to be found in any igneous rocks except where ash falls or nearly cooled lavas have overwhelmed plants and animals. They occur in all types of sedimentary rocks but are generally least common in pure sandstones and most abundant in calcareous shales and limestones. Red sandstones and shales usually have few fossils, except footprints, because the red color is due to complete oxidation, which destroys organic compounds. Even where abundant tracks prove the existence of plentiful life, as in the Triassic redbeds of Connecticut, skeletal remains are rare.

After preservation, fossils may be distorted or completely destroyed during the deformation and recrystallization of rocks involved in strong folding or thrusting. Even the compaction of some types of sediment, notably black muds, causes shells or bone to be squeezed flat (Fig. 34). The flow of weak rocks during folding commonly distorts fossils into grotesque forms. Metamorphic rocks frequently show blurred traces of fossils (as in many marbles), but where recrystallization has been complete, all traces of organic remains are commonly destroyed. Nevertheless, poorly preserved and generally distorted fossils are found locally even in highly metamorphosed rocks. Here they are of great importance for three reasons: (1) they give clear evidence that the rocks were originally sedimentary; (2) their shapes may give evidence as to the nature and amount of distortion the rocks have undergone; and (3) they may serve to date the original rocks, at least approximately.[9]

INTERPRETATION AND RECONSTRUCTION OF FOSSILS

Early Interpretations

History does not record the first observation of fossils. A Jurassic brachiopod has been found among the amulets of Neandertal man at Saint-Léon (Dordogne), France, and there are other evidences of aboriginal fossil hunters. In the writings of the Greeks, there are occasional references to such objects long before the beginning of the Christian Era. Some of these early observers correctly interpreted the organic remains and drew significant inferences from their presence in the rocks. Herodotus, for example, during his African travels about 450 B.C. observed fossil sea shells in Egypt and the Libyan desert, from which he correctly inferred that the Mediterranean had once spread across northern Africa. On the other hand much fancy and mysticism was associated with fossils even by great thinkers like Aristotle who, while believing them to be organic remains, thought they had grown in the rocks. His ideas of how this came about were obscure, but his pupil, Theophrastus, clearly expressed the idea that eggs or seeds buried with accumulating sediment had germinated and grown after burial.

The natural interpretation of fossils as organic remains of some sort seems to have been general until the beginning of the Dark Ages, when the Christian church came to insist upon a belief in a special Creation accomplished in six days, and a beginning of the Earth at a time only a few thousands of years ago. This belief left no place for extinct creatures or great changes in the position of

Figure 28. Floor of Rampart Cave in Lake Mead National Recreation Area, Nevada, covered by the dung of an extinct ground sloth. (R. K. Grater, courtesy of National Park Service.)

Figure 29. Bone bed in lower Miocene deposits at Agate, Nebraska, showing a remarkable concentration of bones of a small twin-horned rhinoceros (*Diceratherium*). Slab preserved in the museum at Scotts Bluff National Monument, Gehring, Nebraska. Courtesy of John W. Henneberger.

land and sea. Under this influence, interest in fossils was so subdued that few references to them appear in the literature of the Dark Ages. With the Renaissance, however, and the growth of natural science, fossils again claimed attention and soon became the subject of a great controversy.

The "Fossil Controversy." The controversy really began in Italy about A.D. 1500, when the digging of canals through Cenozoic marine formations brought to attention abundant shells so obviously like those of the present sea coast that their significance could hardly be doubted. Leonardo da Vinci, who besides being an artist was trained as an engineer, took a great interest in these fossils, and argued clearly that they were shells of animals once living in the places where they were found. There were many who flatly denied this, and for two centuries the controversy raged, advocates of the Organic Theory being frequently subjected to persecution. The most fantastic explanations were invented to avoid the biologic interpretation of fossils. Some were entirely mystical, attributing them to a "plastic force" at work in the rocks, while a few simply declared them "devices of the Devil," placed in the rocks to delude men. One of the most remarkable illustrations of such fanaticism occurred in Germany as late as 1696, when parts of the skeleton of a mammoth were dug from the Pleistocene deposits near Gotha. These fell into the hands of Ernst Tentzel, a teacher in the local gymnasium, who declared them to be the bones of some prehistoric monster. This heretical idea raised a furor, as a result of which the bones were examined by the medical faculty of the school and dismissed as but a "freak of nature."

Eventually when even devout Christians could no longer doubt the organic nature of fossils certain churchmen attributed them to creatures that had been buried by the Flood described in the Scriptures. The extreme to which this fallacy was carried is immortalized in a small Latin volume by Johan Andrias Scheuchzer published in 1726 and entitled *Homo diluvii testis* (The man who is proof of the flood). It contained illustrations and description of articulated skeletons from the Oligocene lake beds near Oeningen, Switzerland (Fig. 35). When the great paleontologist, Cuvier, later restudied one of these skeletons and found it to be only that of a giant salamander, he described and named it *Andrias scheuchzeri!* Two vertebrae were likewise figured by Scheuchzer as "relics of that accursed race that perished with the flood" and his figures were reproduced in the "Copper Bible" of 1731. Cuvier found these to be vertebrae of Mesozoic reptiles.

In 1706 a mastodon tooth discovered in a peat bog near Albany, New York, was sent to Governor Dudley of Massachusetts, who under date of July 10 wrote to Cotton Mather about it as follows:

I suppose all the surgeons in town have seen it, and I am perfectly of the opinion it was a human tooth. I measured it, and as it stood upright it was six inches high lacking one eight, and round 13 inches, lacking one eight, and its weight in the scale was 2 pounds and four ounces, Troy weight.

I am perfectly of the opinion that the tooth will agree only to a human body, for whom the flood only could prepare a funeral; and without doubt he waded as long as he could keep his head above the clouds, but must at length be confounded with all other creatures and the new sediment after the flood gave him the depth we now find.

It is difficult to realize that these words concerning a mastodon tooth were written in pious seriousness and not as a jest! Yet as late as 1784 Thomas Jefferson wrote to Ezra Stiles, President of Yale University, for his opinion about similar remains,

Figure 30. Asphalt trap at Rancho La Brea in Los Angeles. Above, reconstruction of a scene at the asphalt seep during late Pleistocene time by Charles R. Knight. In left foreground a saber-toothed tiger snarls at a group of giant ground sloths while vultures wait overhead, and in the middle distance a herd of Imperial elephants is in view. Lower left, a modern jack rabbit recently trapped in the asphalt; lower right, a mass of fossil bones preserved in the asphalt. (Upper picture courtesy of the American Museum of Natural History; lower pictures courtesy of the Los Angeles Museum.)

Figure 31. Volcanic ash fall from the eruption of Mt. Katmai, Alaska, in 1912. The white line indicates the profile of the mountain before eruption. Timber in the foreground was killed and largely buried by the ash fall. It is estimated that 5 cubic miles of ash and pumice were spread over an area some 200 miles across. (*National Geographic Magazine.*)

to which, after a lengthy discussion, President Stiles concluded "Perhaps the sensible rational and anatomical Virtuosi will judge those dug up at North-Holston, at Claverack and elsewhere . . . (of this enormous Description) and the Mammoths of Siberia all truly belong to an Animal Race in the shape of Men, called Giants in the Scriptures," etc.[10]

Still another illustration will show how little was known of the significance of fossils before the nineteenth century. Johannes Beringer, a teacher at Würtzburg, Germany frequently took his students to nearby shale outcrops to collect fossils. For some unexplained reason the University librarian, George von Eckhardt and a mathematics professor, Ignatz Rodrigue, "salted" the outcrops with small objects carved from marble where they would be found by Professor Beringer. These included flowers, insects, frogs, a seahorse, astronomical objects, and even characters from the Hebrew al-

Figure 32. Imprints of fern leaves on the under surface of a thin lava flow, formed during the eruption of Kilauea in 1868. (Harold S. Palmer.)

phabet. Deceived by the hoax, Beringer believed them to be natural, but apparently realized that they were not true organic remains. He therefore published a volume in 1726 entitled *Lithograhica würceburgensis* in which many of them were figured, and offered the explanation that they had formed in the rocks by natural causes even as concretions and dendrites are formed. Eventually the hoax was discovered, to Professor Beringer's great embarassment, and an inquest was held by the local Prince-Bishop that resulted in the disgrace of both Eckhardt and Rodrigue.°

The controversy over fossils served only to kindle interest in these objects, and by the beginning of the nineteenth century fossil collecting had become a hobby with many devotees in the church and out, one of the first large collections being made at the Vatican. By the year 1800 the organic nature of fossils was almost universally recognized, and learned men were generally agreed that they represent the life of the geologic past.

°This account, differing in some respects from that current in the literature, is based on a restudy of the old record by Heinrich Kirchner: "Die Würzberger Lügensteine im Licht neuer archivalischer Funde", *Deutsch. Geol. Gesell.*, v. 87, pp. 607–615, 1935. I am indebted to my colleague, John Sanders, for bringing it to my attention.

Modern Interpretations

Geographic Significance. There are many groups of animals that live exclusively in the sea. Corals, brachiopods, crinoids, sea urchins, and cephalopods are but a few examples. Their occurrence as fossils in a rock implies the presence of a sea at some former time, even though the fossils are now far inland and at great elevations in the mountains, as are the Eocene fossils at 20,000 feet in the Himalayas. The coral reefs so common in the Silurian limestones of northern Indiana leave no doubt that a great bay or inland sea like Hudson Bay or the Baltic Sea covered Indiana during Silurian time. If we plot the distribution of Silurian rocks that bear marine fossils, we can determine at least the minimum extent of this ancient seaway. If in other regions we find fossil land plants with stumps or roots in place, or if we find abundant bones or shells of land animals, it is evident that

Figure 33. A modern forest killed and in process of being buried by alluvium on the delta of Yahtze River, Alaska. (E. S. Dana.)

Figure 34. Deformation and destruction of fossils. Left, an uncrushed specimen of the trilobite *Isotelus;* center, the same species badly crushed by compaction of the sediment after burial; right, a similar trilobite reduced to a "ghost" when the enclosing shale was crushed and recrystallized into slate. (Yale Peabody Museum.)

the enclosing rocks were formed above sealevel. Fossils thus indicate the past distribution of land and seas.

They may also prove the former existence of land bridges between continents now separated by oceans. For example, the sudden appearance of the "elephants" in North America in Miocene time, long after they had developed in Eurasia, can mean only that America was then connected by a land bridge (Behring) with the Old World. By similar reasoning, it can be shown that at several times in the past North and South America have been separated. At present the species of marine animals on the Atlantic side of Panama and Central America are almost all different from those on the Pacific coast, and there is no way for them to mingle without an impossible migration through the cold waters by way of Cape Horn. Therefore, when in certain of the older rock formations we find the same species of fossils in the Gulf region, along the northwest coast of South America, and in California, it is evident that a strait existed somewhere across the isthmus. Here we have a double check, for when the marine animals were free to cross from the Atlantic to the Pacific side, the land animals in North and South America were isolated and developed independently.

Climatic Implications. Most kinds of animals and plants are now restricted to definite climatic environments. Palms and crocodiles characterize the tropics and subtropics, as the reindeer and musk-ox do the Arctic. The presence of the former as common fossils in the Oligocene rocks of the Dakotas bears a very strong implication that the winters at that time were much milder than now in the Great Plains region. Likewise the presence of fossil musk-ox in New York and Arkansas and of reindeer in France in Pleistocene sediments accords with unmistakable evidence of glacial climates at that time.

In reasoning thus from the known distribution of living types, we are fairly secure for late geologic time, but less and less so as we go back to the older rocks where the species and even the genera are different and may have had different habits. Caution must be exercised even for relatively recent geologic time, since animals and plants are highly adaptive and certain extinct species may have been adjusted to different climatic extremes than living

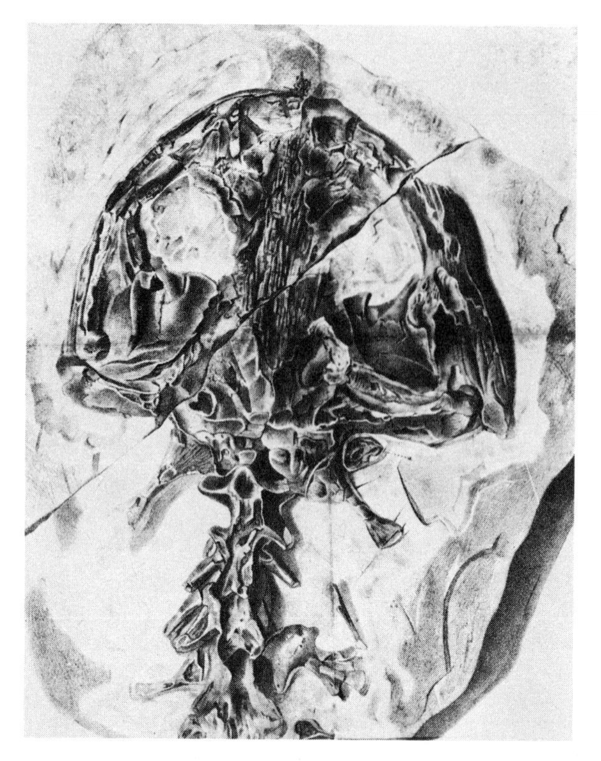

Figure 35. *Homo diluvii testis.* Skull and part of the backbone of a large salamander from the Oligocene lake beds at Oeningen, Switzerland, mistaken by Scheuchzer for the remains of a human drowned during the Biblical Flood. About ½ natural size.

species are. Of course the implication of a *group* of species is more trustworthy than that of one. Cumulative evidence may thus be convincing even for Mesozoic or Paleozoic faunas. For example, since living reptiles and amphibians of every sort become torpid when the temperature drops to near freezing, the inference is justified that this was true for most, at least, of the great Mesozoic reptiles. Small reptiles and amphibia survive cold weather by crawling into holes or burrowing in the ground where they are protected during their helpless condition, but large species, unable to find such refuge, live only in regions of no frost. There is a strong implication here that dinosaurs and other great reptiles of the Mesozoic could live only in regions of warm temperate to tropical climates.

Since 1950 Professor Harold Urey and a group of young colleagues at Chicago have developed a technique for determining the actual temperature of the sea water in which certain marine animals lived, even millions of years ago, by measuring the ratio of common oxygen, O^{16}, to its rare isotope, O^{18}, in the calcium carbonate ($CaCO_3$) built into their shells. Complicated techniques are required for making measurements of sufficient accuracy, and the study of paleotemperatures is still in its infancy, but the results already attained have demonstrated spectacular possibilities.[11]

The method is based on the fact that the ratio of the two isotopes incorporated in the shell as carbonate varies with the temperature at time of shell formation since the ratio of the carbonate dissolved in sea water is a function of the temperature. If, then, the shell has not been altered by recrystallization or by the diffusion of oxygen at a later date, it retains a built-in record of the temperature of the water in which it was formed. Of all the kinds of shells thus far tested the belemnites and foraminifera appear to be the most reliable.

The belemnite, a Mesozoic cousin of the squid, developed an internal shell with a cigar-shaped guard built up by successive additions during growth of the animal, so that it has concentric layers similar to the growth rings of trees. Figure 36 shows the application of this method to a belemnite from the Jurassic rocks of Scotland. The O^{18}/O^{16} ratios determined for successive concentric zones in this shell indicate rhythmic fluctuations of temperature from a winter low of about 15°C. to a summer high of about 22°C. From this data it can be deduced that this animal was born in the spring, lived through three summers, and died in the fourth winter at the age of about 4½ years, and that the temperature range in the shallow sea in which it lived some 140,000,000 years ago was about that of the modern shallow sea off Gibraltar!

This method has had its most important application in the study of deep sea cores which penetrate the Pleistocene sediments of the ocean floors.[12] Since the shells of pelagic foraminifera (Family Globigerinidae) have a built-in record of the temperature of the surface water in which they lived, climatic fluctuations will be recorded by variations in the O^{18}/O^{16} ratio of these shells at different depths in the cores. Of course such fluctuations at a single locality could be due to shifts in the position of warm, or cold, surface currents; but, if and when such fluctuations at widely distributed places in the oceans can be synchronized by radioactive dating, we shall have evidence of worldwide temperature fluctuation that will permit correlation of the sediments of the ocean floor in low latitudes with the record of glacial and interglacial ages on the land.

Documents of Evolution. Since fossils record life from age to age, they show the course life has taken in its gradual development. The facts that the oldest rocks bear only extinct types of relatively small and simple kinds of life, and that more and more complex types appear in successive ages, show that there has been a gradual development or unfolding of life on the Earth. Moreover, series of closely allied species and genera of a single stock, from successive horizons, provide clear instances of gradual evolution. The horse series from the Cenozoic beds of the western United States is a classic example, showing in detail the development of the modern horse from a tiny, forest dwelling ancestor with three toes on each hind foot and four toes on each front foot. Although the comparative study of living animals and plants may give very convincing circumstantial evidence, fossils provide the only historical, documentary evidence that life has evolved from simpler to more and more complex forms.

Dating the Record. Inasmuch as life has evolved gradually, changing from age to age, the rocks of each geologic age bear distinctive types of fossils unlike those of any other age. Conversely, each kind of fossil is an **index** or **guide fossil** to some definite geologic time. For example, trilobites lived only in the Paleozoic Era, and the particular trilobite genus *Olenellus* lived only during Early Cambrian time; whereas the horned dinosaur *Triceratops* lived only in the Cretaceous period, and three-toed horses only in the middle part of the Cenozoic.

During the last hundred years, paleontologists in many parts of the world have cooperated in gathering such a mass of this kind of information that it is now as easy for a trained specialist to identify the relative geologic age of a fossiliferous rock formation as it is to determine the relative place of a sheet in a manuscript by its pagination. Fossils thus make it possible to recognize rocks of the same age in different parts of the Earth and in this way to correlate events and work out the history of

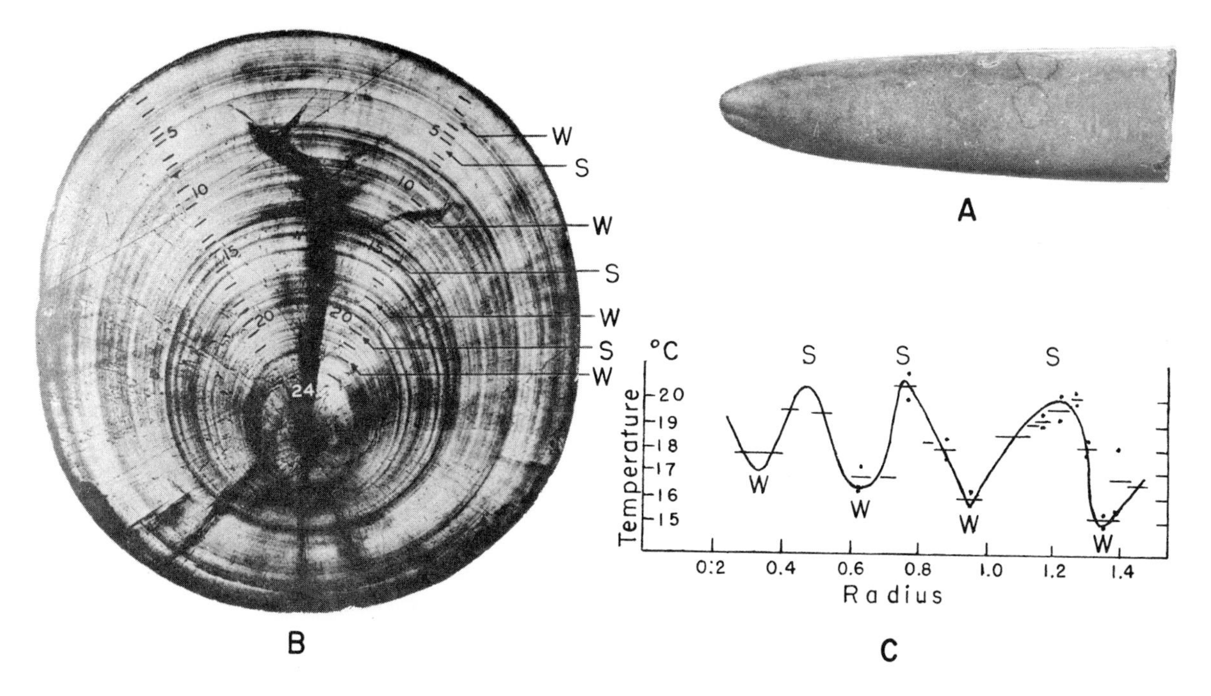

Figure 36. Evidence of paleotemperature. *A*, lateral view of a belemnite shell; *B*, enlarged cross section of a similar shell from the Upper Jurassic rocks of Scotland showing concentric growth layers; C, temperature curve recorded by the O^{18}/O^{16} ratios in successive layers of the shell. (*B* and *C* after Urey, Lowenstam, Epstein, and McKinney.)

the Earth as a whole. They furnish us with a chronology, "on which events are arranged like pearls on a string."

In the previous paragraphs we have assumed as an established fact the gradual evolution of life throughout geologic time. This provides a rational and convincing explanation for the sequence of fossil forms that we find in the rocks. But it is important to realize that **the sequence of fossils was not assumed and does not rest on any theory;** as explained on p. 9 it was revealed by patient exploration and discovery in many regions where there are thick sections of fossiliferous rocks having simple structure, so that the beds are known to be in the normal order of superposition, the oldest at the bottom.

Reconstructions. The majority of fossils represent only the hard parts of creatures. Even these, moreover, are commonly incomplete. The skeleton of an animal may have been scattered by the carnivores that stripped it of its flesh, or erosion may have destroyed the exposed parts before its chance discovery. We cannot, however, be content with the mere description of "vestiges of the dead"; hence paleontologists are ever intent on completing the missing parts and clothing the naked bones, in imagination at least, with flesh and life. Modern museums, therefore, display many fossil skeletons with missing parts restored. In this practice there is no attempt to deceive, for the plaster has a luster different from that of fossil bone and the artificial parts are evident. Nor is the restoration a mere feat of the imagination. The most simple and natural principles are employed in restoring a fragmentary skeleton. For example, if some of the bones in a right limb are lacking but those of the corresponding left limb are preserved, it is obviously safe to model the missing bones as mirror images of those in the opposite limb. Thus, with one side of a skeleton incompletely preserved, the whole can be reconstructed with absolute fidelity because vertebrates are bilaterally symmetrical. Moreover, the bones of a single skeleton fit together when naturally arranged. Even if they were disarticulated and piled in a heap, it would be no more difficult than solving a jigsaw puzzle to fit them together in their proper places, especially when we have articulated skeletons of similar living types for comparison. If the skeleton lacks part of its ribs, those that are preserved may be sufficient to indicate clearly the contour of the body. The missing ones, it is then evident, must be shaped to fit into this plan. A profound knowledge of comparative anatomy will justify still other restorations that might seem to the uninitiated to be guesswork. For example, suppose but four of the neck vertebrae of a mammalian skeleton have been recovered. The specialist will know that three are missing, because all mammals have seven neck vertebrae. Whether the mammal is an elephant or a giraffe, the length of its neck is controlled by the length of the individual vertebrae, not by their number. If the skeleton is that of a bird or a reptile, on the contrary, no such simple decision can be made, for in those groups the number of neck vertebrae varies. Suppose the skeleton is that of a dinosuar, and several, but not all, of the tail vertebrae are present. The number of missing ones may be inferred from the rate of taper in those that are present. If the tail is long and slender, there is a chance here for some error, but even so, the mistake will not be great.

In many instances skeletons are found alone and at least partly articulated. When two or more such skeletons are sufficiently complete to be safely identified as belonging to the same species, the missing parts of one may be reconstructed from the other. Thus, if it so happens that the front end of one has been destroyed by erosion and the tail of the other is missing, we can still restore an entire, but composite, skeleton faithfully representing the species. The restoration of fossil skeletons therefore leaves little to guesswork.

However, the clothing of the bones with flesh in lifelike reconstructions does involve powers of imagination, guided by profound knowledge of comparative anatomy. We can visualize extinct creatures only by comparison with living types. If the evolution of life had been utterly haphazard, this procedure would be futile, but few, if any, of the great groups of animals have become wholly extinct. Genera and species, even families and orders, have died out, but all these had gradually evolved from others, more or less closely related, which still have living descendants. This is one of the reasons why the larger paleontological research institutions are searching the far corners of the Earth for living animals of all kinds.

The first attempts at the reconstruction of extinct

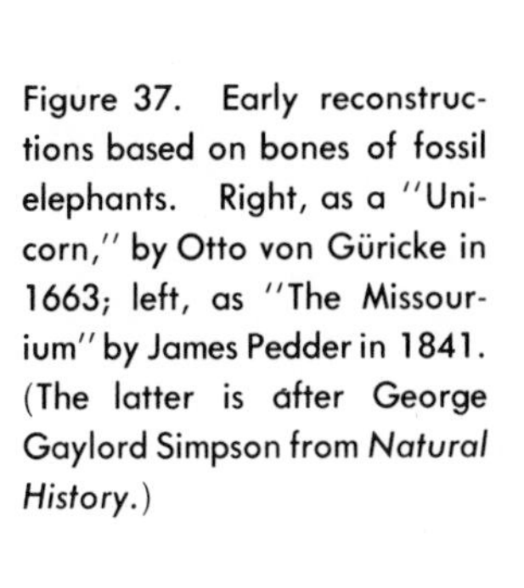

Figure 37. Early reconstructions based on bones of fossil elephants. Right, as a "Unicorn," by Otto von Güricke in 1663; left, as "The Missourium" by James Pedder in 1841. (The latter is after George Gaylord Simpson from *Natural History*.)

animals were made before anyone had a very general knowledge of anatomy or comparative morphology. It is not surprising, therefore, that these early efforts were fantastic. The oldest known attempt is the reconstruction of the unicorn by Otto von Güricke, burgomaster of Magdeburg, in 1663 (Fig. 37). It was composed of various Pleistocene elephant bones, the "horn" being, in reality, a tusk. From such early attempts, based more on legends and myths than on knowledge of animal life, it is a far cry to the critical modern studies where the necessary muscles are modeled on the articulated skeleton one by one, as the fleshy body is built up, and where attention to the muscular facets on the bone and careful comparison with the musculature of related living types reduce the element of speculation to a minimum (Fig. 30).

REFERENCES

1. Kulp, J. Laurence, Lansing E. Tryon, Walter R. Eckelman, and William A. Snell, 1952, Lamont natural radiocarbon measurement, II. *Science*, vol. 116, p. 411.

2. Palmer, Allison R., et al., 1957, Miocene arthropods from The Mojave Desert, California. *U.S. Geol. Surv., Prof. Paper 294–G*, pp. 237–280.

3. Hibbard, Claude W., and Elmer S. Riggs, 1949, Upper Pliocene vertebrates from Keefe Canyon, Meade County, Kansas. *Geol. Soc. Amer., Bull.*, vol. 60, pp. 829–860.

4. Gazin, Charles L., 1942, The Late Cenozoic vertebrate faunas from the San Pedro Valley, Arizona. *U.S. Nat. Mus., Proc.*, vol. 92, pp. 475–518.

5. Kelly, W. A., 1940, Tar as a trap for unwary humans. *Amer. Jour. Sci.*, vol. 238, p. 451–452.

6. Gidley, James W., and Charles L. Gazin, 1933, New Mammalia in the Pleistocene fauna from Cumberland Cave. *Jour. Mammology*, vol. 14, pp. 343–357.

7. Grater, Russell K., 1958, Last stand of the ground sloth. *Arizona Highways*, vol. 34, no. 7, pp. 30–33.

8. Chappell, W. M., J. W. Durham, and D. E. Savage, 1951, Mold of a rhinoceros in basalt, Lower Grand Coulee, Washington. *Geol. Soc. Amer., Bull.*, vol. 62, pp. 907–918.

9. Bucher, Walter H., 1953, Fossils in metamorphic rocks; a review. *Geol. Soc. Amer., Bull.*, vol. 64, pp. 275–300.

10. Anonymous, 1951, Early letters concerning the Mammoth. *Soc. Vertebrates Paleontology, News Bull.*, no. 33, pp. 27–31.

11. Urey, H. C., H. A. Lowenstam, S. Epstein, and C. R. McKinney, 1951, Measurement of paleotemperatures and temperatures of the Upper Cretaceous of England, Denmark, and the southeastern United States. *Geol. Soc., Amer., Bull.*, vol. 62, pp. 399–416.

12. Emiliani, C., 1955, Pleistocene temperatures. *Jour. Geology*, vol. 63, pp. 538–578.

13. Radiocarbon date based on a piece of hide from this specimen preserved in Peabody Museum. Personal communication from Professor Edward S. Deevey, Jr., Director of the Yale Geochronometric Laboratory.

Figure 38. Spiral nebula in Andromeda, a galaxy of stars more than 5,000,-000,000,000,000,000 miles distant, seen obliquely with respect to its plane of rotation. (Lick Observatory.)

Chapter 4. Cosmic History of the Earth

Globed from the atoms falling
slow or swift I see the suns,
I see the systems lift their forms.

TITUS LUCRETIUS CARUS (96–55 B.C.)

Beginnings. THE ORIGIN OF THE WORLD HAS ALways intrigued the mind of thinking man, and few cultures have been without legends of the Creation; but until the Renaissance such beliefs were generally fanciful because men had no real knowledge of the physical universe or of the natural laws that govern it. Even in our scientific age we cannot come to grips with the ultimate—the origin of matter, the beginning of time, and the limits of space lie forever beyond scientific inquiry and human understanding. Nevertheless, it is now clear that the Earth, as such, is not eternal; it was "molded out of stardust" and set wheeling about the Sun a few billions of years ago. Before attempting to understand this cosmic event we must make a brief survey of the universe about us.

EARTH'S PLACE IN THE UNIVERSE

In the limited experience of primitive peoples it seemed evident that the Earth was flat, and was the center of the Universe about which Sun and Moon and stars revolved. Indeed this idea prevailed until the Renaissance, when Columbus and Magellan showed it to be round, and Copernicus indicated it to be only a minor satellite revolving about the Sun. We now know, furthermore, that the Sun is only one of the myriad of stars that make up the Milky Way, and that far out beyond these—"like islands in a sea of space"—lie other vast galaxies of stars known as **spiral nebulae.**

Since distance lends perspective, we can best visualize the organization of our own universe by observing these remote star systems. Typical of these is the great nebula in Andromeda (Fig. 38) which to the unaided eye appears as a faint, fuzzy star, but in the great telescopes is seen to be a myriad of stars grouped in a vast system with the over-all shape of a thin lens. Because we see it obliquely, the Andromeda nebula appears elliptical, but others seen from a polar view appear circular and those seen from the edge as thin lenses. Local concentrations of stars form the brighter luminous spots in the nebula and comprise the spirally twisted streamers or "arms." The shape suggests that such a star-system is in rotation, and analysis of the light coming from opposite limbs of a nebula seen from the edge clearly confirms this inference. Each spiral nebula is a universe of millions of stars in revolution about a common center "like sparks in a cosmic pinwheel."

The great nebula in Andromeda is approximately 900,000 light years away,* but most of the spiral nebulae are still more remote. As the great telescopes peer ever farther into space, they reveal more and more of these island universes, and still we see no indication of a limit to infinity. Earth's place in this vast system is clearly an humble one!

OUR GALACTIC SYSTEM

The ancients observed the belt of faint light that girdles the night sky and called it the Milky Way. Big telescopes later resolved this faint light into individual stars too faint to be distinguished by the eye because of their distance. Together with all the visible stars about us they constitute a spiral nebula of which we are a part. This is our Galactic System. We are in the midst of the nebula, though far from its center, and our sun is one of the minor stars. As we look out through its lesser diameter, the stars appear relatively bright and well spaced, but as we turn toward its periphery, more and more faint stars crowd into view until they are lost in a faint distant glow of the Milky Way. Our Galactic System has an equatorial diameter between 100,000 and 200,000 light years and a polar diameter of probably 10,000 light years; and it rotates on its axis in a period of about 200,000,000 years.[1]

THE SOLAR SYSTEM

Revolving about the Sun are the 9 planets and their moons, more than 1,500 planetoids, and an unknown number of comets and meteors (Fig. 39). The system is completely dominated by the Sun which includes more than 98 percent of its total mass, and holds the other members in its gravitative control while supplying them with light and warmth. These celestial bodies form a close-knit family and evidently have had a common origin. They are our closest neighbors in the Cosmos and deserve further consideration.

*A light year is a unit of distance in astronomy measured by the distance light will travel in a years time at a velocity of 186,000 miles per second—almost six million million miles.

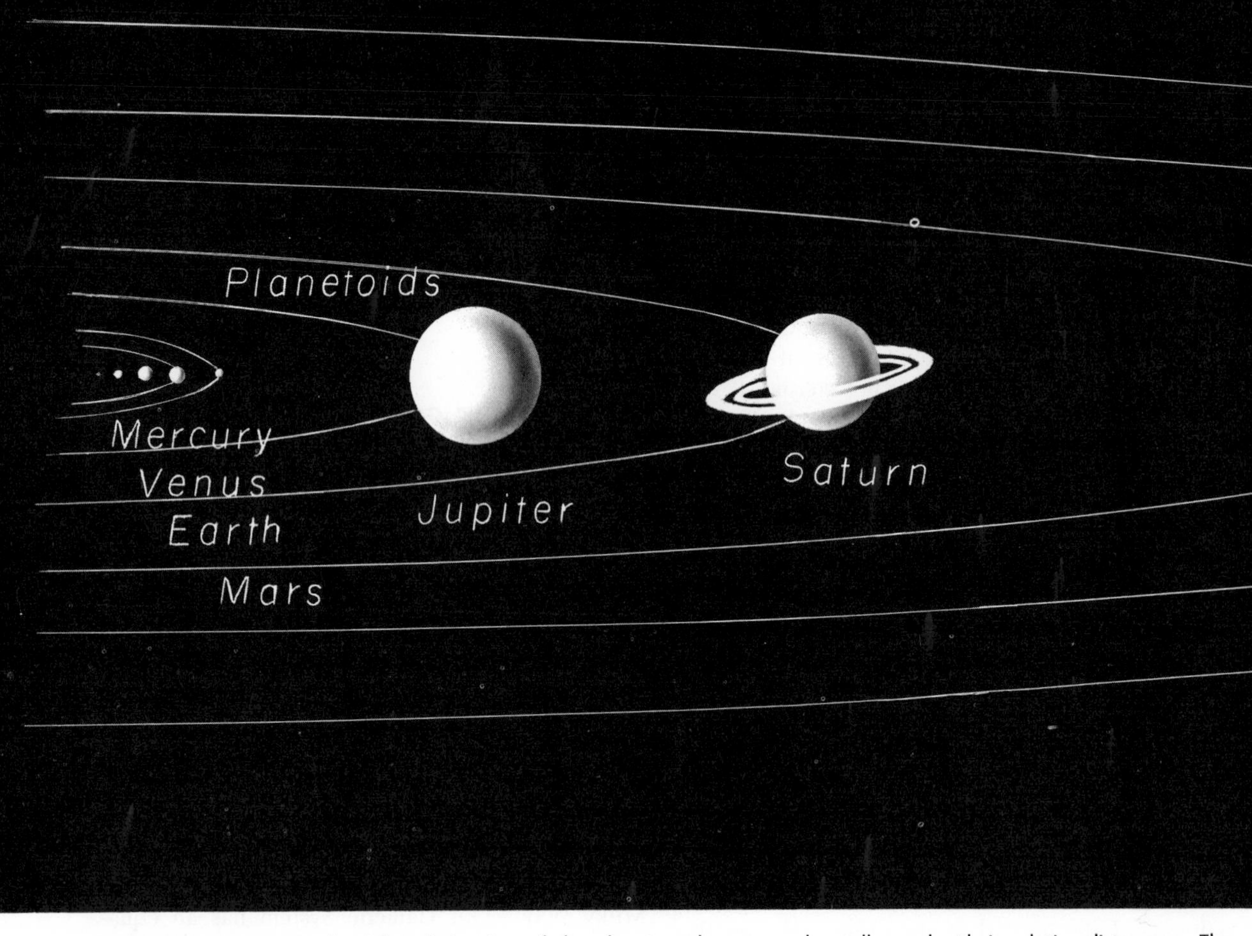

Figure 39. Diagram to show the relative sizes of the planets and, on a much smaller scale, their relative distances. The view is from obliquely above the plane of rotation so that the circular orbits of the planets appear elliptical. On the scale

The Sun. The Sun is a true star some 860,000 miles in diameter and so hot as to be entirely gaseous and self-luminous. Its temperature is about 6000°C. at the surface, increasing inward to some 20,000,000°C. at the center. It is made of the same chemical elements as the Earth, but in quite different proportions, some 99 percent of the Sun's mass consisting of hydrogen and helium.

The radiant energy supplied by the Sun in the form of light and heat is amazing. It spreads equally in all directions so that the Earth intercepts only about one two-billionth of the total output; yet this is sufficient to provide life-giving warmth to the Earth, to enable plants by photosynthesis to build organic compounds, to lift the vapors that return as rain, to keep the atmosphere in motion, and thus to motivate all the forces of erosion—and geologic evidence makes it quite clear that this prodigious flow of energy has not flagged nor greatly varied for more than a thousand million years. Its source was a mystery until atomic energy was understood. Now it seems evident that the interior of the Sun is a furnace in which, by atomic fusion (as in a hydrogen bomb), the lightest element, hydrogen, is being transformed into helium, and perhaps helium and other light elements are being built into heavier ones. As the spectre of hydrogen bombs hangs over a troubled world we are inclined to regard atomic energy with fear, little realizing that our world would be cold and lifeless without it.

The visible disc of the Sun, the **photosphere**, appears in the telescope as a billowy surface of seething, white-hot clouds. Outside this is a much

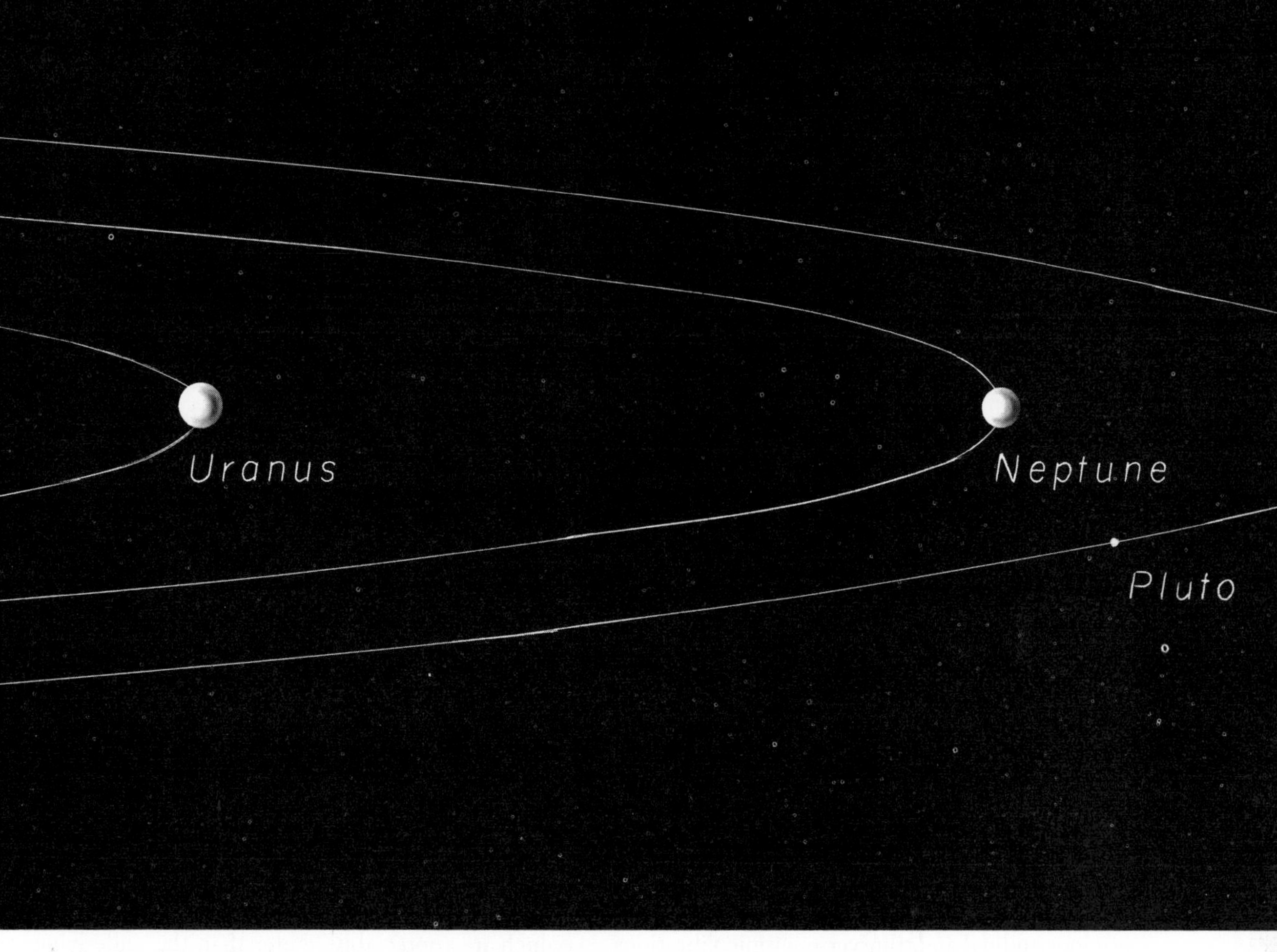

used for the planets, the Sun would be about 7 inches in diameter. On this scale the distance from the Sun to Mercury would be 25 feet, to Earth 64 feet, to Mars 97 feet, to Jupiter 333 feet, and to Neptune 1923 feet.

rarer layer of crimson gas from 5,000 to 10,000 miles thick, which because of its color is known as the **chromosphere**. It is clearly visible at total solar eclipse when the moon blocks out the white light from the photosphere. From the surface of the chromosphere, solar prominences leap out from time to time like great tongues of crimson flame, reaching heights of many thousands of miles and bearing evidence of the explosive energy in the Sun. Outside the chromosphere is the **corona**, a vast halo of extremely rarified and largely ionized gases, seen best at total eclipse, surrounding the Sun and extending far out, with streamers reaching even to the Earth to create the electrical disturbances that frequently interfere with radio and television transmission.

Although it is the center of our Solar System, the Sun is not stationary in space; with its retinue of satellites it is plunging toward the bright star Vega with a velocity of about 11 miles per second, meanwhile rotating on its own axis in a period of about 25 days.*

Earth as a Planet. The planets are nine in number and their relative sizes are shown in Figure 39. They revolve about the Sun in concentric and nearly circular orbits, all moving in a counterclockwise direction as viewed from the North Pole. Earth is about 93,000,000 miles from the Sun, Mercury one-third as far, Jupiter 5 times as far and Neptune over 30 times as far as the Earth.

*There is no prospect of a collision since Vega is extremely remote, and is moving across our path so that we probably will never be nearer to her than we are now.

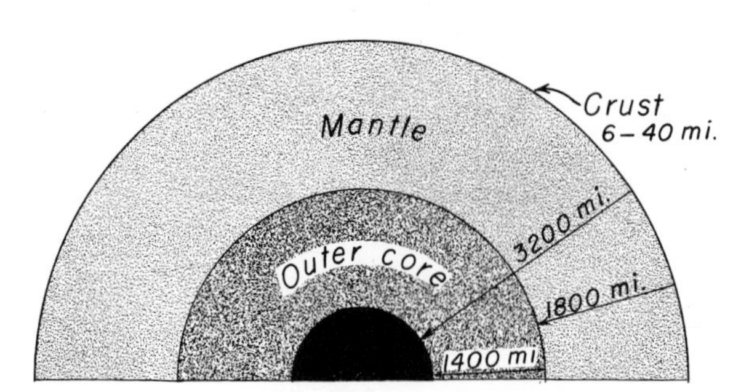

Figure 40. Diagram to show the interior structure of the Earth. (Adapted from Longwell and Flint.)

Earth is a rather small planet, with a diameter of approximately 8,000 miles. It travels at a speed of 18 miles per second in its nearly circular orbit, making a complete revolution about the Sun each year, meanwhile rotating on its polar axis each day.

Since the average density of the Earth (5.5) is about twice that of the surface rocks, the material at great depth is clearly much denser than any rocks we know. For reasons suggested below it is confidently believed that the visible crust is underlain by concentric shells of increasingly dense matter, as indicated in Figure 40. The **mantle** is believed to be composed of ultrabasic rocks. It is clearly rigid to short-term stresses since it transmits both longitudinal and transverse seismic vibrations, and the high velocity of such waves indicates that the rock is appreciably denser than basalt. The **outer core** is believed to consist mostly of metallic iron, with a probable admixture of nickel and chromium, but it must be in a molten condition since it does not transmit transverse seismic vibrations. At the boundary between the mantle and the outer core, however, there is an abrupt acceleration of the longitudinal vibrations, which do go through, and this indicates a sudden increase in density that can mean only change in composition at this level. The **inner core** is believed to be metallic and similar in composition to the outer core, but in a rigid, crystalline state. This condition is inferred from the further acceleration of the longitudinal seismic vibrations that pass through the inner core.

One of the chief bases for believing that the core is metallic is that iron forms such a large part of the average meteorite (p. 62), and meteorites appear to be either fragments of a disrupted planet or possibly the remnants of the building material of which all the planets were formed.

The density stratification indicated in Figure 40 implies that the Earth at some stage in its early history passed through a molten condition when the lighter, silicate minerals rose toward the surface like slag in an iron smelter, while the metals settled toward the center.

The contrast in the physical states of the outer and inner cores throws significant light on temperature conditions deep within the Earth. Since the melting point rises with pressure, the temperature in the outer core must be well above that at which iron melts under surface conditions (1535°C.); yet it can hardly be greater than 4000°K since the inner core is not molten.

At the scale used in Figure 40, the outer crust of the Earth would be thinner than the ink line. Details are therefore shown on a much larger scale in Figure 41. Resting upon the ultrabasic mantle is a layer of basaltic rocks normally about 3 miles thick. This layer forms the floor of the ocean basins except for a surface veneer of oceanic sediments and sedimentary rocks, which seismic evidence shows to be normally less than a mile thick. In each continent, on the contrary, the basalt is overlain by a layer about 20 miles thick (locally up to 40 miles) composed of granitic rocks (which are appreciably lighter than the underlying basalt). Such a vast plate of relatively light, granitic rock, resting in isostatic equilibrium on the basic layers of the crust, floats higher than the rest, just as the vast tabular icebergs in the Antarctic seas float with their surface above sealevel. And where mountain ranges rise far above the surrounding plains, they are compensated for by downward thickening of the granitic plate just as pressure ridges project downward in the floe ice of the polar seas. Thus the major relief features of the Earth reflect the structure of the crust, the continental masses standing on the average about one-half mile above sealevel and the ocean floors on the average some 3 miles below sealevel. This being true, it is inherently improbable that large parts of the continents have ever subsided to become part of the deep ocean basins. They could do so only if large injections of ultrabasic lavas from great depth increased the average specific gravity of the continental plate to that of the basic layers of the crust. On the contrary, the continents may have grown peripherally where sediments, largely made of siliceous materials, accumulated to great thickness at their edges to form the continental shelves. Such deposits, later subjected to orogeny, could be metamorphosed into rocks of granitic composition.

Earth's atmosphere is relatively thin and its composition quite exceptional as compared with that of other planets. It consists largely of nitrogen (76 percent by weight) and oxygen (23 percent), with less than 1 percent argon, only a trace of carbon dioxide (0.03 percent), and a variable amount of water vapor.

The Moon as a Satellite. As the nearest of all the celestial bodies the Moon is in some respects the most interesting, and it may be the most significant as regards the cosmic history of the Earth. Having a diameter of only about 2,100 miles and a mean density of 3.46, its mass is only one-eightieth that of the Earth, and the force of gravity at its surface is only one-sixth as great as it is here. Since its distance is slightly less than 240,000 miles, large telescopes reveal its surface features in great detail (Fig. 42). Indeed, photographs taken with the 200-inch telescope on Mount Palomar show it as though it were only 200 miles away.

Its stark barren surface is never obscured by clouds or haze because it is completely devoid of atmosphere. The reason for this is well understood. The molecules of a gas are in violent motion, jostling each other like so many ping-pong balls, and are thus kept apart. In the upper reaches of the atmosphere where the molecules are far apart, some fly out into space without collision. If the force of gravity is sufficient they eventually fall back, like spent missiles, and rejoin the atmosphere, but if they exceed a critical velocity they never return. For any celestial body there is, therefore, a critical **escape velocity.** On Earth this amounts to about 7 miles per second, but on the Moon it is about 1.5 miles. This is well below the normal molecular velocity of any of the gases, and the Moon, therefore, has never been able to hold an atmosphere.

The great dark patches, visible to the naked eye, were thought by the ancients to be seas and were named **maria** (L. *mare*, sea). Indeed they would be seas if water were present on the Moon, but actually they are flat desert plains lying well below the level of the surrounding highlands. They appear dark only because their smooth surfaces do not reflect the Sun's light as effectively as the rugged uplands.

The most striking feature of the lunar landscape is the plexus of craters that covers much of its higher parts. The craters range in size from less than a mile to more than 100 miles in diameter. Most of them have relatively flat floors and steep lofty rims. In depths they range up to more than 3 miles. They obviously differ greatly in age, some

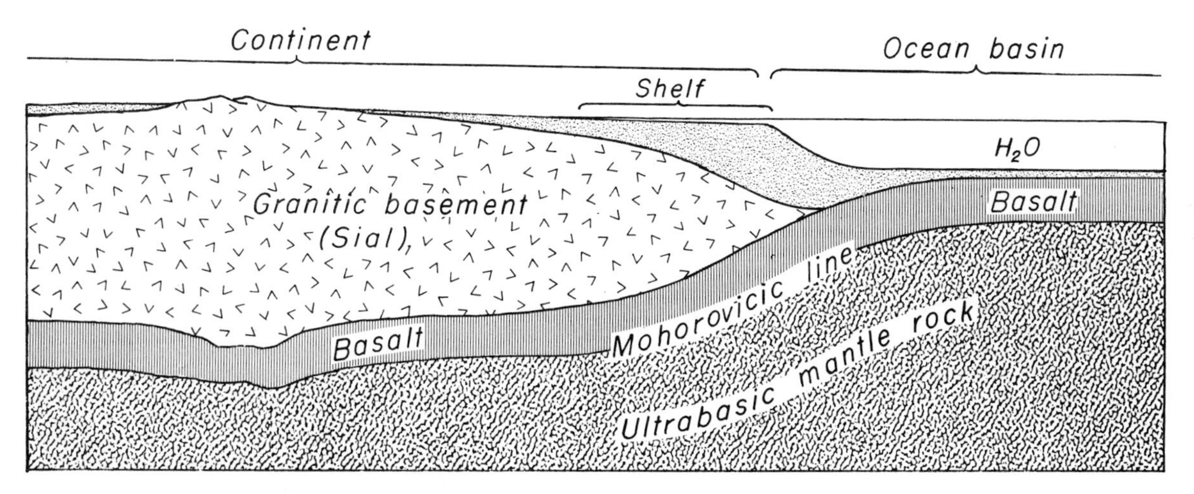

Figure 41. Structure of the crust of the Earth. (Adapted from J. T. Wilson in G. P. Kuiper (ed.) *The Earth as a Planet*, 1954, Univ. of Chicago Press.)

Figure 42*B*. Mare Serenitatis and adjacent territory on the Moon. This is the large mare above the center of Figure 41. (Yerkes Observatory.)

← Figure 42*A*. Surface of the Moon at third quarter. (Lick Observatory.)

Figure 43. Meteor Crater in Arizona. An oblique aerial view looking westward toward San Francisco Mountains. The crater is approximately 4,000 feet across and 550 feet deep. (Spence Air Photos.)

of the older ones having subdued rims, whereas the younger ones have sharp lofty rims. The younger commonly cut the rims of the older. Since the Moon lacks an atmosphere, its surface has never been modified by erosion and we see here the cumulative effect of crater formation throughout the ages. The rims of the older craters have been subdued as the rocks crumbled and slumped under the extreme temperature changes as night followed day, and in part they are blanketed by dust from the younger craters; otherwise they have stood changeless since they were formed.

The origin of the lunar craters has long been a subject of controversy, some students of the Moon interpreting them as volcanoes whereas others believe they are craters produced by the infall of great meteors.[2] In either event the effects of a great explosion on the Moon would differ in important respects from that of an equivalent blast at the Earth's surface. The weak force of gravity would allow ejected material to be hurled to much greater distances and, in the absence of an atmosphere (as in a vacuum), dust-size particles would travel as fast as coarse blocks of stone and would fall back as quickly to form a steep and symmetrical rim. The great size of the craters is therefore not an obstacle to the volcanic interpretation. On the other hand, if lava had welled out in great flows through the rim, as it commonly does in terrestrial volcanoes, such flows should be plainly visible on the Moon. There are none.

In recent years most astronomers have come to believe that the craters were formed by great meteors which, after plunging into the Moon, exploded as their kinetic energy was suddenly transformed into heat. Meteor Crater in Arizona (Fig. 43) was formed in this way, and a few even larger ones are now known on the Earth. If these were simple impact craters, many of them should be unsymmetrical since meteors come from random directions and most of them would strike at low angles; but inasmuch as they are explosion craters, formed after the meteors had embedded themselves below the surface, they should all be essentially symmetrical as, indeed, they are. If a meteor merely struck a grazing blow it might plow a deep furrow for many miles in the loose surface of the Moon and then break up without imbedding itself. Several such trenches may be observed (Fig. 42).

This interpretation suggests that the Moon has grown by sweeping up the meteors that were in or near its path. If this be true, meteors represent the building material of which the Earth also was formed. The lack of erosion on the Moon has left the record clear to see, whereas on Earth all but a few of the youngest craters have been destroyed.

The origin of the maria remains a problem. The random fall of meteors should have distributed the craters fairly evenly over the face of the Moon, yet very few are present in the maria. This implies that craters once formed in these dark areas have been buried or destroyed at a late stage in the Moon's growth. The maria could not then be vast explosion craters formed by colossal meteors during an early stage of the Moon's history as some have suggested, and they could not be plains simply "built up" by vast lava flows that buried pre-existing craters, since they lie hundreds or even thousands of feet lower than the surrounding highlands. Possibly these are areas where the surface layer of the Moon was melted down by internal heat and then covered by lava that welled out over the surface, but in the light of what we know of the Earth's major relief features (Fig. 40) we may assume that the maria are low because the underlying crust is heavier than elsewhere.

Other Planets. Mercury, the innermost planet, is only 3,000 miles in diameter and is too small to hold an atmosphere. It is therefore a lifeless, changeless, desert world probably much like the moon. Venus is almost equal to Earth in size and has an atmosphere probably as dense as ours, but it is perpetually cloudy so that the rocky surface of the planet is never visible. Spectroscopic analysis of the reflected light proves the atmosphere of Venus to be quite unlike ours, consisting largely of CO_2.[3] If water is present it must be very rare, and free oxygen is probably lacking. The clouds are believed to be formed by dust particles. Mars, the ruddy planet beyond us, is 4,200 miles in diameter and barely large enough to hold a tenuous atmosphere which, like that of Venus, is largely made of CO_2 with very little if any H_2O and no free oxygen. Telescopes reveal small white polar caps that come and go with the seasons and are believed to be films of hoarfrost formed of frozen CO_2 or possibly of H_2O.

Jupiter, the giant among the planets, has an apparent diameter of 88,600 miles but its low specific gravity (1.36) proves it to be largely gaseous. It is believed to have a core perhaps 8 times as big as the Earth, formed almost entirely of solid hydrogen and helium, surrounded by a vast atmosphere largely of hydrogen and helium gases.[4] Because of its perpetual cloud cover, the solid body of the planet can never be seen. Spectroscopic analysis of its reflected light shows that the major constituent of its outer atmosphere is ammonia (NH_3) with methane (CH_4) in second place, and that H_2O and free O_2 are rare or absent.[3] The clouds are inferred to be formed by particles of frozen ammonia (just as the high cirrus clouds in Earth's atmosphere are formed of ice particles). The temperature at the surface of the clouds on Jupiter ranges between 100 and 140°C. below zero.

Saturn, the great ringed planet, has an apparent diameter of 74,000 miles but is even more largely gaseous than Jupiter, its mean density being less than that of water (0.72). Its upper atmosphere resembles that of Jupiter except that methane (CH_4) predominates over ammonia (NH_4). No evidence has been found of free O_2, N_2, or H_2O.[3]

Uranus and Neptune are so faint and far away that spectroscopic analysis of their reflected light is difficult and unsatisfactory, and we have little secure data beyond the fact that they are largely gaseous. Pluto is much smaller and more remote and is little known.

From this survey it is evident that the minor planets, Mercury, Venus, Earth, and Mars, are relatively small, solid bodies, whereas the major planets, Jupiter, Saturn, Uranus, and Neptune, are vastly larger but are mostly gaseous. Furthermore, the atmosphere of Earth is unique in its composition. On the other planets the predominant gases are compounds of carbon, hydrogen, and nitrogen (CH_4, CO_2, NH_3). Only Earth has free O_2, free N_2 with a small trace of CO_2, and much H_2O. As explained on page 64 this is believed to be an acquired condition; its primeval atmosphere, like that of the other planets, probably consisted of hydrogen and carbon compounds.

Satellites of the Other Planets. Mercury and Venus have no moons, but Mars has two, Jupiter

Figure 44. Halley's comet, May 5, 1910. (Photograph by Ferdinand Ellerman, *Mt. Wilson Observatory.*)

twelve, Saturn nine, Uranus five, and Neptune two. These satellites are all much smaller than our Moon. They revolve about their respective planets in nearly circular and concentric orbits and, with a few exceptions, move nearly in the common plane of the entire Solar System. The large satellite systems of Jupiter and Saturn are like scaled-down replicas of the Solar System. As exceptions to this regularity, however, the eighth, ninth, and eleventh satellites of Jupiter and the ninth of Saturn are retrograde (revolving clockwise as seen from the North Pole of the Solar System); the inner satellite of Mars revolves faster than its planet rotates and therefore rises in the west and sets in the east; and the satellites of Uranus and Neptune revolve in orbits at a high angle to those of the rest of the Solar System. These irregularities may be due to capture of satellites originally belonging to other planets.

Planetoids. With a single exception the orbits of the planets are spaced so that each is a little more than twice the distance of the next nearest from the Sun. The exception is that, according to this scheme, a planet is missing between Mars and Jupiter. This is the belt of the planetoids—small solid, planetlike bodies ranging in size from 5 or 10 miles up to 485 miles in diameter—each revolving in its own orbit about the Sun. Many of these orbits are distinctly elliptical and some actually cross, so that close approach or even collision between planetoids appears possible. Thus far more than 1,500 planetoids have been discovered.

Since they occupy a belt where a planet should exist, there has been much speculation as to whether the planetoids are fragments of a former planet disrupted by tidal forces, or are samples of the original material that for some reason failed to be gathered into a planet when the Solar System was formed.

Comets. Comets appear from time to time as faint luminous objects in the night sky, grow brighter as they approach the Sun, and then fade again in a period of months as they recede in highly elliptical orbits. Each displays a dense nucleus in its head, surrounded by a gaseous envelope that streams out into a long tail (Fig. 44). In its journey about the Sun the comet grows brighter and its tail grows longer during its approach; the tail is constantly directed away from the Sun, trailing behind as it approaches, then swinging through a wide arc at perihelion and rushing ahead like the flame of a blow torch as the comet recedes. This behavior clearly suggests that the tail is made of particles driven away from the head of the comet by the radiant energy of the Sun. Spectroscopic analysis of the light shows the comet's tail to consist of ionized gases, chiefly C_2, CO, and CN, and from this it is inferred that the nucleus of the head is a solid mass, or perhaps a swarm of masses, of the ices of H_2O, methane (CH_4) and ammonia (NH_3).[5] It should be noted that these are the predominant gases of the upper atmospheres of the major planets.

Although comets are part of the Solar System their motions are much more irregular than those of the planets and planetoids. Each has a definite, highly elliptical orbit, but as a group they are not concentric and do not lie close to a common plane. They frequently cross the planetary orbits and, on occasion, come near collision with a planet. In 1886, when Brook's Comet with a period of 27 years, came near Jupiter, it was drawn into a smaller orbit in which it now returns every 7 years. Although it was so strongly deflected by the pull of Jupiter, the small satellites of the planet were not appreciably disturbed, and from this it is evident that the mass of the comet is trivial as compared with that of even the smallest satellite.

Meteors. The "shooting stars" that streak across the night sky are **meteors**. Each is a solid object (a meteorite) heated to incandescence by friction as it plunges into the atmosphere from outer space. It is estimated that some millions of meteors fall daily; but most of them are no larger

Figure 45. The Weston Meteorite. This stony meteorite was one of several seen to fall in the town of Weston, Connecticut, on the morning of December 14, 1807. The meteor was first seen over Rutland, Vermont, where it appeared as a "fire ball" about one-fourth the diameter of the full moon. To observers in Connecticut it appeared to have one-half to two-thirds the diameter of the moon, and was estimated to be traveling at a velocity of more than 3 miles per second while still some 18 miles above the Earth. A loud explosion immediately preceded the rain of meteorites to the ground. This specimen, weighing about 33 lbs., plunged through the sod in a pasture field and buried itself a foot or so below the surface. It was the first fall of a meteorite to be observed and the first accounts of it were received with scepticism even by learned men. Thomas Jefferson, for example, who besides being President of the United States was also president of the American Philosophical Society, wrote to Daniel Salmon on February 15, 1808, "It may be difficult to explain how the stone you possess came into the position in which it was found. But is it easier to explain how it got into the clouds from whence it is supposed to have fallen?" (Yale Peabody Museum.)

than sand grains and are completely vaporized before reaching the surface. Large ones occasionally drive through the atmosphere so quickly that only a surface shell is vaporized before they drop to Earth. If their velocity is sufficient they then plunge into the crust like a projectile and explode, as their energy of flight is suddenly transformed into heat, producing a crater (Fig. 43). In such cases most of the meteoric material disappears as vapors; but if the velocity of infall is low, the meteorite lands with only a seared surface. In 1954, for example, an 8½-pound meteorite plunged through the roof of a house at Sylacauga, Alabama, striking a woman who suffered only slight injury.[6]

The Weston meteorite (Fig. 45), weighing 33 pounds, was observed to fall in 1807, breaking the sod and coming to rest just under the surface. The meteorite that formed Meteor Crater (Fig. 43) must have weighed thousands of tons, and Chubb Crater in northern Ungava records an ancient meteor, probably a mile or more in diameter, that plowed into solid granite and left a crater almost two miles across.

Meteors commonly travel in swarms that pass the Earth like dust storms, and some of these reappear from the same direction at regular intervals, proving that they are part of the Solar System and travel in orbits about the Sun. They appear to be samples of the "star dust" out of which Earth and the other planets were formed. Accordingly there is much interest in their mineral composition and in the relative abundance of the chemical elements of which they are made. They fall generally into two major classes, **metallic meteorites** formed of iron with appreciable amounts of nickel and cobalt, and **stony meteorites** made of a variety of silicate minerals. Many of these include radioactive elements, from which absolute age determinations can be made. It may be significant that the best determined ages all fall about 4,500,000,000 years B.P. (before the present).

ORIGIN OF THE SOLAR SYSTEM

In their majestic courses the planets revolve in the same sense about the Sun, moving in concentric orbits in a common plane. Surely they and their satellites are children of the Sun. But in what manner were they born? Several hypotheses have been advanced during the last hundred years, and two of these for a time seemed highly promising, but when critically examined each in turn proved inadequate.[7] The spectacular advances in both physics and astronomy during recent years have provided new insights, however, that give renewed promise of a real understanding of the way in which the Solar System came into being. It may be profitable, therefore, to examine the present status of the problem even though it is still in the realm of speculation.

Hypothesis of Tidal Disruption. An hypothesis much in favor during the first part of this century assumes that the Sun traveled alone until it almost collided with another star; in this encounter, tidal stresses generated by the pull of the passing star partly disrupted the Sun and set the fragments flying in a plane about it, like sparks from a giant pinwheel; this debris was then slowly gathered together to form the planets and their satellites, the residue being left over in the form of planetoids and meteors. As thus conceived, the Solar System was born of a stellar catastrophe a few billions of years ago.

In its original form this theory was developed by Chamberlin and Moulton, geologist and astronomer, respectively, at the University of Chicago, and is known as the **planetesimal hypothesis.** It assumed that the explosive forces in the Sun caused the ejected material to be discharged in the form of enormous belches of incandescent gas, which upon cooling condensed into small solid particles to form swarms of meteors that fell into elliptic orbits about the Sun. These solid particles of which the planets were to be formed were termed **planetesimals.** It was conceived that a few of these swarms, formed of the largest belches of gas, had sufficient mass to set up a mutual gravitative field; this drew them together to form the nucleus of a planet which then slowly grew by the meteoric rain of other planetesimals in or near its path as it continued to circle the Sun. The satellites were similarly formed of smaller concentrations too far from the course of the growing planets to be intercepted, but near enough to be captured and brought under their gravitative control.

When, upon critical study, the hypothesis in this form was found to be untenable, two British astronomers, Jeffreys and Jeans developed a modification. This assumed that at the time of tidal disruption the explosive energies in the Sun were relatively unimportant, and the ejected material was discharged in the form of a vast stream of incandescent gas reaching out to the present orbit of Pluto; it was then segmented into units which condensed to a molten and finally a solid stage to form the several planets.

While this, the **gaseous-tidal hypothesis,** avoided some of the difficulties encountered by the planetesimal hypothesis, it also fails to account for the remarkable fact that the giant Jupiter, traveling in its vast orbit, carries about 60 percent of the angular momentum of the entire system. That is to say, it would have required 1.5 times as much force to launch Jupiter into its orbit as to set the Sun spinning and place all the other members of the system in orbit. No way has been conceived whereby tidal disruption, in any form, could concentrate so much of the energy in a single planet. For this and numerous other reasons that, for lack of space, cannot be discussed here, such hypotheses now seem to be unacceptable.

Evolution from a Gaseous Nebula. The first attempt to account for the origin of the Solar System on a scientific basis was that of the French mathematician, Laplace, who in 1796 supposed that at one time all the matter now comprised in the System formed a gaseous nebula, so distended by heat that its diameter somewhat exceeded the orbit of Pluto, slowly rotating in space. He argued that in cooling it would rotate faster and faster until centrifugal force at the periphery equaled the pull of gravity, whereupon a gaseous ring would be shed as the central mass continued to shrink. Such a ring would eventually break and contract into a gaseous sphere revolving about the central mass in a circular orbit. By repetition of this process Laplace pictured the formation of the planets one after another as successive rings were shed.

The beautiful simplicity of this scheme made an immediate appeal, and Laplace's hypothesis had a great vogue during the nineteenth century. When confronted with mathematical analysis, however, it proved to be entirely untenable and has long since been abandoned.

During recent decades, however, several astronomers have advanced modified forms of the **gaseous-nebular hypothesis,** and we now seem on the threshold of a satisfactory explanation.

According to a version recently developed by Kuiper, [3] the Sun, at an earlier stage in its development, was surrounded by a diffuse nebula of gases and solid dust particles extending beyond the limits of the orbit of Pluto. At this time the Sun was cooler than it is now and the surrounding nebula was relatively cool, thus resembling some of those now observed about other stars. As this vast "dust cloud" revolved with the Sun, turbulent eddies developed, in a sense analogous to the great cyclonic storms—the lows and highs—that so commonly disturb Earth's present atmosphere. Such eddies are believed from time to time to have concentrated sufficient mass to develop local gravitative fields to which dust particles and molecules of gas were drawn and held. Here the dust particles condensed to form solid cores and were surrounded by gaseous envelopes. Thus, as turbulent eddies formed and reformed, the larger nuclei grew into protoplanets while smaller ones formed the nuclei of minor members of the Solar System—the satellites, the planetoids, and meteors. Originally, then, each of the planets was largely gaseous, with a solid core, and the minor planets were relatively much larger than now. At this early stage the Sun was cooler than it is now and not nearly as bright, and the protoplanets may have been cool.

But upon further condensation radioactivity came into play and the cores of the protoplanets developed internal heat while the Sun was developing its present brightness and radiant energy. With this change the lighter gases surrounding the planets (chiefly hydrogen and helium) began to leak away into space. During this stage the loss from the planets relatively near the Sun was very great as the gas molecules were literally driven away into space even as those in the tails of comets are now driven off. Mercury, being both small and near the Sun, and unable to hold any of its gases, was stripped down to its solid core. Venus and Earth were large enough to hold a very small part of their primeval gaseous envelopes, but Mars was too small to hold more than a trace. On the contrary, giant Jupiter, far out in space, suffered little loss and may have picked up some of the

TABLE 1. RELATIVE ABUNDANCE OF THE COMMONEST ELEMENTS IN THE PRESENT SOLAR ATMOSPHERE

(Adapted from Mason, after Unsöld.)

Element	Abundance
H	5100.
He	1000.
O	28.
Fe	2.7
N	2.1
Mg	1.7
C	1.0
Si	1.0
S	0.43
Al	0.10
Na	0.10

gases driven away from the inner planets. It therefore more nearly represents the original protoplanets, having a relatively small solid core surrounded by a vast gaseous envelope. Saturn, Uranus, and Neptune, being still farther out, are likewise largely gaseous.

This version of the nebular hypothesis explains readily the circular and concentric orbits of the planets, their rotation in a common plane, and the vast difference between the minor and major planets. The momentum of Jupiter, inherited from the time when the nebula revolved as a unit about the Sun, offers no difficulty.

It is perhaps too early to be sure whether quantitative study will require further modifications of this theory, but it now appears to be nearer the truth than any previously considered explanation of the origin of our world.

COSMIC HISTORY OF THE EARTH

According to the hypothesis just sketched, Earth grew from a nucleus that began as a local condensation deep within a vast solar nebula. Within its gravitative field the dust particles composed of the heavier elements were gradually drawn closer together until they condensed to form a solid body surrounded by a gaseous atmosphere. Traveling in a circular orbit inherited from the rotation of the nebula, it grew by sweeping up the diffuse matter and the lesser condensations that lay within or near its path. As its mass increased, its gravitative field widened until it was able to clear a broad belt along its course. One of the secondary condensations in this zone was too far away, however, to be drawn into the growing Earth, but near enough to be captured and drawn into orbit about it; this was to become the moon. Meanwhile each of the other planets was developing in a comparable manner, and the central part of the nebula was contracting to form the ancestral Sun, still large and diffuse and relatively cool.

In the original nebula the elements were presumably present in approximately the ratios indicated in Table 1 in which the abundance of silica (Si) is chosen as unity. It appears probable, however, that dust particles comprised of the heavier elements were more concentrated deep within the nebula than in its outer part which consisted chiefly of the lightest elements, hydrogen and helium. If this be true, the inner planets were, from the start, made of heavier matter than the outer ones.

As the system evolved, moreover, a new factor came into play that vastly increased this contrast. As the Sun gradually condensed to smaller radius, its temperature rose, and it began to pour out radiant energy. As it thus warmed the atmospheres of the inner planets, the heat increased the molecular velocity of their component gases until it exceeded the escape velocity, and the lighter gases began to leak away into space. Thus, by the time the radiant energy of the Sun had reached its present intensity, the minor planets had lost all, or nearly all, of their lighter elements which were literally blown away. Meanwhile the major planets were so far from the Sun as to be less affected, and so large that they could hold even the lightest gases. Indeed, they may have captured part of the gases that leaked away from the minor planets. Thus the original contrast in size and composition between the minor and major planets reached its present magnitude as the minor planets decreased in size through the loss of their more volatile constituents, and were reduced to solid earthlike bodies, while the major planets grew in size and remained largely gaseous.

Evolution of the Atmosphere. During its early history the solid Earth must have consisted largely of silicate rocks and iron. It was too small to retain hydrogen and helium, and if free oxygen were present it was quickly depleted through oxidation of the iron and silicates. Nitrogen, on the other hand, being relatively inert, may have been present in some abundance.

In view of the relative abundance of carbon and its remarkable affinity for hydrogen, oxygen, and nitrogen, the primeval planetary atmospheres should have consisted chiefly of the following gases: hydrogen and helium (on major planets), methane (CH_4), ammonia (NH_3), CO_2, CO, H_2O, and N. Free oxygen could not exist in such association, and it is evident that Earth's unique atmosphere of free oxygen and nitrogen with only a trace of CO_2 must have evolved during a later stage of Earth history.

At present two widely divergent views are current as to the composition of Earth's primeval atmosphere. One school[9] holds that it consisted largely of methane (CH_4) and ammonia (NH_3); the other[10] that it was comprised chiefly of CO_2 with some N and H_2O. In support of the latter view, Rubey[10] has pointed out that methane and ammonia would form in the presence of abundant free hydrogen, but in its absence the normal carbon compounds would be CO_2 or CO. In view of the fact that CH_4 and NH_3 have been identified only on the major planets where hydrogen is abundant and that CO_2 is the dominant gas in the atmospheres of Venus and Mars (the only minor planets, except Earth, that have been able to hold an atmosphere), the inference is very strong that the second school is right. How then was a primeval atmosphere of CO_2, H_2O, and N_2 transformed into one of N_2, O_2, and H_2O with only a trace of CO_2?

In the first place, CO_2 has been continually used in the weathering of the silicate rocks to form carbonates and is thus kept to a minimum even though CO_2 has been continually supplied by volcanic emanations throughout geologic time. In the second, H_2O is dissociated into H and O_2 in the upper reaches of the atmosphere where the H readily escapes whereas the O_2, being heavier, is retained. Rubey[10] presents convincing evidence, furthermore, that H_2O has been sweated out of the interior of the Earth throughout geologic time, as discussed in the next paragraph, so that a constant supply of water vapor has been maintained in the atmosphere, from which a steadily increasing supply of O_2 could be generated. Nearly all of our present atmosphere has thus been secondarily derived during geologic time; very little is inherited from the primeval stage.

Origin of the Ocean Water. In scholarly discussions too technical to review here, Rubey[10] has advanced convincing reasons for believing that the ocean water has been sweated out of the interior of the Earth during geologic time. This began when the young Earth began to be heated internally by radioactivity. As the mantle approached the melting point, "degassing" of the silicates released H_2O which worked its way to the surface, accompanying the rising magmas to escape as volcanic emanations or as juvenile water working its way up through the outer crust. If this be true, the volume of ocean water has been continually rising throughout geologic time and is still increasing.

Growth of Continents and Ocean Basins. In its primeval stage the mantle of the Earth must have been fairly homogeneous, since it was formed by the condensation of discrete solid particles in a gaseous medium. The original rocky surface may therefore have had but slight relief, and there may not have been enough water to cover it.

Upon condensation, however, the radioactive elements widely disseminated through the silicate rocks began to generate heat. Since rock is a poor conductor, the heat gradually built up to a point where some of the materials with the lowest melting point became fluid. Then the lighter materials began to work their way upward while the iron migrated downward. Thus volcanic activity was initiated on the Earth. Thus also the ocean water began to accumulate. It is possible that for a time the Earth was covered with a universal but very shallow ocean. However, where large masses of the igneous rocks, sweated out from below, accumulated at or near the surface, they formed rock masses relatively lighter than the average rocks, and these masses therefore tended to rise isostatically as ice bergs rise above the sea. Such masses then appeared as islands in a shallow sea. With continued volcanism such islands grew in size and were welded into larger land masses—the nuclei of the continents. According to this hypothesis the continents have grown throughout geologic time and the ocean basins have deepened, relatively, as the great granitic plates that underlie the continents were gradually forged. In the meantime the iron has migrated down to form the core, and a rough density stratification within the solid Earth has been attained.

REFERENCES

1. Gamow, George, 1958, *Matter, Earth, and Sky*, Prentice-Hall, Englewood Cliffs, New Jersey, pp. 520–525.

2. Menzel, Donald H., 1958, Exploring our neighbor world, the Moon. *National Geographic Magazine*, vol. 113, pp. 277–296.

Urey, Harold C., 1952, *The Planets, Their Origin and Development.* Yale University Press, New Haven, Connecticut.

3. Kuiper, G. P. (ed.), 1952, Planetary atmospheres and their origin. In: *The Atmospheres of the Earth and Planets*, 2nd ed., University of Chicago Press, Chicago, pp. 306–405.

4. Wildt, Rupert, 1958, Inside the planets. *Publ. Astronomical Society of the Pacific*, vol. 20, pp. 237–250.

5. Beirmann, Ludwig F. and Rhea Lüst, 1958, The Tails of Comets. *Scientific American*, vol. 199, no. 4, pp. 44–50.

6. Swindel, George W., Jr., and Walter B. Jones, 1955, *Meteoritics*, Vol. 1. pp. 125–132.

7. Jones, Sir Harold Spencer, 1958, The origin of the solar system. *Endeavor*, vol. 17, no. 67, pp. 140–144.

8. Mason, Brian, 1958, *Principles of Geochemistry*, 2nd ed. John Wiley and Sons, New York, p. 15.

9. Oparin, A. I., 1953, *The Origin of Life*, English translation of Second Edition. Dover Publications, Inc., New York, pp. 1–270.

Urey, Harold C., 1952, *The Planets: Their Origin and Development.* Yale University Press, New Haven, Connecticut, p. 1–245.

10. Rubey, W. W., 1955, Development of the hydrosphere and atmosphere, with special reference to probable composition of the early atmosphere. *Geol. Soc., Amer., Special Paper 62*, pp. 631–650.

Figure 46. The Tree of Animal Life. Animals below the wavy white line are aquatic; those above are adapted to land life. (Simplified from a colored wall chart by Heintz and Störmer. Reproduced through the courtesy of Ward's Natural Science Establishment.)

Chapter 5. The Constant Change of Living Things

A fire-mist and a planet,
A crystal and a cell,
A jellyfish and a saurian,
And caves where the cave men dwell;
Then a sense of law and beauty
And a face turned from the clod—
Some call it Evolution,
And others call it God.

WILLIAM HERBERT CARRUTH

THE ORIGIN OF LIFE

One cannot contemplate the pageant of life stretching down through the corridors of time without wondering how it all started. Indeed, philosophers of all ages have speculated on the origin of life, and their beliefs have fallen generally into one of two categories: either (1) it began by a *supernatural* act of creation, or (2) it developed spontaneously from inorganic matter.

To seek a natural explanation is not, as some have thought, more materialistic than Special Creation, for if a Divine Creator produced the physical universe, surely He also established the physical and chemical laws that govern it; the alternatives are merely whether the creation of life was accomplished by the operation of these natural laws or whether in some capricious manner they were set aside.

Belief in spontaneous generation was common during the Middle Ages when worms were thought to develop from mud, maggots from decaying flesh, and mold from refuse. But the experiments of Pasteur, about 1860, convincingly proved that maggots develop from eggs laid by flies, and even germs of disease and decay do not appear in sterilized organic matter except when contaminated by living organisms from outside sources. Since then, abundant experience in medicine and in food preservation has made it clear that life is not spontaneously generated in the modern world. For this there are two chief reasons: (1) In the presence of free oxygen organic matter is readily destroyed by oxidation and is reduced largely to CO_2 and H_2O. Thus, for example, in the forests where organic tissue is rapidly built up, the fallen leaves and trees disappear about as fast as they are formed, and whether they are consumed by fire, or by the slower process of decay, the end products are the same. (2) The modern world is populated by an enormous complex of living creatures that feed upon and destroy organic matter—especially the ever-present molds and bacteria that cause putrefaction and decay.

But if the Earth developed from a gaseous nebula as outlined in the preceding chapter, it passed through an early stage when neither of these inhibitions existed, for until life had appeared, it was an utterly sterile world. Furthermore, contrary to previous conception, the primeval atmosphere for a time probably contained no free oxygen but was composed largely of carbon dioxide and water vapor.

Of all the elements, carbon is unique in its ability to unite with a great variety of other elements to form metastable compounds, and to join relatively simple units into long chains or rings (Fig. 47) and thus to build up large and complex molecules such as the proteins of which living matter is made.

Synthetic chemistry in recent years has discovered ways of building up many kinds of polymers (e.g., synthetic rubber, plastics, rayon, nylon). In industry catalyzers are used to speed up such reactions, but they do not *cause* chemical reactions—they merely *speed up* reactions that can and do take place naturally.

Now, on our primitive planet, bathed in an atmosphere of carbon dioxide, a great variety of organic compounds must have formed; and in a sterile and oxygen-free world they may have persisted, accumulating in the seas and lakes until some of the shallow waters were virtual soups of organic compounds. This then was the environment, so different from our modern world, under which life may have begun naturally.[2]

The problem is not simple, for a living organism not only includes a great variety of such compounds but has them organized in very definite and almost infinitely complex systems, so that some serve as catalyzers while others react in complex ways to store and again to free the energy that is manifest in living things.

The first great source of such energy was sunlight, which is still the means by which plants build up organic matter through photosynthesis; and when free oxygen began to appear in the atmosphere a still more effective source of energy was available in the oxidation of proteins. This is the present source of energy in animal metabolism.

Thus far, by deductive reasoning, we have pictured conditions under which proteins may have formed and the simplest types of life may have developed in nature. Recently laboratory experiments have gone one step further. In the geochemical laboratory at Chicago Dr. S. L. Miller[3] circulated a mixture of the gases methane (CH_4), ammonia (NH_3), water vapor (H_2O) and hydrogen (H_2) over an electric discharge (to supply energy), and after a time found that the water in the bottom of the apparatus contained certain amino acids that are the basic units of which proteins are made. No living tissue has yet been synthetically produced—and possibly none ever will be, for the organization of the proteins in even the simplest forms of life is amazingly complex. But the new insights in both astronomy and chemistry suggest that we are on the threshold of discoveries that will enable us to understand how life began when the world was young.*

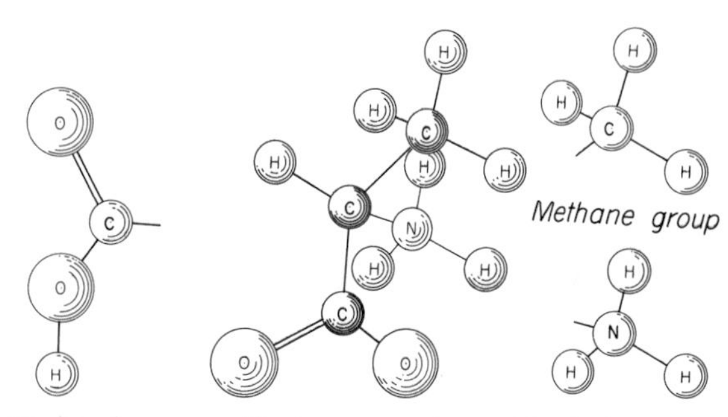

Glycine + Glycine = Glycylglycine + Water

Portion of a polypeptide chain — a protein

Figure 47. The building of organic compounds. Alanine, one of the amino acids, is a fundamental building unit of proteins. The center figure above shows the space relations and the relative sizes of the atoms of carbon, hydrogen, nitrogen, and oxygen in this molecule which is produced by the combination of simpler units shown beside it. The central figure indicates how two molecules of another organic compound, glycine, unite to form a larger and more complex molecule. In the proteins such simple units are repeated in long chains or complex configurations held together by carbon atoms. The lower figure represents part of a single and relatively simple protein molecule.

In the proteins certain of the hydrogen atoms may be replaced by others such as sulphur or potassium, which are represented by the letter *R* in this figure.

In his experiment Dr. Miller synthesized both alanine and glycine.

Adapted from figures in *General Chemistry* by Linus Pauling.

THE DOCTRINE OF EVOLUTION

A thoughtful person can hardly survey the great diversity of life about him without wondering how the many kinds of animals and plants came to be. And if he contemplates the fossil record and finds that in each geologic age the Earth was inhabited by still different types of life, that question becomes more insistent. Thus far two, and only two answers have been suggested—the first is Special Creation; the second, Evolution.

The first theory, that of Creation, assumes that each kind of animal and plant was "molded from the dust of the Earth" and "given the breath of life" in its present form, each being a special and independent creation. To primitive people who knew but a few hundred kinds of animals and plants, and had no knowledge of biology, this seemed the simplest and most acceptable explanation, as natural as the belief that the Earth was flat and that it formed the center of the Universe about which Sun and Moon and stars revolved. From such early speculation this theory was incorporated in the ancient Hebrew scriptures, and so, for centuries, it exerted a profound influence on the thought of the Christian world.

The long and extensive experience of breeding domestic animals and plants suggested a different origin. It is known, for example, that all modern breeds of dog can be traced back to a single species of wild dog, that all our domestic horses have come from one or two species of wild pony, and that the many breeds of cattle have sprung from one, or at most a few, wild ancestors. If it has been possible, within a few thousand years, to change a wild dog into forms as diverse as the whippet, the bulldog, and the poodle, and if, by careful selection and breeding, it has been possible to transform the scrawny wild pony of central Asia into the sleek Arabian race horse, the toylike Shetland pony, and the ponderous Percheron, then we can only wonder

*This subject is too vast and too technical to be adequately presented here. Those interested will find a scholarly treatment comprising an entire volume by Oparin[2] and an interesting and readable shorter discussion in an article by Wald.[3]

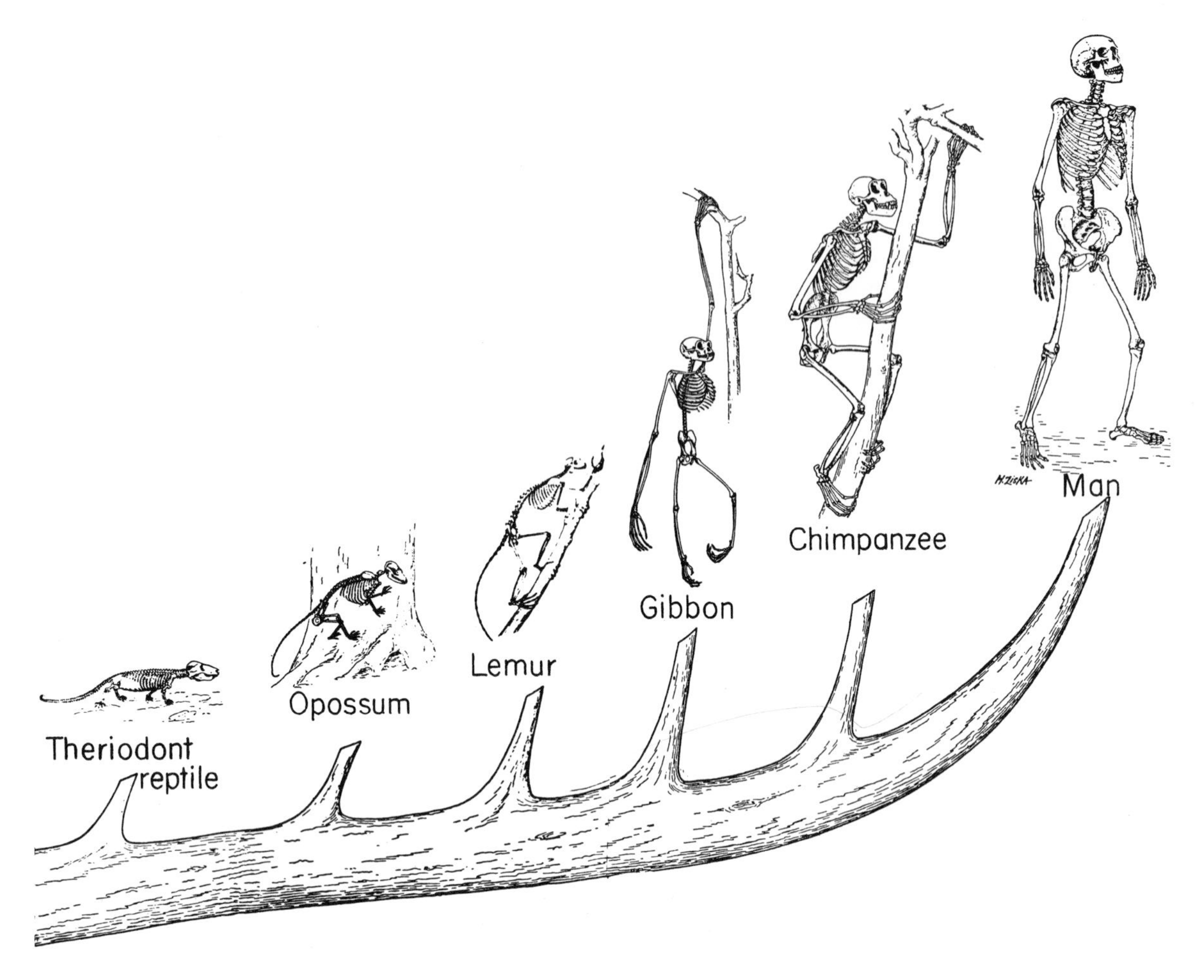

Figure 48. Series of skeletons from reptiles to man, showing homologies of skeletal elements. (American Museum of Natural History.)

if in similar fashion each kind of wild life has developed from some other, by gradual change and specialization. This line of thought led to the doctrine of Organic Evolution, which is the belief that from some geologically remote, primitive form of life all the diverse kinds of animals and plants have developed, each **evolving** from some previous form by gradual and orderly change. According to this conception, all creatures are genetically related, like the members of a great human family, and the degree of relationship of different groups of animals and plants may be presented by the branches of a family tree (Fig. 46).

It may be noted that *evolution* is no less a *special* Creation than that conceived in the Scriptures; it is only a *different method* of creation—one that is still taking place about us and that we can hope to understand. There is still much to learn about the ways and means by which evolution is brought about, but enlightened people can no longer doubt that it *is* the *method of creation,* and it is now universally accepted as a guiding principle in all fields of biology.

Evidence of Evolution

The evidence of evolution is so varied and so extensive that volumes would be required to review it all, and most of it is too technical for simple presentation. Therefore, we can hope here only to suggest the *nature* of the evidence. Our illustrations are chosen from three distinct lines of investigation, the first two biologic, the third geologic.

Comparative Anatomy: Homologous Structures. It is a striking fact that in related groups of animals a given organ or anatomical structure is built on a common plan. This is illustrated repeatedly in Figure 48, for, in spite of the impressive differences between reptile, lemur, and man, the skeleton in all three is constructed on the same fundamental plan, and its elements can be matched bone for bone. The forelimb in each includes a single upper arm bone (humerus), a pair of forearm bones (ulna and radius), a series of wrist bones (metacarpals), and five digits.

If we extend the comparison to distantly related mammals such as the bat, the seal, and the dog (Fig. 49), we find great modifications of the limbs for different habits of life; yet the arm of a man, the wing of a bat, the flipper of a seal, and the foreleg of a dog are built with the same skeletal elements, the dissimilarities being due essentially to differences in size and proportions of individual bones. Organs that thus agree in fundamental structure are said to be **homologous** (Gr. *omologia*, agreement).

A study of the muscles and of the internal organs would greatly multiply the examples of homologous structures in the animals mentioned. Such likenesses indicate kinship and descent, with modification, from a common five-toed ancestor; they are inexplicable on any other basis.

Vestigial structures—those that have lost their function—afford perhaps the most telling evidence from comparative anatomy (Fig. 52). Such, for example, are the ear muscles in man, which are homologous with those that move the ears of the lower mammals, but in most humans are no longer under voluntary control and serve no useful purpose. Another vestigial structure is the human appendix, which seems to be only a source of danger, although its homologue in many lower animals is an important part of the digestive system. About 180 such useless features have been recorded in the human body. One of the striking and unfortunate misfits of our anatomy is the way in which the viscera are supported in the body cavity. All the mammals, save man and the apes, walk on all fours, with the body in a horizontal position, and the delicate mesenteries that hold the various organs in place are well fitted to this posture. In standing upright, however, man has brought the body into a vertical position in which the mesenteries, supporting the viscera and arranged as in the quadrupeds, are inadequate and inefficient. As a result, human beings suffer from "fallen stomach," prolapse of the womb, paunchiness, and hernia. Surely, if a body were created

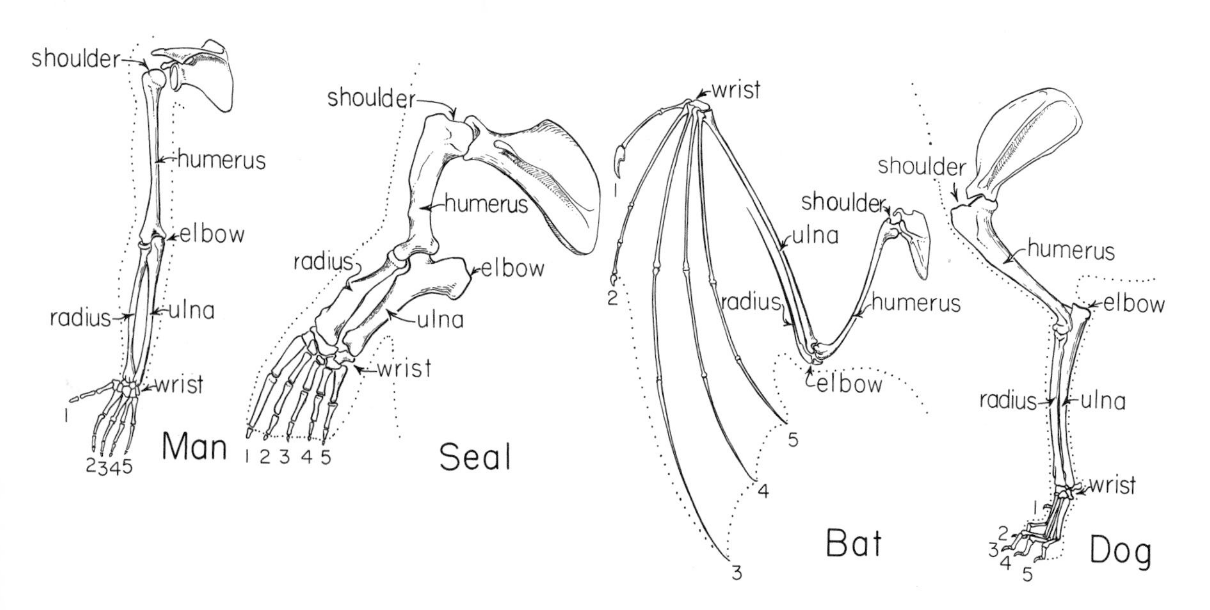

Figure 49. Forelimbs of man, seal, bat, and dog.

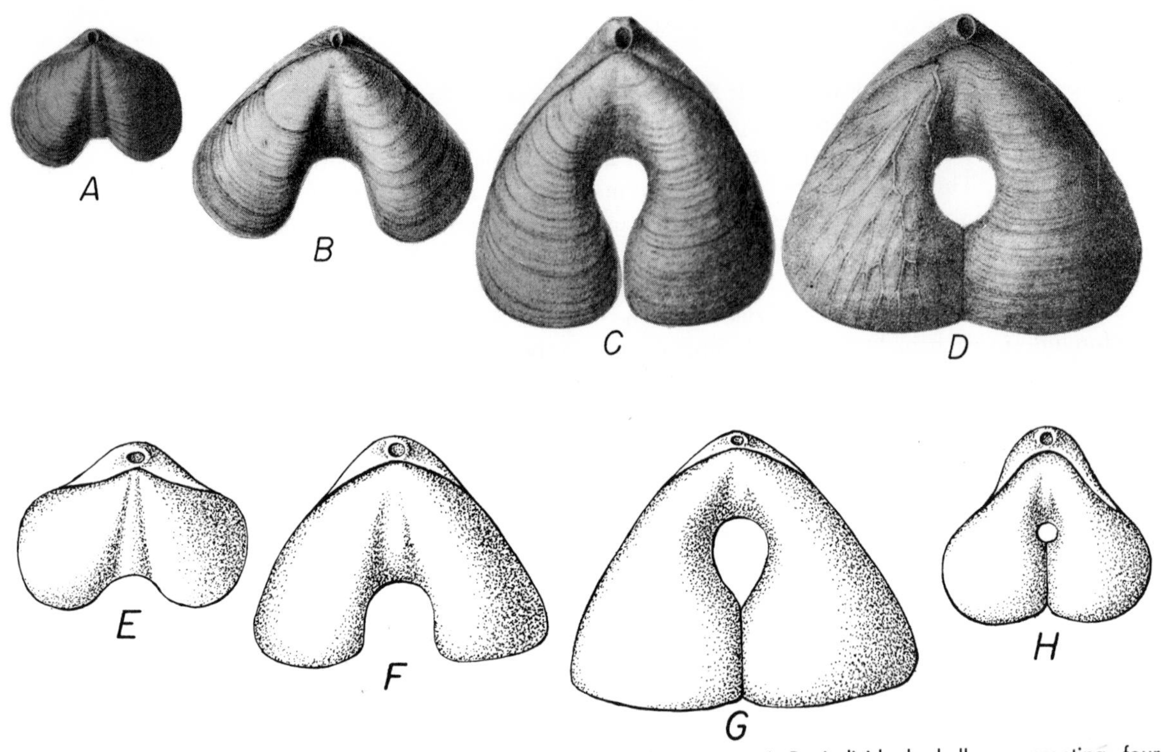

Figure 50. Individual and racial history of the keyhole brachiopod, *Pygope*. *A–D*, individual shells representing four growth stages in a single species (*P. diphyoides*); *E–H*, adult shells of distinct species from successive geologic ages showing the racial history of the genus. *E*, *F*, and *G* are from Jurassic horizons and *H* from the early Cretaceous.

de novo, it would not be endowed with useless and dangerous appendages *aping* those that are functional in other animals; and the human body would hardly have been given the most inefficient and troublesome visceral support of all the mammals, one that is efficient for the quadrupeds but not for man. Such vestigial structures admit of no other rational explanation than that man is related to other animals by common descent from ancestors in which these structures were functional.

Embryology: The Law of Recapitulation. Each individual begins as a single cell and by repeated cell division grows and passes through a remarkable series of embryological and juvenile stages before assuming its normal adult form. This orderly sequence of developmental stages constitutes its **ontogeny**.

One of the great biological discoveries of the last century is that the ontogeny repeats briefly (and in many cases imperfectly) the racial history. Stated as a natural law, **ontogeny recapitulates phylogeny.** The amphibians (for example, the frog and the salamander) provide an illustration of such recapitulation. They lay their eggs in the water, and these hatch into tadpoles that are in essential respects fishlike, breathing by means of gills and having no lungs or limbs. But during growth the gills are resorbed, lungs are formed, legs bud out from the body, and, after a transition period, the animal may leave the water to spend the rest of its days on land. This remarkable metamorphosis implies that the remote ancestors of the amphibia were fishes, from which they descended by migrating from the water to the lands, with all the modifications which that migration imposed.

Recapitulation really means that an animal has inherited from its ancestors a certain ontogeny which it repeats up to the point at which its own peculiar specialization begins. The amphibians inherited from their remote ancestors, the fishes, the capacity to lay only small eggs without much yolk and without shells. Such eggs can survive and hatch only in water, and the young, of necessity, breathe by means of gills. The amphibians were never able to improve on this habit and so, throughout the ages, have returned annually to the water to spawn.

Many fossil shells preserve a record of their own ontogeny. Consider, for example, the keyhole shell, *Pygope*, among the Jurassic brachiopods (Fig. 50). The adult shell has a hole passing through its middle, like the hole in a doughnut. A young one, however, has the shape shown in *A;* a slightly older one, *B;* and a half-grown shell, *C*. The lines of growth on the adult shell, *D*, recording its margin at many stages of development, show that it passed through all the shapes preserved in the young shells. It is obvious that the very young shell was not perforated but had a shallow notch at its front margin, and during growth it became deeply bilobed and the notch became deep and rounded; eventually the lobes converged and grew together, thus transforming the notch into a hole. This ontogeny would imply that *Pygope* descended from a remote ancestor which at maturity was shaped much like the young shell, *A*, and that, during the ages, the race underwent progressive changes of shape similar to those repeated in the ontogeny of *Pygope*. In actual fact, a series of species has been found in successive horizons in the Jurassic and Cretaceous rocks of Europe which prove that the racial development *did* follow this course (Fig. 50*E–H*).

Another illustration of ontogeny is afforded by the straight-shelled ammonite, *Baculites*, of late Cretaceous age (Fig. 51). Although most of the shell is straight, the tip is tightly coiled, and the inference is, therefore, that its remote ancestors were coiled (as, in fact, nearly all ammonites were).

Insofar as the early ontogenetic stages are inherited from ancestors, they clearly indicate the general nature of the ancestral stock of any animal. Thus, closely related animals should be closely alike in the early ontogeny, and conversely, animals that are closely alike in their youth are probably genetically related, even though they specialize and become dissimilar at maturity.

Paleontology: The Documentary Evidence. If life has evolved gradually since early geologic time, the fossils preserved in successive formations should record many intermediate stages between forms now widely differentiated, and should provide connecting links between even widely distinct stocks of animals and plants. In following chapters we shall have occasion to note many such cases, some of which have played a major role in establishing the doctrine of descent. The study of embryology and comparative anatomy provide only circumstantial evidence of evolution, but the fossil remains of evolving series constitute actual documentary evidence that the changes occurred.

The origin of the keyhole shell discussed above is an example; the ontogeny led us to infer how the perforation developed, but the discovery of fossil shells representing the inferred changes in successive Jurassic and Cretaceous formations affords the documentary proof in the case.

The skeleton of the horse's leg displays interesting vestigial structures whose significance is likewise clearly shown by the fossil record. In the hind leg, for example, if we begin with the hip joint (Fig. 52), it is easy to identify the thigh bone and the knee cap, and below these the paired lower leg bones, the tibia and fibula. The hock is really the heel, as shown by its relations to the short tarsals, and below the latter are the elongated toe bones.

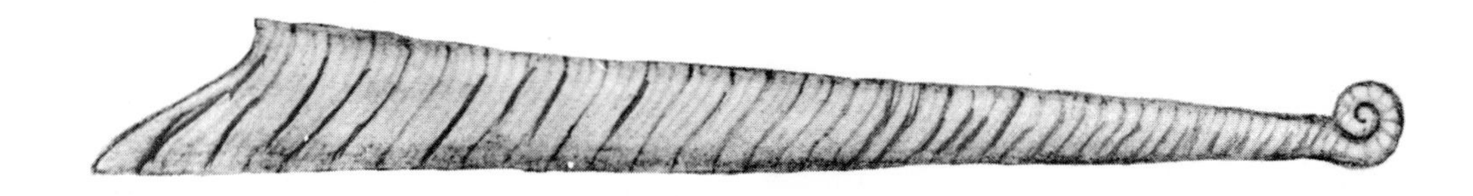

Figure 51. Shell of a straight ammonite (*Baculites*) from the Upper Cretaceous. Its coiled tip was inherited from coiled ancestors.

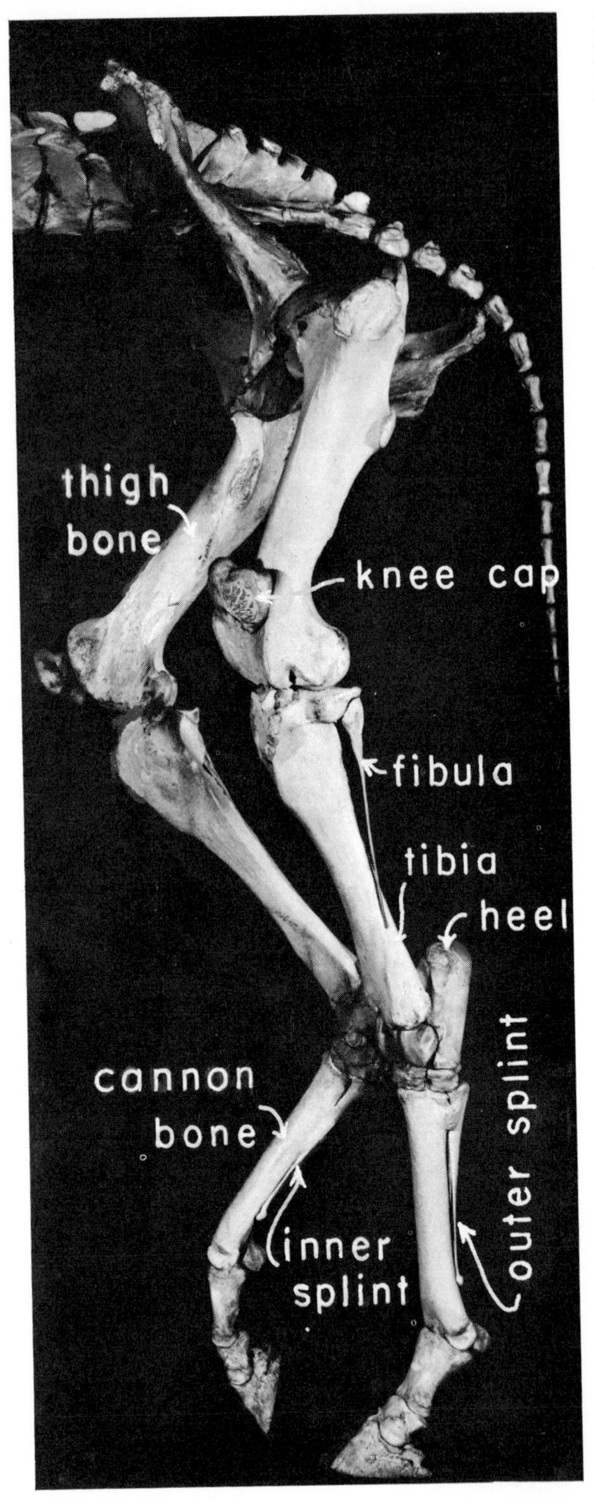

Figure 52. Skeleton of hind legs of a modern horse showing vestigial structures. (American Museum of Natural History.)

From this examination we may conclude that the horse walks on the *end* of one toe and that the lower part of the leg has been greatly lengthened as the heel came up off the ground (please examine also Fig. 348, p. 409).

Now in primitive mammals, and even in the specialized ones that use their hands and feet for grasping or digging, the paired lower limb bones are subequal in size and provide for a rotary motion of the hands and feet. But in the horse, which can bend its leg only fore and aft at the heel, the fibula is reduced to a mere sliver, and its lower end does not even make contact with the foot bones. The presence of this vestigial fibula implies, however, that the remote ancestor of the horse had a less specialized limb with freer movement of the foot. And on each side of the main toe bone (the cannon bone) there is a slender bone known as the **splint**, which can be nothing but the vestige of another toe. The splint bones clearly imply that the ancestor of the modern horse had three toes, as do the rhinoceros and the tapir.

The series of fossil horses recovered from successive Cenozoic formations in the western United States proves this inference to be true beyond any doubt. For example (Fig. 348), all the fossil horses from the Pleistocene, and most of those from the Pliocene, are like the modern horse, but *all* those of the Miocene have three toes on each foot. In these, however, the side toes are slender and in most species apparently were functionless, probably dangling like the dewclaws of cattle. In the underlying Oligocene beds, on the contrary, the three toes are subequal in size on each foot, and all shared in bearing the animal's weight. Finally, in the still older Eocene strata, vestiges of a fourth toe have been found in the front feet. No fully five-toed ancestor has yet been identified, but there can be no doubt that such a one existed. Illustrations of the paleontological evidence of evolution could be multiplied to any length, for they form the essence of the geological history of life.

Ways and Means of Evolution

Variation. The principle of heredity is that "like begets like," the parents passing on to its offspring all its distinctive characters. However, no individual is exactly like its parent, nor is it precisely like any of its brothers and sisters, even of

Figure 53. Adaptive specialization of the beak in the crossbill, *Loxia*. The parrot crossbill (left) feeds on pine cones; the common crossbill (center) feeds on spruce cones; and the Himalayan crossbill (right) feeds on the small soft cones of the larch. Slightly larger than natural size. (Data from David Lack.)

the same brood; and commonly there is an appreciable variation among individuals of the same species. Thanks to recent progress in the science of genetics we now understand a good deal about the way in which variations arise, but the facts are too complex and technical for brief presentation. Regardless of the cause, experience indicates that, in spite of the heredity principle, variations, mostly slight, occur in each new generation.

Struggle for Existence. All kinds of animals and plants produce more offspring than can possibly survive. Many of the lower animals lay thousands or even millions of eggs each year—the salmon as many as 28,000,000 and the oyster more than 100,000,000—and a plant such as the elm or maple tree produces innumerable seeds. This means that among such organisms only one out of millions live to maturity; otherwise the population of any species would rapidly increase. Even in the higher animals such as man, where few offspring are born, more die young than survive to maturity.

Thus, throughout Nature there is an intense and never-ceasing struggle on the part of all kinds of organisms to exist and to grow and to reproduce their own kind. The struggle is against the environment, against enemies that devour or those that cause disease; commonly it is against members of the same kind, in competition for food, or even for "a place in the sun." Life's struggle is exceedingly harsh toward the young, and success is the rare exception.

Natural Selection. In a struggle so severe, any advantage, however slight, may decide between life and death. And of the many trivial variations that appear in any species, some will be advantageous and individuals possessing them will tend to survive, while others, less favored, will tend to be exterminated. For example, if the species is an animal living in an environment where fleetness is necessary to escape carnivorous enemies, the slow and the underdeveloped young in the herd have little chance to reach maturity, whereas, on the average, the most precocious will survive and pass on their characteristics to new descendants. In this way Nature selects, as a breeder of stock might do, eliminating the unfit (unfit for a particular environment) and permitting only the fit to continue the race. And so, in spite of endless and random variations from generation to generation, only selected ones will survive. By this method Nature has evolved new species from old, to meet new or changed environments.

A single illustration may serve to show how such adaptations are produced (Fig. 53). The crossbill, which ranges over Europe from the Alps to Siberia, lives on the seeds of evergreens. In the Alps it feeds on pine cones, which are tough and hard and require a stout, thick bill if the bird is to break them apart and extract the nut. In Siberia, however, it has to feed on cedar cones instead of pine, and in these the seeds lie deeper but are not so well protected, and here a longer, more slender beak is a decided advantage. Now when the crossbill appeared in Europe (whether by migration or evolution), those birds that varied toward long slender bills could not survive through a hard winter in a pine-clad region where the competition for food was keen, because their fragile beaks could not break enough pine cones. The birds with short, stout beaks fared much better. Conversely, the short-beaked birds could hardly survive in the cedar forests because they could not reach the nuts; there, the birds with longer and more slender beaks survived. Thus it has come about that, through many generations of natural selection, the crossbill of Siberia has a slender beak with the upper jaw protruding about one-tenth of an inch beyond the lower, whereas the crossbills of the Alps have short, stout beaks.

Isolation. A species is a population of individuals capable of interbreeding. If it spreads over a large region of varied environments, as the crossbill has done, more or less isolated communities may specialize in different directions as they become adapted to new types of food or new habits of life. Thus new geographic races or subspecies arise. Until the specialization has reached a critical limit, however, a subspecies is still capable of interbreeding with related subspecies. Where the geographic habitats of two subspecies are contiguous or overlap somewhat, interbreeding does take place and the characters of the two subspecies blend and lose their distinctiveness. Likewise, if a few individuals of one subspecies should migrate into a province occupied by a related subspecies, interbreeding with the larger population will so dilute their contribution to the common gene pool that within a few generations their peculiarities will disappear. For the same reason it is improbable that a new subspecies could arise in direct competition with a parent subspecies. However, where subspecies are geographically isolated for a sufficient length of time, the specializations of each may become so great that they are incapable of interbreeding. Each thus becomes a distinct species. Isolation is thus an important factor in speciation. This was perceived by Darwin more than a century ago when he visited the Gallapagos Islands and found the finches, presumably derived from the mainland of South America, to be widespread but with a distinct species on each island.

Two species with identical habits could not long survive in direct competition because one would be more successful and would soon drive out or exterminate the other; but even closely related species adapted to different feeding habits or to different niches in the environment may successfully survive in a single area since they cannot interbreed and do not directly compete one with the other.

Illustrations could be multiplied ad infinitum if space permitted, for the whole complex of life is a maze of adaptations to special habits and conditions.

The ways and means of evolution are still the subject of intense research, but the truth of the general doctrine is no longer to doubt.

REFERENCES

1. Rubey, W. W., 1955, Development of the hydrosphere and atmosphere, with special reference to probable composition of the early atmosphere. *Geol. Soc. Amer., Special Paper* 62, pp. 631–650.

2. Oparin, A. I., 1953, *Origin of Life*, 2nd ed. Dover Publications, New York, pp. 1–270.

Wald, George, 1954, The origin of life. *Scientific American*, vol. 191, no. 2, pp. 44–53.

3. Miller, Stanley L., 1953, A production of amino acids under possible primitive earth conditions. *Science*, vol. 117, pp. 528, 529.

Figure 54. South wall of the Grand Canyon near Bright Angel Creek, showing the Vishnu schist overlain with profound unconformity by the Tonto sandstone of Cambrian age and succeeding Paleozoic formations. (U.S. Geological Survey.)

Chapter 6. The Cryptozoic Eon: Precambrian History of the Earth

What seest thou else
In the dark backward and abysm of time?
THE TEMPEST, ACT 1, SCENE 2

The Ruins of Time. EARTH'S BEGINNING WAS followed by long eras that are veiled in the shadows of antiquity. Enormous groups of ancient rocks, lying in tangled confusion below the Paleozoic, form an impressive record of those early times; but without fossils to date them, each is like a fragment of an unpaged manuscript. With local exceptions they have been intensely deformed; in large part they have suffered strong metamorphism; and only remnants have escaped erosion or burial by younger formations.

Human history presents similar difficulties. The millennia that preceded written records are known to us only from scattered ruins. The buried cities of Mesopotamia, the stone implements of Neanderthal man, and the skulls of *Pithecanthropus* record chapters of human history no less real because they are only vaguely known. In this spirit we must approach the early history of the Earth. We are dealing with fragments of the record that have escaped the ravages of time.

Distribution of Cryptozoic Rocks. Although presumably world wide in extent, the Precambrian rocks are covered by younger formations in approximately four-fifths of the land areas of the world. Exposures are limited to (1) the cores of mountain ranges where great uplift and deep erosion have laid them bare, (2) to a few gorges, such as the Grand Canyon, cut deeply into high plateaus, and (3) to the so-called shields° which are stable areas that since Precambrian time have never been deeply covered. Each continent displays at least one shield (Fig. 55). In general these were sites of extensive orogeny during the Cryptozoic Eon, then became stable, and subsequently have been great interior plains.

NATURE OF THE CRYPTOZOIC RECORD

The early history of the Earth can be sketched only in broad terms until we have enough radioactive dates to correlate the records of widely scattered regions. Meanwhile study of a few representative areas will illustrate the nature of

°This term was suggested because the chief areas of such ancient rocks are gently arched like the surface of a medieval shield of battle.

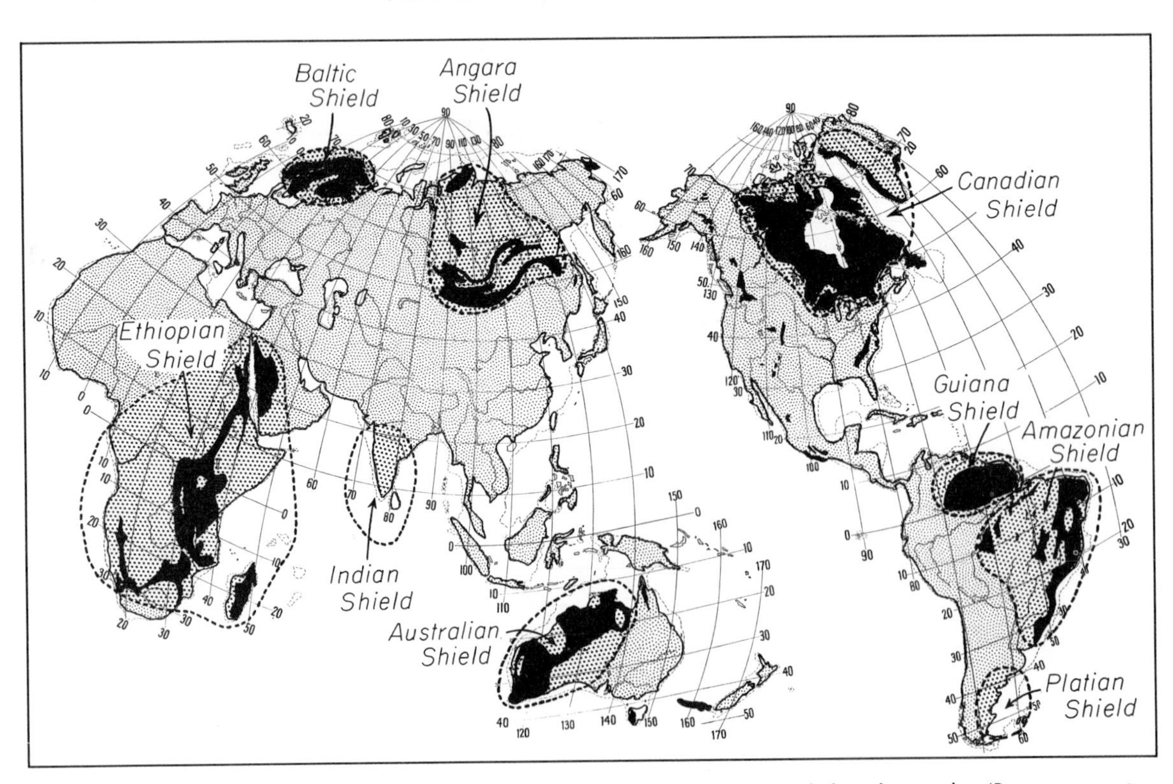

Figure 55. Areas of Precambrian outcrops (black). The several shields are stippled and named. (Basemap courtesy of the American Museum of Natural History.)

usually metamorphic Granite, foliated Cambrian

Figure 56. Vishnu schist in the bottom of the Grand Canyon at the mouth of Bright Angel Creek. The darker rocks are greenish schists, shattered and shot through with pink granite, which appears lighter.

Figure 57. North wall of the Grand Canyon opposite Bass Trail showing the Grand Canyon System dipping to the

the Precambrian rocks and the problems they present.

Grand Canyon Section

One of the most significant exposures of the Precambrian rocks may be seen in the walls of the Grand Canyon of the Colorado River. Here Lower Cambrian formations, still essentially horizontal and undisturbed, overlie with profound unconformity two distinct systems* of Cryptozoic formations.

The older of these, walling the Inner Gorge (Figs. 54, 56), is the Vishnu System of mica-, quartz-, and hornblende-schists, intruded locally by granite and pegmatite dikes. In large part the planes of foliation stand nearly vertical, but in places they are gnarled and crumpled. Quartzites occur at many places in the complex and, although thoroughly recrystallized, they preserve local evidence of stratification and even of cross-bedding, thus betraying a sedimentary origin. The associated schists are inferred to have been muddy sandstones and shales. The Vishnu System, then, represents a sedimentary series of very great but undetermined thickness that was isoclinally folded and strongly metamorphosed in an ancient mountain system. These rocks are believed to be equivalent, in part at least, to the "Older Precambrian" exposed in the ranges of south central Arizona which, although strongly folded are less metamorphosed, are clearly of sedimentary origin, and have a thickness of some 15,000 feet.

Resting on the Vishnu schists with profound unconformity is a great thickness of unmetamorphosed sedimentary formations comprised in the Grand Canyon System. These once covered the whole region in regular, horizontal beds, but before Cambrian time they were broken into great fault blocks and then eroded to a peneplaned surface in which only the downfaulted portions survived. The walls of the Grand Canyon west of the mouth of Little Colorado River show a simple conformable sequence of these strata more than 2

*By long established usage major stratigraphic units of Precambrian rocks are termed systems even though, in the absence of fossils for world-wide correlation, each is a provincial unit, recognizable on a lithologic basis, and should be called a *group*. In this book, however, we shall defer to the established custom of Precambrian geologists.

right and overlain with profound unconformity by horizontal Cambrian (Tonto) sandstone. (U.S. Geological Survey.)

miles thick (Fig. 57). It begins with a basal conglomerate, resting on the peneplaned surface of the Vishnu schist, that is succeeded by a limestone followed by shales and quartzites. The limestones and parts of the shales were deposited in shallow water, but bright red zones marked by abundant mudcracks show that in part they were formed above sealevel. The region is inferred to have been the site of a vast delta plane over which submarine and subaerial deposition alternated. Since the surface thus remained near sealevel, the region obviously subsided slowly to the extent of several thousands of feet while deposition was in progress. These formations are lithologically similar to Paleozoic and younger strata, and the redbeds prove that free oxygen was abundant in the atmosphere then as now. Some of the limy beds bear calcareous algal deposits (Fig. 58) and abundant trails of some wormlike animal were recently discovered on a ripple-marked surface near the base of the system.[1]

The Precambrian history of this part of North America may now be summarized with the aid of the block diagrams shown in Figure 59. Block *A* represents the earliest stage we know, when the rocks deep in the roots of a primeval mountain system had been folded and recrystallized to form the Vishnu schist. The surface relief is purely symbolic and is without direct evidence, but the character of the schists clearly indicates that we are dealing with the roots of mountains. The masses of bedded quartzite that locally plunge down through them were once horizontal layers of sand; they now betray vestiges of mountain folds otherwise obliterated by the intense pressure and heat to which they were subjected while deep within the zone of flow. The granitic intrusions were probably formed at this time. This intense deformation extended far beyond the Grand Canyon region. In south-central Arizona it produced intense folding and imbricate thrusting, accompanied by granitic intrusion on a large scale. For that area the orogeny has been named the **Mazatzal Revolution.**[2]

Whatever the nature and height of those ancient mountains, they were worn down eventually to a remarkably flat peneplane (block *B*). The region then began slowly to subside, probably as part of a vast geosyncline that extended northward through Montana (Fig. 60). and the Grand Canyon

Figure 58. Calcareous algae (*Greysonia basaltica*) from the Newland limestone in the Beltian Series 8 miles west of White Sulphur Springs, Montana. Similar forms occur in the Grand Canyon System. (Yale Peabody Museum.)

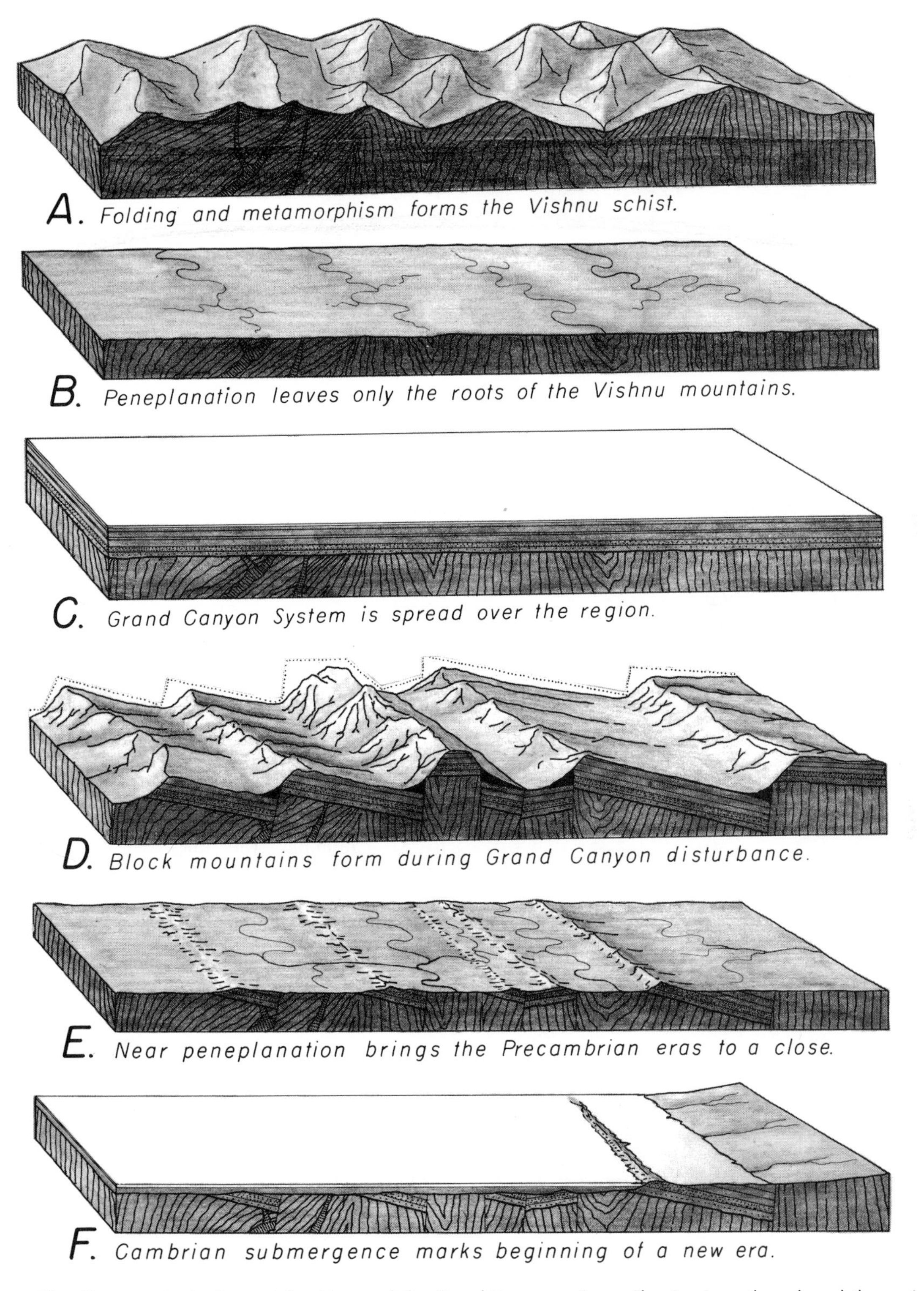

Figure 59. Six stages in the Precambrian history of the Grand Canyon region. The view is northward, and the sections represent an east-west distance of about 15 miles. The solid black shading in block *D* represents alluvium about the flanks of the Grand Canyon Ranges. The great wedge of Grand Canyon formations near the right end of block *F* is pictured in Figure 57.

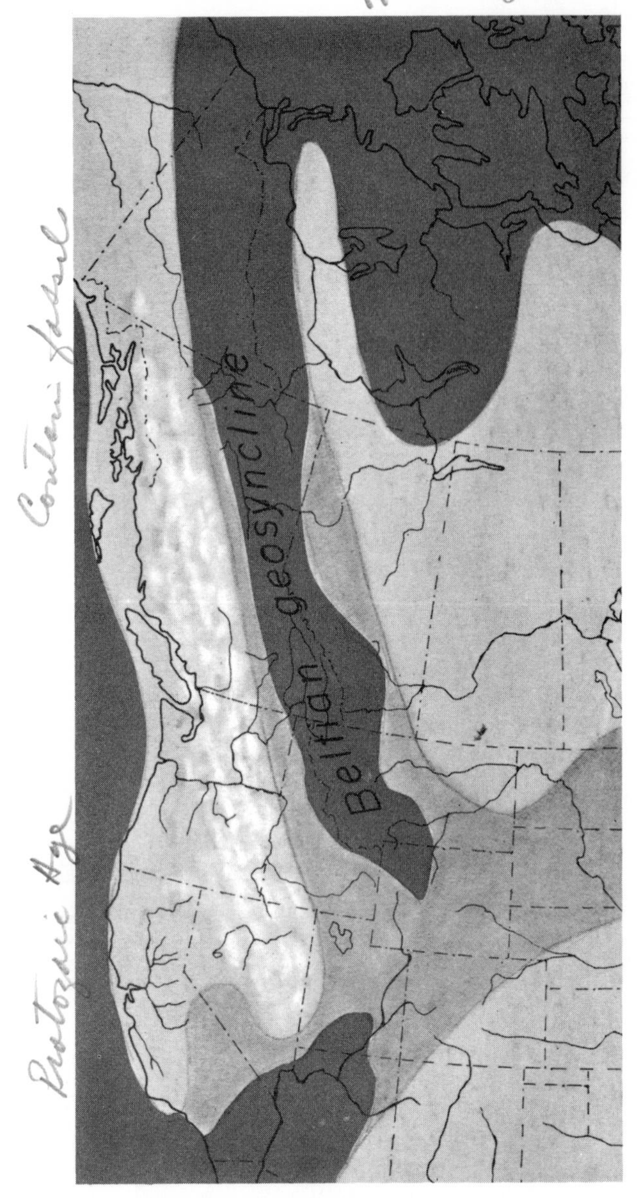

Figure 60. The Beltian Geosyncline. (After Fenton and Fenton.)

deposits accumulated, layer upon layer, until they had a thickness of more than 12,000 feet (block *C*). For a short time during deposition lava flows occurred locally.

Eventually the region was uplifted and, with but slight folding, was broken by great normal faults that gave rise to a system of block mountains much like those that now form the Basin and Range Province east of the Sierra Nevada. This episode of mountain making has been named the **Grand Canyon Disturbance.** Of course, these blocks suffered erosion as they rose, so that their height at any particular time cannot be determined. However, remnants of a dozen or so great blocks are still preserved, and their bounding faults are clearly evident, so that the size and orientation of the ranges can be plotted; and if we project the dip of the beds in portions of the fault blocks still extant, the restored edges reach elevations more than 2 miles above their present surface (block *D*).

In time these mountains were destroyed and the region was again almost peneplaned (block *E*) before the early Cambrian seas spread over it to mark the beginning of a new era (block *F*).

There are, then, two profound unconformities in this section, each representing an immense lost interval during which the entire region was slowly reduced by erosion from bold mountainous relief to a peneplane. It is probable that the hiatus above the Vishnu schist (blocks *A* and *B* of Fig. 59) represents as much time as all the post-Cambrian rocks together.

Rocky Mountain Region

From Utah and Colorado northward through Wyoming, Montana, and Idaho, and far into British Columbia, the Rocky Mountains have brought extensive areas of Precambrian rocks to the surface. They fall generally into two groups or systems separated by profound unconformity, as in the Grand Canyon region.

Early Precambrian Formations. The older rocks vary in character from range to range and may represent widely different spans of time, but they are similar in being strongly deformed and considerably metamorphosed. In many places they are overlain with profound unconformity by much younger and but slightly metamorphosed Precambrian strata. In this regard they resemble the Vishnu schists farther south. In a considerable area about the Beartooth Mountains of southern Montana, granites cutting this older sequence have recently been dated by lead/uranium ratios as 2,750,000,000 years old.[3] They are thus among the oldest rocks known.

Beltian System. The later Precambrian rocks of this region have been named the **Beltian System** for fine exposures in the Belt Mountains of southwestern Montana, but they extend northward into Canada and are exposed in a belt some 300 miles wide in which they range from more than 35,000 feet thick in the west to about 12,000 feet in the east. Exceptionally fine exposures occur in Glacier National Park near the northwest corner of Montana, where a thickness of 25,530 feet has been measured (Fig. 61).[4]

In the Little Belt Mountains of Montana eight formations were described, most of which can be recognized over a large region. Especially noteworthy are two great limestones, a lower one about 2,000 feet thick and a higher one some 4,000 feet thick. The basal formation comprises sandstone and quartzite, but the remaining five units are shales. The shales are in part sandy, and are mostly gray; however, one unit of mudcracked red shale, some 1,500 feet thick occurs near the middle of the system, and thinner units of redbeds occur in the upper part.

In western Montana sections can be compared along an east-west line for some 200 miles, and this brings out the significant fact that the system is much thicker and more largely detrital toward the west where the great limestones are replaced by shale and sandstone.[5] From this it is clear that much of the detrital sediment was coming from a land mass still farther west, probably in Washington and western British Columbia.

The gray shales of the Beltian System commonly show oscillation ripples, indicating deposition under shallow standing water, but the mudcracked redbeds were laid down on low fluvial plains.

Figure 61. The "Garden Wall" overlooking Iceberg Lake in Glacier National Park. This towering cliff exposes about 2,000 feet of the Siyeh formation of the Beltian System. The Collenia bed is a reef of calcareous algae. (Photograph by Heilman, courtesy of Great Northern Railway.)

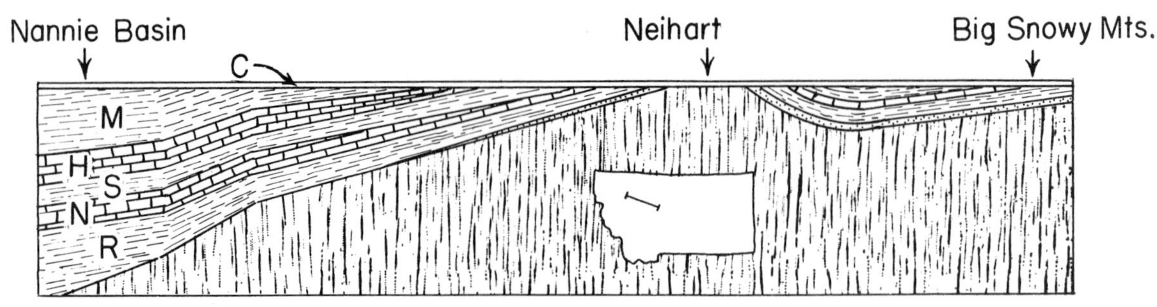

Figure 62. Idealized and restored section of the Beltian System in Montana, showing its unconformable relation to the Cambrian (C). The section is about 200 miles long and the vertical scale is exaggerated about 4 times. In Nannie Basin the Beltian rocks exceed 10 miles in thickness. The unconformity is due to gentle warping, regional uplift, and long erosion before Cambrian deposition began. *H*, Helena limestone; *M*, Missoula formation; *N*, Newland limestone; *R*, Ravalli redbeds; *S*, Spokane shale.

Reeflike deposits of calcareous algae (Fig. 76) are locally prominent in the limestones and in some of the gray shales, and rare trails of wormlike animals (Fig. 78) have been found. In Glacier National Park basic lava flows are interbedded with the sediments at several horizons. These are mostly thin, only locally ranging up to 300 feet thick.

The regional distribution, great thickness, and abundant evidence of shallow deposition clearly indicate that the Beltian System was formed in a broad geosyncline and was probably continuous with the Grand Canyon System to the south (Fig. 60).

Since over such a large area the Beltian formations are but slightly metamorphosed and generally appear conformable with the overlying Cambrian formations, they have long been regarded as *Late* Precambrian, but recent dating by radioactive data shows how deceptive physical appearances can be. In the Coeur d'Alene district of Idaho, Beltian rocks are cut by pegmatite veins (in Sunshine Mine) whose age proves to be 1,130,000,000 years.[6]

Cambrian strata generally overlie the Beltian System and appear to be conformable, as though no uplift or disturbance had occurred before Cambrian time. Regional study has shown, however, that the Cambrian system is transgressive on different parts of the Beltian System and in places rests on pre-Beltian metamorphics (Fig. 62).[5] It is therefore evident that the region had been uplifted, warped, and very perfectly peneplaned before Cambrian deposition began. The uplift probably occurred while the Grand Canyon disturbance was under way farther south and peneplanation probably was contemporaneous in both regions.

Canadian Shield

This is the largest and most studied area of Precambrian rocks in the world. Fabulously rich deposits of iron, nickel, copper, silver, and gold have stimulated exploration and intensive local study. Much of its 2,000,000 square miles lies in unsettled barrens of the North, however, and scarcely a fourth of it has actually been seen by geologists; moreover its geologic history is so involved and its structure so complex that it still abounds in unsolved problems.

About three-fourths of the Shield is formed of granite and banded gneiss (Figs. 63, 64A, 64B), the rest consisting of relatively small and irregular patches of sedimentary rocks and associated volcanics resting upon the granite basement. The sedimentary rocks are in most places intensely deformed and strongly metamorphosed. Isolated, like islands in a sea of granite, they cannot be correlated by lateral tracing and, in the absence of fossils, their relative ages can be judged only by physical appearance, except where, in recent years, radioactive minerals have yielded absolute dates. Before attempting a general synthesis of the Precambrian history of the Shield, therefore, it will be helpful to examine the local history of four representative areas, the Rainy Lake region, the Huronian area, the Lake Superior area, and the Grenville area.

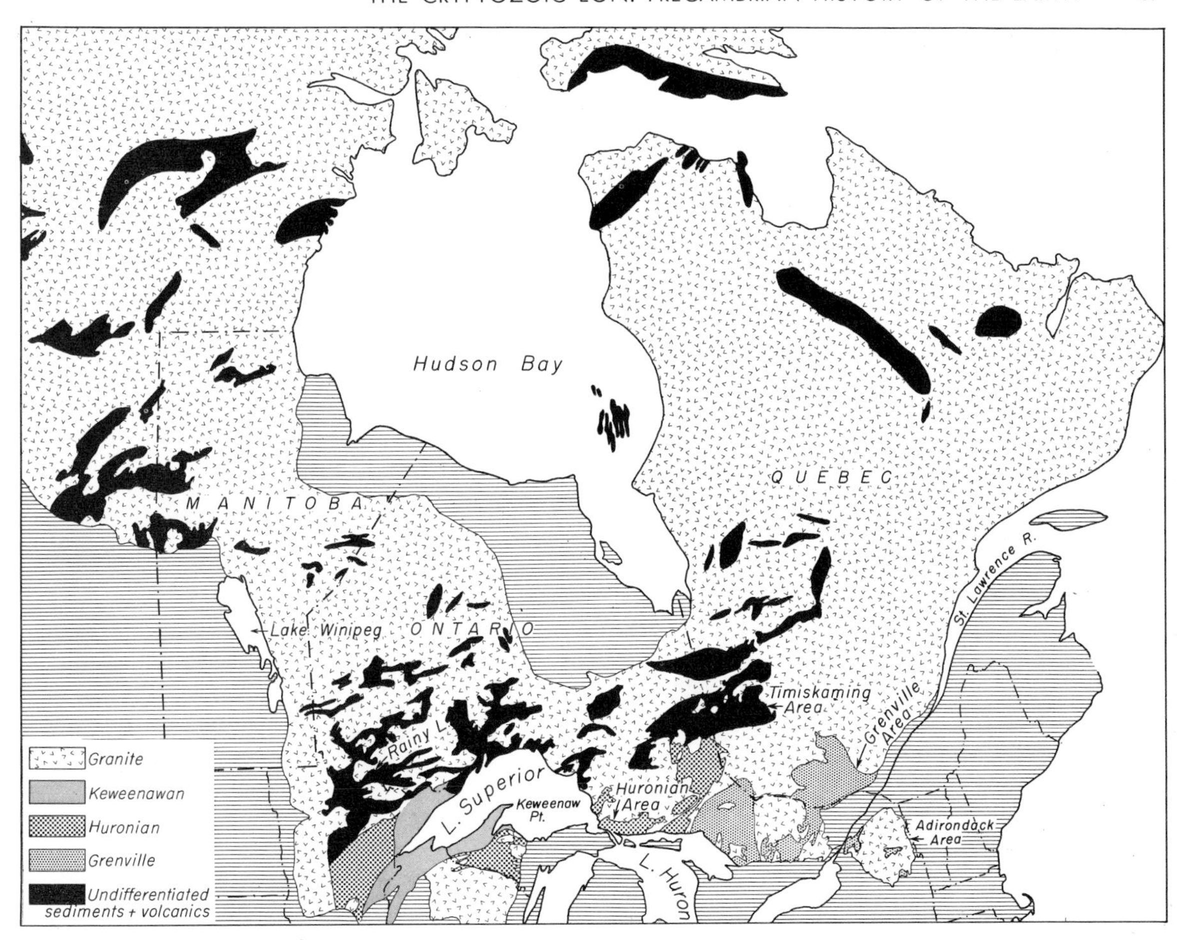

Figure 63. Geologic map of the southern part of the Canadian Shield. Data from the Geologic Map of North America published by the Geological Society of America, 1946. Overlying Phanerozoic rocks are horizontally lined.

Figure 64A. Laurentian gneiss, Grenville Township, Quebec. The dark layers are rich in pyroxenes. The foliation dips steeply to the right. (M. E. Wilson, Geological Survey of Canada.)

Figure 64*B*. Crumpled Grenville limestone (light) with interjected layers of Laurentian gneiss (dark). Prescott County, Ontario. The break in the beds near the left margin marks a fault.

Rainy Lake Region. In 1883, A. C. Lawson, a young geologist just out of college, was sent by the Geological Survey of Canada to examine the region about Rainy Lake and along the Seine River, which flows eastward into Lake Superior and forms the boundary between Canada and Minnesota (Fig. 65). Here he made two discoveries of fundamental significance in Precambrian geology.[7]

Up to this time it was believed that the granite of the Shield was part of the "original crust" of the once molten Earth upon which the sedimentary rocks and associated volcanics had accumulated. Lawson first mapped and studied a sequence of some 20,000 feet of lava flows and interbedded sedimentary rocks to which he gave the name **Keewatin Series.** When he studied its marginal contacts, he found the underlying granite to be intrusive into the Keewatin rocks (Fig. 66A). Furthermore, he found "greenstone" inclusions in the granite which were obviously pieces of the Keewatin lavas that had sunk into the granitic magma before it solidified. From these observations he drew the obvious, but at that time the astonishing, conclusion that the granite is younger than the overlying rocks. Subsequent work in other areas has proved this to be a general relation throughout the Canadian Shield—the original floor upon which the ancient sedimentary rocks were laid down is unknown; it has been engulfed or buried by magmas that welled up to form granite bathyliths.

Although strongly deformed and largely altered to greenstone, the Keewatin lavas locally preserve amygdaloidal and "pillow" structures proving that they were surface flows. In Rice Bay area (Fig. 65) they are domed over a large granite stock; but in many places they are abruptly cut across by masses of granite and, in general, they are strongly metamorphosed and deformed, dipping at steep angles in close folds. It is evident that we are dealing here with the roots of ancient mountains the cores of which were formed of granite bathyliths. The Keewatin Series once covered a much larger area and formed a roof into which the granite was intruded.

Lawson later recognized a second thick sequence of sedimentary rocks in this region which he named the **Seine Series** for exposures along the Seine River east of Rainy Lake.[8] These overlie the Keewatin rocks with profound unconformity and in basal conglomerates include boulders of the old granite (Fig. 66B). Obviously a long period of erosion had reduced the relief and laid bare the granitic cores of the Keewatin mountains before deposition of the Seine Series began.

Lawson's second great discovery was that the Seine Series in turn has been intruded by granite which must therefore be still younger (Fig. 67). Having misidentified the older granite as "Laurentian" he then named the younger the **Algoman granite.** We now know from radioactive dating that the "Laurentian" granite of this region is about 2,200,000,000 years old, and the Algoman granite is tentatively correlated with others farther east that are only half as old.[9] Here, then, we

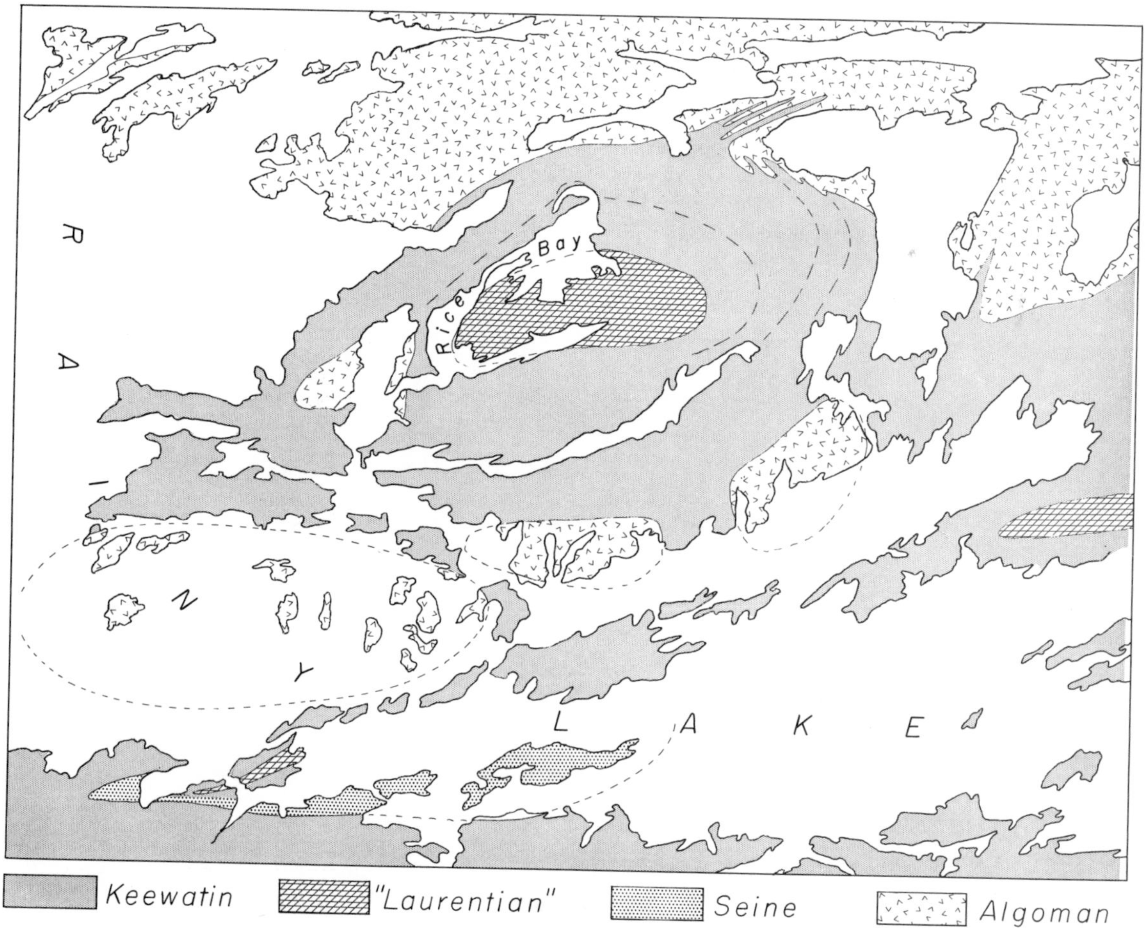

Figure 65. Geologic map of Rainy Lake region, after Lawson.

Figure 66A. Intrusive contact of Algonian granite gneiss (light) and Coutchiching sedimentary unit (schists) of the Keewatin Series between Gash Point and Back Point on the shore of Rainy Lake. The gneiss penetrates the schist in all directions and extends away to the right, and the schist extends to the left. It was here that Lawson discovered the intrusive relation of the granites of the Canadian Shield. (A. C. Lawson, Geological Survey of Canada.)

Figure 66B. Basal conglomerate of the Seine Series in which the lighter colored boulders were derived from the ''Laurentian'' granite that is intrusive into the Keewatin Series. West of Mathieu. (A. C. Lawson, Geological Survey of Canada.)

have two granites similar in appearance but differing in age by perhaps a billion years, yet except where they are in contact with the Seine Series they cannot be distinguished!

This region thus illustrates one of the basic problems of the Canadian Shield—the granite floor is not of one age, but is a complex of bathylithic intrusions formed at widely different times but which look so much alike that correlation from one area to another on physical appearance is completely unreliable.

Huronian Area. The north shore of Lake Huron is bordered by a wide belt of sedimentary formations named the **Huronian System**.[10] They consist of sandstones, shales, and conglomerates, still lying nearly horizontal and only slightly metamorphosed over most of the area. They total about 12,000 feet in thickness and have been separated into two major units, the Bruce Series below and the Cobalt Series above. These beds strike under a cover of Paleozoic rocks in the Upper Peninsula of Michigan but reappear in northern Wisconsin and central Minnesota, where they are generally of finer grain than in the type region, and carry most of the "iron formations" of the Lake Superior region (see page 95). Here also they are associated with the overlying Animikian Series which is classified as Upper Huronian. With this addition the Huronian System is probably 20,000 feet thick, and is divided as follows:

Upper Huronian (Animikian) Series
Middle Huronian (Cobalt) Series
Lower Huronian (Bruce) Series

Special interest attaches to the Middle Huronian Series for two reasons. First, its basal unit, north of Lake Huron, is a remarkable conglomerate, known as the **Gowganda tillite** (Fig. 68), that includes faceted and striated boulders as much as 10 feet in diameter (Fig. 69) and, in at least two places, may be seen resting on a grooved and striated floor, attesting to its glacial origin.[11] Patches of the tillite, locally as much as 600 feet thick, have been identified over an area that stretches for nearly 1,000 miles from west to east, indicating that at the beginning of Middle Huronian time the southern margin of the Canadian Shield was covered by an ice sheet of large dimensions.

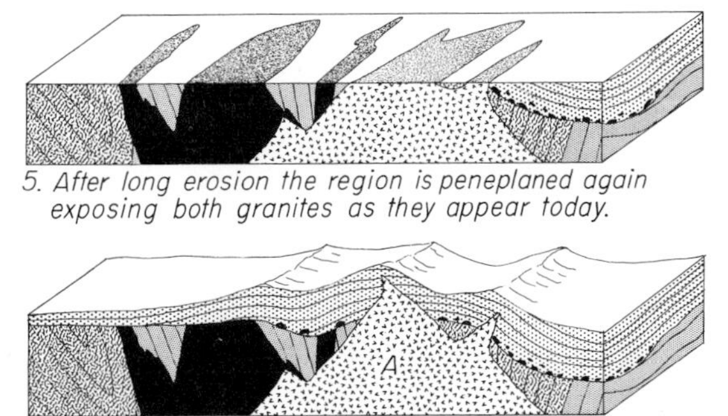

5. After long erosion the region is peneplaned again exposing both granites as they appear today.

4. During later orogeny the Algoman granite is intruded.

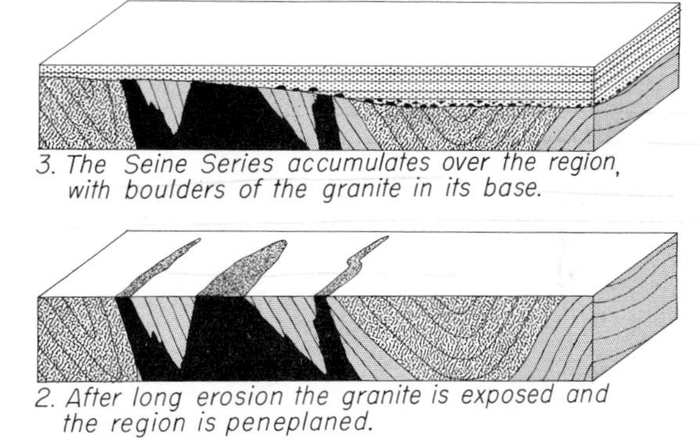

3. The Seine Series accumulates over the region, with boulders of the granite in its base.

2. After long erosion the granite is exposed and the region is peneplaned.

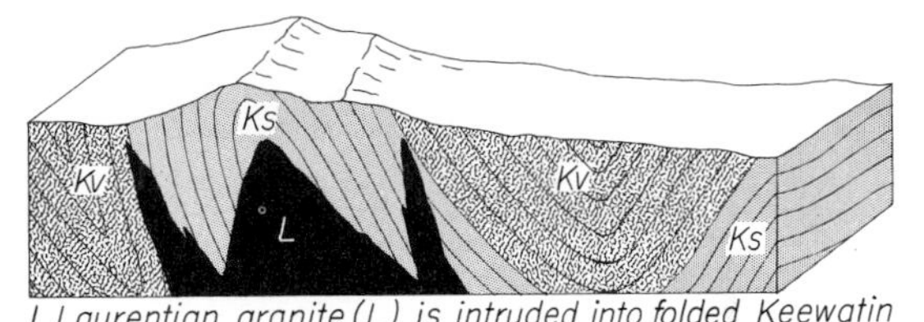

1. Laurentian granite (L) is intruded into folded Keewatin sedimentaries (Ks) and volcanics (Kv).

Figure 67. Block diagrams to show the relation of the two granites in the Rainy Lake region.

The second feature of importance is the concentration of vast amounts of iron in the Middle Huronian rocks of Wisconsin and Minnesota described on page 95.

Lake Superior Area. Overlying the Huronian rocks on the south side of Lake Superior is the **Keweenawan System** of redbeds and basic lava flows. The redbeds include sandstones, siltstones, and shales with lesser amounts of conglomerate, and have an aggregate thickness of some 15,000 feet. They are interbedded with, and succeeded by, basic lava flows totaling probably 35,000 feet in thickness. The surfaces of successive flows are still rough and slaggy and much of the lava,

Figure 68. Gowganda tillite near the base of the Cobalt Series at Drummond mine, near Cobalt, Ontario. The large boulder at the right above is 30 inches across. (C. W. Knight, Ontario Bureau of Mines.)

originally vesicular, is now amygdaloidal. The volume of these flows has been estimated at 24,000 cubic miles. This enormous outpouring of molten rock allowed the crustal rocks to sag, forming the great structural basin now occupied by Lake Superior (Fig. 70). With the upwelling of these lavas came copper-bearing solutions that in places filled the vesicles of the lava with metallic copper and in other places cemented the pebbles of interbedded conglomerates (see page 97).

The Keweenawan rocks are for the most part unmetamorphosed and they lie unconformably above the Huronian. They are believed to be among the youngest of the Precambrian rocks.

Grenville Area. In the region of Montreal and Ottawa, as in the Adirondack Mountains of New York, the granite is overlain by the **Grenville System** of deformed and strongly metamorphosed sedimentary rocks. This is the type region of the **Laurentian granite,** (Fig. 63) so named by Sir William Logan about a century ago for exposures in the Laurentide Mountains along the north side of the St. Lawrence River.

In the Grenville area the rocks are badly deformed and were originally thought to be among the oldest of the Precambrian formations, but radioactive dating has proved them to be only about 1,100,000,000 years old.[9]

Late Precambrian Orogeny. At least three great ranges of mountains are clearly recorded by the structures in thick masses of sedimentary formations in the eastern part of the Canadian Shield (Fig. 71). The Penokean-Killarney Range ran east-west across the Great Lakes region; the Belcher Range ran roughly north-south along the east side of Hudson Bay and is recorded in the

Figure 69. Striated boulder from the Gowganda tillite at Cobalt, Ontario. Slightly enlarged. (Royal Ontario Museum.)

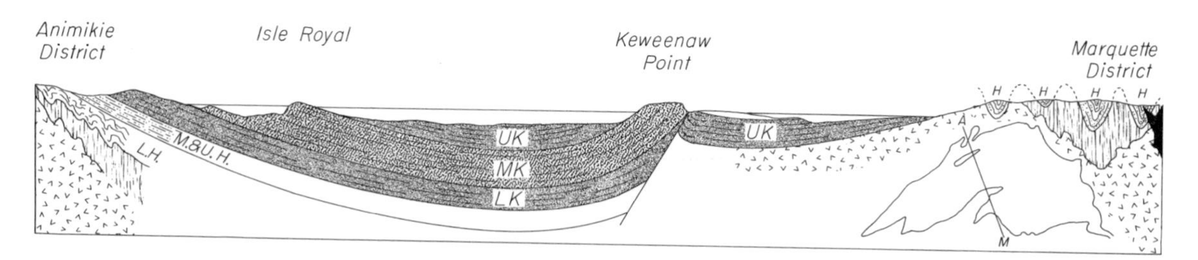

Figure 70. Structure section across Lake Superior showing relations of the Keweenawan formations. H., Huronian undivided; L.H., Lower Huronian; M.&U.H., Middle and Upper Huronian undivided; L.K., Lower Keweenawan sedimentaries; M.K., Middle Keweenawan lavas; U.K., Upper Keweenawan sedimentaries.

Figure 71. Late Precambrian mountains.

steeply folded rocks in Belcher Islands; the Labrador Range ran northwest-southeast along the western border of Labrador.

There is still uncertainty as to the exact time of this deformation. In the Lake Superior region local deformation occurred after Early Huronian, again after Middle Huronian, and yet again after Late Huronian deposition, and finally the entire Keweenawan System was involved in the deformation that created the Lake Superior structural basin. In connection with the post-Keweenawan movement granites were intruded along the axis of the Penokean Range (in southern Minnesota, central Wisconsin, and northeast of Lake Huron). These granites have been identified as of Keweenawan age. "The principal folding of the Upper Huronian, as well as of the Middle and Lower Huronian, dates from this period."[10]

RECAPITULATION AND INTERPRETATION OF THE RECORD

Loss of the "Original Crust." It would be a matter of great interest if we could discover beneath the oldest sediments some portions of the original surface of the Earth, for they might reveal critical evidence bearing on the Earth's origin and might show whether it had been molten. In the regions thus far studied, however, we have seen no certain evidence of such primal rocks.

Colossal Igneous Activity. It stirs the imagination to contemplate the 2,000,000 square miles of granite gneiss that floors the Canadian Shield, and to realize that it all came into place as fluid magma, which congealed beneath a cover of older rocks now long since removed by erosion. The relatively small areas of sedimentary formations that lie infolded among these bathyliths, as remnants of their former cover, convey the impression that during these primeval eras the crust of the Earth was repeatedly broken and largely engulfed in upwellings of molten material that dwarf all post-Cambrian igneous activity.

Of course, the intrusions were distributed over an immensely long period of time, and probably no vast subsurface area was all fluid at once, for the individual bathyliths are only tens or scores of miles across. Moreover, we are impressed by the extent of the granitic rocks because profound erosion has stripped the bathyliths of their roofs and laid bare horizons that were once several miles below the surface. Nevertheless, the regional extent of the folding and recrystallization of the old surface formations, and the vast stretches of granitic rocks, testify to the wide extent of the early igneous activity.

Great Diastrophism and Erosion. In each of the regions studied, two features of the record stand in antithesis one to the other. Great sequences of conformable beds mark periods of quiet when the region for long ages subsided slowly as it received its sheets of bedded sediments. In some cases there are reasons to believe these sediments to be parts of great deltas or extensive floodplains, but in other instances the deposition was in shallow inland seas like Hudson Bay or the Baltic.

In contrast to these evidences of quiet and long-continued accumulation are great unconformities that imply periods of crustal unrest, mountain-making, uplift, and destruction. It is clear, then, that long intervals of quiet have alternated with times of diastrophic change. In the Grand Canyon there are two profound unconformities. In the Lake Superior region there were at least three episodes of regional diastrophism and granitic intrusion, one following the Keewatin deposition, a much greater one (Algoman) succeeding the Early Precambrian, and the last (Penokean) coming late in the era. The second of these resulted in the strong folding of the Early Precambrian formations over a vast area along the southern part of the Canadian Shield, even in places which have escaped all subsequent deformation. It appears to have been the most widespread revolution experienced by the Shield and to have been followed by one of the longest intervals of erosion known anywhere. The Penokean disturbance, which came late in the Precambrian in this region, has already been described. It was followed by another of the great periods of erosion, one that is recognized in many parts of the world as the great break separating the rocks of Cambrian and later times from all that existed before.

In each of the regions studied it is evident that the record of Precambrian time is far from complete. It is probable, however, that the great breaks seen in one region are represented by sedimentary rocks in some other parts of the world. When we have secured enough radioactive dates from widely separated regions, it may be possible to build up a composite record of the whole of the Cryptozoic Eon; but at present we are only digging among the ruins.

Attempts at Subdivision of the Precambrian Record. During the early half of this century it was common practice to recognize two major divisions of the Cryptozoic Eon, the **Archeozoic Era** and the **Proterozoic Era**. This was based on the premise that the two eras were separated generally by a profound hiatus and that the Archeozoic rocks were largely igneous and were the older, whereas the Proterozoic rocks were largely of sedimentary origin even though generally deformed and metamorphosed. Correlations from one area to another or from one continent to another were based on such lithologic characters. If the rocks were intensely deformed (as are the Vishnu schists) they were assumed to be Archeozoic, but if they appeared young or if they were igneous rocks cutting supposedly young sedimentary rocks they were judged to be Proterozoic. Radioactive dating during recent decades has shown that such correlations are completely invalid and that there were probably several times of widespread granitic intrusion and orogeny, and several times, rather than one, of widespread erosion and peneplanation. Attempts to distinguish between Archeozoic and Proterozoic rocks are therefore likely to be misleading. The Precambrian rocks are known to range in age from roughly 600,000,000 to 3,000,000,000 years, a span some five times as long as the combined length of the three Phanerozoic eras. Probably several eras are represented in the older rocks, and when enough absolute dates are established on the basis of radioactive minerals to permit interregional correlation, a scheme of subdivision useful for worldwide classification may be possible. For the present, however, only local or regional subdivisions appear to be valid and useful.

A fine review of the many areas of sedimentary and volcanic rocks of the Canadian Shield will be found in *The Proterozoic in Canada.*[12]

MINERAL WEALTH

The Precambrian rocks of the Canadian Shield have yielded iron, copper, nickel, silver, and gold beyond the dreams of Midas. The iron is the sole sedimentary deposit, the other metals occurring in association with the igneous rocks. The exploitation of these metallic riches has played no small part in the industrial development of both the United States and Canada.

Iron. For many years, 80 percent or more of the iron produced annually in the United States has come from the Precambrian rocks of the Lake Superior district (Fig. 72). In the prewar year 1939 the output from this area amounted to 45,000,000 tons and was valued at $135,000,000. It rose to a high of 91,000,000 tons in 1943, declined in the early postwar years, then rose to an all-time high of 110,096,199 tons in 1955.

The production is chiefly from the Middle Huronian rocks,[10] though some ore is mined also from the Lower Huronian and, in the Vermilion Range, from the Keewatin rocks. The ranges are more or less linear belts of outcrop of the dipping and folded iron ore formations. That of Mesabi, which produces twice as much as all the others together, will serve for illustration (Fig. 73*A*). It is part of the Middle Huronian Series, which dips gently southeast. The iron formation consisted originally of cherty iron carbonate and greenalite (an iron silicate). This primary ore is not used, however, partly because it is only about 25 percent iron, and partly because the silicate is too refractory to smelt. During the weathering of the outcrop in Pre-

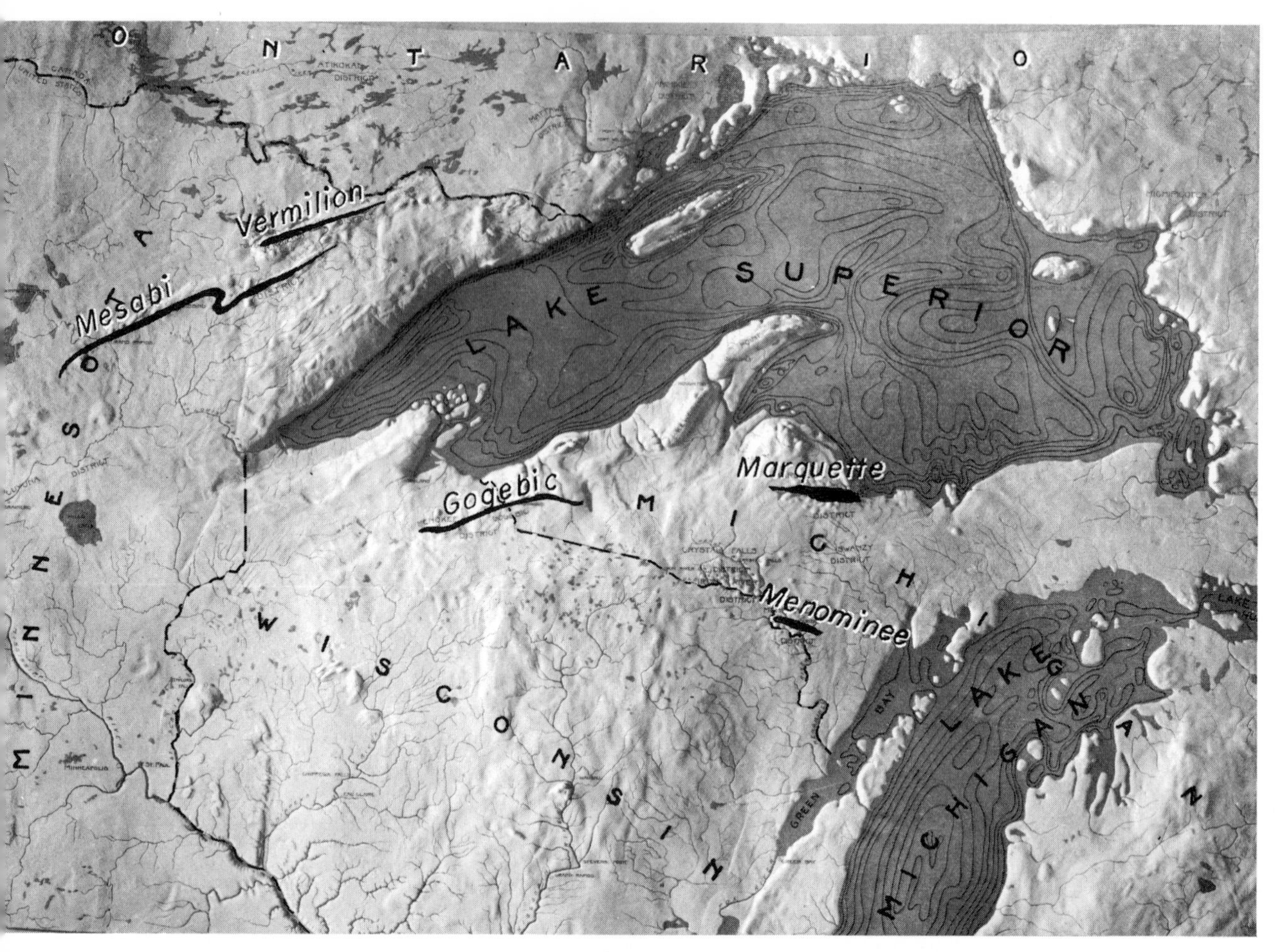

Figure 72. Model of the Lake Superior region showing distribution of the chief "iron ranges." (Photograph of the model used by permission of the Director, U.S. Geological Survey.)

cambrian time, however, the calcite and silica were partly carried away in solution, and the iron was oxidized and concentrated by descending solutions into large ore bodies that will yield over 50 percent of iron. The rich ore bodies lie at the surface in the Mesabi Range and are mined by power shovels in enormous open cuts (Fig. 73*B*). In the Gogebic Range of Michigan, where similar iron formations are more strongly folded, the enrichment followed more definite conduits and reached to depths of about 3,000 feet below the present surface, so that underground mining is necessary.

It is remarkable that some of the greatest iron mines of Europe are also in the Late Precambrian rocks (at Kiruna, Sweden), and that another of the greatest known iron deposits is in the Precambrian rocks of Brazil (Minas Geraes).

A colossal deposit of rich oxide ore, similar to that of the Mesabi Range was discovered in 1937 on Burnt Creek near Knoby Lake on the boundary between Quebec and Labrador. Lying in the midst of the subarctic wastes it could not be immediately exploited, but extensive prospecting indicated that the ore body was great enough to justify the expenditure of more than $200,000,000 in building a railroad north from the port of Seven Islands on the St. Lawrence River and building a settlement adequate to house the mining operations. This has now been done and the area is expected to produce some 25,000,000 tons of rich ore annually. This important development was one of the chief reasons for building the St. Lawrence Seaway, which will permit cheap transportation of the ore into the steel-making centers of the states bordering the Great Lakes.

Copper. Native copper occurs in the lavas and conglomerates of Keweenaw Peninsula and was known and worked by the Indians long before the advent of white men. It forms amygdules in the scoriaceous lavas and not only serves as a cement between the pebbles in the conglomerate, but also has partly replaced the pebbles themselves. As the copper is concentrated in certain beds, and the series dips steeply to the northwest, the producing area is a belt only 3 to 6 miles wide, running for about 70 miles along the axis of the peninsula. The famous Calumet and Hecla mine is located on this belt. At its peak of production in 1916 this region alone produced 135,000 tons of copper, valued at $66,300,000. The yield had declined to 30,400 tons in 1945, but the grand total for the hundred years, 1845–1945, was over 4,800,000 tons, slightly more than one-seventh of the total production of the entire United States. Production in 1956 was 61,526 tons.

Nickel. Over 70 percent of the world's nickel is now secured from the mining district of Sudbury, Ontario, where a great sill of gabbro, presumably of Keweenawan age, has a border of nickel-copper ore. The production from this small area increased from about 40,000 tons of nickel in 1933 to more than 105,000 tons in 1938; it reached a peak of

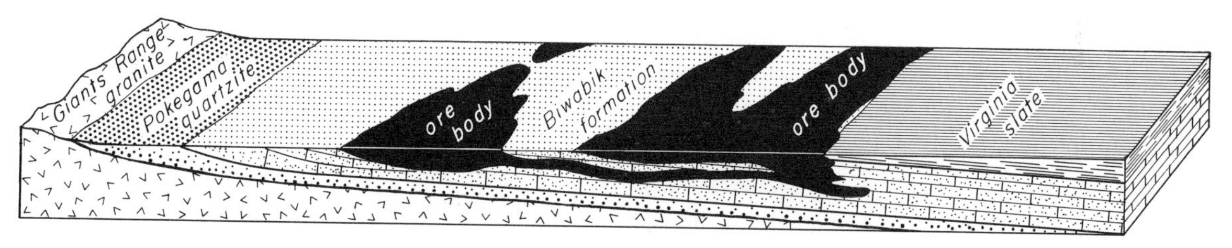

Figure 73A. Block diagram showing a section across the Mesabi Range at Hibbing, Minnesota. Length of section about 4½ miles. (Adapted from Van Hise and Leith, U.S. Geological Survey.)

Figure 73B. Open-cut mine in the Mesabi Range, Minnesota. (L. P. Gallagher.)

130,642 tons in 1943 and dropped back to about 110,000 tons in 1945.

Silver. Silver is found in many localities in the southern part of the Canadian Shield, generally in veins associated with basic intrusives of Keweenawan age. In some places the veins occur in Keewatin or Timiskaming rocks and in others in the Upper Huronian, but in all, the mineralization is closely restricted to the vicinity of the younger intrusives, which were the "orebringers."

At present the greatest production is from a small area (about 6 square miles) around Cobalt, Ontario, where native silver occurs in veins associated with a great sill of dolerite. The richness of some of these veins is phenomenal, yields of 7,000 ounces of silver per ton of ore being recorded. A number of lesser silver camps of similar nature are found within a radius of 75 miles west of Lake Timiskaming. Port Arthur, on the northwest shore of Lake Superior, is another silver camp where both the Upper Huronian and the Keewatin rocks have been intruded by Keweenawan magmas.

Gold. There are likewise many occurrences of gold in the southern part of the Canadian Shield. The most spectacular production has been about Porcupine, a locality nearly 100 miles northwest of Lake Timiskaming. Although not discovered until 1912, it soon became one of the greatest gold camps in the world, and in the twelve years up to 1924 produced over $135, 000,000 worth of gold. Its total output to 1947 has been nearly 20,000,000 ounces. The Hollinger mine is the chief producer of the area and one of the richest gold mines known. In 1938 its production of gold and silver together was valued at $15,000,000.

In the Porcupine district the gold occurs chiefly in the metallic form, and in veins associated with granitic intrusions (syenite porphyry) in the Keewatin lavas and Timiskaming sedimentaries. As these ore-bringing intrusives are unconformably overlain by Middle Huronian strata, they are considered to be genetically related to the Algoman granite. In recent years the Kirkland Lake district has surpassed the Porcupine. These and other districts in the Canadian Shield have made Canada forge ahead in gold production to third rank among the countries of the world. In 1957 it produced about 4,420,000 ounces of gold, which was more than twice the output of the United States. About one-third of the gold produced in the United States comes from a small area in the Precambrian core of the Black Hills near Deadwood, South Dakota, where, in 1957, 568,000 ounces were yielded by the great Homestake mine. South Africa produces about one-half of the world's gold, and there also it comes from Precambrian rocks.

Since all these valuable metals—gold, silver, copper, nickel, and cobalt—are in veins associated with intrusives, it is clear that the great igneous activity of Precambrian time in the Canadian Shield has a very direct human and economic interest. In the single prewar year of 1938, these deposits in Canada yielded about $250,000,000 in mineral wealth.

After the close of the Keweenawan epoch no important ore deposits, so far as is known, were formed within or near the Canadian Shield. The upsurges of magma during this vast Late Precambrian upwelling "seem to have exhausted the treasure-house". [13]

PRECAMBRIAN ROCKS OF OTHER CONTINENTS

Scandinavia. Much of Scandinavia is made of Precambrian formations, that have long been the subject of study. After a life devoted to the interpretation of these rocks, Sederholm, the distinguished geologist of Finland, concludes that at least four great cycles of Precambrian sedimentation occurred in these northern lands of the Baltic Shield, and that each of them was separated from the next by a period of mountain folding and a long interval of erosion. [14]

Australia. Precambrian rocks form the surface of nearly one-third of the continent of Australia, chiefly in the central and western parts (Fig. 55), where they reach a vast thickness and rival in complexity those of the Canadian Shield. They fall into three well-defined groups, each separated from the next by a profound unconformity. The lowest forms a "basal complex" of gneisses and schists associated with much-altered sediments and lava flows. The second is similar in complexity but has a basal conglomerate with boulders of the older rocks, and is separated from the latter by a regional unconformity. The youngest group of the Precambrian rocks in Australia comprises a very thick conformable sequence of strata with interbedded tillite. It was separated from the older systems by a period of intensive orogeny and granitic intrusions on a vast scale. This igneous activity produced the phenomenal gold deposits of Kalgoorlie and the rich lead and silver ores of Broken Hill. In fact, it was the most important ore-forming epoch in all the history of Australia.

The late Precambrian rocks are so much less deformed than the rocks below, that they were long thought to be part of the Cambrian. "It was perhaps the most extensive and, in some respects, is the most interesting sedimentary formation in the whole of Australia. It now covers an area of about 310,000 square miles, and the sea in which it was deposited formerly covered fully half the entire area of Australia."[15] In New South Wales, where this system has a thickness of probably 13,000 feet, it includes at least three horizons of interbedded tillite, of which the greatest, the **Sturtian tillite**, is locally 600 feet thick.

Africa. A large part of the continent of Africa south of the Sahara is formed of Precambrian rocks (Fig. 55), and, although not fully studied, they evidently compare well in thickness and complexity with those of Australia and North America. Here, as elsewhere, the ancient complex includes thick systems of sedimentary rocks and volcanics which have been deformed and intruded by vast granitic bathyliths. Here also rich deposits of precious metals were a by-product of the igneous activity. The most phenomenal of the African deposits are the gold-bearing conglomerates of the Witwatersrand in the Transvaal, which up to 1930 had yielded over $5,000,000,000 worth of the metal. Between 1940 and 1945, the Witwatersrand reached a peak production of more than 14,000,000 ounces in a single year, valued at over $500,000,000. This is approximately half the world production.

CLIMATES

In rocks so old and so generally devoid of fossils there is little to indicate what the normal climates of the Precambrian actually were. The thick lime-

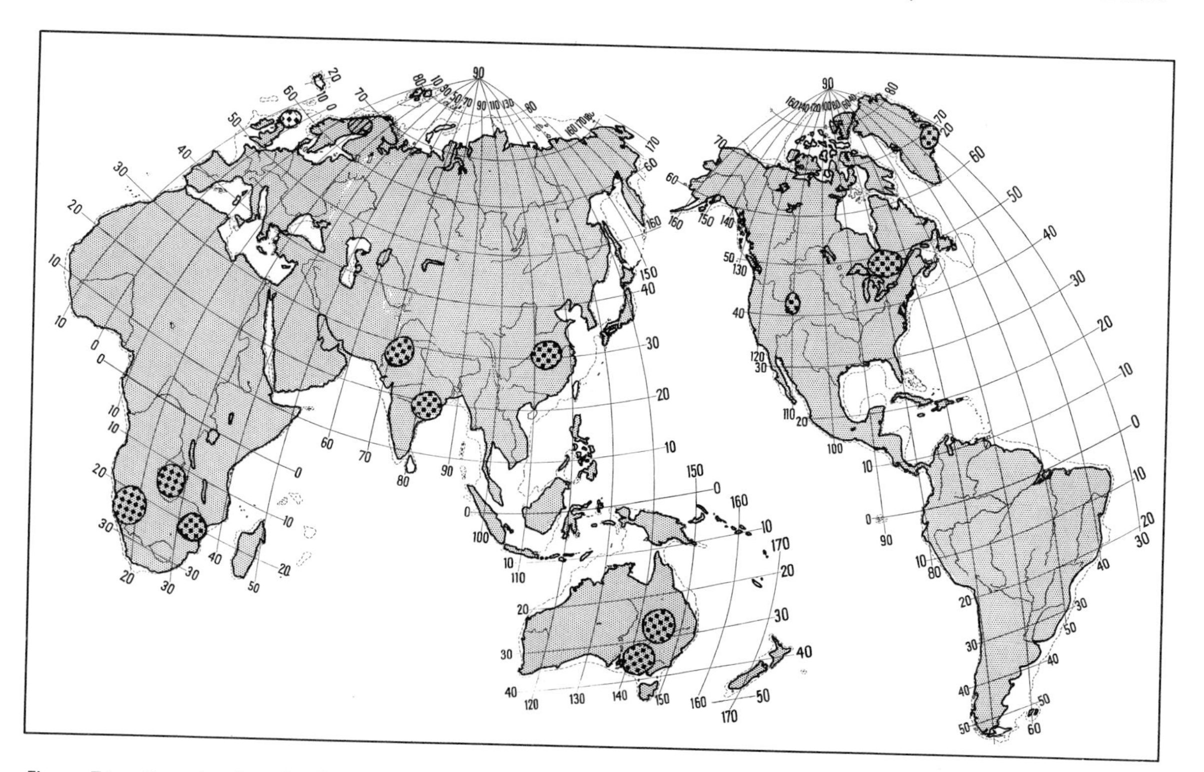

Figure 74. Map showing distribution of Precambrian glaciation (coarsely stippled areas). (Basemap courtesy of the American Museum of Natural History.)

Figure 75. Precambrian tillite in Utah. South side of Little Mountain west of Ogden. The compass above the large angular block is 3 inches across. (Elliot Blackwelder.)

stones were probably deposited in rather warm seas, and the mudcracked redbeds clearly imply marked seasonal rainfall. Most of the other formations, however, are equivocal in the light of our present understanding.

The most remarkable and direct evidence of Precambrian climate is the glacial deposits which occur in many parts of the world and represent at least two times of extensive continental glaciation, one in the middle Precambrian and the other near its close (Fig. 74).

The Huronian (Gowganda) tillite has been mentioned. Its distribution over the southern part of the Canadian Shield shows that a continental ice sheet more than a thousand miles in diameter lay over central Canada for a time during the Huronian epoch.

Glacial deposits are widespread in northern Utah beneath the Cambrian formations, cropping out in the islands in Great Salt Lake and in the mountain ranges both east and southwest of the lake (Fig. 75). Tillite and glacio-fluvial deposits occur at different horizons in a series of sandy and shaly formations that exceed 12,000 feet in thickness and are supposedly of Precambrian age, possibly Beltian.

The tillite includes boulders of many kinds of rock, some of them as much as 10 feet in diameter, enclosed in a non-bedded, slaty matrix. Some of the boulders are faceted and striated. The tillite reaches the exceptional thickness of 700 feet at one locality and 1,100 feet at another, but is generally much thinner. Its age, unfortunately, is not definitely fixed. The series bearing the tillite rests upon a much older and intensely metamorphosed group of schists, and is overlain with local unconformity by beds high in the Lower Cambrian. The glaciation is believed to have occurred late in the Cryptozoic Eon.

Perhaps the greatest record of Precambrian glaciation exists in Australia, where ancient tillite is found at three horizons in a very thick series of late Precambrian formations. One of the finest displays of the glacial deposits is in the Flinders Range of south-central Australia, where the **Sturtian tillite**, exceeding 600 feet in thickness, forms the backbone of the range and is exposed in great cliffs. It consists of a non-bedded matrix of ancient "rock flour" and angular chips, in which boulders of many kinds of rock are embedded.[15] These boulders are in part rounded and in part angular, and some of them are faceted and striated. The underlying, well-bedded strata include scattered boulders of glacial origin that are believed to have been dropped from icebergs in a body of water in front of the ice sheet. The Sturtian tillite is about 16,000 feet below the base of the Cambrian system in this section.[16] The glacial deposits are known to extend for at least 300 miles from south to north.

Glacial deposits are strikingly developed at several different horizons in the very thick Precambrian section of southern Africa.[17] The **Chuos tillite** of the state of Southwest Africa lies within the "Primitive Systems", the lowest of three major divisions of the Precambrian rocks. It has been recognized over an area of some 20,000 square miles and locally attains a thickness of 1,500 feet. Over most of this area it has the character of a moraine, but toward the south it is replaced by marine beds with widely scattered boulders believed to have been rafted to sea by icebergs. The center of ice accumulation obviously lay north of the 20th parallel. The **Griquatown tillite** of the northern part of Cape Colony lies in the Transvaal

Figure 76. Reef of calcareous algae in the Siyeh Formation in Hole-in-the-wall Cirque, Glacier National Park, Montana. (C. L. and M. A. Fenton.)

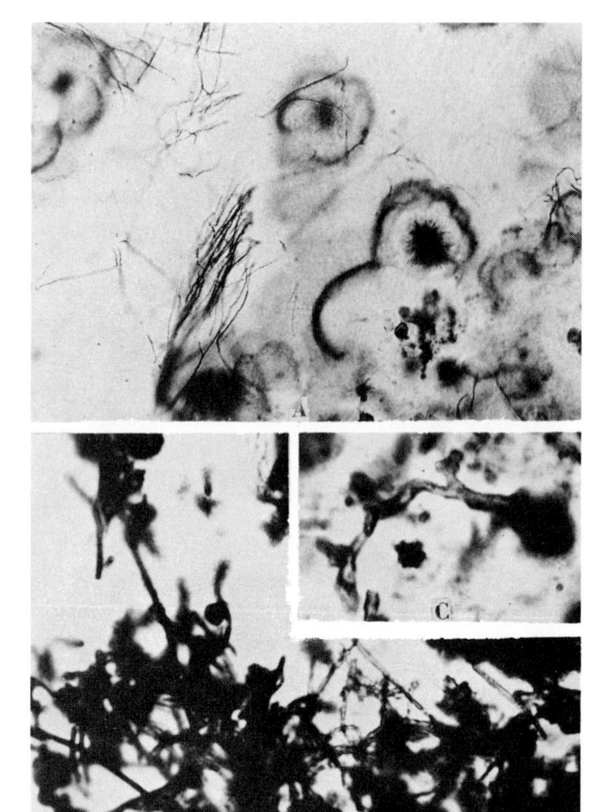

Figure 77. Algae and fungi from the Gunflint chert 4 miles west of Schreiber, Ontario. *A*, colonies and free filiaments of algae (×190); *B*, colony of fungus (×423); *C*, fungus mycelium (×700). (Photographs from Elso S. Barghoorn.)

System of late Precambrian age and may be contemporaneous with the **Numees tillite** of western Cape Colony and others in Katanga, west of Lake Tanganyika.

In the Yangtze Valley of China there are also extensive deposits of Precambrian glaciers. Scattered exposures of tillite indicate that glacier ice once spread over an area of at least 800 miles from east to west across central China during Precambrian time.

There are other tillites, less certainly dated but probably of late Precambrian age, in Norway, East Greenland, India, and Australia. Certain of these underlie the Cambrian so closely that some geologists believe they belong in the Cambrian rather than the Precambrian.

Before the enormous length of the Precambrian was appreciated, the discovery of these evidences of early glaciation seemed a serious obstacle to the belief that the Earth was originally molten. To the older geologists, who conceived of the Earth in these early times as a hot planet clothed in dense vapors of a vast primal atmosphere, it was, indeed, a shocking discovery. In view of our present knowledge, however, the oldest of the known glacial times may have followed the formation of the Earth by 500,000,000 years or more. Precambrian glaciation has, therefore, no greater bearing on the mode of origin of the Earth than later times of refrigeration. As we shall see, climatic changes on the Earth have been periodic, with fluctuations between mildness and glaciation since early geologic time. The glacial times of the Precambrian were undoubtedly but relatively short episodes in the climatic fluctuations of those early ages. It must not be supposed that the world was generally cold for long times.

EVIDENCES OF LIFE BEFORE THE CAMBRIAN

For more than 50 years an eager search for fossils has gone on wherever Precambrian rocks have been studied—and the reward has been amazingly slight.

The most abundant fossils are the deposits of calcareous algae, one of the most primitive tribes of microscopic plants that grow in moldlike colonies, precipitating calcium carbonate to build up globular or irregular structures with a fine concentric lamination (Fig. 76). Such plants are common in the modern oceans and in lakes and streams. They have formed characteristic limy deposits of the same sort in all ages since early in the Precambrian. They are abundant in certain of the limestones and calcareous shales in the Beltian System in Montana (Fig. 58) and in limy zones in the Grand Canyon System. Similar structures occur in the iron-bearing rocks about Hudson Bay and in Michigan and Minnesota, some of them in the upper part of the Keewatin System in Minnesota. No higher types of plants are indicated in any part of the Precambrian record.

The oldest known fossils have been found in cherts in the Gunflint formation (Middle Huronian) in Ontario.[18] The assemblage includes two kinds of blue-green algae, two kinds of very primitive fungus, and possibly a flagellate (Fig. 77). This fortunate discovery is the more amazing because the objects are microscopic, yet show definitive structures. Their preservation was probably possible because they were enclosed in silica soon after burial.

The best evidences of animal life are the trails and burrows of wormlike creatures in some of the Beltian rocks (Fig. 78). Recently the impression of a supposed jellyfish was reported from near the middle of the Grand Canyon System.

A number of other alleged fossils have been reported but are now suspected of being concretions or other inorganic structures. The first of such objects to claim attention was named *Eozoön canadense* ("dawn animal of Canada"). These are hemispherical masses from a few inches to a few feet across, showing a crude concentric lamination of alternating layers of calcite and serpentine. The best and the original examples came from Côte St. Pierre about 35 miles east of Ottawa in a zone of intense contact metamorphism about 300 feet across, where the Grenville limestone is intruded by granite. In view of this occurrence, and of the fact that serpentine is a metamorphic mineral and is never found in undoubted fossils, *Eozoön* is now considered to be an inorganic structure. However, undoubted calcareous algae similar to those of the Beltian occur also in the Grenville limestone.[19]

Figure 78. Worm burrows packed with sand in the Siyeh formation of the Beltian System. Dawson Park, Glacier National Park, Montana. (C. L. and M. A. Fenton.)

Another alleged fossil was found in the Early Precambrian (Seine Series) at Steeprock Lake in Ontario. It takes the form of hemispherical or rounded masses showing a faint radial structure, but microsections prove that the material consists of fine quartz crystals. The structure can be so perfectly matched in near-Recent concretions that there is now no reason to believe these things to be organic deposits.

Thus, the record boils down to calcareous algae, fungi, and the trails and burrows of a few wormlike animals, certainly not an impressive array to represent the life record of more than three-fourths of the history of the Earth!

On the other hand, a vast amount of carbon is disseminated in the Precambrian shales and schists. Later sedimentary deposits contain much carbon of organic origin which appears as coal, or as hydrocarbons, or as disseminated particles in dark shales. No other source is known for such disseminated carbon in sedimentary rocks, and the belief is therefore commonly held that the graphite and disseminated carbon in Precambrian rocks are also of organic source. Nevertheless, it appears probable that the hydrothermal reactions at the borders of large intrusive masses could break down molecules of calcium carbonate ($CaCO_3$) and free the carbon. The graphite in some Precambrian contact metamorphic deposits is believed therefore to be of such inorganic origin, and some students have argued that all the Precambrian graphite might be inorganic.

We may infer, therefore, that life probably was abundant in the seas of late Precambrian time, but was soft-tissued like that of the Middle Cambrian Burgess shale (p. 122), so that there was little chance for actual preservation as fossils.

Probably the greatest contrast between that primeval world and the world of today lies in the primitive character of both plant and animal life. No forests then mantled the mountain slopes, no prairies covered the plains, and no animals inhabited the desolate lands. Only in the sea was there a beginning of the organic host that in later times would possess the whole world.

REFERENCES

1. Alf, Raymond M., 1959, Possible fossils from the early Proterozoic Bass Formation, Grand Canyon, Arizona. *Plateau*, vol. 31, pp. 60–63.

2. Wilson, E. D., 1939, Pre-Cambrian Mazatzal revolution in central Arizona. *Geol. Soc. Amer., Bull.*, vol. 50, pp. 1113–1164.

3. Gast, P. W., J. L. Kulp, and L. E. Long, 1958, Absolute age of early Precambrian rocks in the Bighorn Basin of Wyoming and Montana, and Southeastern Manitoba. *Amer. Geophysical Union, Trans.*, vol. 39, pp. 322–334.

4. Fenton, C. L., and M. A. Fenton, 1937, Belt Series of the North, *Geol. Soc. Amer., Bull.*, vol. 48, pp. 1873–1970.

5. Deiss, Charles, 1935, Cambrian-Algonkian unconformity in western Montana. *Geol. Soc. Amer., Bull.*, vol. 46, pp. 95–124.

6. Eckelmann, Walter R. and J. Laurence Kulp, 1957, Uranium-lead method of age determination, Part II: North American Localities. *Geol. Soc. Amer., Bull.*, vol. 68, pp. 1117–1140.

7. Lawson, A. C., 1885, Report on the geology of the Lake of the Woods region, with special reference to the Keewatin (Huronian?) belt of the Archean rocks. *Canadian Geol. Surv., Ann. Report 1: CC*, pp. 1–151.

8. Lawson, A. C., 1913, The Archean geology of Rainy Lake re-studied. *Canadian Geol. Surv., Mem. 40*, pp. 1–115.

9. Knopf, Adolph, 1955, Bathyliths in time. *Geol. Soc. Amer., Special Paper 62*, pp. 685–702.

10. Leith, C. K., R. J. Lund, and A. Leith, 1935, Pre-Cambrian rocks of the Lake Superior region. *U.S. Geol. Surv., Prof. Paper 184*, pp. 1–34.

11. Coleman, A. P., 1926, *Ice Ages Recent and Ancient.* Macmillan, New York, pp. 1–296.

12. Gill, James E., (ed.), 1957, *The Proterozoic in Canada.* University of Toronto Press, Toronto, pp. 1–191.

13. Coleman, A. P., 1915, The Proterozoic of the Canadian Shield and its problems. In: *Problems of American Geology,* Yale University Press, New Haven, Connecticut, pp. 81–161.

14. Sederholm, J. J., 1932, On the geology of Fennoscandia. *Commission Geologique de Finlande, Bull. 98*, pp. 1–30.

15. David, Sir T. W. E., 1932, *Explanatory Notes to Accompany a New Geologic Map of the Commonwealth of Australia.* Sidney, Australia, pp. 1–177.

16. Fairbridge, Rhodes W., 1953, *Australian Stratigraphy,* 2nd ed. The University Bookshop, Nedlands, Western Australia.

17. Du Toit, A. L., 1953, *Geology of South Africa,* 3rd ed. Hafner Publishing Co., New York, pp. 1–611.

18. Tyler, S. A., and E. S. Barghoorn, 1954, Occurrence of Structurally Preserved Plants in Pre-Cambrian Rocks of the Canadian Shield. *Science*, vol. 119, pp. 606–608.

19. Wilson, Morley E., 1939, The Canadian Shield. In: *Geologie der Erde: Geology of North America,* vol. 1, pp. 232–311.

PART II

PART II

THE PALEOZOIC WORLD

Figure 79. West side of Helena Ridge northwest of Banff, Alberta, exposing 3,750 feet of Cambrian strata. Cathedral dolostone to Eldon dolostone, Middle Cambrian; Pika formation to Bosworth dolostone, Upper Cambrian. (Stephen C. Porter.)

Chapter 7. The Cambrian Period

The race of man shall perish, but the eyes
Of trilobites eternal be in stone,
And seem to stare about in mild surprise
At changes greater than they have yet known.

T. A. CONRAD

A Date of Reckoning. WITH THE BASAL CAMBRIAN rocks, fossils make their appearance in abundance, supplying at once a record of life and a certain means of correlating the physical record from place to place. Henceforth events in all parts of the world can be pieced together as parts of a continuous story, and it is possible to present the history of a whole continent, or of the whole world, in systematic fashion, period by period. Thus, the beginning of the Cambrian is a date of reckoning in geologic history.

PALEOGEOGRAPHY AND PHYSICAL HISTORY OF NORTH AMERICA

The Cambrian Submergence. At the very outset of the Paleozoic Era the Cambrian seas began to encroach upon the lowest lands, and before the close of the period covered more than 30 percent of the present continent. When the older Cambrian rocks are plotted on a map, however, a striking relation is shown (Fig. 80). They are not distributed over the present lowlands or along the margins of the continent, but are limited to two comparatively narrow belts well inland. In these places Cambrian formations attain a great thickness and abound in marine fossils, showing that seas were present here for a very long time. Since the sediments are of types that form in shallow water, it is clear that these places were vast troughs, subsiding slowly as they filled; that is, they were typical **geosynclines.** The eastern seaway followed the trend of the present Appalachian folds and is therefore known as the **Appalachian Geosyncline;** the western, centered in the Cordilleran region, is known as the **Cordilleran Geosyncline.**

East of the Appalachian Geosyncline lay **Appalachia,** a land mass of unknown eastward extent that was to form the Atlantic margin of the continent throughout the long Paleozoic Era, rising at times to mountainous heights and supplying most of the sediment that filled the geosyncline. A similar marginal land, **Cascadia,** lay to the west of the Cordilleran Geosyncline, while the vast interior of the continent was a low plain. The mutual relations of these five major structural features of the North American continent are shown in Figure 81.

Before the close of the Cambrian, another geosyncline, the **Ouachita Trough,** took form across northern Mexico, Texas, and Oklahoma; and a borderland, **Llanoria,** lay to the south of it along the present Gulf border.

These seven elements presisted as the dominant features of the North American continent through all the changes of the Paleozoic Era—three borderlands, three geosynclines, and a great stable interior. The borderlands were from time to time worn low, but were repeatedly uplifted; they were the mobile areas—the lands of Paleozoic mountains—while the interior of the continent remained relatively low and quiet until near the end of the era. The geosynclines trapped most of the debris eroded from the adjacent lands and would soon have been filled if they had not continued to sink. In them we find the most complete record of Paleozoic times in strata that reach an aggregate thickness of 30,000 to almost 50,000 feet along the axes of the troughs. During much of the era they were occupied by shallow seas, but at times they were drained by uplift or filled somewhat above sealevel with fluvial sediments.

Cambrian rocks are now exposed in only a small part of the area of these old geosynclines, because in many places they are buried by younger formations and in others they have been removed by post-Cambrian erosion. But wherever the rocks in two outcrops carry the same marine fossils, it is clear that they were formed in a common seaway. Conversely, where the faunas in one area are conspicuously different from those in another, a barrier may be indicated. In the Lower Cambrian formations of the Cordilleran Trough, for example, certain genera and species occur south of Idaho that are not found in Canada, and vice versa. The absence of Early Cambrian rocks in Idaho and western Montana would seem to confirm that a land barrier had blocked the trough here. Detailed study of the lithology in adjacent outcrops adds to the evidence, for the formations become coarser and unfossiliferous as we approach Idaho from either north or south. It is inferred, therefore, that the Cambrian seas invaded the Cordilleran Geosyncline in separate embayments that did not quite meet until near the close of Early Cambrian time. In the East, likewise, it is inferred that the **Acadian Trough** (Fig. 80) was separated from the Appalachian Trough during most of Cambrian time because the faunas in the Acadian belt are so distinct from those farther northwest.

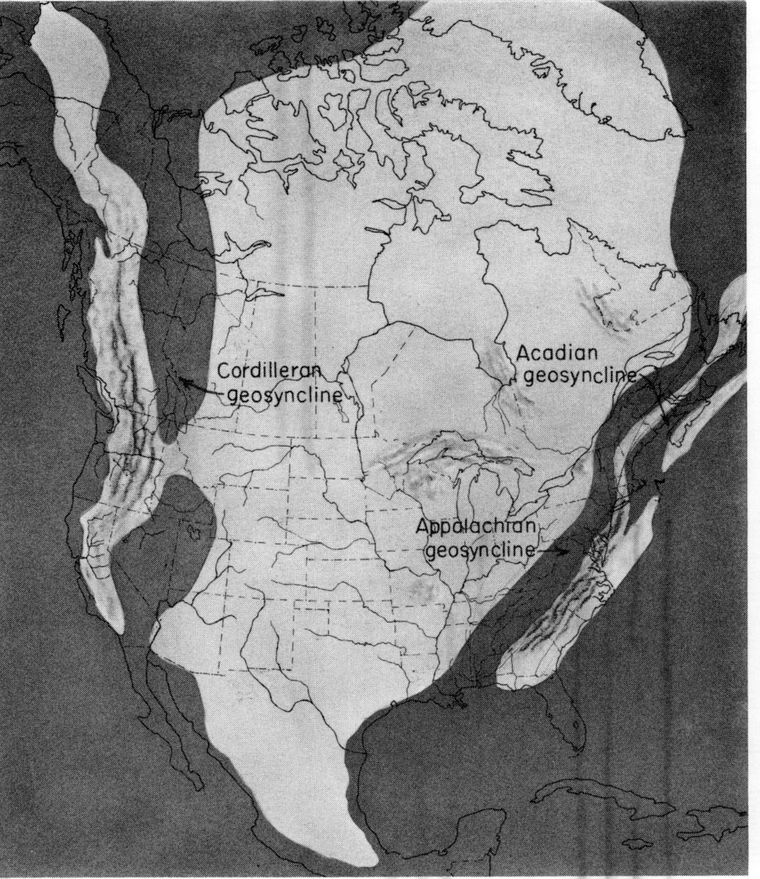

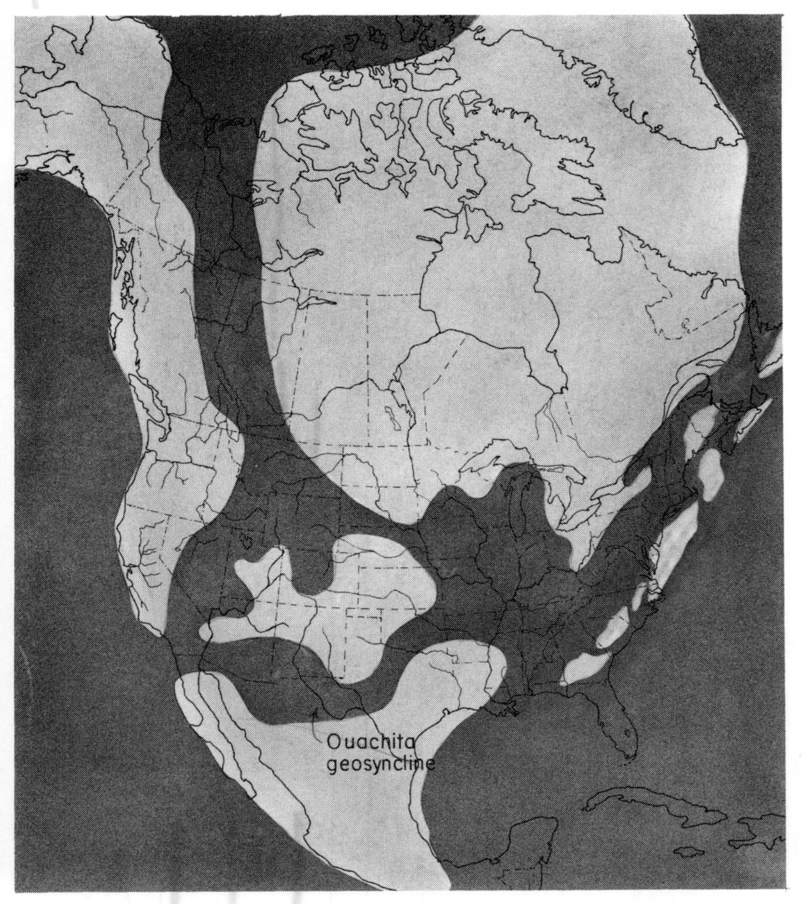

Figure 80. Cambrian Paleogeography. Left, maximum extent of the Early Cambrian seas. Hills remain where the late Precambrian ranges stood on the Canadian Shield; marginal highlands existed along both east and west margins of the continent. Right, Late Cambrian seaways. Appalachia was now reduced to lowland and probably was largely submerged, leaving only a chain of islands. The islands shown are symbolic; there is no direct evidence for their size or shape.

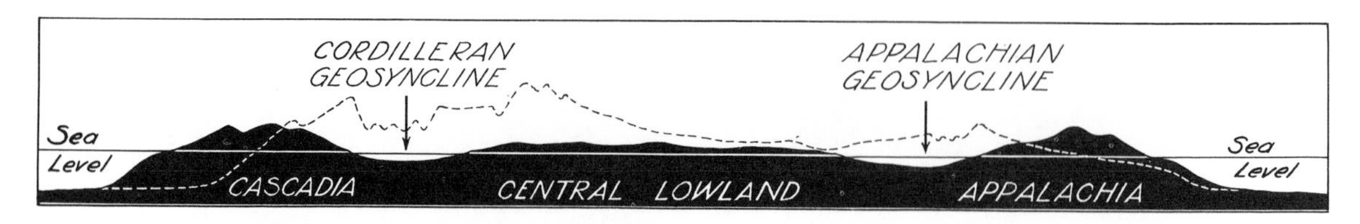

Figure 81. Profile across the North American continent in Cambrian time (black) to show the relation of the geosynclines and broderlands to the modern continent (broken line). The section runs through San Francisco and Washington, D.C. Vertical scale greatly exaggerated.

The Early Cambrian seas were restricted to the geosynclines and probably at no time covered more than 10 percent of the continent. The Lower Cambrian deposits in both troughs are predominantly quartzites, ranging from a thousand feet or less to several thousands of feet in thickness, and in the Appalachian Trough the basal part includes large amounts of conglomerate. In this respect the Lower Cambrian formations contrast with those of Middle and Upper Cambrian time which are largely calcareous. This suggests that a vast sandy mantle had been forming over the widespread Precambrian crystalline rocks before Cambrian time, and warping and uplift early in the period provided sufficient relief to cause most of the loose sand to be transported into the sinking geosynclines. Concentration of the conglomerates along the east side of the Appalachian Trough indicates that Appalachia was a conspicuous highland at this time undergoing rapid erosion.

During the period the highlands were progressively reduced; before the end of Middle Cambrian time the Cordilleran sea had begun to creep eastward across the low interior of the continent; and by Late Cambrian time fully 30 percent of North America was submerged (Fig. 80) and the remaining land was so low as to supply but little detrital sediment. In short, a major erosion cycle had been completed, affecting virtually the whole continent. Appalachia may then have been reduced to a chain of low islands (the pattern represented in Figure 80 is purely symbolic since we have no direct evidence for the topography in Appalachia at this time).

The Upper Cambrian formations of the North Central states (South Dakota, Minnesota, Wisconsin, and Iowa) contrast with equivalent deposits in most of the rest of the continent in being predominantly of sandstone and siltstone. These widespread but relatively thin sandy deposits were clearly derived from the mantle that still blanketed the Canadian Shield. Tongues of sand from this source reach as far to the southeast as central Pennsylvania.

It should be understood that the spread of the Cambrian seas was so gradual that it would not have been perceptible to an observer if one had existed. The movements undoubtedly were like the broad crustal warpings that have drowned parts of the coastal belts in recent geologic time and are still continuing. The northern part of the Baltic coast of Sweden, for example, is rising at the rate of about 1 centimeter a year. In the course of a normal human lifetime this rise would amount to less than 3 feet, but in 10,000 years it would tilt all the water out of the Baltic Sea and transform it into dry land, or if continued for a million years would uplift the region as high as Mount Everest, as noted by Shand.[1] The drowning of our mid-Atlantic coastal belt in late geologic time was certainly produced by equally slow downwarping.

Nor should we imagine that the Cambrian submergence was as simple as here sketched. Evidently the spread and final retreat of the Cambrian seas were largely the result of a world-wide rise and fall of sealevel, for contemporaneous changes were marked in other continents. The rise in sealevel may have been due in part to filling of the seas by sediments eroded from the lands, or to broad upwarping of parts of the ocean floor; and the retreat may have been caused by disturbances in other parts of the world, which deepened the ocean basins, thus drawing off the waters from the continents. Whatever the cause of this major cycle of submergence and emergence, minor oscillations were superposed upon it. Twice during the period the seas were greatly restricted if not entirely withdrawn from the continent, thus producing natural breaks in the record that make it convenient to separate the Cambrian *System* into three *series*, Lower, Middle, and Upper. Furthermore, while sealevel was rising and falling, the continent itself was slowly warping, even as it is today, and, accordingly, the outlines of the inland seas shifted widely during the period. The geosynclines, however, were the most continuously depressed areas and remained the most persistent seaways.

Close of the Period. The Cambrian submergence was followed by a gentle lowering of sealevel that drained the inland seas and left the continent fully exposed but very low and flat. This emergence caused a break in the sedimentary record, separating the Cambrian from the Ordovician period. During the exposure, however, no marked uplift occurred in North America; accordingly, the Cambrian formations suffered little erosion, and when renewed submergence brought the Ordovician seas again into the geosynclines, the new deposits were laid over the Cambrian with slight physical evidence of the break. In many places, therefore, the boundary between the Cambrian and the Ordovician is not well marked and, in unfossiliferous areas, is still the subject of controversy.

This stands in contrast with conditions in western Europe, notably Wales, where the Cambrian formations include much volcanic material and are unconformably overlain by the Ordovician, indicating that uplift, disturbance, and considerable erosion occurred at the end of the Cambrian. This is the type region where the Cambrian and Ordovician systems were established.

STRATIGRAPHY OF THE CAMBRIAN ROCKS

Stratigraphy is the study of the stratified rocks, their nature, distribution, and interpretation. As noted in Chapter 1, the character of a sedimentary deposit indicates the conditions under which it was laid down, and at the same time reflects the character of the adjacent lands. The Cambrian strata are in this way the basis for the interpretations of the physical history sketched above.

Subdivisions of the Cambrian System. Although the Cambrian System of rocks was first studied and named in Wales (1835), a country which the Romans called Cambria, it is more grandly displayed in the mountains of western North America, where a vast thickness of evenly bedded strata is exposed like pages of a colossal manuscript preserving the history of Cambrian time (Figs. 83, 85). In different parts of this area the thick Cambrian section is divisible into numerous formations, some local and others recognizable over considerable distances. Throughout the whole Cordilleran geosyncline it is possible to group these formations, however, into three great **series** representing three distinct **epochs** of Cambrian time (Figs. 82 and 84).

In accordance with the custom of using geographic names for geologic units, the Lower Cambrian has been called the **Waucoban Series,** for the very long section at Waucoba Springs, California; the Middle Cambrian, the **Albertan,** for the fine sections in the Canadian Rockies of Alberta; and the Upper Cambrian, the **Croixian** (pronounced *croy·an*), for the exposures about St. Croix Falls, Minnesota. The threefold division of the Cambrian is recognizable throughout the world, though local names are used in different countries.

The **Lower Cambrian** formations are characterized by faunas in which the spartailed trilobite *Olenellus* is conspicuous (Fig. 82), and Pl. 1, fig. 10). Since extensive experience has shown that no species of this genus occurs above the Lower Cambrian, *Olenellus* is accepted as a **guide fossil** or **index** to the Lower Cambrian Series.

Above the zone of *Olenellus* come large-tailed trilobites of several genera, such as *Olenoides* and *Bathyuriscus* (Fig. 82, and Pl. 1, fig. 3), which are equally distinctive of the **Middle Cambrian** formations. Finally, the **Upper Cambrian** faunas are characterized by the trilobite *Crepicephalus* (Fig. 82, and Pl. 1, fig. 2) and by other genera which are confined exclusively to that epoch.

With *Olenellus* are associated many other types of trilobites, brachiopods, etc., that together represent the life of Early Cambrian time. The assemblage found with *Bathyuriscus* is largely different, for while many of the genera ranged from Early into Middle Cambrian time, the species are wholly distinct. Hence it is possible to distinguish the two series even where neither *Olenellus* nor *Bathyuriscus* occurs. Likewise, Middle and Upper Cambrian formations can be distinguished by the general composition of their faunas.

Chart I. Correlation of important Cambrian sections

Series	Stages	Canadian Rockies	House R., Utah	Wyo.–Mont.	Texas (Llano)	Okla. (Arbuckl)	Mo. (Ozarks)	Minn.–Wisc.	Southern Appalach.	Central Appalach.	Stages	Series
Croixian	Trempeleau.	Goodsir ls.; Mons	Notch Peak ls.	Gallatin fm.: Grove Cr. fm	Wilberns fm.: San Saba ls.; Pedernalis dol.	Butterly dol.; Signal Mt. ls.	Eminence dol.; Potosi dol.	Madison dol.; Jordan ss.; Lodi sh.; St. Lawrence	Copper Ridge dol.	Gatesburg fm.; Conococheague ls.	Trempeleau.	Croixian
	Franconian	Goodsir ls.; Lyell ls.; Sabine ls.	Notch Peak ls.; Orr fm.	Gallatin fm.: Snowy R. fm; Pilgrim ls.	Wilberns fm.: Pt. Peak sh.; Morgan Cr. ls.	Royer dol.; Ft. Sill ls.; Honey Cr. fm.	Doe Run; Derby dol.; Davis dol.	Reno ss.; Mazomanie member; Tomah ss.	Copper Ridge dol.	Gatesburg fm.; Conococheague ls.	Franconian	
	Dresbach.	Bosworth fm.; Arctomys sh.; Sullivan	Weeks ls.	Gallatin fm.: Maurice f.	Lion Mt. ss.; Cap Mt. f.; Hickory ss.	Reagan ss.	Bonneterre dol.; Lamotte ss.	Galesville ss.; Eau Claire sh.; Mt. Simon ss.	Maynardville ls.; Nolichucky sh.	Warrior fm.; Conococheague ls.	Dresbach.	
Albertan	(Stages not established)	Pika f.; Eldon dol.; Stephens fm.; Cathedral dol.; Ptarmigan f.	Marjum fm.; Wheeler ls.; Swasey fm.; Dome ls.; Howell ls.	Gros Ventre fm.: Park sh.; Meaghre ls.; Wolsey sh.; Flathead ss.					Conasauga shale: Nolichucky sh.; Maryville ls.; Rogersville sh.; Rutledge ls.	Elbrook fm.		Albertan
Waucoban		Mt. Whyte fm.; St. Piran ss.; Ft. Mountain ss.	Tatow ls.; Pioche sh.; Prospect Mt. ss.						Rome fm.; Shady dol.; Erwin qtz.; Hampton sh.; Unicoi ss.	Waynesboro f.; Tomstown dol.; Antietam qtz.; Harpers sh.; Chickies qtz.		Waucoban

The cause of the abrupt change in the faunas between Early and Middle Cambrian time must be sought in a temporary withdrawal of the seas from the geosynclines, followed by an interval of non-deposition during which *Olenellus* died out and species of other genera evolved, so that the eventual return of marine waters into the geosyncline introduced a migrant Middle Cambrian fauna that had been developing in the marginal seas during the interval of non-deposition. Emergences of this sort, more or less complete, have caused the breaks between series, just as greater and more extensive emergences have separated the systems and divided off the periods of time. The Lower Cambrian emergence is confirmed in most places by an abrupt change in the character of the sediments or by erosional unconformity or by basal conglomerates in the overlying series. The emergence was accompanied by no pronounced crustal disturbance, however; hence no angular discordance exists, and the Middle Cambrian seas returned to almost the same areas that had been flooded before. The emergence between the Middle and Late Cambrian epochs was apparently less extensive, and in North America no generally recognizable physical change marks the boundary between Middle and Upper Cambrian rocks and its position is determined by correlation with the rocks in Wales where the system was established. As now understood, it falls between two well-defined trilobite zones, the **Cedaria zone** being referred to the top of the Middle Cambrian and the **Crepicephalus zone** to the base of the Upper Cambrian.

Cambrian Rocks of the Cordilleran Trough. Along the axis of the Cordilleran Geosyncline the Cambrian strata are several thousands of feet thick, and are now magnificently exposed as a result of uplift in the modern mountains. The Canadian Rockies of Alberta provide many exposures like those of Figures 83 and 85, where the entire thickness of Cambrian rocks may be seen in a single view. Other fine sections are found in the Rockies of Montana and Wyoming and in the basin ranges of Utah and Nevada.

In general, throughout this region, the Lower Cambrian deposits consist chiefly of quartzite, and exceed half a mile in thickness. Some zones are shaly, and others, especially in the upper part, are calcareous, but the overwhelming predominance of sandy sediments is remarkable. These sands were derived from the crystalline Precambrian rocks that had been weathering during the preceding interval. In some of the thickest sections, the basal part is unfossiliferous and probably was laid down in advance of the sea, but the presence of trilobites and other fossils indicates that most of the deposits are marine. The water must have been shallow, however, to permit the sand to be transported and spread evenly over the floor of the geosyncline.

The Middle Cambrian formations are predominantly limestones, all the way from Nevada to Alberta, indicating that by this time the bordering lands had been largely stripped of their sandy mantle or were so low that little detrital sediment was being carried to the sea. These calcareous formations range from half a mile to a mile in thickness in the Canadian Rockies and in Utah and Nevada. During this epoch the geosyncline widened somewhat, and the sea tended to spread farther east than in Early Cambrian time; along this margin, where the Mid-Cambrian comes to rest directly on the Precambrian, it, too, is sandy like the Lower Cambrian (Fig. 84).

The Upper Cambrian Series is largely dolostone and limestone throughout most of the Cordilleran Trough, and is commonly 3,000 to 4,000 feet thick. Many of the towering white cliffs of the Canadian Rockies are made of these limestones (Fig. 85).

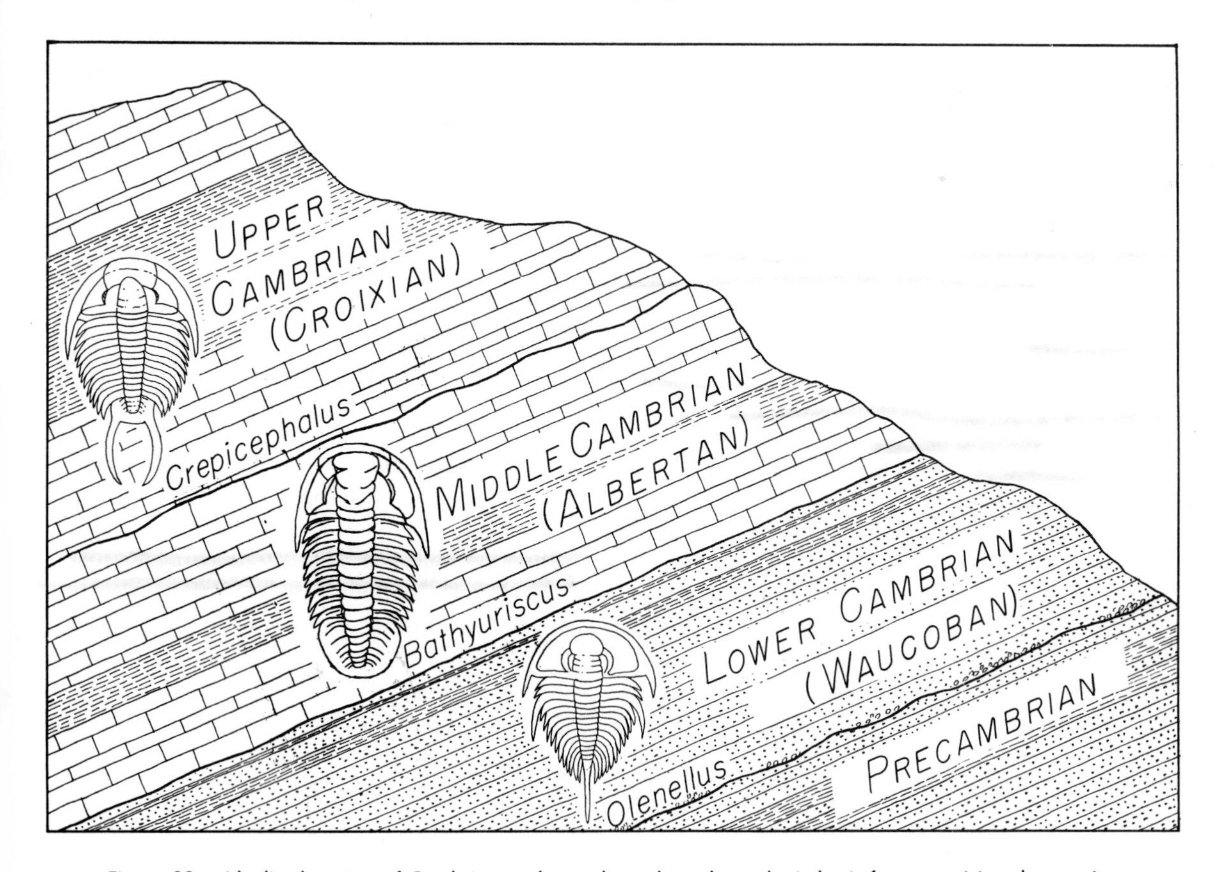

Figure 82. Idealized section of Cambrian rocks to show the paleontologic basis for recognizing three series.

Figure 83. South face of Mt. Bosworth, from Kicking Horse Pass, Alberta, showing in simple succession more than a mile of Cambrian strata. (Charles D. Walcott.)

Cambrian Rocks of the Appalachian Trough. In the Appalachian Trough the Lower Cambrian strata are predominantly detrital as they are in the west, whereas the Middle and Upper Cambrian consists largely of limestone and dolostone. This change in facies (lithologic expression) is due in part to the fact that Appalachia was undergoing rapid erosion during Early Cambrian time but was too low to supply much detrital sediment during the later epochs. Perhaps equally important, during the Early Cambrian the geosyncline was bordered on both east and west by a surface of Precambrian crystalline rocks, that had been weathering so long that an extensive sandy mantle was at hand to be swept into the newly formed geosyncline.

From Pennsylvania southward the detrital part of the Lower Cambrian Series ranges from 3,000 to 4,000 feet in thickness, and its thick quartzites, being exceptionally resistant, are prominent ridge-makers in the eastern part of the fold belt.

The Middle and Upper Cambrian dolostones are sparingly fossiliferous and have been difficult to differentiate and to separate from the overlying Ordovician dolostones. They underlie a large part of the limestone valleys in the fold belt.

Cambrian formations are thick in the northern part of the Appalachian Geosyncline, expecially in eastern New York and the Champlain Valley of Vermont and in Newfoundland; but in the Champlain Valley they have been so badly deformed by later orogeny that the stratigraphy is still not well known.

Around the north and east flanks of the Adirondacks, the Upper Cambrian overlaps into the Precambrian granite and is largely detrital, consisting

of the sand swept off the old Adirondack Dome. Here it is known as the **Potsdam sandstone** (Fig. 86).

Cambrian Deposits of the Mississippi Basin. The late Middle Cambrian and Upper Cambrian seas gradually flooded across the low interior of the continent, lapping northward upon the ancient crystalline land of the Canadian Shield. Spreading thus across a region deeply covered by a residual mantle (much of which was wind-blown sand), they reworked this loose material into sandy and silty formations of vast areal extent but no great thickness. The exposures of these formations in the region of St. Croix Falls in Minnesota and Wisconsin are regarded as the type section of the Upper Cambrian, and give us the name Croixian Series. Here they attain a total thickness of scarcely 1,000 feet.

Farther south, in the Ozark region of Missouri, the Upper Cambrian formations lap up onto the flanks of Precambrian hills which were progressively submerged during late Cambrian time (Fig. 87). At the base of this section is 300 to 400 feet of sand like that of the upper Mississippi Valley, but the rest of the section is mostly dolostone, in part highly siliceous or cherty. This section represents the Ouachita Trough and, in general, is similar to beds exposed farther west in the Arbuckle Mountains of Oklahoma and the Llano Uplift of central Texas. It is noteworthy that throughout this region the very youngest Middle Cambrian rests directly on Precambrian crystallines.

Climate. We have no direct evidence as to the climate of this remote period. The tillites which underlie the Cambrian in various parts of the

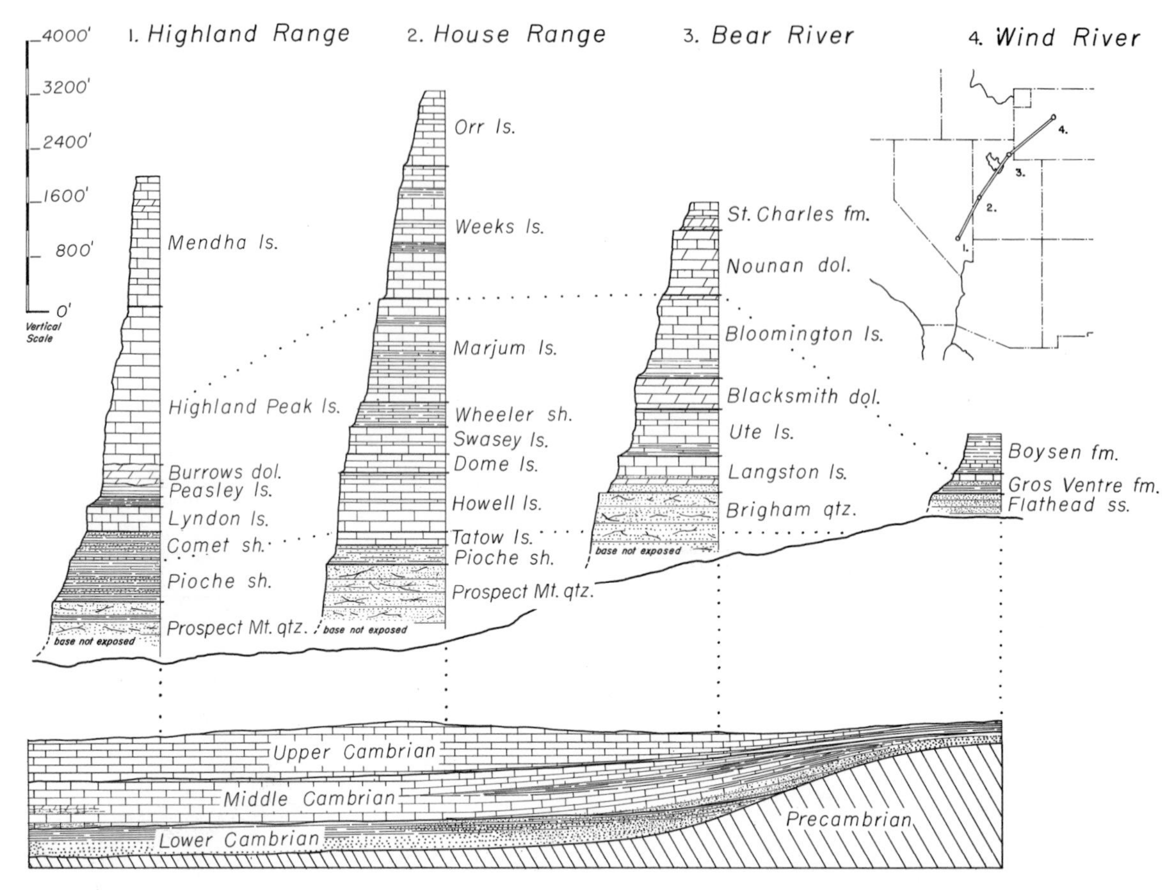

Figure 84. Cambrian rocks of the Cordilleran Trough. Above, four columnar sections whose position is indicated on the inset map; below, a restored stratigraphic section drawn on a vertical scale only ¼ that of the columnar sections. (Data from Charles Deiss and from Harry E. Wheeler.)

world have been described in the discussion of the Precambrian. Although some geologists regard them as basal Cambrian, we believe they belong with the underlying system. In any event, the extensive limy reefs of the Archaeocyathina (Fig. 89) in the Lower Cambrian are believed to imply a mild climate, since physico-chemical conditions greatly favor the precipitation of limy deposits in *warm* waters. The wide distribution of many of the Cambrian species from low to high latitudes clearly suggests that climatic belts were less sharply defined than at present. The extensive deposition of pure limestones and dolostones during Late Cambrian times as far north as Quebec, Newfoundland, and northern Greenland likewise gives evidence of mild temperatures at these high latitudes.

LIFE OF THE CAMBRIAN

The Curtain Rises. At the dawn of the Cambrian, life had already existed on the Earth for possibly a thousand million years. It is small wonder, therefore, that nearly all the great branches of the animal kingdom were represented, and that complex forms of arthropods, such as trilobites, held the center of the stage. Although exceedingly rare in the Precambrian rocks, fossils appear in abundance at the base of the Cambrian, revealing this highly varied life as though a curtain had suddenly lifted on a drama already in progress.

The lands must then have presented scenes of stark desolation, for Cambrian rocks bear almost no direct evidence of terrestrial life of any sort. Primitive soft-tissued plants, such as lichens, prob-

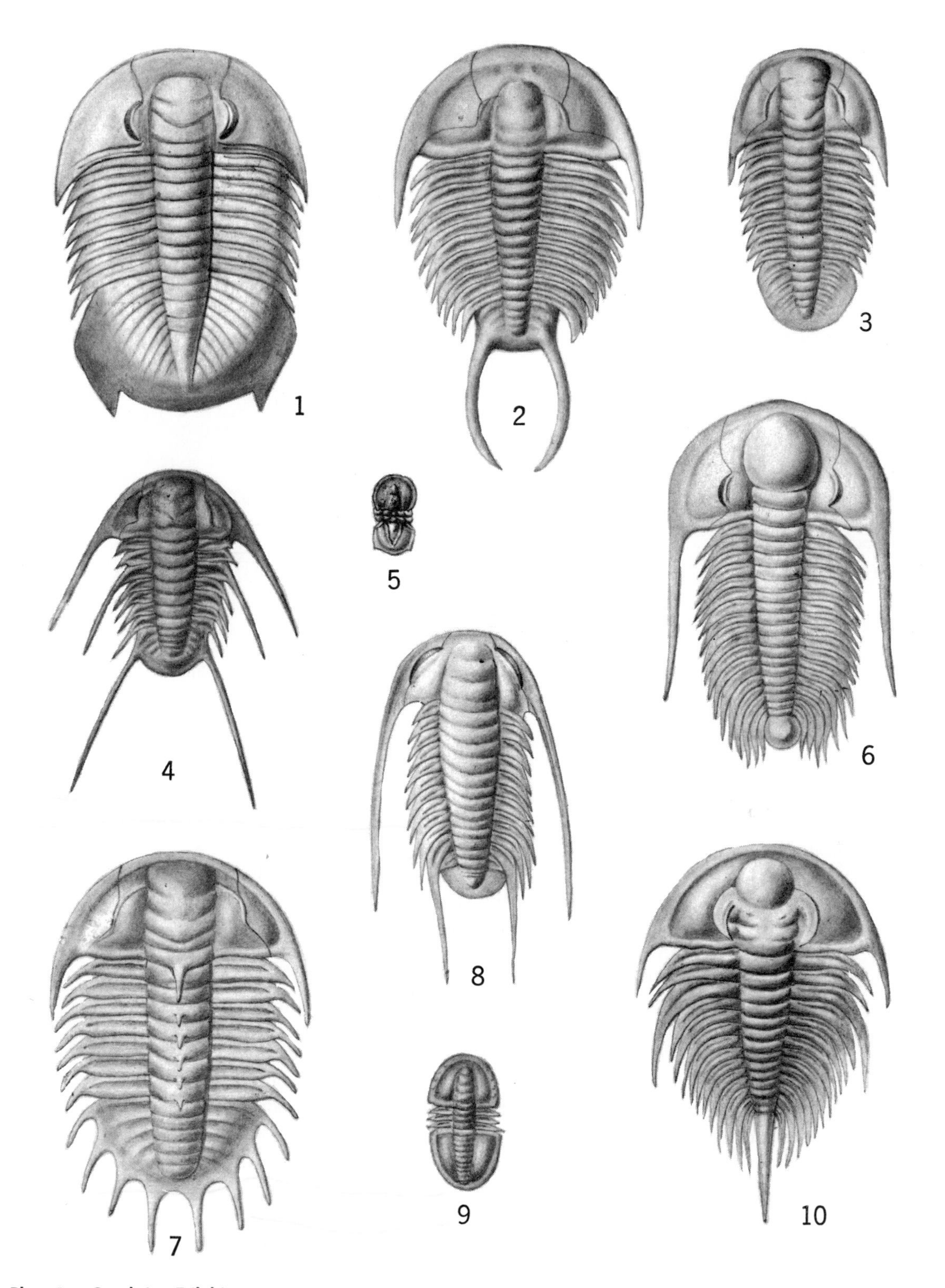

Plate 1. Cambrian Trilobites.

Upper Cambrian: Figure 1, *Dikelocephalus minnesotensis;* 2, *Tricrepicephalus texanus.* Middle Cambrian: Figure 3, *Bathyuriscus rotundatus;* 4, *Albertella helena;* 5, *Agnostus interstrictus;* 6, *Paradoxides harlani;* 7, *Olenoides curticei.* Lower Cambrian: Figure 8, *Bathynotus holopyga;* 9, *Eodiscus speciosus;* 10, *Olenellus thompsoni.* All natural size except 6, which is about $\frac{1}{6}$ natural size. (Drawn by L. S. Douglass.)

Figure 85. Mount Lefroy in the Canadian Rockies northwest of Banff, Alberta. This peak, with an altitude of 11,660 feet, is made of Middle and Upper Cambrian limestones. (Natman.)

ably clothed the moist lowlands, but, lacking roots and vascular tissue by which to draw moisture from the ground, these lowly plants could not thrive in the dry regions.

In recent years spores of land plants have been reported from the Lower Cambrian in the Baltic coast of the USSR,[2] and both spores and plant tissue in the Middle Cambrian of eastern Siberia.[3] The latter are alleged to represent primitive vascular plants. Animals had not yet learned to breathe air and so far as now known, did not appear on the land until Silurian time.

The seas, however, teemed with invertebrate animals of many kinds that found both food and shelter among the varied and abundant seaweeds. On the whole, it was a strange and unfamiliar assemblage of animals, primitive in many respects and all of comparatively small size.

Stars of the Cast. The dominant creatures of the Cambrian seas were the **trilobites** (Fig. 88), swimming and groveling arthropods which became so numerous and varied as to make up fully 60 percent of the known fauna (see Pl. 1). They are by far the most important fossils in the Cambrian rocks. In their day they boasted the greatest size if not the highest intelligence of any animals upon the Earth. Even so, they were small, generally ranging between 1 and 4 inches in length. The giant of Cambrian forms was *Paradoxides harlani* (Fig. 88, and Pl. 1, fig. 6), whose abundant remains in Middle Cambrian slates near Boston indicate a creature about 18 inches long and probably not over 10 pounds in weight. It is a striking commentary on the history of life that such feeble folk held undisputed sway over the Earth throughout Cambrian time—a span exceeding that of human existence by perhaps a hundredfold.

Next to the trilobites in importance came a horde of **brachiopods**, which constituted another 30 percent of the Cambrian faunas (Pl. 2, figs. 1–7). During the early and middle epochs of the period these were mostly very small, primitive types (Atremata) with phosphatic shells. They must have been exceedingly numerous locally, for in places their shells now cover the bedding planes

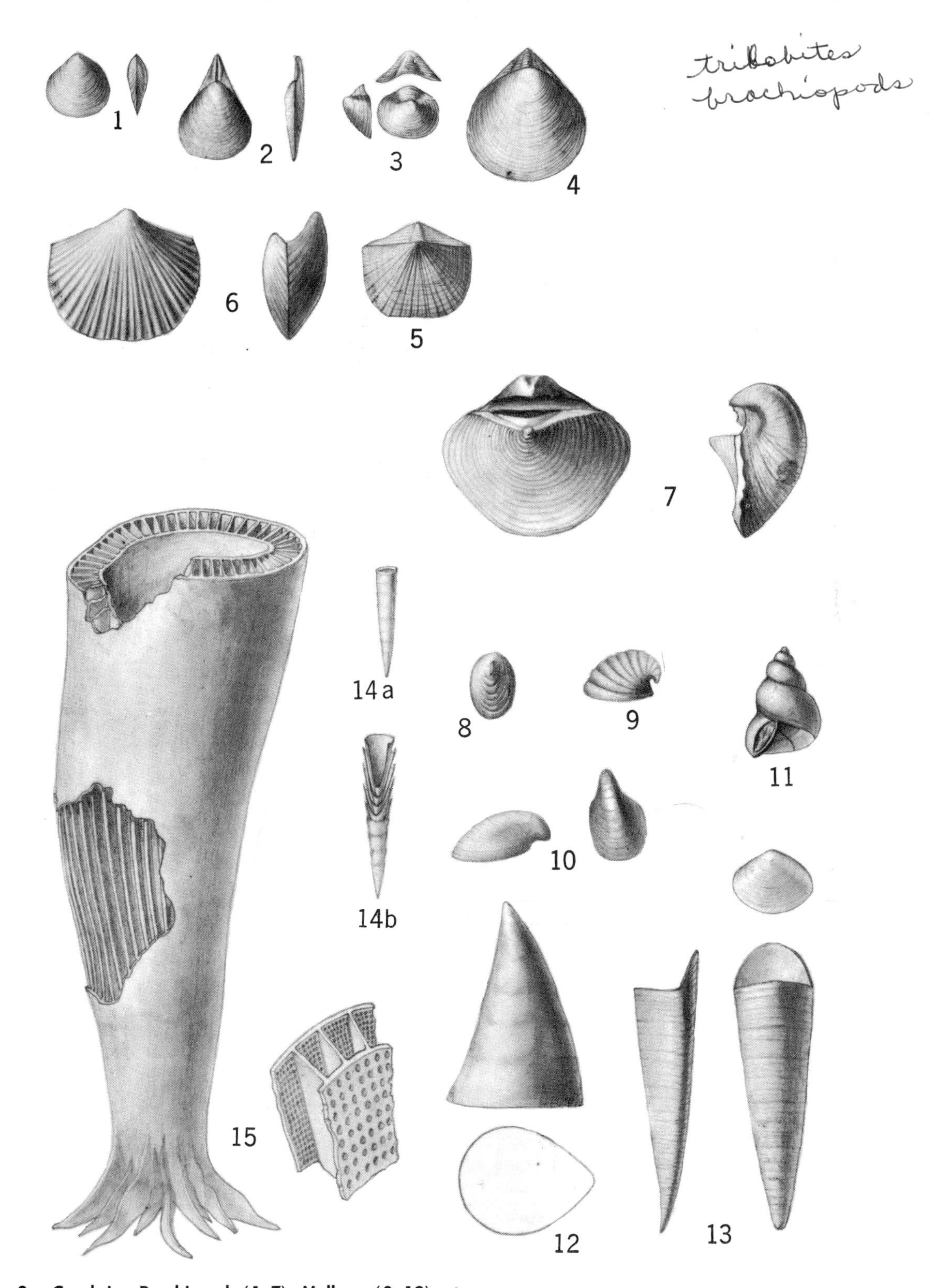

Plate 2. Cambrian Brachiopods (1–7); Molluscs (8–12), etc.

Figure 1, *Dicellomus politus* (ventral and lateral views); 2, *Lingulepis pinnaformis;* 3, *Paterina bella;* 4, *Obolus aurora;* 5, *Billingsella coloradoensis;* 6, *Eoorthis texana* (ventral and lateral views); 7, *Kutorgina cingulata* (dorsal and lateral views); 8, 9, *Helcionella rugosa* and var. *paupera;* 10, *Helcionella* sp. (2 views); 11, *Matherella saratogensis;* 12, *Hypseloconus elongatus* (side view and outline); 13, *Hyolithes princeps* (lateral and dorsal views and operculum); 14, *Salterella rugosa* (entire and weathered shells); 15, *Cambrocyathus profundus* (lateral view and enlarged detail). All slightly enlarged, except Figure 15 in part. Drawings by L. S. Douglass.

Figure 86. Upper Cambrian (Potsdam) sandstone. Ausable Chasm near Keeseville, New York. (Carl O. Dunbar.)

of the Cambrian rocks. In the Late Cambrian, more progressive types with calcareous shells began to rise into prominence, foreshadowing their dominance in the Ordovician Period following.

The **Archeocyathina** played the role of reef-builders in the Early Cambrian seas (Fig. 89, and Pl. 2, fig. 15). They formed vase-shaped to cylindrical skeletons of calcite, characterized by having two walls, one inside the other, separated by limy plates or bars. Both walls were sievelike. Their biologic relations are still uncertain. They generally grew over one another in tangled profusion as sponges do, and they left an imposing record in the Lower Cambrian rocks in the form of reefs which are found in many parts of the world (California, New York, Quebec, Labrador, Newfoundland, Siberia, Sardinia, Spain, Australia, and Antarctica). In Australia they range through fully 200 feet of limestones and extend for more than 400 miles; it is a strange coincidence that this greatest of all Paleozoic reefs should occupy a region closely paralleling the Great Barrier Reef of the east coast of Australia, the largest of all modern coral reefs.

Mention must also be made of the calcareous alga, ***Cryptozoön,*** that formed smaller but widely

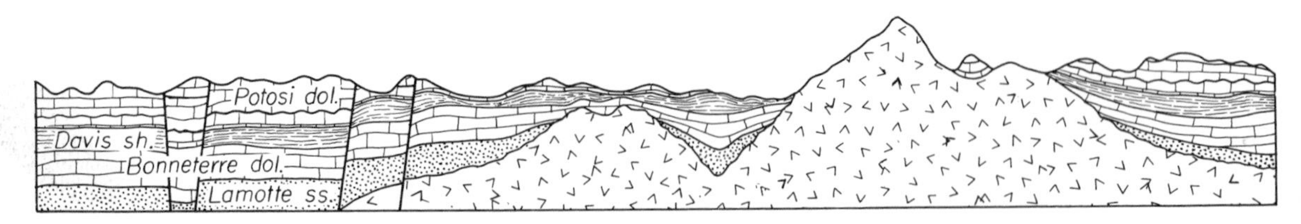

Figure 87. Cambrian formations near the crest of the Ozark Dome. The unconformable onlap of successive formations on the Precambrian granite core shows that the dome was progressively submerged during Cambrian deposition. Length of section about 12 miles; vertical scale 5 times the horizontal. Normal faults near the left end are of post-Cambrian date. (After C. L. Dake, Missouri Bureau of Geology and Mines.)

distributed reefs throughout Cambrian time (Figs. 90 and 91). These deposits are hemispherical, irregular, or spreading masses of finely laminated calcite precipitated layer upon layer by moldlike colonies of microscopic blue-green algae. The limy precipitate preserves only the gross form of the colony, not that of the individual plants.

Worms in considerable variety must have been present, and some of the sand flats apparently were full of them, since the sandstones are in places replete with their burrows, making the so-called pipe-rocks (*Scolithus*, etc.). These are especially common in the Upper Cambrian sandstones of New York and Wisconsin and in the Lower Cambrian of Tennessee, Virginia, and Sweden.

Minor Characters. The remaining phyla play a very minor part in the fossil record of the Cambrian, partly because many of the modern classes had not yet evolved, but probably in greater degree because they had not developed shells capable of fossilization. **Protozoa** have been reported from Siberia[4] but are otherwise unknown; simple "**glass sponges**" with siliceous spicules are locally abundant; and **coelenterates** are of no importance, though doubtful impressions of jellyfish have been found locally in the Lower Cambrian of New York, Vermont, and the Baltic countries, a supposed sea anemone has been found in the Middle Cambrian Burgess shale, and numerous jellyfish have been described from the Lower Cambrian of Australia.[5] The ancestors of the true corals had not yet learned to secrete lime. **Echinoderms** are represented by small, primitive cystoids, but no starfish, sea-urchins, or crinoids are known; nor were there any bryozoans.

Although the **mollusks** constitute the bulk of the shell-bearing animals of modern seas, they were relatively few in Cambrian time. The **gastropods** were first to appear, and are represented by two distinct tribes in the Lower Cambrian rocks. The first group includes very small and primitive **snail** shells scarcely attaining a breadth of half an inch and having the form of a low cone or of a spiral less than one-quarter of an inch across with only two or three volutions. The snails remained inconspicuous until near the close of the Cambrian, when a rapid evolution set in that foreshadowed the prominence they were to assume in the next period. Much more common than snails were the **hyolithids** (Pl. 2, fig, 13), doubtfully allied to the modern pteropods or sea butterflies, which are gastropods

Figure 88. Restoration of the Cambrian trilobite, *Paradoxides harlani*, one of the giants of its time. About ¼ natural size.

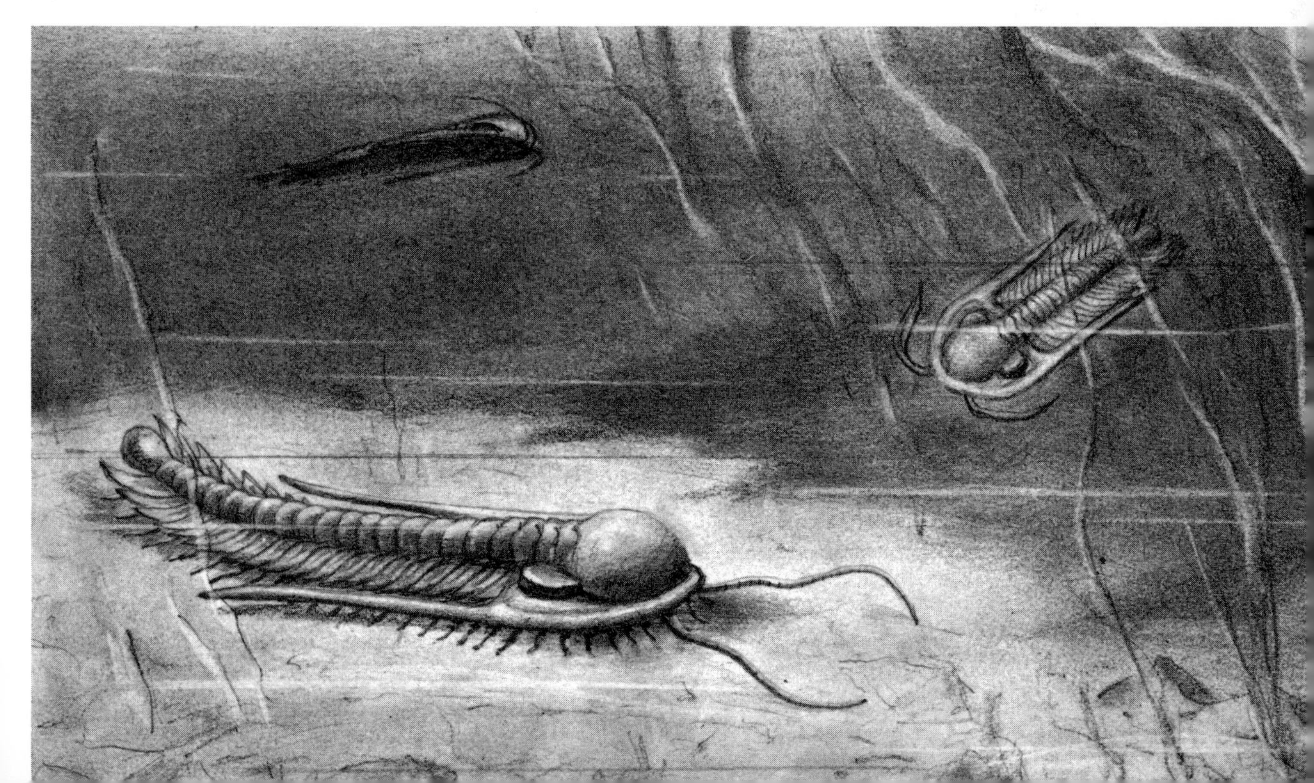

Figure 89. Weathered surface of Lower Cambrian reef limestone made of Archeocyathina. Millimeter scale at left margin. (T. G. Taylor.)

peculiarly modified for a swimming habit. The small scabbard-shaped shells of *Hyolithes* occur locally in such abundance as to form thin layers of limestones.

Pelecypods appear to have been absent throughout the Cambrian, and **cephalopods** appeared only near the close of the period and are among the rarest of Cambrian fossils. Two genera of minute conical shells from the Lower Cambrian rocks have been considered to be cephalopods, but this now seems highly doubtful. These are *Salterella* (Pl. 2, fig. 14) and *Volborthella,* both of which are confined to the Lower Cambrian.

The Burgess Shale Fauna. Probably the most significant fossil locality yet known was discovered by C. D. Walcott (Fig. 92) in 1910, in a bed of slaty black shale of Middle Cambrian date high up on the slope of Mt. Wapta above the town of Field, British Columbia. The fossils are preserved as delicate carbon films on the bedding planes where bedding and cleavage coincide. Each is a mere lustrous film, the residue of a soft body pressed as flat as the ink on this page, but it preserves with amazing detail the form of delicate external appendages and, in many instances, shows the presence of viscera. From this single bed, only a few feet thick, Walcott described 70 genera and 130 species, almost all of which were delicate soft-bodied animals of types elsewhere completely unknown. Among these are sponges, jellyfish, and a remarkable array of annelid worms in which not only the body form but also bristles, scales, and even intestinal tract are preserved. The most interesting, however, are the highly varied primitive arthropods, which include, besides trilobites with limbs and antennae, delicate forms like those of the modern brine-shrimp. Of particular interest is a fossil **onychophoran**[6] (*Aysheaia,* Pl 3, fig. 4; and Fig. 93). A single genus of this strangely isolated stock

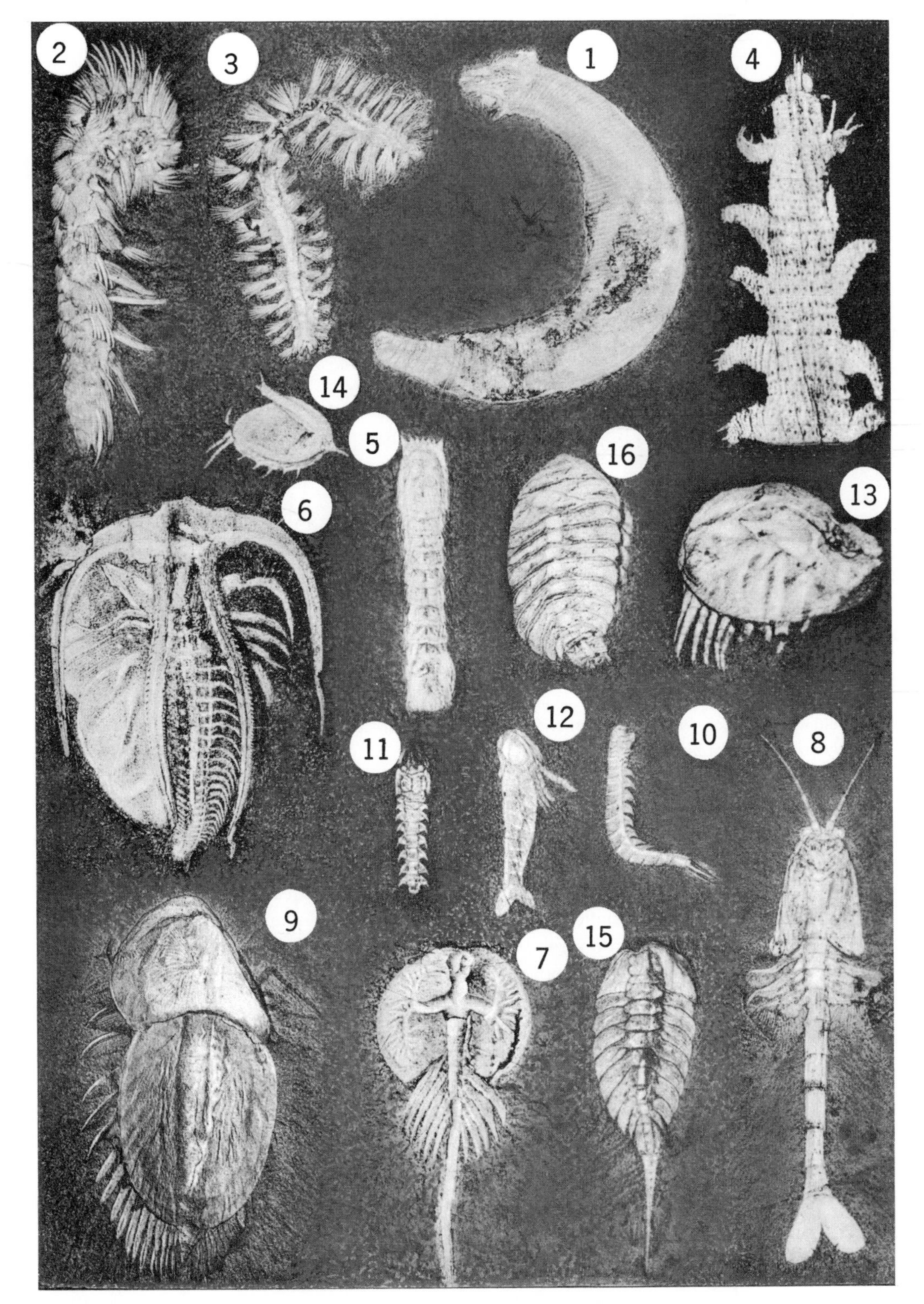

Plate 3. Middle Cambrian Fossils from the Burgess Shale, near Field, British Columbia.

Figures 1–3, annelids (Chaetopoda); 4, an onychophoran (see Figure 87); 5–16, trilobiloidea.

Figure 1, *Ottoia prolifica;* 2, *Canadia spinosa;* 3, *C. setigera;* 4, *Aysheaia pedunculata;* 5, *Mollisonia gracilis;* 6, *Marrella splendens;* 7, *Burgessia bella;* 8, *Waptia fieldensis;* 9, *Naraoia compacta;* 10, 11, *Yohoia tenuis;* 12, *Y. plena;* 13, *Hymenocaris ? circularis;* 14, *H.? parva;* 15, *Molaria spinifera.* Figures enlarged $\times$ 1½ or $\times$ 2. (After Walcott, 1911–1912.)

Figure 90. Colonies of calcareous algae weathering out of the Upper Cambrian Gros Ventre formation in Grand Teton quadrangle, Wyoming. (Elliot Blackwelder.)

still survives and has long been recognized by zoologists as a persistently primitive type, structurally like the expected common ancestor of annelid worms and arthropods. It was confidently believed by comparative anatomists to be a relic of a very ancient stock, but, since it is as softbodied as a caterpillar, there seemed no hope of a fossil record until the Burgess shale was discovered.

The Burgess shale fauna is important chiefly because of the perspective it gives. Here we get one clear view of the world of soft-bodied creatures that inhabited the early Paleozoic seas. Without these fossils we could only infer that life was abundant, and guess what it was like; and we might have believed that trilobites were more abundant than other animals just because they are the common fossils. This glimpse of the primitive soft-bodied creatures of the Cambrian sea proves the incompleteness of the fossil record; it also presents an exciting challenge. The wonderful discovery came by accident as a pack horse, high up on a mountain trail, turned over a slab of slate that caught the eye of a trained paleontologist. It was a spot where the forces of nature had conspired to preserve an almost incredible record from the past; there must be many others yet undiscovered—perhaps some in the Precambrian slates!

One may infer the circumstances under which this unusual deposit formed. Muds so fine of grain and so rich in decaying organic matter must have formed a soft, oozy sea floor, deficient in oxygen and reeking in hydrogen sulphide. Occasional storm waves stirring the bottom muds liberated the H_2S and allowed it to rise toward the surface, poisoning such swimming or floating organisms as were present. The locality of Mt. Wapta was probably a depression somewhat deeper than the surrounding sea floor, and when the dying organisms drifted into it they settled below wave base and were never again disturbed. Because of the poisoned water, no scavengers were present to devour them and so they remained whole, with limbs and other delicate appendages intact. Comparable mass destruction of organisms by H_2S gas rising from mud bottoms has been observed in modern seas.

Stage of Evolution Represented. Although the vast length of Precambrian time was not suspected when Walcott, in 1890, first brought out the richness and variety of Early Cambrian life, the zoologist Brooks exclaimed that these forms, instead of being "the simple, unspecialized ancestors of modern animals, are most intensely modern themselves in the zoological sense and . . . belong to the same order of nature as that which prevails at the present day." Obviously the evidences of the truly primitive stages of life and of their differentiation into the great phyla must be sought far earlier than the Cambrian. It is a tantalizing thought that probably far more than half the drama of evolution had been enacted before the rising curtain gives us a clear glimpse into the Cambrian scene.

Even though it is now established that a great variety of animals must have existed long before, the sudden appearance of abundant fossils in the Cambrian is remarkable. Precambrian fossils are chiefly those of lowly, lime-secreting algae, with possible representatives of two animal phyla, the protozoa and worms; but the Cambrian strata of North America alone have yielded at least 1,200 different kinds of animals, including sponges, coelenterates, worms, brachiopods, gastropods, echinoderms, and arthropods. The difference implies that some great change took place in the organization of animals during the interval between the Precambrian and the Cambrian. This undoubtedly involved the use of external armor in the form of shells of chitin (a nitrogenous substance similar to our finger nails) or of calcium carbonate. Precambrian animals were probably unarmored and, therefore, like the soft-tissued creatures of the Cambrian, were scarcely capable of preservation except under extraordinary conditions. The great variety of such forms in the Middle Cambrian Burgess shale, most of which are recorded nowhere else, shows clearly how abundant and how varied soft-bodied animals may have been in Precambrian time. The suddenness of the appearance of armor in several phyla at the beginning of the Cambrian

Figure 91. Natural exposure of part of a reef of the calcareous alga, *Cryptozoon proliferum.* Glacial scour during the Pleistocene Epoch removed the summits of these hemispheric colonies and exposed them in cross section. Saratoga, New York. (H. P. Cushing, New York State Geological Survey.)

may be more apparent than real, for the interval preceding the Cambrian is one of the greatest breaks in the geologic record and probably represents some tens of millions of years during which the evolution of shells was taking place.

The cause of the development of shells in many stocks of animal life in the time between the Precambrian and the Cambrian has been a subject of much speculation. Brooks[7] has suggested that before this time marine animals were chiefly small free-floating or swimming creatures like the larvae of existing types, and that near the close of the Precambrian they began to inhabit suitable parts of the shallow sea floor, then rapidly increased in size, experienced for the first time the effects of crowding and keen competition, and hence required protective armor. It has also been postulated that the Precambrian oceans may have been so deficient in dissolved carbonates that limy shells could not be formed, that the lime brought to the sea by rivers may have been chemically precipitated as fast as it was supplied because of the decaying organic matter on the sea floor before scavenging

Figure 92. Charles D. Walcott (1850–1927), leading student of Cambrian faunas.

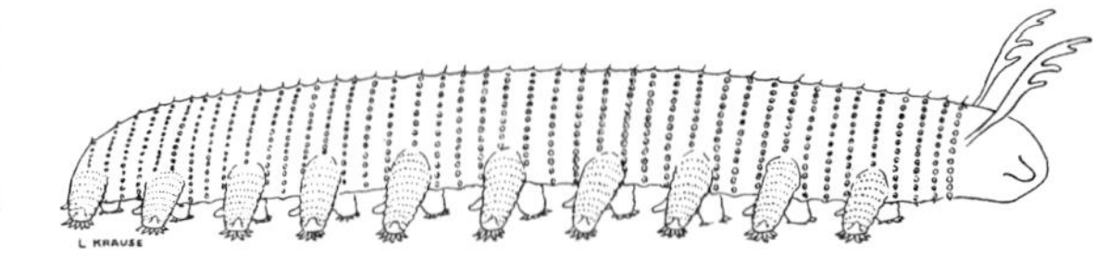

Figure 93. Restoration of a Middle Cambrian onycophoran, *Aysheaia pedunculata*. Slightly enlarged. (After G. E. Hutchinson.)

types of life had developed.[8] This hypothesis does not really solve our problem, however, because even in the absence of lime, animals could still make their shells of chitin, as, in fact, most of the Lower Cambrian types did. Moreover, the abundance of deposits of calcareous algae in Precambrian formations rather strongly controverts the suggestion of a deficiency of lime in the oceans.

The development of actively predacious habits may have been the first great stimulus to the development of protective armor. It is not improbable that all Precambrian animals were herbivorous or scavenging, and that the development of the active carnivorous habit coincided with the great change that marks the lost interval before the Cambrian.

Faunal Realms. The modern shells along the New England coast are entirely different from those to be found on the coast of California, because the Atlantic and Pacific oceans have been effectively separated by land barriers while the modern species were evolving. Thus each ocean has become a great faunal realm so far as the marine invertebrates are concerned. How great the faunal differences are is strikingly shown at Panama, where Dall has listed 517 species of shell-bearing invertebrates from the Atlantic side and 805 from the Pacific, yet finds but 24 common to both oceans, though the barrier is less than 50 miles across! Obviously, marine animals could migrate more easily from our Atlantic coast to that of Europe than by way of the Arctic or Antarctic into the Pacific. Accordingly, there is much closer resemblance between the modern marine faunas of western Europe and eastern United States than between those of the east and west coasts of North America. It is therefore clear that, during a submergence of the continent, a sea which entered the interior from the Atlantic realm would bring animals quite distinct from those of a western seaway. Some of the Cambrian faunas show this distinction quite as definitely as the modern ones.

The Early Cambrian oceans seem to have been somewhat openly connected, so that intermigration was easy and the leading types of life are much alike in various parts of the world. The faunas of this epoch are therefore said to be **cosmopolitan.** On the contrary, the Middle Cambrian faunas of the Pacific and Atlantic realms are largely different. The former is characterized by the large-tailed trilobites of the tribe of *Bathyuriscus,* none of which is present in the Atlantic realm. In the latter, various species of the trilobite *Paradoxides* are common, though none has ever been found in the Pacific realm. Thus it is known that the Acadian Trough in Middle Cambrian time was flooded from the Atlantic, bringing *Paradoxides* into this seaway across Newfoundland, Nova Scotia, and eastern New England at least as far as Boston (and by way of a special trough into northern Vermont), with species closely allied to those of Europe. The southern part of the Appalachian Trough at the same time contained no *Paradoxides,* but was inhabited by genera that occur in the Cordilleran Trough and the Pacific realm.

The distinction between realms is equally clear and more striking when we come to the Late Cambrian and find the *Dikelocephalus* fauna spreading from the southwestern margin of the United States across Nevada, Texas, and Oklahoma, northward into Minnesota, and eastward into the Appalachian Trough, while in Europe the contemporaneous seas swarmed with the tribe of *Olenus,* another large-tailed form.

Within each great realm there are provinces less sharply isolated by differences in temperature, depth, facies, or salinity. Thus the modern fauna of the Florida coast is unlike that of New England or Labrador, and even the two sides of Florida have somewhat different assemblages. A very slight change in salinity makes a great difference in the richness of the faunas of Long Island Sound and the New Jersey coast. Likewise, changes in temperature, due to Cape Cod's deflection of the cold Labrador current from the coast, are responsible for a marked difference in the faunas of the eastern and southern coasts of New England. In the same way, an embayment from Hudson Bay would bring into the continent a very different life assemblage from that of a Gulf embayment, though both would have the general impress of the Atlantic realm.

During the early stages of any general submergence, we should, therefore, expect localized faunas in distinct embayments. Should two or more such embayments eventually unite, the faunas would mingle, a keen struggle between competing types would ensue, many species would become extinct, and the resultant fauna would take on a more cosmopolitan aspect. This was the case in Early and in Late Cambrian times. Many of the apparently sudden changes in the faunas of the geologic past probably mean not so much a break in time as a downbreaking of barriers and an ingress of migrants.

REFERENCES

1. Shand, S. J., 1938, *Earth-lore; geology without jargon,* 2nd ed. E. P. Dutton, New York, pp. 1–144.

2. Naumova, S. N., 1949, Spory nizhnego kembriya [Spores of the Lower Cambrian]. *Akad. Nauk USSR, Izv. Ser. Geol.,* no. 4, pp. 49–56. [In Russian]

3. Krystofovitch, A. N., 1953, Nakhodka Plaunobraznogo Rasteniya v kembrii vostochnoi Sibiri [Discovery of lycopodiaceous plants in the East-Siberian Cambrian]. *Akad. Nauk. USSR, Doklady,* vol. 91, pp. 1377–1379.

Le Clercq, S., 1956, Evidence of vascular plants in the Cambrian. *Evolution,* vol. 10, pp. 109–114.

4. Reitliger, E. A., 1948, Kembriiske foraminifera Yakutii [Cambrian foraminifera of Yakutsk]. *Moscow Soc. Naturalists, Bull.,* vol. 53, *Geol. Sec.,* vol. 23, pp. 77–81.

5. Sprigg, R. G., 1949, Early Cambrian "jellyfishes" of Ediacara, South Australia, and Mt. John, Kimberley District, Western Australia. *Royal Soc. S. Australia, Trans.,* vol. 73, pp. 72–88.

6. Hutchinson, G. E., 1930, Restudy of some Burgess shale fossils. *U.S. Nat. Museum, Proc.,* vol. 78, art. 11, 24 pages.

7. Brooks, W. K., 1894, The origin of the oldest fossils and the discovery of the bottom of the ocean. *Jour. Geol.,* vol. 2, pp. 455–479.

8. Daly, R. A., 1907, The limeless ocean of Pre-Cambrian time. *Amer. Jour. Sci., 4th Ser.,* vol. 23, pp. 93–115.

Trenton Gorge near Trenton Falls, New York. Here west Canada Creek descends over a series of falls revealing some 300 feet of thin bedded limestone. This is the type section of the Trenton limestone. This view shows the middle part of the section (Sherman Falls limestone). Within 40 miles to the east the equivalent beds are black shale (Fig. 107). (Carl O. Dunbar.)

Chapter 8. The Ordovician Period

Yes, small in size were most created things
And shells and corallines the chief of these.

T. A. CONRAD

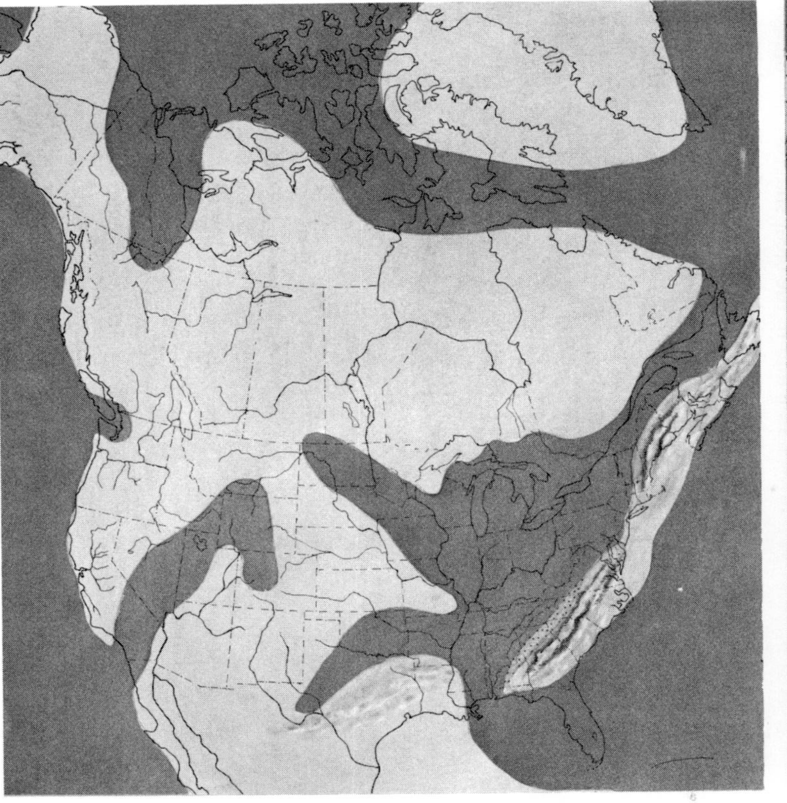

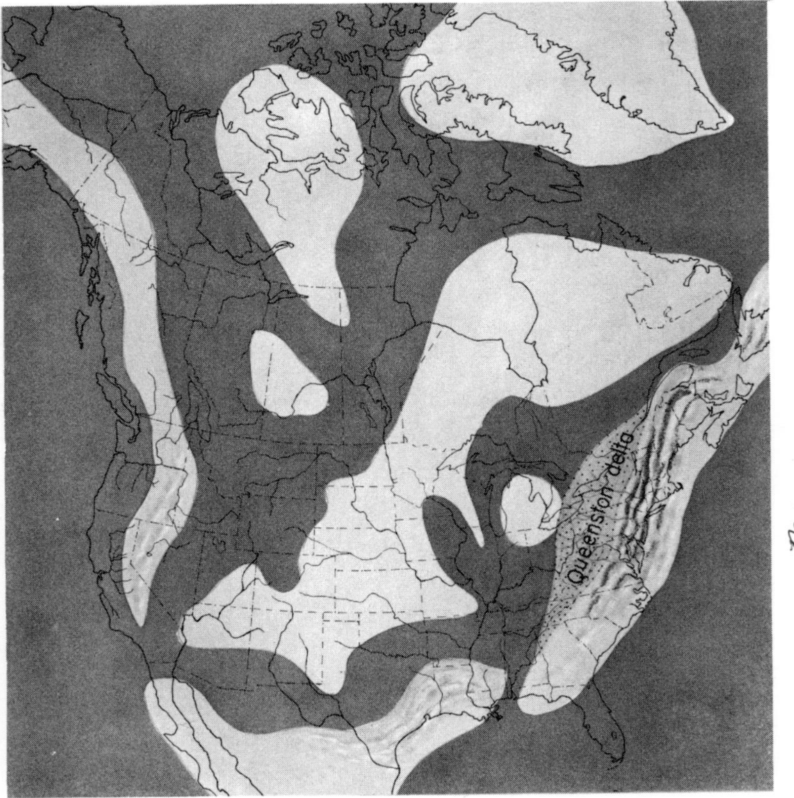

Figure 94. Ordovician paleogeography of North America. Left, maximum submergence during Middle Ordovician time; right, maximum submergence of Late Ordovician time. In the latter, note the Taconian Mountains, bordered on the west by the broad, low Queenston Delta.

Greatest of All Submergences. THE POST-Cambrian emergence was only temporary. The continent still lay but little above sealevel, and the Ordovician submergence brought marine waters creeping over the lowlands from east, west, north, and south in shallow epeiric seas that first flooded the geosynclines and eventually spread over much of the interior, covering at the maximum fully half of the present continent and reducing it to a group of great islands almost awash with the sea. No other submergence has been quite so extensive in North America.

Since the continent was so flat, gentle warping frequently altered the outlines of land and sea as the shorelines shifted back and forth; many maps would be required to present in detail the slow ebb and flow of the great inland seas. The two maps here presented (Fig. 94) indicate temporary stages in an ever-changing scene. The left shows the maximum submergence during Middle Ordovician time and the right the maximum Late Ordovician submergence.

The Early Ordovician submergence was about as extensive as the Middle and is recorded in widespread limestones and dolostones carrying similar or identical fossils across the continent, indicating that the seas were generally clear and shallow. In New England and the Maritime Provinces of Canada, however, thick deposits of dark shale with graptolite faunas indicate deeper water and higher land in the northern part of Appalachia. In Arkansas and Trans-Pecos Texas, likewise, graptolite-bearing slates and shales were formed by muds coming out of uplands that lay to the south—an old land mass known as Llanoria. And, finally, in the Beaverfoot-Brisco Range of British Columbia, similar thick dark shales are found, grading eastward into limestone and thus indicating a source in uplands farther west. From Pennsylvania southward to Alabama, however, the Lower Ordovician maintains its dolostone facies to the easternmost outcrops, indicating that the southern and central parts of the marginal land, Appalachia, were very low if not largely submerged.

Early in Middle Ordovician time, on the contrary, Appalachia began to rise, and mud was carried into the eastern part of the geosyncline all the way from Newfoundland to Alabama, forming thick deposits of dark shale that grade westward into limestones. For a time, uplift in the southern part of Appalachia was sufficient to provide sediment in sufficient volume to build a broad compound delta along the western flank of the highlands in Georgia and the Carolinas, pushing the shoreline westward. This has been called the **Blount Delta.** At this time an extensive sheet of sand (Bays formation) spread westward into eastern Tennessee, and two beds of volcanic ash near its top indicate that active volcanoes existed in the highlands to the east.

During Late Ordovician time uplift was progressive farther north along the whole of Appalachia, and a vast coastal lowland was formed along its western flank, finally pushing the shoreline back into Ohio and southern Ontario. This was the subaerial part of the vast **Queenston Delta** (Fig. 95). This progressive uplift in Appalachia was to culminate at the end of the period in the **Taconian Disturbance.**

Elsewhere the continent remained generally stable and in the clear shallow seas limestones were deposited widely across the United States and the Canadian Shield. An exception of some importance was an uplift in western Nevada (possibly extending northward into eastern Oregon and Washington) that had begun early in the period and continued intermittently during Ordovician time shedding detrital sediments into the sea that then covered parts of central and northwestern Nevada and southeastern Idaho. Here the Lower Ordovician dolostone facies grades northwestward into black graptolite-bearing shales, and the Middle Ordovician is represented by the Eureka quartzite.

Four Stable "Domes." In the midst of these extensive seaways four relatively small areas stood out as presistent lands. These were: (1) the **Ozark Dome** of southeastern Missouri, (2) the **Highlands of Wisconsin,** (3) the **Adirondack Dome** of northeastern New York, and (4) the **Cincinnati Arch,** with its southern extremity sometimes distinguished as the **Nashville Dome.** From the viewpoint of isostasy, each was a positive area tending to rise slightly as the surrounding regions subsided. Although none were highlands, all persisted as landmarks through-

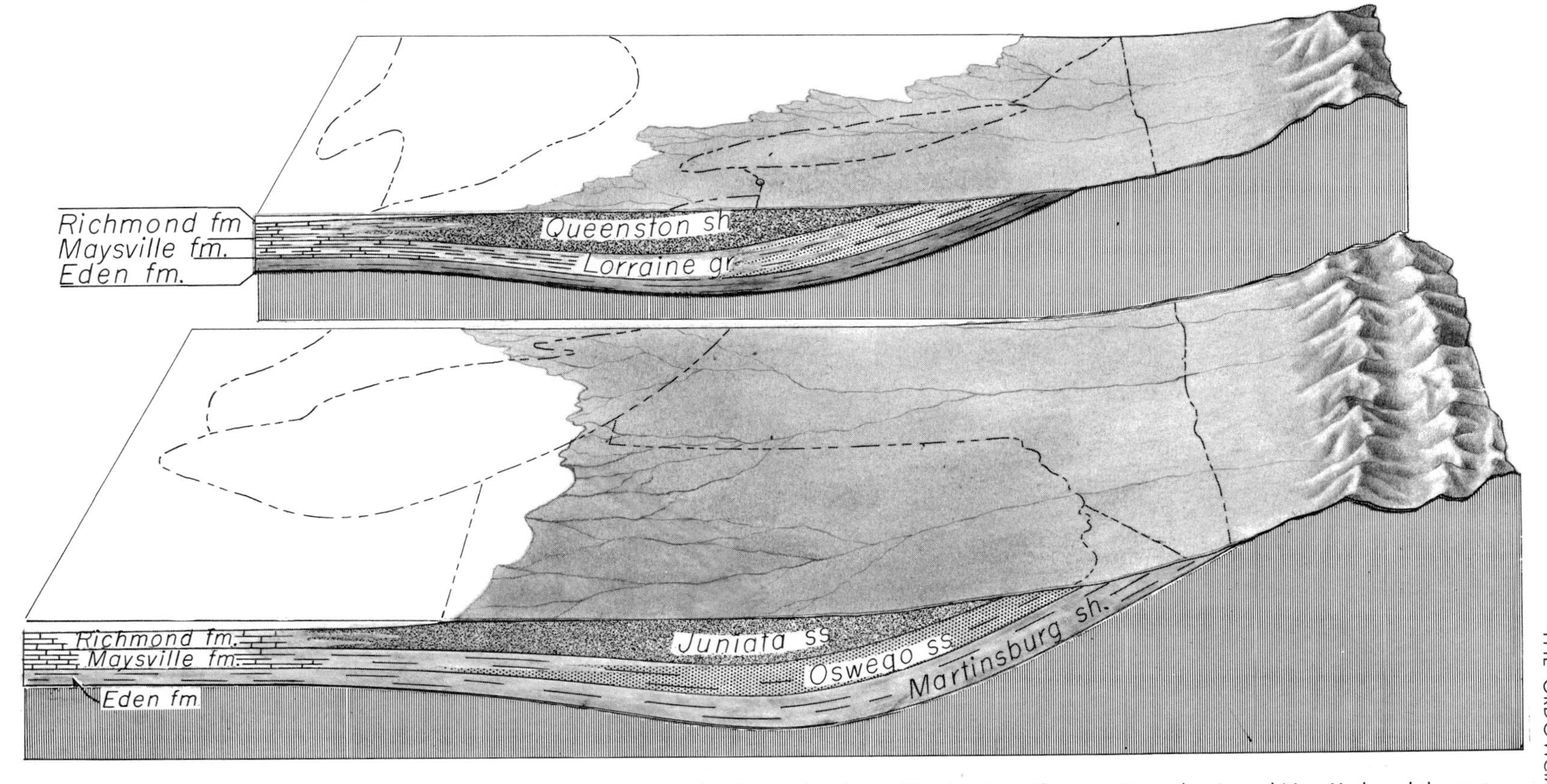

Figure 95. Block diagram of the Queenston Delta as it existed at the end of Ordovician time. The view is north across Pennsylvania and New York and the eastern part of the Great Lakes. The edge of the Taconian highlands is shown at the extreme right. The block has been parted along an east-west cut. Length of front face about 600 miles. Vertical scale greatly exaggerated but not uniform; the Eden, Maysville, and Richmond formations are relatively much thinner than represented.

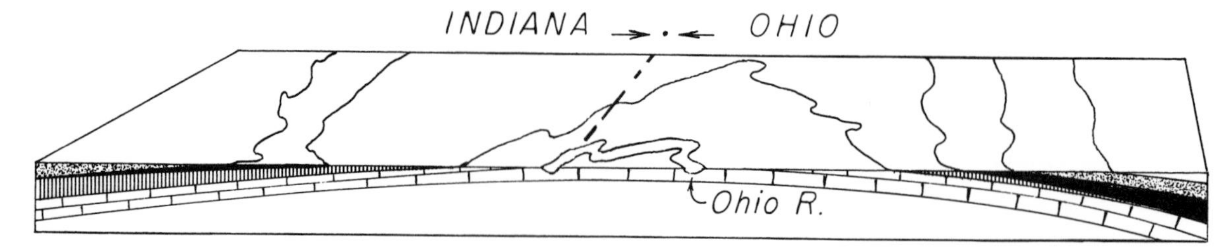

Figure 96. Block diagram showing in its front face an east-west section across the Cincinnati Arch near Cincinnati, Ohio. The Ordovician System is represented as limestone, the Silurian is vertically lined; the Devonian is black; and the Mississippian is stippled. (Adapted from a section by G. D. Hubbard.)

out most of Paleozoic time, flanked about by successive epeiric seas. They are now areas of relatively ancient rocks encircled by younger strata that dip gently away from the central area, and for this reason they are spoken of as **domes** or **arches** (Figs. 87 and 96).

The most significant of the four was the Cincinnati Arch, which ran northward from the vicinity of Nashville, Tennessee, through Cincinnati and western Lake Erie into Ontario, thus paralleling the western side of the Appalachian Geosyncline. At many times during the Paleozoic Era it served as a barrier separating the Appalachian seaways from those farther west. Even when partly submerged, it formed a threshold to limit the westward spread of detrital sediments derived from Appalachia.

The Cincinnati Arch was never mountainous, or even a highland, and it seems remarkable that a structure so broad and low should have been so persistent. It began to form during the Middle Ordovician, was definitely outlined in the Silurian, and was slightly emergent at different times during the remainder of the Paleozoic Era.

Temporary Emergences and the Subdivisions of the Period. Twice during the period there was gentle but apparently complete emergence of the continent. During these intervals the freshly formed sediments were exposed to erosion and locally more or less widely removed, though no folding or pronounced uplift distorted the exposed beds. At the same time crowding of the marine invertebrates occured upon the shallow continental shelves and more or less rapid evolution resulted as diverse emigrants from the epeiric seas were driven into competition. As a result, the following submergence in each instance brought into the new seaways immigrant faunas in which the species and many of the genera were unlike those of the previous invasion. Thus, as in the Cambrian, the Ordovician System of formations is divisible into three series, each separated from the next by a widespread (though not prolonged) stratigraphic break, and each marked by distinctive faunas.

The Early Ordovician has been named the **Canadian Epoch** for exposures in extreme southeastern Canada; the Middle Ordovician is known as the **Champlainian Epoch** for its striking development along the Champlain Valley; and the Late Ordovician has been called the **Cincinnatian Epoch** for exposures about Cincinnati, Ohio.

The system is exceptionally well displayed in New York State, where it was first comprehensively studied and classified. The succession of formations there exposed is therefore regarded as the **standard section**, with which others in America are compared. From this region also many of the Ordovician names are derived.

Taconian Disturbance and the Close of the Period. During the Ordovician Period Appalachia was rising again, at first slowly and then with acceleration. This, the Taconian Disturbance, culminated at the close of the period in a chain of fold mountains that extended from Newfoundland through the Maritime Provinces of Canada and New England and reached at least as far south as Alabama. It resulted in close folding and westward overthrusting of the older rocks that now occupy a disturbed belt along the south side of the St. Lawrence and the east side of the Hudson Valley (Fig. 94). Sir William Logan long ago recognized that a great thrust fault follows the St. Lawrence Valley, separating the intensely deformed rocks of its south shore from the relatively undisturbed ones on the north side. This dislocation has since become known as **Logan's line.** It was the locus of late Ordovician overthrusting (Fig. 97). South of New England the mountains were east of the modern Valley and Ridge Province in what is now the Piedmon. belt. Radioactive dating of the old rocks in the Piedmont indicate large scale igneous intrusions and strong metamorphism in late Ordovician time.[1]

The disturbance began early in the period with local warping in northern Vermont and spread northeastward into Quebec and Newfoundland, where submarine thrust faulting gave rise to talus and landslide deposits on the sea floor; these deposits are now preserved as limestone breccias, locally of great thickness and of remarkable coarseness (Fig. 98). Actually such movements had begun in western Newfoundland in Middle Cambrian time and continued intermittently through the Late Cambrian and then spread more widely during Early Ordovician time.[2] The regional uplift in northern Appalachia stimulated erosion and resulted in an enormous volume of detrital sediment being carried into the geosyncline. During the Early Ordovician, these sediments were mostly fine dark muds, but as uplift continued, they included more and more sand and gravel and finally culminated in thick sandstones and conglomerates of Late Ordovician age that spread widely over areas where limestone had previously been forming.

This **first generation** of Appalachians no longer exists as mountains. The highest peaks disappeared through erosion before half a geologic period had passed, and the late Silurian sea advanced over the peneplaned folds; but a record was left in (1) the unconformity between Ordovician and younger rocks in the disturbed area and (2) the coarse detrital sediments deposited in the geosyncline.

Most of New England and Maritime Canada suffered two later disturbances, one in the Devonian and another in the Permian, and these largely mask the results of the Taconian Disturbance; but in several places along the western margin of the disturbed belt, Ordovician formations can still be seen in folds truncated by erosion and overlain with striking unconformity by Silurian or younger beds. Fine examples may be observed along the Hudson Valley from Kingston to Catskill (Figs. 99 and 100). In eastern Quebec (Gaspé), also, the

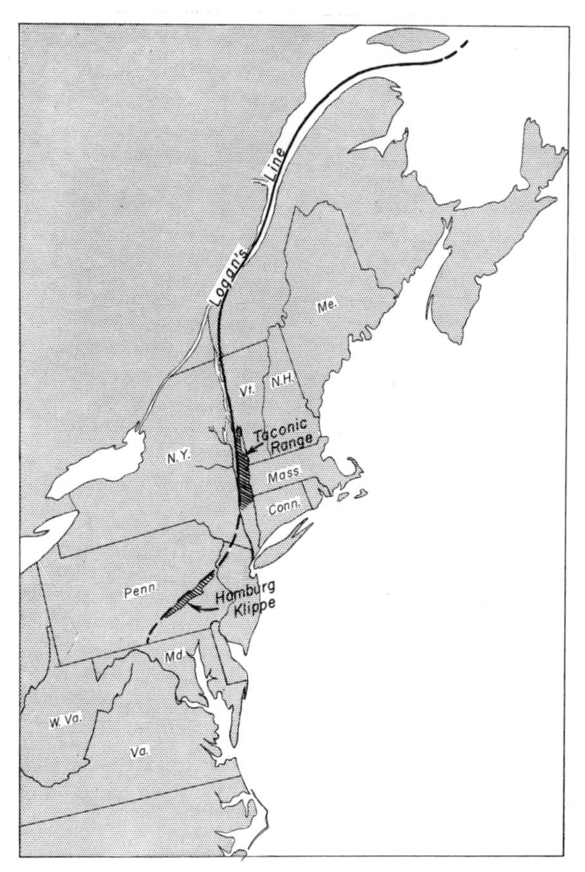

Figure 97. Logan's Line, a major belt of Late Ordovician thrust faulting to the east of which the Ordovician and older strata are intensely deformed. Immediately to the west of this line the structure remained simple until near the end of the Paleozoic Era.

Ordovician formations are much more metamorphosed and deformed than the Silurian, and commonly are overlain by the latter with angular discordance. These relations are well shown in the Matapedia Valley and farther east along the Bay of Chaleur.

Volcanic Activity. The Taconian Disturbance was accompanied by volcanic activity, the first recorded in this region since before the Cambrian. Local volcanoes were in eruption in early Middle Ordovician time, spreading ash falls over the Appalachian Geosyncline from Alabama to New York, and even as far west as Wisconsin, Minnesota, and Iowa. In central Pennsylvania, 14 such ash beds have been recognized, intercalated in Middle

Figure 98. Cow Head breccia, a talus deposit of limestone blocks formed along the front of a submarine thrust fault early in Middle Ordovician time. Cow Head Island, western Newfoundland. Hammer above center gives the scale. (Carl O. Dunbar.)

Figure 100. Unconformable contact of the late Silurian (Manlius) limestone on closely folded Middle Ordovician (Hudson River) shale at Becraft Mountain near Hudson, New York. Dotted line follows the contact. Dip and strike symbols indicate the bedding at two places in the crumpled shale. (Carl O. Dunbar.)

Ordovician marine limestones (4 in the Black River group and 10 in the Trenton group),[3] and in Alabama 2 are recognized. The ash beds vary in thickness up to more than 7 feet, but commonly are only a few inches thick. A basic lava flow is associated with one of the ash beds near Jonestown, Pennsylvania,[4] and pillow lava occurs in Middle Ordovician shales at Stark's Knob in eastern New York. The Ammonoosic volcanics of New Hampshire are also probably of this date. The greatest display of volcanic activity, however, is found farther to the northeast, in Quebec, where the **Mictaw group** is made up of shales and volcanic tuff of great but undetermined thickness. Eastern Newfoundland has tuff and pillow lavas interbedded with graptolite shales and fossiliferous limestones of Middle Ordovician age, and such volcanic rocks spread widely across the center of the island. Pillow lavas and agglomerate of great thickness are associated with the Ordovician sediments from Bay of Islands south to Port au Port Bay on the west coast of Newfoundland (Fig. 101).

Igneous and metamorphic rocks in the Piedmont of the southeastern states have long been attributed to Taconic orogeny, but their dates, which fall around 360,000,000 years, now indicate late Devonian time. Nevertheless, volcanic ash beds and thick detrital formations in the Ordovician of Tennessee and Alabama indicate disturbance farther east. Possibly its record in the Piedmont was eclipsed by the Devonian orogeny.

← Figure 99. Unconformable contact of upper Silurian (Manlius) limestone on Middle Ordovician (Hudson River) sandstone at the Alsen Quarry south of Catskill, New York. The Silurian beds strike N 35° E and dip 20° NW, whereas the Ordovician beds strike N 5° E and dip 55° E. (Chester R. Longwell.)

Figure 101. Thick lava flow in the Middle Ordovician sequence near the mouth of Fox Island River on the east coast of Port au Port Bay, western Newfoundland. (Carl O. Dunbar.)

CLIMATE

Few species of animals or plants now range from southern United States into Canada, and probably none save man and his dog range from the subtropics into arctic latitudes. Alligators and palms do not live in Greenland, nor musk-ox and walrus in Florida, for each is imprisoned by the limits of a definite climatic belt. Ordovician faunas, however, show little regard for latitude, many of the same species occuring in Kentucky, southern Ontario, the Mackenzie Valley, and northern Greenland. In the Upper Ordovician limestones there are small coral reefs widely distributed throughout arctic Canada, from Manitoba to Alaska and northern Greenland, all made of a few common species some of which occur also in Wyoming and New Mexico. We cannot escape the conclusion, therefore, that climatic zones were less marked then than now, and that arctic America was not ice-bound at that time. The wide distribution of vast limestones and dolostones bears the same implication, for if parts of the oceans had been much warmer than others, they would have been the chief places of limestone deposition.

Tillites in the Varangerfjord region of northern Norway, long thought to be probably of Ordovician age, are now thought to be Precambrian.[5]

NATURE AND DISTRIBUTION OF THE ORDOVICIAN ROCKS

Canadian Formations. The Lower Ordovician strata present two strikingly different facies (lithologic expressions), the one of dark shale, rich in graptolites, and the other of dolostone with limy-shelled fossils.

The dark-shale facies occurs to the south of the St. Lawrence River all the way from Gaspé to Quebec City, and thence southward on both flanks of the Notre Dame and Green mountains through Vermont and eastern New York to New Jersey. It represents the fine dark mud derived from Appalachia and deposited in quiet, stagnant water along the eastern margin of the Appalachian Geosyncline. The presence of the four-branched graptolite genus, *Tetragraptus* (Fig. 102), distinguishes it readily from similar but younger shales, and at the same time shows a close connection with similar deposits of the same age in western Europe.

These dark strata are the **Deepkill shales,** so named for a locality in New York but also widely recognized elsewhere in eastern North America. Throughout eastern Quebec they bear a number of interbedded layers or lenses of limestone breccia that have been the object of much speculation. The limestone fragments are angular and show no bedded arrangement or size sorting, yet their fossils indicate that some were derived from Lower Cambrian formations, others from Upper Cambrian beds, and the majority from Lower Ordovician formations only a little older than the enclosing shales. Since the fragments are not rounded, they could not have suffered long transportation, and since they were derived from formations of widely different ages, ordinary erosional processes could not have brought them together. In Newfoundland thick and very coarse breccias of this type have been found actually associated with submarine thrust faults where they accumulated as talus or landslide deposits in front of the overthrust masses. Probably the breccias in Quebec also owe their origin to thrust faulting, either on the sea floor or in adjacent Appalachia.

Chart 2. Correlation of important Ordovician sections

Series	Stages	Utah–Nevada	Okla. (Arbuckle)	Mo. (Ozarks)	Tenn. Nashville	Ohio Cincinnati	Tenn. (eastern)	Virginia	Penn. (Central)	New York	Stages	Series
Cincinnatian	Richmond		Sylvan sh. Fernvale	Girardeau Orchard C. Fernvale	Sequatchie ls.	Richmond: Elkhorn Saluda Liberty Waynesb. Arnheim	Sequatchie fm.	Sequatchie fm.	Juniata ss.		Richmond	Cincinnatian
Cincinnatian	Maysv.	Fish Haven dol. Hansen ls.			Liepers ls.	Maysv.: Mt. Auburn Corryville Bellevue Fairmont Mt. Hope	Martinsburg sh	Martinsburg sh.	Bald Eagle	Oswego ss. Pulaski ss.	Maysv.	Cincinnatian
Cincinnatian	Eden	Fish Haven dol. Hansen ls.			Inmans ls.	Eden: McMick. Southgate Economy Fulton	Martinsburg sh	Martinsburg sh.	Reedsville sh.	Whetstone Gulf sh.	Eden	Cincinnatian
Champlainian	Trentonian	Eureka qtz.	Viola ls.	Kimmswick ls. Decorah	Catheys ls. Bigby ls. Hermitage Carters ls.	Cynthiana (not exposed)	Chickamauga ls. Martinsburg sh	Eggleston ls. Moccasin f.	Antes sh Coburn ls. Salona ls. Nealmont ls.	Atwater Cr. sh. Cobourg ls. Sherman F. ls. Kirkfield ls. Rockland ls. Normanskill sh.	Trentonian	Champlainian
Champlainian	Black R.		Bromide ls. (Simpson gr.)	Plattin gr.	Lebanon Ridley ls. Pierce ls. Murfrees.	(not exposed)	Chickamauga ls. Bays Ottosee Sevier Athens	Witten fm. Gratton ls. Ben Bolt ls. Peery ls. Ward Cove ls.	Hunter ls. Hatter ls.	Chaumont ls. Lowville ls. Pamelia ls. Normanskill sh.	Black R.	Champlainian
Champlainian	Chazyan	Swan Pk.	Simpson gr.: Tulip Cr. McLish Oil Cr. Joins	Joachim St. Peter ss. Everton	(not exposed)	(not exposed)	Lenoir ls.	Lincolnshire ls. Elway ls. Blackford ls.	Loysburg ls.	Valcour ls. Crown Pt. ls. Day Pt. ls. Deepkill sh.	Chazyan	Champlainian
Canadian		Garden City ls. Pogonip ls.	West Spr. Creek ls. Kindblade ls. Cool Cr. ls. McKenzie Hill ls.	Black Rock Smithville Powell Cotter Jeff. City Roubidoux Gasconade	(not exposed)	(not exposed)	Knox dol.: Mascot dol. Kingsport dol. Longview dol. Chepultepec dol.	Knox dol.: Mascot dol. Kingsport dol. Longview dol. Chepultepec dol.	Bellefonte Axeman ls. Nittany dol. Stonehenge ls. Larke dol.	Beekmantown dol. Tribes Hill ls. Deepkill sh.		Canadian

Figure 102. Characteristic Lower Ordovician graptolites on a slab of black shale. Such four-branched colonies belong to the genus *Tetragraptus*. Lower Ordovician, Levis, Quebec. (Yale Peabody Museum.)

The Deepkill shale is now limited to the country south and east of Logan's line and cannot now be traced into calcareous deposits of the same age. Immediately to the northwest of this disturbed zone, the Lower Ordovician is well developed but in a dolostone facies that extends down the Appalachian Trough from Quebec City through the Champlain Valley into New York and Pennsylvania and thence to Virginia and Alabama. In this trough it ranges from about 1,500 to more than 4,000 feet thick and is divisible into numerous formations that bear local names. The dolostone is light gray in color and has several peculiarities. At various horizons the beds are mudcracked, indicating that the sea floor was repeatedly exposed. In many places thin polygons loosened by the desiccation cracks were swept together by returning currents to form lenses of "edgewise conglomerate." Reefs formed by the calcareous alga, *Cryptozoön,* are very common and widely distributed (Fig. 103), but other fossils are as a rule extremely rare. There is almost no detrital material. Quite clearly it is a marine deposit, yet the water was extremely shallow and the sea floor was frequently exposed over wide areas. Similar deposits in Oklahoma, Texas, and New Mexico indicate a remarkable extent of the same peculiar environment. In the Ozark region, and from there northward into Minnesota, the Canadian formations are likewise predominantly of dolostone and bear abundant *Cryptozoön* deposits.

In the Canadian Rockies both the graptolitic and the dolomitic facies are well shown, the latter represented in the center of the geosyncline by cherty limestone and dolostone (Sarbach formation), which, farther west, near the old shoreline of Cascadia, grade over into gray and black shales (Glenogle formation) carrying the *Tetragraptus* fauna.

Post-Canadian Emergence. Nowhere in North America is there any evidence of transition strata from the Canadian into the Champlainian. There is a complete break here, which means that the whole continent was dry land for a long time. How long cannot be told, but the marked difference between the faunas of the Canadian and the Champlainian indicates a considerable lapse of time. It is for this reason that some stratigraphers have been inclined to regard the Canadian as a distinct period.

Champlainian Formations. The Middle Ordovician formations generally present a contrast with the rocks below, being mostly limestone and calcareous shale instead of dolostone. However, along the eastern border of the old Appalachian Geosyncline they also present a black-shale facies all the way from New York to Alabama. Local names are used for the whole or various parts of this facies in different regions, but they refer to parts of a continuous belt of dark shales and represent the fine mud eroded from Appalachia and deposited near the shore while limestones were forming farther west. This is the lower part of the Martinsburg shale* of the "slate belt" of New Jersey and the central Appalachian region and the equivalent Normanskill and Canajoharie shales of New York.

Between Albany and Utica, New York, the bluffs of the Mohawk Valley show a complete lateral gradation from flaggy sandstone (Schenectady flags) (Fig. 108) through black shale (Canajoharie) (Fig. 107) into the Trenton limestone (Figs. 105 and 106) as represented in Figure 104.[6] To the south in the Appalachian Trough the same relation exists between the lower part of the Martinsburg shale and the Mid-Ordovician limestones farther west (Fig. 109). Since the shales and limestone interfinger in a broad transition zone, it is evident that they are of the same age and were formed in an open seaway with no barrier between, the mud settling near shore and the purer, limy sediment farther out. It is interesting to note that the upper

*Black shales of Lower Ordovician age have also been erroneously embraced in the Martinsburg in places in the central Appalachian region.

Figure 103. Surface of a Cryptozoon reef in the St. George dolostone (Lower Ordovician) near Port au Port, western Newfoundland. The bed is tilted to the right by post-Ordovician deformation. (Carl O. Dunbar.)

Oswego
Rome
Utica
Little Falls
Canajoharie
Amsterdam
Schenectady
Probable surface at close of Lorraine deposition
Oswego sandstone
Lorraine sandstone
Appalachian Geosyncline
Utica shale
Trenton limestone
Black River limestone
Adirondack Arch
Canajoharie shale
Schenectady flags
Black River ls.
0 25 50
Scale in miles
Vt.
N.H.
N.Y.
Mass.
Penn.
A.
B.

Figure 104. Idealized section across central eastern New York showing changes of facies in the Middle and Upper Ordovician formations resulting from progressive uplift in Appalachia. The Adirondack Arch extending southward from the Adirondack Dome formed a peninsula in the Middle Ordovician sea during the early part of the Champlain Epoch preventing the westward spread of mud and sand beyond the geosyncline. It was submerged after middle Trenton time and black mud then spread rapidly across central New York. As Appalachia continued to rise, sands also spread farther and farther, reaching into western New York by the middle of the Late Ordovician Epoch. The Lorraine sandstone is marine, but the Oswego sandstone is largely fluvial, proving that the shoreline by this time had been pushed westward beyond Oswego. Vertical scale greatly exaggerated. (Data from papers by Marshall Kay.)

Figure 105 and chapter opening. Trenton Gorge near Trenton Falls, New York. Here west Canada Creek descends over a series of falls revealing some 300 feet of thin bedded limestone. This is the type section of the Trenton limestone. This view shows the middle part of the section (Sherman Falls limestone). Within 40 miles to the east the equivalent beds are black shale (Figure 107). (Carl O. Dunbar.)

Figure 106. Typical outcrop of Trenton limestone in Trenton Gorge. (Carl O. Dunbar.)

Figure 107. Type section of the Canajoharie black shale above the dam on Canajoharie Creek at Canajoharie, New York. Equivalent beds in the limestone facies are shown in Figure 105. (Carl O. Dunbar.)

shales spread more and more to the west at the expense of the limestone. This shows that Appalachia was already beginning to rise in Middle Ordovician time and was being stripped of its old mantle, which was carried into the Appalachian seaway in ever-increasing volume.

West of this shale belt the Middle Ordovician is generally limestone throughout the eastern United States, tending to pass locally into dolostone in the upper Mississippi Valley. Two stages are widely recognized, the older (Chazyan) being named for classical exposures in the Champlain Valley of New York, and the younger (Mohawkian) for the extensive display along the Mohawk Valley.

Cincinnatian Formations. Throughout the eastern United States the Upper Ordovician formations show a further change from limestone to shales and sandstone, reflecting the progressive uplift in Appalachia. At the beginning of the epoch mud swept westward as far as Cincinnati, forming black shales in the Appalachian Trough and bluish calcareous shales farther west. While shales and thin-bedded limestone continued to form in the longitude of Cincinnati, the sediments to the east became coarser and coarser, finally passing into conglomerates and non-marine sandstones.

The Queenston Delta. These higher Ordovician sediments of New York and Pennsylvania represent part of a large delta formed on the west side of Appalachia, as shown in Figure 95. During the first half of the epoch the landward part of the delta was very small, and the sediments were largely, if not entirely, marine. As erosion increased in rising Appalachia, however, the shoreline was crowded gradually westward until a low delta plain stretched from the foothills to beyond the region of Niagara. As the region of deposition was slowly subsiding, sediments accumulated over the landward front of the delta as well as over its submerged portion. Those in the former region, under the climatic environment then obtaining, were largely oxidized to a red color, while the submarine sediments turned gray. Thus the barren, red Queenston shales (now exposed in the base of the lower gorge of Niagara) are contemporaneous with fossiliferous Richmond beds of the Lake Huron and Cincinnati regions. Irregular subsidence and building at the delta front caused a to-and-fro migration of the shoreline as the deposits grew, and as a result the Queenston and Richmond formations interfinger over a broad transition zone in Ontario.

Dolostones of the Cordilleran and Arctic Regions. Beyond the limits reached by the sediments from Appalachia, the seas were generally clear, for the western lands remained low. As a result, the Upper Ordovician is represented throughout the Rocky Mountain region and arctic Canada by a remarkably widespread and homogeneous formation of massive, cliff-forming dolostone. In the northern Rockies of the United States, this is known as the Bighorn dolostone (Fig. 110). It is recognized under local names from northern Mexico to Alaska and northwestern Greenland, and, strangely, over this vast area it seldom exceeds a thickness of 300 feet. Its fauna is everywhere much the same, consisting of corals, cephalopods, and large gastropods.

Figure 108. Thin bedded sandstone (Schenectady flags) one mile south of Sloansville, New York. This is the sandy facies of Trenton age. For relations of Trenton limestone, Canajoharie shale, and Schenectady flags see Figure 104. (Carl O. Dunbar.)

MINERAL RESOURCES

Petroleum and Natural Gas. The discovery of petroleum, just before the days of the Civil War, marked the beginning of an industry that was destined to change the course of civilization, for it led to the perfection of the internal-combustion engine and made feasible the automobile, the airplane, and other miracles of our modern age.

The first oil well was driven in Devonian rocks in Pennsylvania in 1859, and Ohio followed with a "pioneer well" in 1883 that tapped the Trenton limestone at a depth of more than 1,000 feet and produced a heavy flow of gas. This was followed by the rapid exploitation of a large oil field on the Wabash arch in northwestern Ohio (Lima field) that derived both oil and gas from Middle Ordovician strata. Between the years 1886 and 1900 it was one of the major American oil fields; later the production greatly declined, and for some years Ordovician rocks were not important producers.

Since 1920 the Ordovician rocks under the Mid-Continent oil fields have assumed great importance in Oklahoma and northern Texas. The earlier production in this region had been from younger strata, chiefly Pennsylvanian, but with deeper drilling the Wilcox sand of Ordovician age has proved to be the greatest producer in the region, and in several fields, such as that of the Oklahoma City pool, has given rise to spectacular gushers and phenomenal production.

Building Stone. Most of the slate produced in America comes from the great shale belt of Ordovician rocks discussed above. The fine muds spread here in Ordovician time were in places so squeezed and metamorphosed by later disturbances that they developed a perfect slaty cleavage. The thicker and more homogeneous beds are quarried and split into shingles for roofing, or slabs for electrical switchboards, or for other industrial uses. A very large proportion (about 80 percent) of the

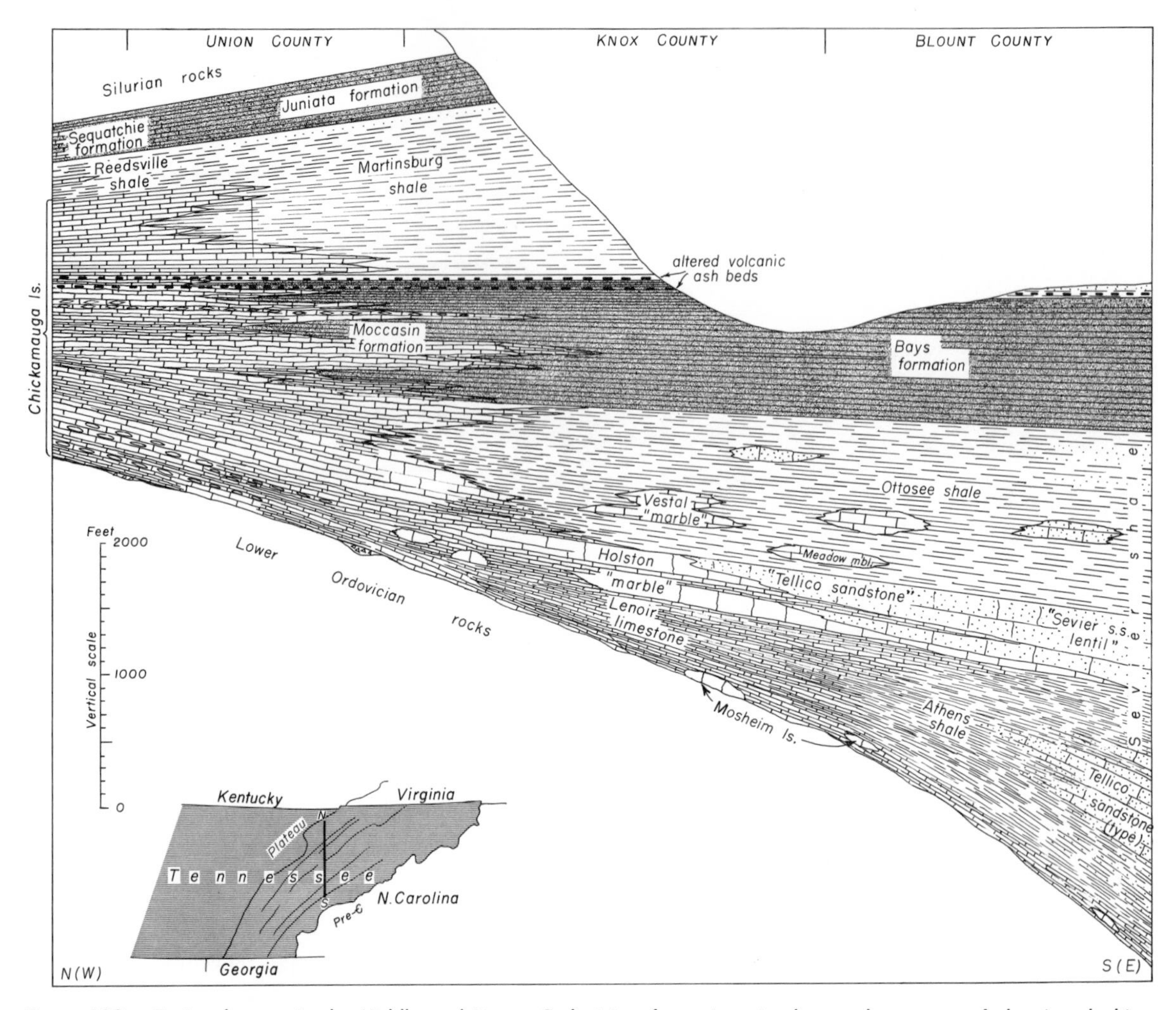

Figure 109. Facies changes in the Middle and Upper Ordovician formations in the southern part of the Appalachian region. This section in Eastern Tennessee shows the predominance of detrital deposits on the southeast, intertonging with and grading laterally into limestones along the northwestern side of the geosyncline. The dark shading of the Bays, Moccasin, and Juniata formations denotes red color. (Adapted from a figure by John Rodgers.)

material quarried is not suitable for the market, and the mountainous piles of refuse in the slate belt form an imposing monument to the industry. The chief producing states are Pennsylvania, Vermont, New York, and Virginia. In 1939 more than 531,380 tons of slate were produced, with a market value in excess of $6,680,000. More than nine-tenths of this slate was of Ordovician age. During the war years the use of roofing slate declined, but industrial uses increased. The value of slate products reached an all-time high of $15,000,000 in 1950 but has steadily declined since then, and was less than $6,000,000 in 1956.

Limestones and **dolostones** of Ordovician and Late Cambrian age, widely spread in the great Appalachian Valley, serve so many uses that their aggregate value would be difficult to estimate. Besides furnishing constructional stone for local use, they are crushed for road metal, burnt for lime to use as fertilizer, whitewash, or mortar, used for flux in the reduction of iron ores, or mixed with shales in the manufacture of cement.

It is a striking fact that most of the **marble** quarried in the United States for interior decoration and finish trim is of Ordovician age. The greatest quarries are near Rutland, in south-central Ver-

Figure 110. Bighorn Canyon opposite the mouth of Big Bull Elk Creek, Bighorn County, Montana. The Bighorn dolostone, about 145 feet thick, forms the spur in the foreground and the lower cliff in the distant canyon wall. The underlying Deadwood sandstone and shale is of Cambrian age. The Madison limestone, about 735 feet thick, forms the upper cliff and is of Mississippian age. Shale of probable Devonian age forms the slope between the Bighorn and the Madison cliffs. (U.S. Geological Survey.)

Figure 111. Entrance to a marble quarry at Proctor, Vermont. Similar quarries in west central Vermont follow the steeply dipping beds of pure white marble to depths as great as 300 feet. The marble is of Middle Ordovician age. (Chester R. Longwell.)

mont, where immense underground mines produce most of the "American Carrara" (Figs. 111, 112). Although the stone is of Ordovician age, its metamorphism from limestone to marble was accomplished by orogeny that came later. Pink and red marbles are secured from the Middle Ordovician of eastern Tennessee, and black marble from Isle La Motte in Lake Champlain. Such colored marbles are used for interior rather than exterior decoration since they fade to a dirty gray when exposed to the weather. In the normal prewar years the annual production of Ordovician marbles exceeded $5,000,000 in value.

Ore Deposits. The chief metalliferous deposits of Ordovician age are the sedimentary iron ores of Belle Isle in eastern Newfoundland. Here the Lower Ordovician strata include six zones of red oölitic hematite that range from a few inches to 50 feet in thickness. The mines now extend under the sea. The annual output averages over 1,000,000 tons.

Lead and zinc ores occur in the Middle Ordovician dolostone in Wisconsin and northwestern Illinois, but since they were formed during a later geologic age, they hardly deserve discussion in the history of this period.

LIFE OF ORDOVICIAN TIME

Primitive Fishes, a Prophecy of Higher Types of Life. The shallow seas remained the chief arena of life as another geologic period drew to a close, for the Ordovician has yielded no proven record of either land animals or land plants. At three widely spaced localities in the Cordilleran region, however, middle Champlainian rocks bear the petrified bony armor plates of very primitive fishes. The first locality to be discovered is in the Harding sandstone near Canyon City, Colorado, whence Walcott announced the finding of fish remains in 1891. The same horizon has since yielded similar fossils in the Bighorn Mountains and in the Black Hills. Another genus was described in 1958 from the Upper Ordovician rocks on the east flank of the Bighorn Mountains.[7] In all these localities the bony plates are fragmentary and show little of the size or character of their owners, but a comparison with well-preserved remains found elsewhere in Late Silurian and Devonian rocks shows clearly that they represent the order of fishes known as the **Ostracodermi** (Figs. 113 and 114). Strange as these fish look, they are yet related to living hagfishes (cyclostomes). From their fragmental nature and their occurrence in cross-bedded sandstone, it seems probable that they inhabited fresh waters, and after death were drifted by the rivers and broken up before arriving in the marine sediments of the littoral zone. As the most ancient relic of vertebrate life they foretell the coming dominance of higher animals—a prophecy that had to wait another geologic period for its fulfillment!

Continued Dominance of Marine Invertebrates. The shallow marine waters of Ordovician times swarmed with a rich variety of invertebrate animals. Although the stocks represented in the Cambrian still held the field, a number of new classes sprang rapidly into prominence, notably the graptolites, true corals, crinoids, bryozoa, and clams (Plates 4 and 5).

The dolostones so widely formed during Early Ordovician time lost the majority of their fossils during deposition as a result of the diagenetic change from calcareous to dolomitic sediment. In the dolostones the fossils most commonly seen are thick-shelled gastropods and cephalopods and *Cryptozoön* algal reefs.

The widespread, limy formations of the Middle Ordovician contain a more complete record of contemporaneous life than any other group of the Paleozoic rocks. More than 2,600 species are known from the Champlainian rocks of North America alone. The host of bryozoans, limy-shelled brachiopods, and crinoids leaves a striking impress on these faunas. Cephalopods and trilo-

Figure 112. Arlington Memorial Amphitheatre in the National Cemetery near Washington, D.C. This and many other monuments in our national capital are made of Vermont marble. (Vermont Marble Company.)

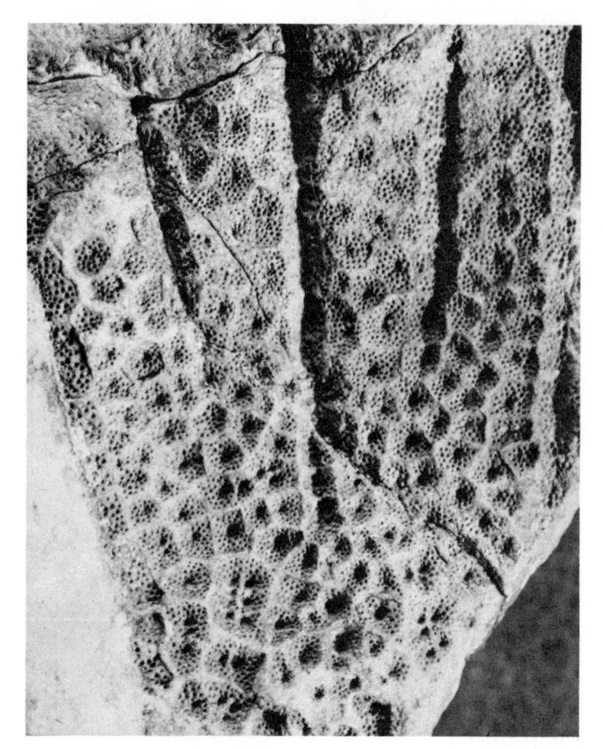

Figure 113. Fragment of bony armor of the oldest known fish, *Astrapsis desiderata,* from the Harding sandstone at Canyon City, Colorado. (W. L. Bryant.)

bites still held a prominent position, and the first true corals made their appearance. During this epoch a straight-shelled cephalopod, *Endoceras proteiforme,* attained the greatest size of any creature of the early Paleozoic world, its chambered shell exceeding a length of 15 feet with a diameter at the front of about 10 inches.

The upper Ordovician faunas resemble those of the Champlainian in general features, though they are neither so prolific nor so abundant in the muddy and sandy formations of the Appalachian Trough nor in the dolostones of the West and the North. In the Cincinnati region, however, the profusion and wonderful preservation of the Late Ordovician life have been an inspiration to amateur collectors and professional geologists as well.

Geographical Restrictions of the Faunas. Faunal realms and provinces existed in Ordovician time as in the Cambrian or the Present, each of the oceans having certain genera and species of its own, notwithstanding a world-wide similarity in the types of life. It is possible thus to distinguish embayments of Atlantic, Arctic, or Pacific source. Some of the faunas of extreme eastern North America likewise show much closer affinity to faunas of Europe than to those of interior North America, which were closer geographically but occupied a distinct embayment. Of course, when the interior seas became as extensive as they were in Middle and Late Ordovician time, the animals from different provinces could migrate and mingle freely until the faunas became nearly cosmopolitan.

Another type of faunal restriction is seen in the

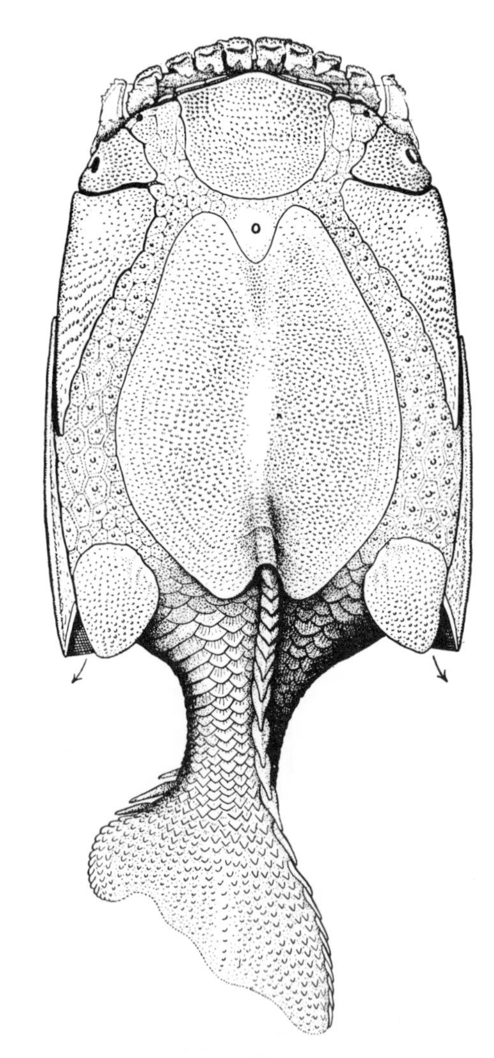

Figure 114. An ostracoderm fish, *Drepanaspis,* from the Lower Devonian beds of Germany. Length about 9 inches. The Ordovician genus *Astraspis* (Figure 113) is believed to have resembled this later and better known genus. (After Patten.)

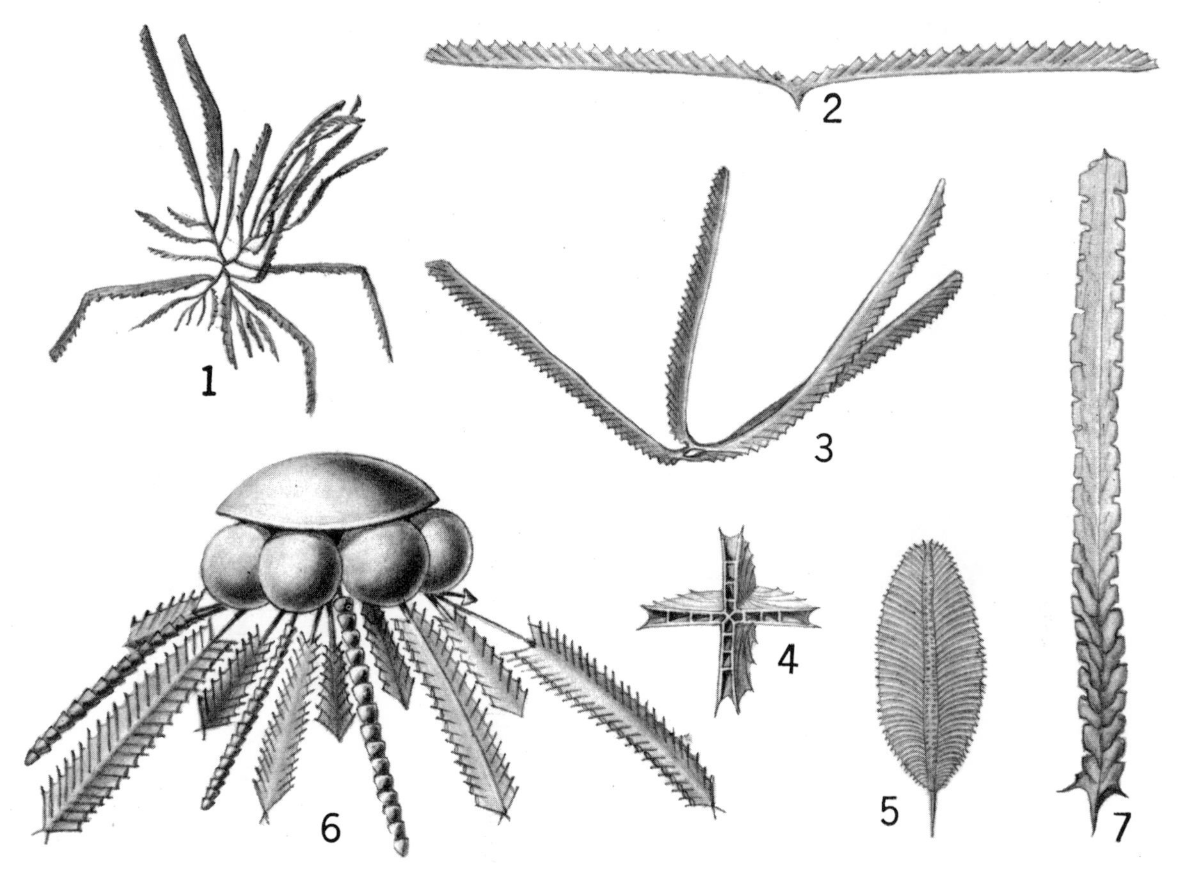

Figure 115. Ordovician graptolites. 1, *Clonograptus flexilis*, a colony of many branches; 2, *Didymograptus nitidus*, a two-branched colony; 3, *Tetragraptus serra*, a four-branched colony; 4, 5, *Phyllograptus typus*, a leaf-shaped colony in cross section and lateral views; 6, *Diplograptus pristis*, a complex colony with float and reproductive pouches; 7, *Climacograptus modestus* (lower part normal, upper part flattened). Slightly enlarged.

striking contrast between contemporaneous faunas of black shale and limestone. The black shales are the deposits of foul, stagnant mud bottoms upon which but few types of animals could live. As a result their fossils are chiefly the floating graptolites, along with small phosphatic brachiopods which may have been attached to seaweed, the mud-loving brachiopod *Lingula*, and the chambered shells of cephalopods which probably floated after death. Certain types of trilobites are also abundant. On the other hand, we find here none of the corals, bryozoa, limy-shelled brachiopods, clams, or gastropods which dwelled of necessity upon a solider and cleaner sea floor, and which made up the faunas now preserved in the limestones and calcareous shales.

This should not be surprising, for the modern sea floors show equally marked local faunas separated only by differences in the bottom environment. The Bay of Naples, for example, includes a limy shoal known as "Pigeon Bank" which is surrounded by slightly deeper water with a soft mud bottom. Here there are known 341 species of shell-bearing invertebrates (capable of fossilization) of which 296 are restricted to the limy shoal and 31 to the mud bottom. An additional 14 species live on both. A group of animals adapted thus to life on a restricted type of sea floor will, of course, be limited to a distinct type or facies of the sediments, and is therefore known as a **facies fauna.** It is evident that the fauna of a Lower Ordovician black shale will show more general resemblance to that of another black shale of Middle or Upper Ordovician age than to a lime-

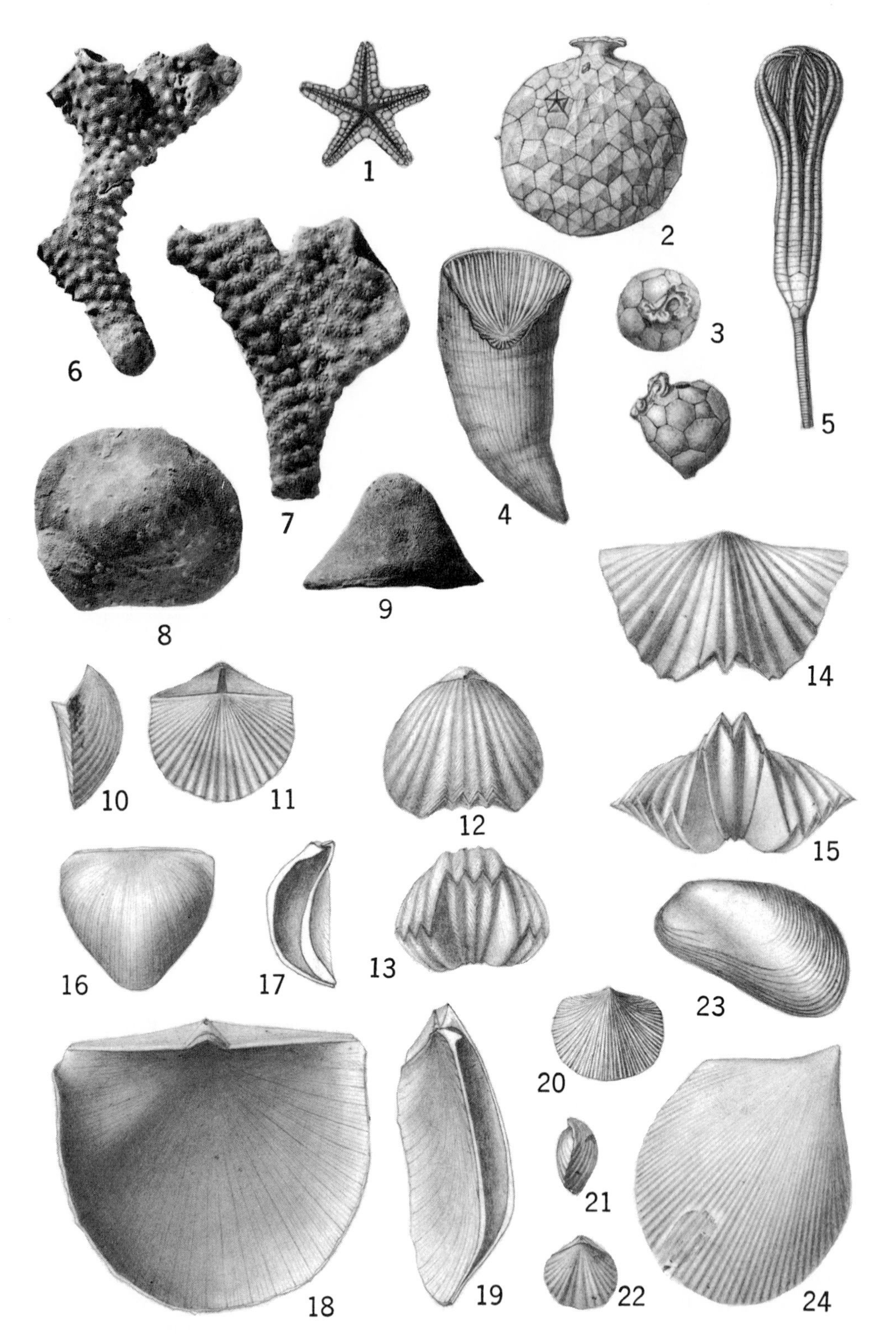

Plate 4. Ordovician Echinoderms (1–3, 5), Coral (4), Bryozoa (6–9), Brachiopods (10–22), and Pelecypods (23–24).

Figure 1, *Hudsonaster narrawayi*, one of the oldest known starfish; 2, 3, the cystoids *Echinosphaerites aurantium* and *Malocystites emmonsi* (upper and side views); 4, *Streptelasma rusticum*; 5, the crinoid *Ectenocrinus grandis*; 6, *Hallopora ramosa* (fragment of a stemlike colony); 7, *Constellaria florida*; 8, 9, *Prasopora simulatrix* (summit and lateral views); 10, 11, *Hesperorthis tricenaria*; 12, 13, *Rhynchotrema capax*; 14, 15, *Platystrophia laticosta*; 16, 17, *Strophomena nutans*; 18, 19, *Rafinesquina alternata* (19, section to show flat living chamber); 20, *Resserella meeki*; 21, 22, *Zygospira modesta*; 23, *Modiolopsis concentrica*; 24, *Byssonychia radiata*. All natural size. Drawings by L. S. Douglass.

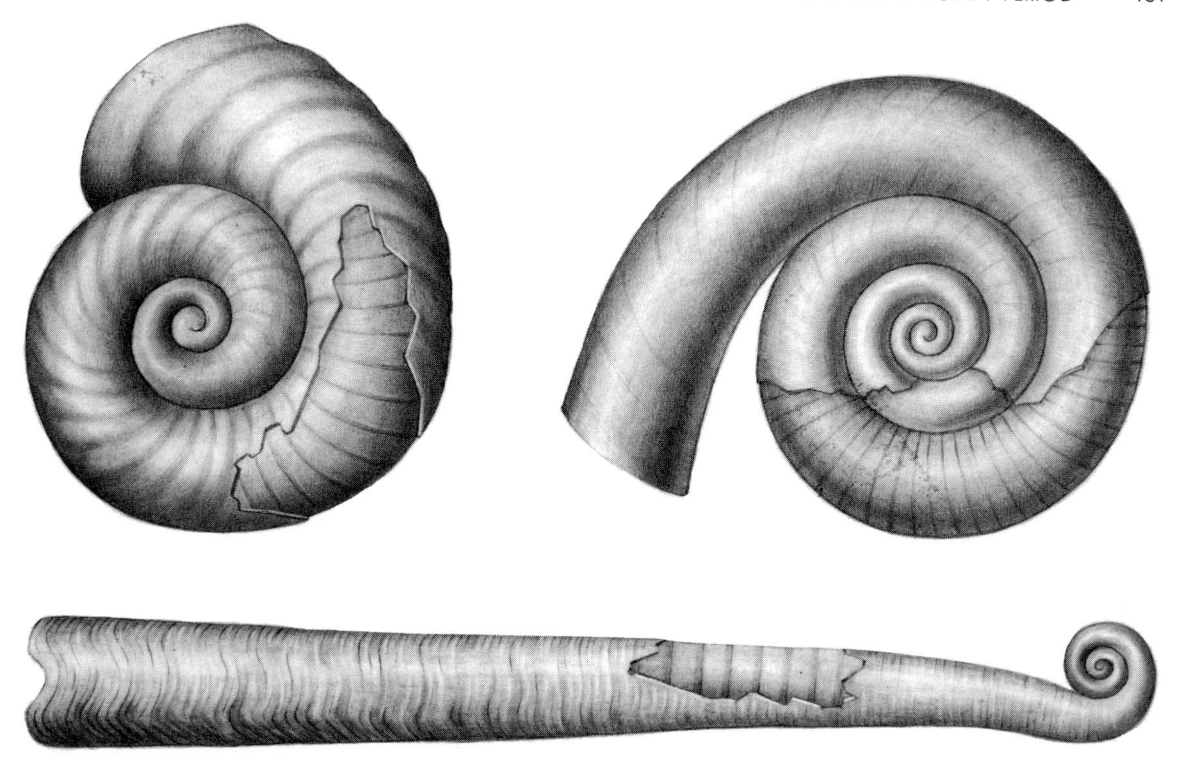

Figure 116. Ordovician cephalopods. Upper left, *Plectoceras occidentale;* upper right, *Schroederoceras eatoni;* lower, *Lituites lituus.* In each specimen a part of the shell is broken away to show the sutures where the septa between chambers joined the shell. About natural size.

stone fauna of its own time. Only the interfingering of the faunas and the sediments where one grades laterally into the other will show the equivalence of dissimilar but contemporaneous facies faunas.

Résumé of the Invertebrate Hosts. Neither Protozoa nor sponges are important in the Ordovician rocks, though both are represented.

The most distinctive animals of the time were the **graptolites,** which became immensely common at the very beginning of the period (Fig. 115). The majority of these were floating creatures, and therefore of world-wide distribution, drifting freely across the open oceans. *Phyllograptus* and *Tetragraptus,* the distinctive genera of the Lower Ordovician black shales, have been found in Canada, the United States, Scandinavia, Wales, Belgium, France, Peru, Bolivia, Australia, and New Zealand. Successive zones characterized by different generic types are of widespread occurrence and form one of our most exact means of determining the equivalence of rocks in widely separated regions.

True **corals** appeared near the very base of the Middle Ordovician Series. A primitive honeycomb (*Lamottia*) formed low reefs as much as 100 feet across, now shown in the Chazy limestone on Isle Lamotte in Lake Champlain. A small, simple horn coral (*Lambeophyllum*) occurs a little higher, associated with small heads of a compound coral (*Foerstephyllum*). There are but a few species, however, though small reefs are widely distributed in the Late Ordovician strata.

Bryozoa (Pl. 4, figs. 6–9) made their first appearance near the base of the Ordovician, but expanded into great variety in the middle and upper part of the system. Probably a thousand kinds are present in the rocks of the Champlainian series alone.

Brachiopods (Pl. 4, figs. 10–22) likewise experienced a rapid evolution, especially those with limy shells, though the primitive types with

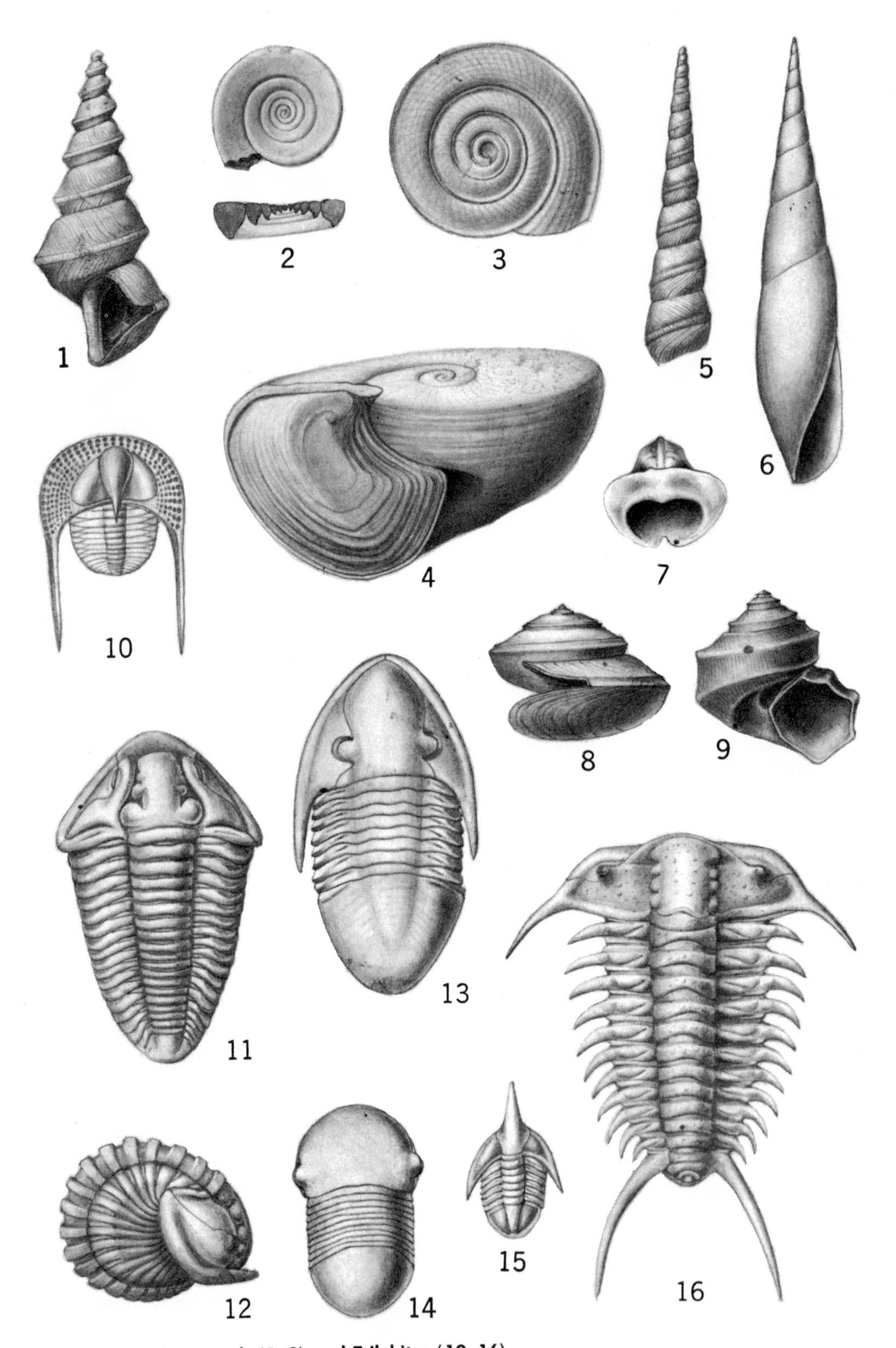

Plate 5. Ordovician Gastropods (1–9) and Trilobites (10–16).

Figure 1, *Lophospira bowdeni;* 2, *Lecanospira compacta;* 3, *Ophileta grandis;* 4, *Maclurites logani* (with operculum); 5, *Hormotoma artemesia;* 6, *Subulites canadensis;* 7, *Bellerophon troosti;* 8, *Eotomaria supracingulata;* 9, *Trochonema umbilicatum;* 10, *Cryptolithus tessellatus;* 11, 12, *Calymene meeki* (dorsal view in crawling position, and side view enrolled); 13, *Isotelus gigas;* 14, *Bumastus trentonensis;* 15, *Ampyx nasutus;* 16, *Ceraurus pleurexanthemus.* All natural size except 2 and 13 which grew to 3 times this size. (Drawings by L. S. Douglass.)

Figure 117. Bean-shaped shells of a large ostracod on the surface of a layer of mid-Ordovician limestone.

corneous or phosphatic shells which had been so prominent in the Cambrian declined rapidly. The majority of the brachiopods were now "square-shouldered" and almost all had radially striate or ribbed shells. Only a very few had calcareous gill supports in the form of spiralia.

Echinoderms were represented by a variety of **cystoids** and by numerous **crinoids**, along with the first rare **starfish** and the earliest known **blastoids** (Protoblastoidea) (Pl. 4, figs. 1–3,5).

Gastropods (Pl. 5, figs. 1–9) showed a surprising evolution into probably as many species as there were of brachiopods, though they were as a rule not so abundant individually as the latter, nor so well preserved. Species with low, widely, coiled shells greatly predominated, but many had already attained high graceful spires.

Clams are exceedingly rare until we come to the Champlainian and are first abundant and widely spread in the sandy formations of the Upper Ordovician of the Appalachian Trough (Pl. 4, figs. 23–24).

Cephalopods (Fig. 116) are represented by both straight and loosely coiled shells in great variety, the former including a number of species of large size. As a class, these were the largest invertebrates of their time.

Trilobites (Pl. 5, figs. 10–16) were still exceedingly numerous and varied, probably attaining the climax of their evolution during this period. If we may judge by their varied form, they were adapted to a wide range of conditions. One striking trend of the times is seen in two of the commonest families, which tended to lose the trilobation of their carapace and the marks of segmentation in both head and tail shields, giving rise to "bald-headed" types like *Bumastus* and *Isotelus* (Pl. 5, figs. 13, 14). The little groveler, *Cryptolithus*, with its pitted frill (Pl. 5, fig. 10), is very characteristic of Ordovician time.

Finally, we must note the first occurrence of the **Ostracoda**, minute crustaceans with bean-shaped, bivalved shells completely enclosing the body, as do those of small clams (Fig. 117).

REFERENCES

1. Rodgers, John, 1952, Absolute ages of radioactive minerals from the Appalachian region. *Amer. Jour. Sci.*, vol. 250, pp. 411–427.

Kulp, Laurence and L. E. Long, 1958, Chronology of major metamorphic events in southeastern United States. *Amer. Geophysical Union, Trans.*, vol. 39, p. 522.

2. Kindle, C. H., and H. B. Whittington, 1958, Stratigraphy of the Cow Head region, western Newfoundland. *Geol. Soc. Amer., Bull.*, vol. 69, pp. 315–342.

3. Whitcomb, L., 1932, Correlation by Ordovician bentonite. *Jour. Geol.*, vol. 40, pp. 522–534.

4. Stose, G. W. and A. I. Jonas, 1927, Ordovician shale and associated lava in southeastern Pennsylvania. *Geol. Soc. Amer., Bull.*, vol. 38, pp. 505–536.

5. Holtedahl, O., 1919, On the Paleozoic formations of Finmarken in northern Norway. *Amer. Jour. Sci., 4th Ser.*, vol. 47, pp. 85–107.

6. Kay, Marshall, 1937, Stratigraphy of the Trenton Group. *Geol. Soc. Amer., Bull.*, vol. 48, pp. 233–302.

7. Ørvig, Tor, 1958, *Pycnaspis splendens*, new genus, new species, a new ostracoderm from the Ordovician of North America. *U.S. Nat. Museum, Proc.*, vol. 108, no. 3391, pp. 1–23.

Figure 118. Silurian section in the gorge below Niagara Falls. This view is upstream along the American side of the gorge. Compare Figure 128.

Chapter 9. The Silurian Period

Coral reefs were the cities of those days.

A. O. THOMAS

Founding of the Silurian System. BEFORE 1830 the geologic succession was unknown below the "Old Red" sandstone that underlies the Coal Measures of England. The older rocks were then looked upon as a chaos of deformed and nearly unfossiliferous beds holding little promise that a clear sequence could be determined. To their solution there came a remarkable young Scotsman, Roderick Impey Murchison (Fig. 119), whose rise to fame began with his recognition of the Silurian System.

After six years in public school and two at a military academy he joined the army at the age of 15 and served through the Napoleonic wars. With the return of peace he retired to his estate in the northwest highlands of Scotland to become a gentleman of leisure. Fortunately he soon came under the influence of Sir Humphry Davy, who persuaded him to go to London and take courses in chemistry and allied subjects. There the lectures in geology aroused in him an interest that was fanned into enthusiasm as he tramped the hills in company with two of the foremost geologists of the day, William Buckland of Oxford and Adam Sedgwick of Cambridge. At the age of 32 he set himself the task of reading and gaining a self-made education in geology. His spectacular rise from this start to become one of the most distinguished scientists of his time, and, eventually, the director of the Geological Survey of Great Britain, is one of the inspiring chapters in the history of geology.

Figure 119. Sir Roderick Impey Murchison (1792–1871).

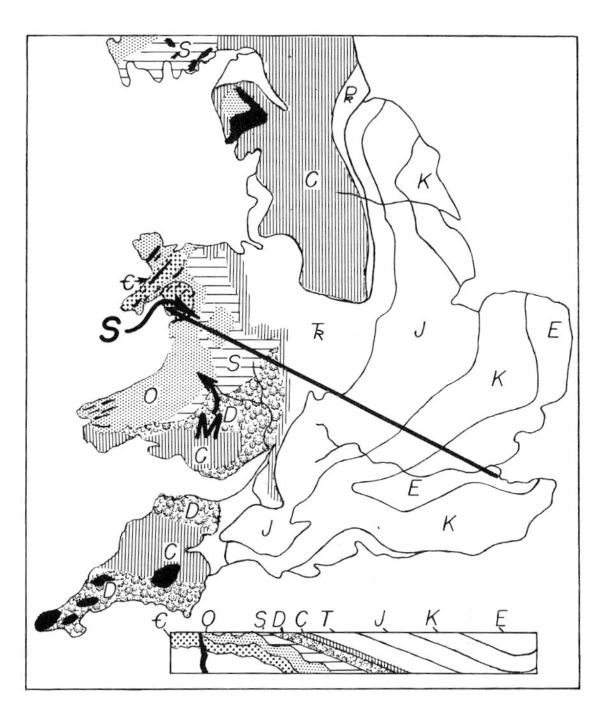

Figure 120. Geologic map of England and Wales with cross section from London to northwest Wales. Darts indicate the starting point of work by Murchison (M) and Sedgwick (S) on the Silurian and Cambrian systems, respectively. Black areas are igneous intrusives.

Murchison's first extensive work was the description of the Silurian System. In 1831 he and Sedgwick resolved to attempt the unraveling of the "Primitive Series" which lay below the Old Red and formed most of the country of Wales. Murchison began his investigations at the base of the Old Red and worked westward (Fig. 120). Here he found that the older rocks, though deformed, formed a regular succession of gray shales and limestones rich in distinctive fossils. By 1835 he had worked out a succession of thousands of feet of such strata which he defined as a new geologic system. Seeking a classical name, he called it Silurian after an ancient Celtic tribe (the Silures) which Caesar's legions had encountered there during the Roman conquest. His great volume, *The Silurian System* (1838), is now a classic in geology.

Sedgwick had meanwhile worked out a great sequence of rocks in the much-disturbed region of northwestern Wales (Fig. 120), and this he simultaneously defined as the Cambrian System. In 1835 both Sedgwick and Murchison supposed the

Cambrian System to lie entirely below the Silurian, but as work progressed, it became evident that the two overlapped, and that the lower half of the Silurian was included in the Cambrian. When Sedgwick subsequently showed the presence of an important faunal and physical break in the midst of the Silurian, Murchison still insisted on restricting the name Cambrian to older and generally unfossiliferous rocks. A bitter controversy ensued which not only estranged these two great pioneers but split the geologists of Europe into two camps for more than a generation.

In 1879 Professor Lapworth of Birmingham proposed to cut the Gordian knot by removing the debatable "Lower Silurian" to a distinct system, the Ordovician, and after many years of discussion this solution has now received wide acceptance.

PHYSICAL HISTORY

Patterns of Lands and Seas. As the Silurian Period opened, Appalachia was still mountainous but the rest of North America was almost flat. Slow submergence soon brought the sea in over the eastern half of the continent as indicated in Figure 121. A low barrier just south of the present Great Lakes is inferred to have separated northern and southern embayment since important elements of the faunas did not cross this line. The only Lower Silurian deposits known in the western part of the continent are in the lower part of the Mackenzie Valley and possibly in the Panhandle of Alaska.

By Middle Silurian time, however, the eastern seaways were united to cover much of the Mississippi Valley region and the central part of the Canadian Shield. Meanwhile the arctic embayment reached south of Great Slave Lake; a small embayment covered Panhandle Alaska; and a southwestern embayment crossed southern California and flooded northward across eastern Nevada and most of Utah and southern Idaho, while a southern arm spread eastward across southern Arizona and New Mexico (Fig. 121). It is noteworthy that except in the Appalachian region the widespread Middle Silurian formations are nearly all calcareous; evidently these inland seas were shallow and clear and the adjacent lands were very low.

Appalachia was appreciably lower than in Early Silurian time and was supplying mud rather than sand to the geosyncline, but it was still undergoing movement and its northern portion was the scene of considerable volcanic activity. Two rapidly subsiding troughs in this region, one in northern Quebec and another in the region of the Bay of Fundy, were filled with thick Silurian deposits.

Volcanoes in Northern Appalachia. Eastern Maine and southern New Brunswick bore a chain of active volcanoes during much of Silurian time and the trough that developed along their margin was largely filled with ash falls and lava flows. About Eastport, Maine these layered volcanics reach the impressive thickness of some 10,000 feet. Here deposition was at least partly submarine since the section includes numerous lenses of fossiliferous sedimentary rocks.

Northern Quebec was farther from the highlands, and along the shores of Bay Chaleur the thick Silurian sections include marine shale followed by some thousands of feet of highly fossiliferous limestones. At Black Cape on the north shore of Bay Chaleur, however, the limestone sequence is interrupted by some 4,000 feet of lava flows. Here the base of the lava includes abundant corals and brachiopods which it overwhelmed as it poured out over the sea floor.

In north-central Newfoundland where the Silurian section is very thick and all detrital, it includes some 1,600 feet of rhyolite and andesitic flows.

A local volcanic field occurred also in the Panhandle of Alaska where the thick sequence of Silurian limestones is interrupted by lava flows and beds of agglomerate and volcanic ash.

With these exceptions however, the continent appears to have been stable and free of volcanic activity.

Quiet Close of the Period in America. In Late Silurian time North America was largely emergent (Fig. 122) and a lingering inland sea became almost landlocked and, under strongly arid climate became a "dead sea" in which vast deposits of salt were formed. Even so, the bordering lands remained low and the detrital sediment carried into the Salina Sea were fine-grained muds. Indeed, as a final episode, the sea became clear and had more normal salinity as indicated by the Manlius limestone which extends eastward to the Hudson Valley, eastern Pennsylvania, and central Mary-

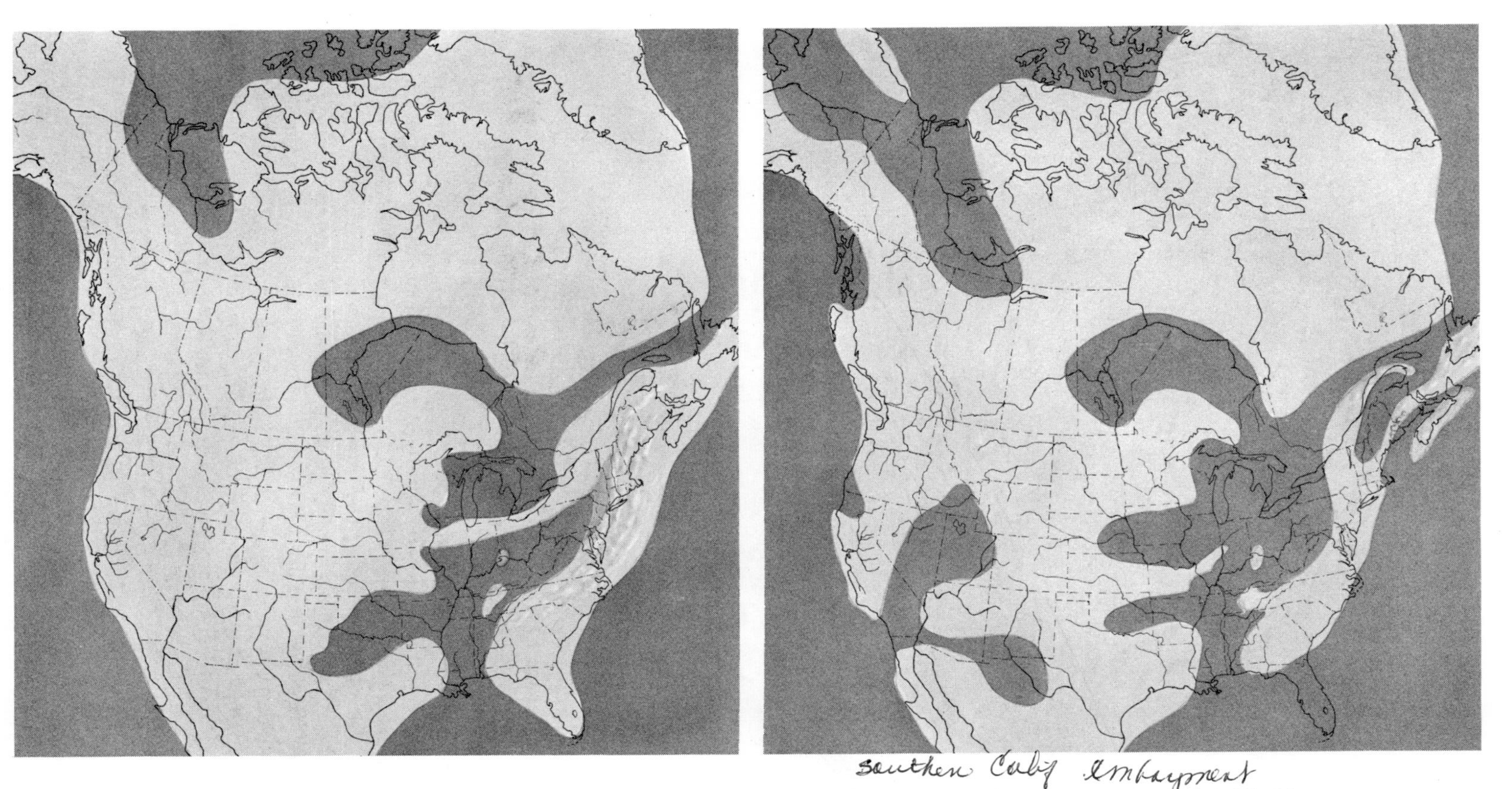

Figure 121. Silurian paleogeography. Left, maximum spread of the Lower Silurian seas; right, maximum spread of Middle Silurian seas.

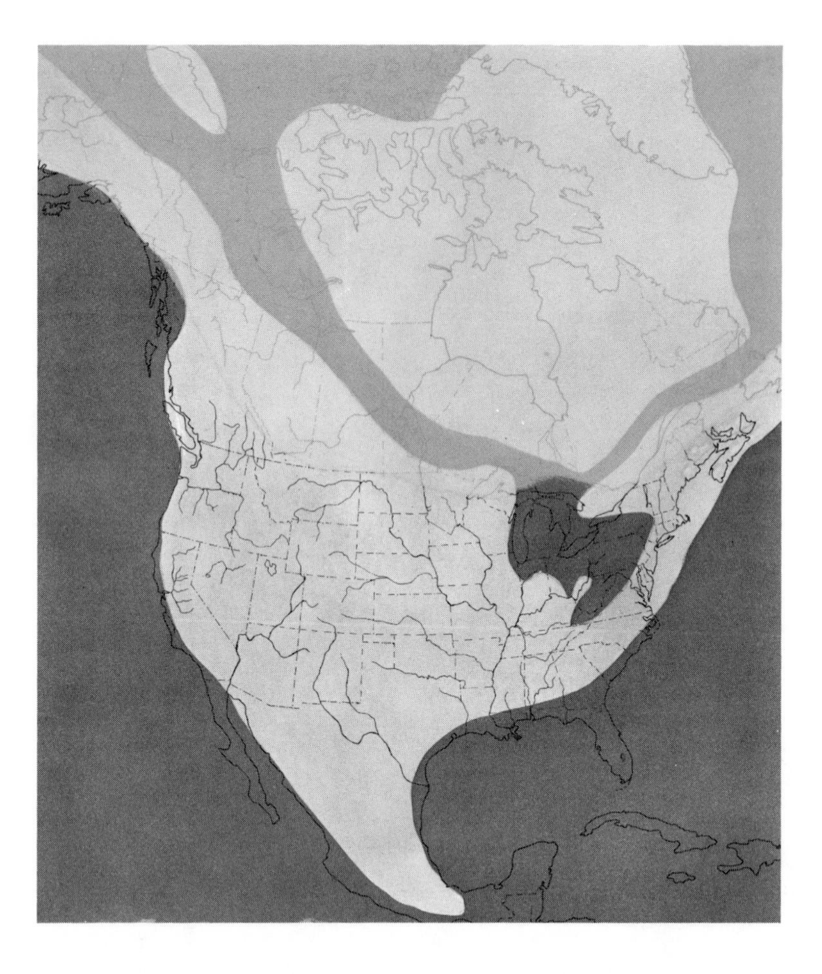

Figure 122. Late Silurian paleogeography, showing the Salina Sea. Possible inlets to the northwest and to the northeast are suggested, but since there is no direct evidence for either, this part of the map is veiled.

land, overlapping the earlier Silurian deposits to rest on the deformed Ordovician shales (Fig. 124). At this time Appalachia must have been essentially peneplaned.

Caledonian Disturbance of Europe. Europe, on the contrary, was the scene of crustal unrest during Silurian time that culminated in the Caledonian disturbance at the close of the period. This produced a majestic range of mountains running from southern Wales across Scotland and northeastward through Scandinavia (Fig. 123).

The Caledonian Range followed the axis of a geosyncline that had been developing since early Cambrian time and was bordered by a marginal land, apparently a volcanic arc, on the northwest. The early Paleozoic record is especially clear in Wales and Scotland where both the Ordovician and Silurian systems are almost entirely detrital and include impressive amounts of volcanics in the form of ash beds, flows, and dikes. The Caledonian disturbance crushed the geosynclinal deposits and thickened the crust here so that after Silurian time it ceased to behave as a geosyncline. In Scandinavia the orogenic forces came from the northwest, folding the Silurian and older rocks and carrying them eastward in a series of great thrusts. Throughout the length of Norway and Sweden, a distance exceeding 1,100 miles, the pre-Devonian formations were folded, overturned, and overthrust with eastward movement on individual faults as much as 20 to 40 miles. The mountains in Scotland and Wales seem to have paralleled those in Norway, but here the thrusts were to the west.

Central East Greenland was intensely deformed at the same time and was the scene of a mountain range that roughly paralleled the Caledonian Mountains. Still another range stretched eastward across northern France and southern Germany into northern Austria. Thus, in western Europe late Silurian time was marked by widespread orogeny, while North America (with the exception of extreme eastern Greenland) was stable.

STRATIGRAPHY

Influence of the Taconian Range. During Early and Middle Silurian time the Appalachian Trough received abundant sandy sediments from the east as the highlands in Appalachia were gradually worn down. This material, trapped between Appalachia and the Cincinnati Arch, kept the geosyncline silted up to near or above sealevel, oscillating between shallow sea floor and low coastal plain. Along the eastern margin of the geosyncline, the Tuscarora sandstone stretches all the way from New York to Alabama, averaging more than 500 feet in thickness and reaching a maximum of more than 1,000 feet in southeastern New York where it is conglomeratic (Fig. 124). This is one of the most extensive sheets of nearly pure quartz sand on the continent and is the great ridgemaker in the Appalachian folds from New York to eastern Tennessee. Other names are applied locally (Clinch, Medina, Albion) but they all refer to parts of this vast, continuous sheet of sandstone. It thins gradually southward and more rapidly to the west and northwest where it is succeeded by and partly replaced by shales. In southeastern New York and northeastern Pennsylvania,

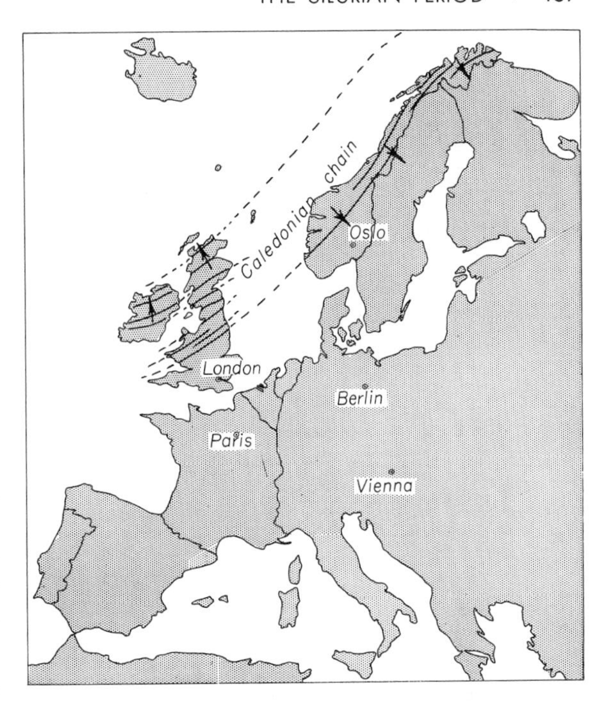

Figure 123. Map showing the location of Late Silurian, Caledonian, orogeny in Europe.

deposition of quartz sand and gravel continued from the beginning to near the middle of the period, but elsewhere in the Appalachian Trough deposition of sand ceased about the end of the Early Silurian Epoch and only fine muds were transported into the geosyncline to form the

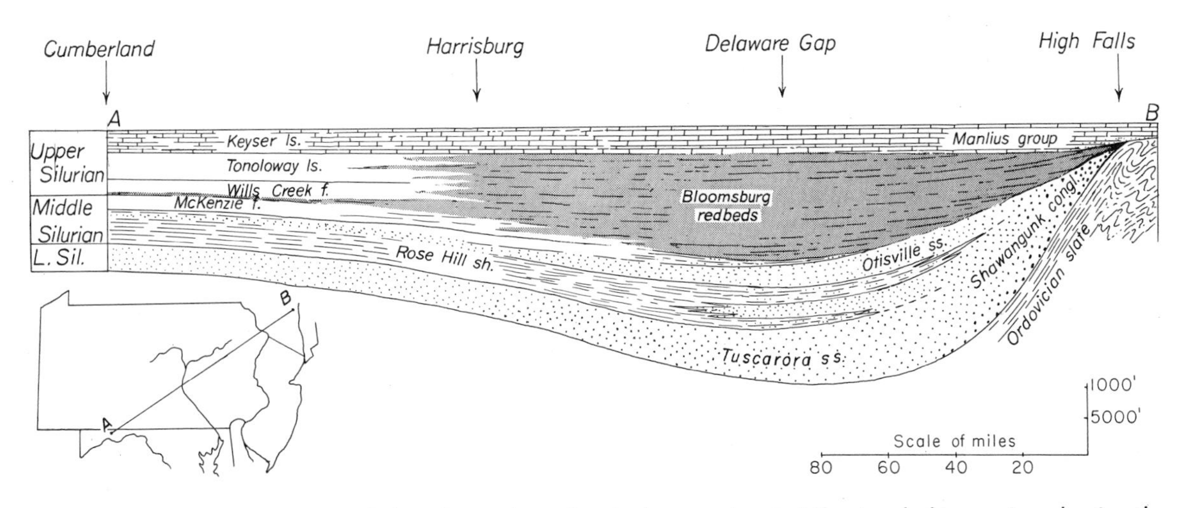

Figure 124. Stratigraphic section of the Silurian formations in the central part of the Appalachian region, showing the influence of the rising Taconian highlands in Appalachia. The section runs obliquely across the geosyncline.

Chart 3. Correlation of important Silurian sections

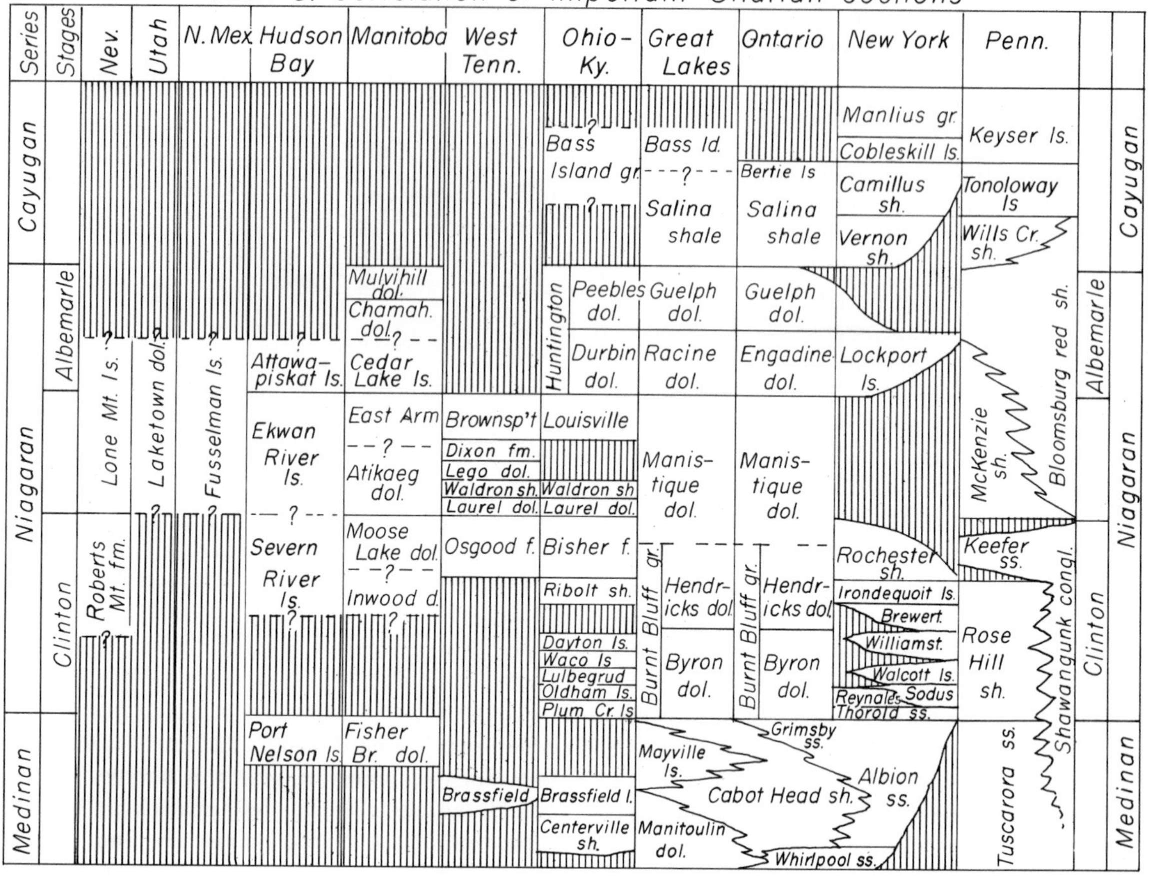

Series	Stages	Nev.	Utah	N. Mex.	Hudson Bay	Manitoba	West Tenn.	Ohio-Ky.	Great Lakes	Ontario	New York	Penn.	Stages	Series
Cayugan								? Bass Island gr. ?	Bass Id. --?-- Salina shale	Bertie ls Salina shale	Manlius gr. Cobleskill ls. Camillus sh. Vernon sh.	Keyser ls. Tonoloway ls Wills Cr. sh.		Cayugan
Niagaran	Albemarle	Lone Mt. ls. ?	Laketown dol. ?	Fusselman ls. ?	? Attawapiskat ls.	Mulvihill dol. Chamah. dol. ? Cedar Lake ls.		Huntington: Peebles dol. Durbin dol.	Guelph dol. Racine dol.	Guelph dol. Engadine dol.	Lockport ls.	McKenzie sh. Bloomsburg red sh.	Albemarle	Niagaran
Niagaran		Lone Mt. ls.	Laketown dol. ?	Fusselman ls. ?	Ekwan River ls. --?--	East Arm --?-- Atikaeg dol.	Brownsp't Dixon fm. Lego dol. Waldron sh. Laurel dol.	Louisville Waldron sh Laurel dol.	Manistique dol.	Manistique dol.		McKenzie sh. Bloomsburg red sh.		Niagaran
Niagaran	Clinton	Roberts Mt. fm. ?			Severn River ls. ?	Moose Lake dol. --?-- Inwood d. ?	Osgood f.	Bisher f. Ribolt sh. Dayton ls. Waco ls Lulbegrud Oldham ls. Plum Cr. ls	Burnt Bluff gr.: Hendricks dol Byron dol.	Burnt Bluff gr.: Hendricks dol Byron dol.	Rochester sh. Irondequoit ls. Brewert. Williamst. Walcott ls. Reynales, Sodus Thorold ss.	Keefer ss. Rose Hill sh. Shawangunk congl.	Clinton	Niagaran
Medinan					Port Nelson ls	Fisher Br. dol.	Brassfield	Brassfield l. Centerville sh.	Mayville ls. Cabot Head sh. Manitoulin dol.	Grimsby ss. Cabot Head sh. Whirlpool ss.	Albion ss. Whirlpool ss.	Tuscarora ss. Shawangunk congl.		Medinan

Middle Silurian shales. The Tuscarora sandstone and its northeastern facies, the Shawangunk conglomerate (Fig. 124), were clearly derived from the old Taconian highlands in Appalachia, which must have been rugged and subject to rapid erosion during the Early Silurian Epoch, but thereafter it was generally so low as to supply only fine muds. The eastern margin of the geosyncline in Early Silurian time is still recorded in southeastern New York where the Shawangunk conglomerate thins to a feathered edge (near Rosendale) and overlaps unconformably on the deformed Ordovician slates. Indeed, the Shawangunk conglomerate was probably deposited on a coastal plain east of the shoreline since marine fossils first make their appearance several miles to the southwest. North of Rosendale the basal Silurian sandstone is completely overlapped by the highest Silurian (Manlius limestone) and by Lower Devonian formations, but it reappears in the lowlands of central and western New York, where it is known as the Medina sandstone. At Niagara Falls it is only about 100 feet thick and a short distance farther west it grades laterally into shale and still further west (in Ontario) into limestone.

In the Gaspé Peninsula of eastern Quebec where the Silurian formations rest unconformably on the metamorphosed and folded Ordovician, the basal Silurian also includes conglomerates and thick sandstones.

A striking contrast is seen, however, if we journey 70 miles across the Gulf of St. Lawrence to Anticosti Island, where the Late Ordovician and Early Silurian are both represented by flat-lying formations of calcareous shale or limestone. There is no evidence here of the Taconian orogeny, in either the structure or the sediments. Moreover, there are younger Ordovician beds on Anticosti

(Gamache formation) than any known elsewhere on the continent, showing that the Ordovician seas lingered longest here. The explanation of this striking contrast in the record of Anticosti Island and Gaspé lies in the fact that Gaspé was originally much farther south and its rocks have been overthrust many miles to the north by a later disturbance, bringing rocks from the eastern part of the geosyncline near those originally deposited far from the Taconian Range.

The westward gradation of the Early Silurian deposits from sandstone into shale and finally into limestone is exceptionally well displayed in nearly continuous exposures that follow the base of the Niagara cuesta from Rochester, New York, through Niagara Falls and across the Ontario Peninsula into the Manitoulin Islands (Figs. 125 and 126).

Middle Silurian Limestones and Coral Reefs. West of the Cincinnati Arch even the Early Silurian formations are of limestone (Fig. 127). Although of considerable areal extent (Fig. 122), they are commonly a few feet or a few tens of feet thick and represent only a small part of this epoch, but it is notable that there were no uplands within adequate reach to supply even muds to this part of the interior sea.

Middle Silurian formations are far more widespread and are considerably thicker, but they, too, are almost entirely made of limestone (locally dolostone in the upper Mississippi Valley). Even where widely distributed across the Canadian Shield, they are predominantly calcareous.

The grand exposures about Niagara Falls (Figs. 118 and 128) display most of the Middle Silurian in its typical development, resting upon the sandy phase of the Lower Silurian. The lip of the falls is formed by the thick-bedded Lockport dolostone, which also rims the gorge in cliffs more than 100 feet high (Fig. 118). This resistant formation, overlying the weak shales below, holds up the Niagara cuesta across western New York, the peninsula of Ontario, and the Manitoulin Islands north of Lake Huron. It extends southward under cover of younger formations, to appear again about the flanks of the Cincinnati Arch. Large outliers occur farther north in Canada, one of the greatest being along the west shore of Hudson Bay.

The rocks exposed above the brink of the falls and along the upper rapids represent the base of the **Guelph dolostone**. This formation is typically developed only in Ontario and Ohio, where it is characterized by a peculiar fauna of gastropods, a large clam (*Megalomus*), and heavy-shelled, hingeless brachiopods (trimerellids). The Guelph fauna appears not to have reached much to the south of central Ohio. The Lockport limestone grades westward into dolostone, and to the south and west

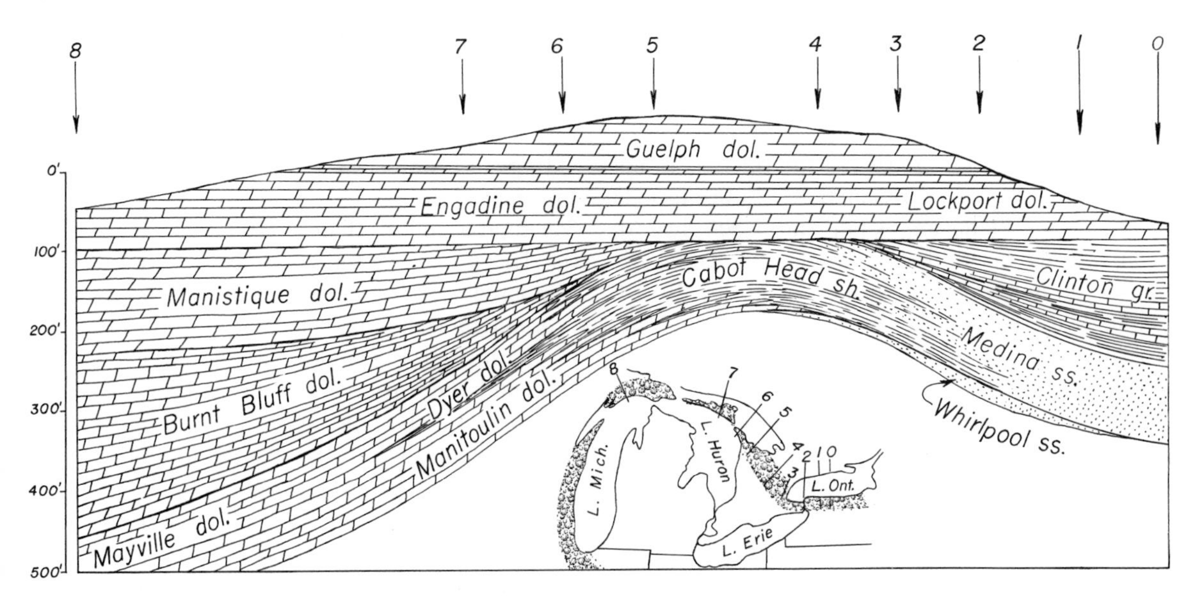

Figure 125. Stratigraphic section of the Silurian formations along the Niagara cuesta from central New York to northern Michigan. The inset map shows the outcrop belt and the location of eight numbered sections.

Figure 126. Whirlpool sandstone, basal member of the Medina sandstone, resting paraconformably on the red Queenston shale of late Ordovician age. This is a beach deposit. (Carl O. Dunbar.)

of Lake Michigan is less easily separated from the Guelph, the two forming a thick group of dolostone beds that extends underground into Kansas and Nebraska, cropping out locally in Iowa.

Below the Lockport formation at the falls and in the gorge at Niagara lies the Clinton group, here much thinner than in the Appalachian region and likewise more calcareous.

The Silurian of western North America is not well known but is represented by 1,000 feet of dolostone in Idaho and Utah and 1,500 feet of similar beds in southern Nevada. Great thicknesses of dolostone are exposed also in British Columbia, the Mackenzie Valley, the Arctic Archipelago, and southern Alaska.

Throughout the extent of the limy Niagaran formations, corals were common and at many places made small reefs. Limestones and dolostones with reef structures occur in the Medinan series, but are especially common in the Niagaran of Indiana, northern Illinois, southern Wisconsin, Iowa, and Ontario north at least to Lake Huron. Some of the oldest of these reefs were made by bryozoans (Fig. 129), but the majority were formed by various kinds of stony corals (Tabulata, Tetracoralla, and hydrocorallines like the stromatoporoids). These reefs vary in size from several feet to more than a mile across, and in height from a few feet up to 75 feet. All are unstratified masses made up of entire or broken skeletons, buried in a matrix of coral sand and mud.

Upper Silurian Desert Deposits and Waterlimes. In central New York the salt-bearing shales of the **Salina group**, more than 1,000 feet thick, succeed the Niagaran limestone. Here the lower half is composed of bright red unfossiliferous shale (Vernon), and the upper half of gray shale (Camillus) with several beds of rock salt. The salt (Fig. 130) underlies an area measuring 150 miles from east to west and extends southward under southern New York, northern Pennsylvania, and Ohio. Several distinct beds occur at intervals in the shale, individual beds of pure salt reaching a thickness as great as 80 feet. At Ithaca, New York, where the formation lies between 2,000 and 3,000 feet underground, there are seven beds of salt with an aggregate thickness of 250 feet; but the greatest ac-

Figure 127. Early Silurian, Sexton Creek, limestone resting paraconformably on Late Ordovician at Girardeau, Missouri. The contact is at the man's chin. The Sexton Creek limestone (some 30 feet thick) is equivalent in age to the lower part of the Tuscarora sandstone of the Appalachian region.

cumulation of Silurian salt is deeply buried under the center of the Michigan Basin, where deep wells reveal salt beds aggregating 1,600 feet in thickness.[1]

Even where no salt remains, the impressions of large crystals of halite (salt hoppers) are common in the Camillus shale (Fig. 131) indicating deposition under saturated brine.

Southeastward toward Appalachia the entire series passes into barren redbeds, but southwestward in central Pennsylvania (Fig. 124) interbedded limestones (Tonoloway) bear abundant marine fossils at many horizons.

After the salt deposition the marine waters again spread widely over the New York desert, and a series of thin persistent dolostones and waterlimes was left as the final record of the Silurian Period. Waterlime is an impure calcareous sediment with a large admixture of silt, possibly the wind-blown dust from the neighboring arid lands; it was once much used in making cement.

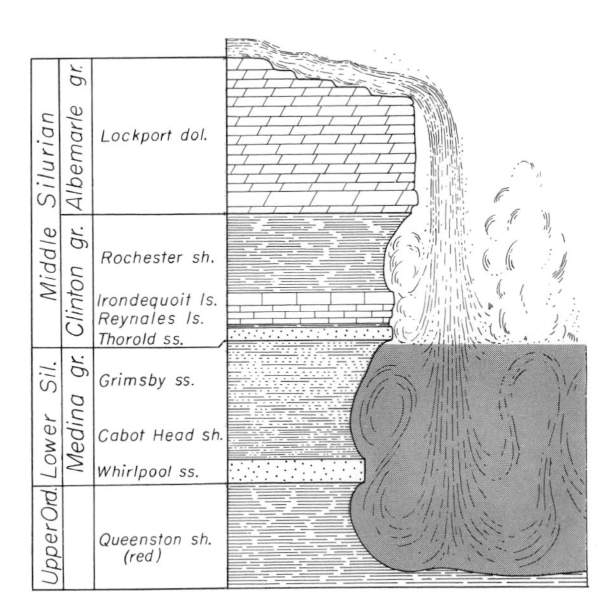

Figure 128. Classical section of the Lower and Middle Silurian formations exposed in the Gorge at Niagara Falls.

Figure 129. Small bryozoan reef in the Irondequoit limestone of the Clinton group in Niagara Gorge. The reef is 25 feet across and projects several feet into the overlying Rochester shale. (Charles Schuchert.)

Figure 130. Salt mine in the Salina shale (Upper Silurian) at Retsof, central New York. The tunnel is cut in solid rock salt, and the cars are loaded with salt on their way to the shaft. (Retsof Mining Company.)

Figure 131. Salt hoppers in the Camillus shale at Camillus, New York. These are impressions of skeletal salt crystals that settled into the mud and were later dissolved. (Carl O. Dunbar.)

CLIMATE

Cosmopolitan Climate of the Middle Silurian. The coral reefs and coral-bearing strata distributed widely throughout the Middle Silurian limestones show that mild temperatures again extended into the arctic region. The evidence lies not so much in the mere existence of the reefs and corals as in the fact that the species are everywhere identical or much alike, whether in Kentucky, New York, the Hudson Bay region, or within the Arctic Circle, as at Polaris Bay, northern Greenland. The wide extent of the limestones and dolostones confirms the evidence of the corals. Other groups of invertebrates, notably the cephalopods, show an equal disregard for latitude. Certain species found in Iowa are clearly migrants from Europe by way of the polar region. Most remarkable of these is the four-sided coral, *Goniophyllum* (Fig. 132), which, unlike all others, had an operculum, or cover, of four limy plates.

Late Silurian Deserts. As the continent emerged during Late Silurian time (Fig. 122), arid conditions spread over the eastern United States, and a large area including Michigan, Ontario, New York, and Pennsylvania took on the characters of a desert basin. In the midst of this region, a lingering arm of the inland sea shrank to a "dead sea" in which vast quantities of salt and gypsum were precipitated. The red Vernon shales of the Salina group probably represent the muds of a barren coastal plain, where free access of the air to the soil during long periods of drought kept the enclosed iron thoroughly oxidized. The gray shales, deposited under hypersaline waters, include salt and gypsum at many horizons over an area of nearly 100,000 square miles. Since the deposition of 1 cubic foot of salt (sodium chloride) would require the evaporation of about 80 cubic feet of normal sea water, it is clear that severely arid conditions must have persisted here for a very long time. It is not to be inferred that the water was deep, however; there was probably an intermittent inflow of more sea water from the outer ocean to balance the evaporation and supply the salt. Indeed, the abundant mudcracks in the gray shales (Fig. 133) indicate that wide mud flats were repeatedly exposed.

Recent study of liquid inclusions in the salt crystals[2] indicates that the temperature of the water at time of deposition ranged from 32 to 48°C. (The surface temperature in the modern tropical oceans is about 27°C. and that in the Mediterranean is only 21°C.; but in a lake in the desert

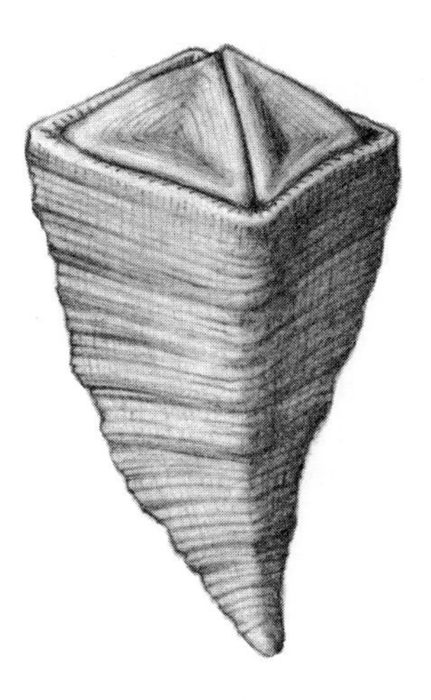

Figure 132. A distinctive coral, *Goniophyllum,* that arrived in the Great Lakes region in Middle Silurian time, having migrated from Europe via the Arctic seaway.

Figure 133. Mudcracked layers of impure limestone in the Salina shale at Roundtop, Maryland. These beds were probably exposed during one of the episodes of extreme evaporation when the inland sea had shrunk and salt was being deposited farther north. (Charles Schuchert.)

near the Caspian Sea temperatures as high as 70°C. have been recorded.)

The cause for the aridity may have been the flatness of the extended land mass, which offered no elevations to chill the westerly winds after they had crossed the interior of the continent.

ECONOMIC PRODUCTS

Clinton Iron Ore. The red iron ore mined in the Birmingham region of Alabama now supplies about 10 percent of the iron produced annually in the United States and is the only important domestic competitor of the Precambrian ores of the Lake Superior region.

The Silurian ore is an oölite of the red oxide, hematite, occurring in thin, lenticular beds alternating with the gray shales of the Clinton group. The ore locally includes abundant marine fossils and commonly has replaced broken bits of the shells. It was originally deposited as a sedimentary accumulation on the Silurian sea floor. One or more beds of ore can be found at most of the outcrops of the Clinton shales all the way from New York to Alabama, but the thickness is generally only a few inches to a foot or two, rising locally to 3 or 4 feet.

Before the Civil War the Silurian iron was extensively exploited in the region of Clinton, New York, but since the discovery of the vast iron deposits in the Lake Superior region most of the Silurian mines have been driven out of competition. In the vicinity of Birmingham, Alabama, however, the Clinton ore beds reach their maximum development, the "Big Seam" having a thickness of 40 feet, of which 15 to 17 feet is rich enough to be workable. Here, in immediate proximity to the Big Warrior coal field, the ore is profitably and extensively mined. It is estimated that over 600,000,000 tons of this ore are still available underground.

Salt. Salt is another important mineral product of the Silurian rocks. During the years 1943–1945 the average annual production of salt from the Silurian rocks of New York State was in excess of 2,900,000 tons and had a value of nearly $10,000,000. This was slightly less than 20 percent of all the salt mined in the United States. The salt is obtained chiefly by forcing water down deep drill holes and pumping up the brine to be evaporated and refined; it is also mined and sold in blocks to be used as salt licks for cattle.

SILURIAN LIFE

Continued Reign of Marine Invertebrates. Silurian life was a modification, through lineal descent, of that of the Ordovician, with no drastic innovations. Marine invertebrates still predominated, almost to the exclusion of other forms of life (Pl. 6). Some of the invertebrate stocks, however, already showed evidences of decline, whereas others, of little importance to the Ordovician, now sprang into prominence.

The **graptolites**, for example, had greatly declined and are found at only a few limited horizons in the American Silurian, though in Europe they were

Figure 134. Three characteristic types of eurypterids. Left, *Eusarcus scorpionis* (× ½); center, *Pterygotus buffaloensis* (× 1/25); right *Eurypterus remipes* (× ⅓). (After Clarke and Ruedemann.)

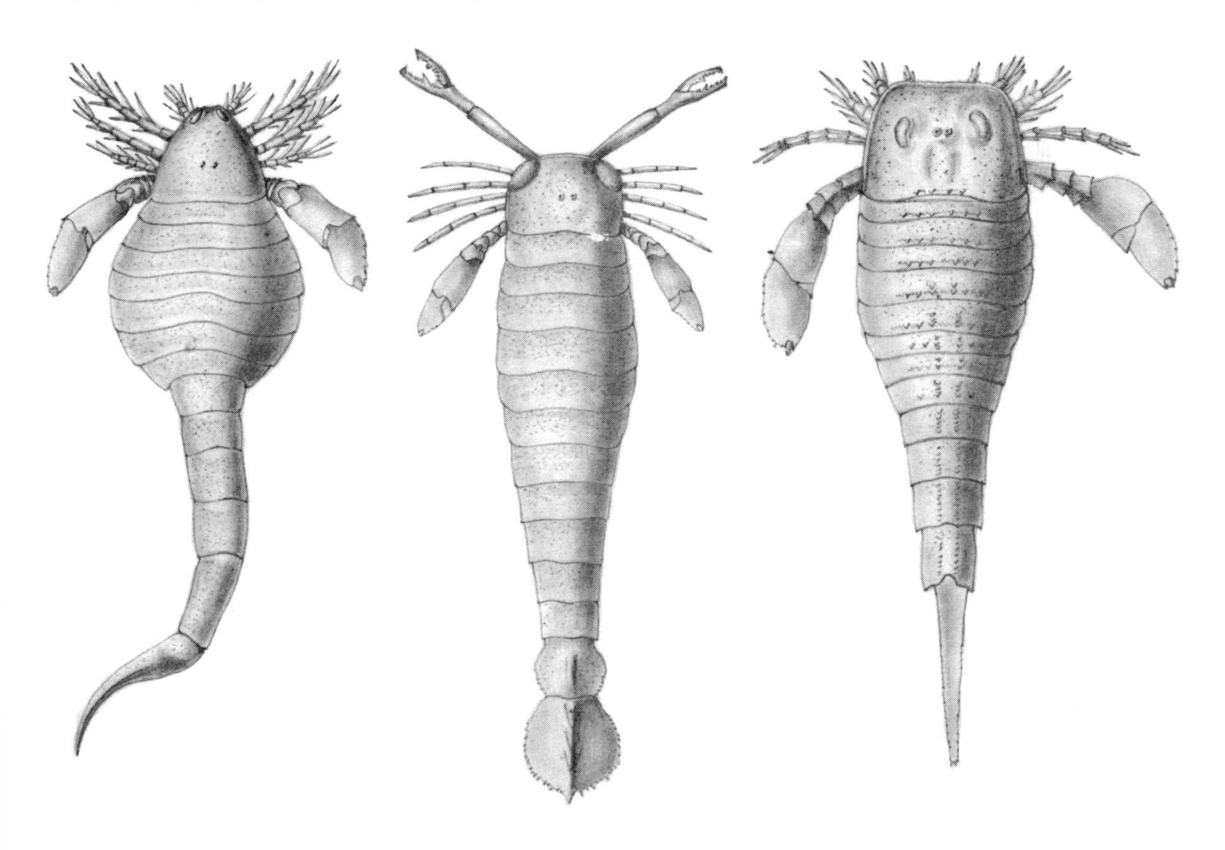

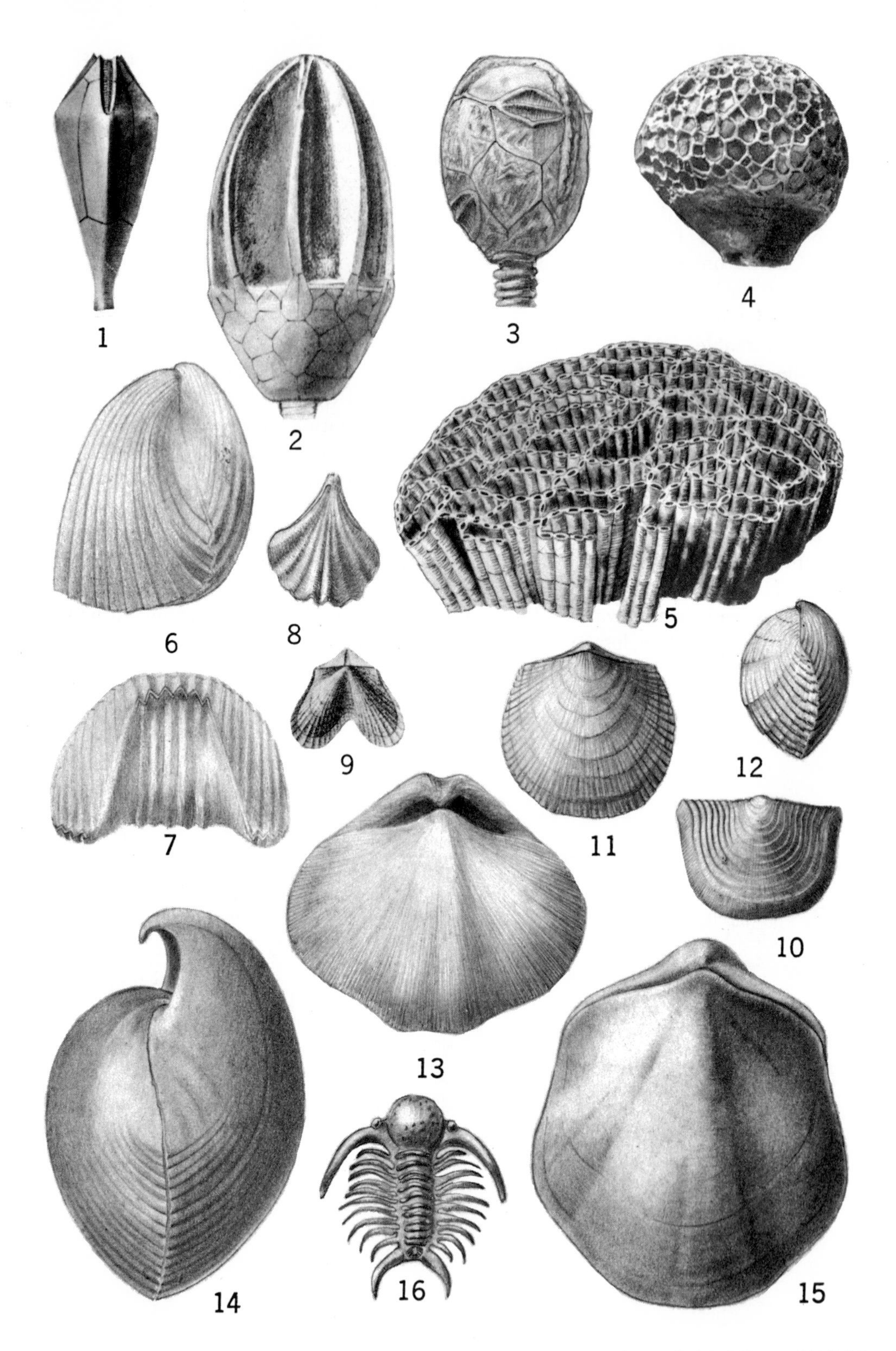

Plate 6. Silurian Blastoid (1), Crinoid (2), Cystoid (3), Corals (4, 5), Brachiopods (6–15), and Trilobite (16).

Figure 1, *Troostocrinus reinwardti;* 2, *Eucalyptocrinus crassus;* 3, *Lepadocrinites manlius;* 4, *Favosites forbesi,* a honeycomb coral; 5, *Halysites catenularius,* a chain coral; 6, 7, *Uncinulus stricklandi;* 8, *Rhynchotreta americana;* 9, *Bilobites bilobus;* 10, *Leptaena rhomboidalis;* 11, 12, *Atrypa reticularis;* 13, *Eospirifer radiatus;* 14, *Conchidium laqueatum;* 15, *Pentamerus oblongus;* 16, *Deiphion forbesi barrandei.* All natural size. (Drawn by R. G. Creadick.)

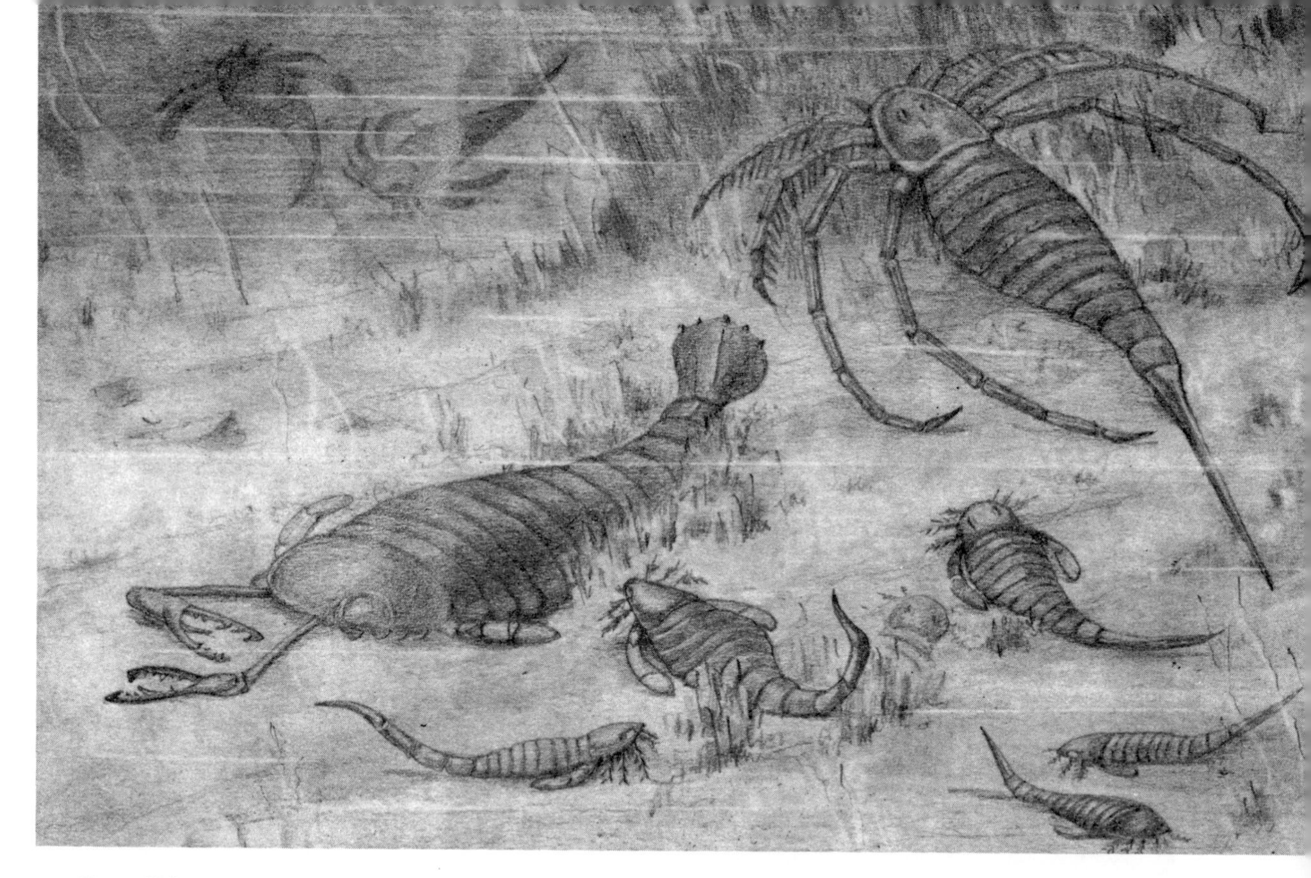

Figure 135. Restoration of Eurypterids on a Silurian sea floor. About 1/10 natural size. (After Ruedemann.)

Figure 136. A primitive fish (*Pharyngolepis oblongus*) from the uppermost Silurian (Downtonian beds) of Norway. Above, a reconstruction; below, dorsal view of a specimen in the rock. About ⅔ natural size. (After Kiaer.)

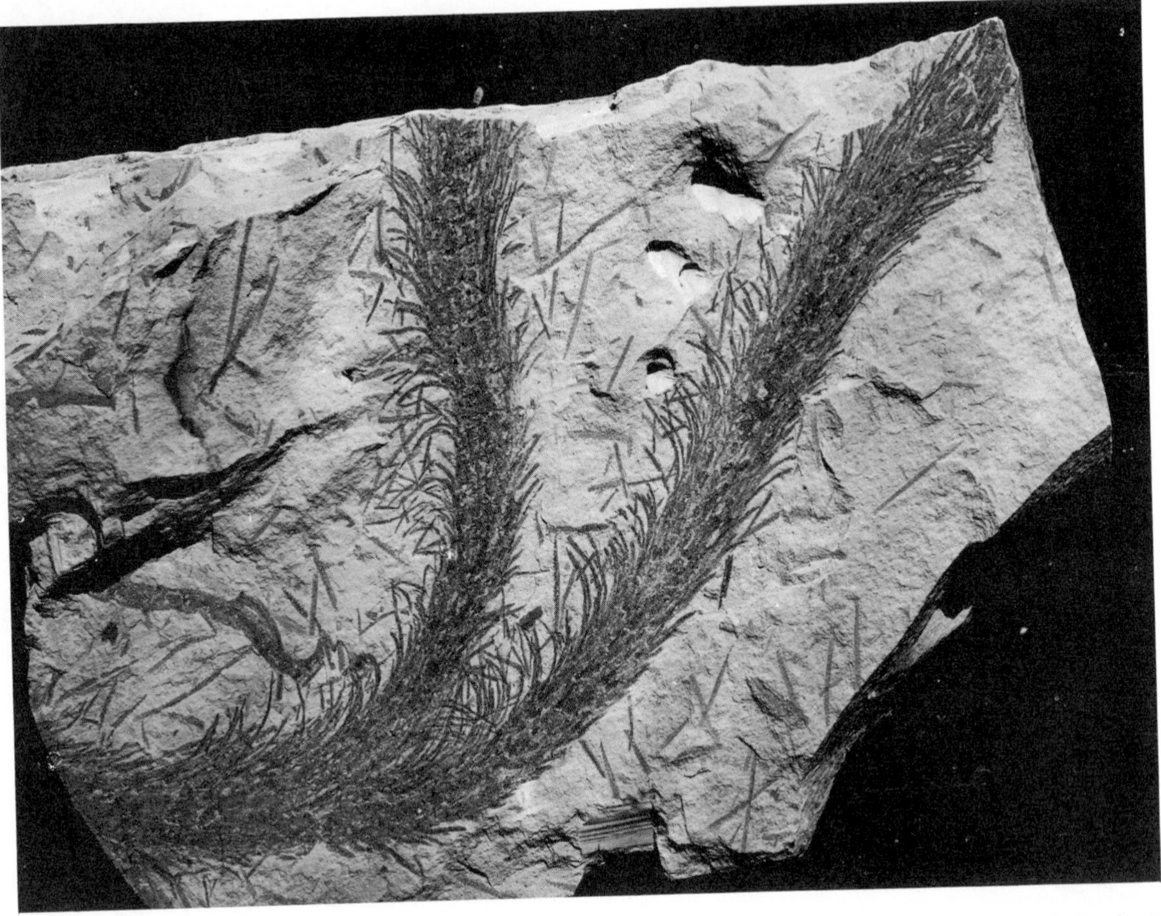

Figure 137. Leafy, branched plant, *Baragwanathia longifolia,* from the Upper Silurian rocks of Australia. The locality is a quarry 19 miles from Woods Point in the province of Victoria. On the slab with this supposed land plant occur abundant specimens of a Silurian graptolite, *Monograptus uncinatus* var. *orbatus.* (R. J. Tillyard.)

still numerically abundant but mostly of one genus, *Monograptus*.

Corals, on the contrary, showed an extraordinary expansion into many genera and species including honeycombs (**Favosites**), chain corals (**Halysites**), cup corals, and compound types of tetracorals. In the clear Niagaran seas they formed reefs of widespread distribution (Pl. 6, figs. 4, 5).

Bryozoa were still very common and locally made small reefs (Fig. 129).

Brachiopods showed a marked expansion. To the flattish and square-shouldered types were added globular, short-hinged forms with pointed beaks and plicated shells. Spire-bearing types also for the first time became common (Pl. 6, figs. 6–15).

Among the echinoderms, **cystoids** (Pl. 6, fig. 3) were rather common, **blastoids** (Pl. 6, fig. 1) just beginning, **starfish** and **echinoids** exceedingly rare. **Crinoids** (Pl. 6, fig. 2), on the contrary, experienced a remarkable evolution and grew in the greatest profusion, their calcareous plates contributing largely to the limy sediments of the clearer seas. Growing as they did on graceful, slender stems, these "lilies of the sea" undoubtedly furnished the most colorful spots upon the Earth.

The mollusks were generally much less conspicuous than in the preceding period, but in some of the late Niagaran dolostones heavy-shelled **gastropods** are abundant. Nautiloids and clams were both present but hardly noteworthy.

Trilobites had passed their climax but still remained common. A number of types showed a tendency toward bizarre development of spines, which may have been a protective measure against the evolving fishes (Pl. 6, fig. 16).

The **eurypterids,** or sea scorpions, formed perhaps the most striking and distinctive element in the late Silurian faunas (Figs. 134 and 135). They are very localized in their occurrence and practically confined to a few limited horizons, but they are common fossils where they do occur. They were sparingly represented in the Ordovician but in the Silurian rose to a meteoric climax only to decline abruptly in the next period, after which they were very rare. Most of them were small animals from a few inches to a foot or so in length, but a few species attained large dimensions. The largest American species (*Pterygotus buffaloensis*) is found in the Bertie waterlime of western New York, where fragments of exceptionally large individuals have led to an estimate of a body length of 7 feet or a length of 9 feet over-all, with pincers extended. This creature ranks as the greatest arthropod of all time.

Ostracods continued in great abundance, and some species now attained a relatively large size, the greatest, however, scarcely reaching a length of 1 inch.

Fishes. Fishes undoubtedly lived in the streams throughout this period, but their remains are exceedingly rare, consisting essentially of small, bony tubercles and armor plates which studded the skin of certain of the primitive Ostracodermi in lieu of scales. In the highest Silurian beds on the Island of Oesel in the Baltic and in the highest Silurian beds of Norway, however, remarkably preserved but very primitive fishes (Fig. 136) have been found in abundance. These have no well-defined jaws, and in this and other primitive characteristics they appear to be ancestral to the modern hagfish or cyclostome.

Beginnings of Terrestrial Life. Fragments of **land plants** have been described from the Silurian rocks of Gotland, England, and Australia. The remains are few, however, and very fragmentary, consisting of bits of stems some pieces of which bear small, bractlike leaves. One of the Australian types (Fig. 137) bears slender leaves 2 centimeters long and 1 millimeter broad. It appears to be most closely related to the modern "ground pines."

> These Silurian fossils are the oldest examples of what appear to be terrestrial plants. . . . They do not tell us very much; but they afford evidence of two Silurian types, probably terrestrial, which agree closely with forms characteristic of the earlier Devonian floras and of a third type that appears to be peculiar to this meagre Pre-Devonian flora.[3]

Soft-tissued algae and fungi may have been abundant in regions of sufficient moisture and suitable climate.

Possibly the **first air-breathing animals** were **scorpions** and **millipeds,** both of which have been found rarely in the Upper Silurian rocks. These first-known scorpions are small creatures, not over 2½ inches long, and their resemblance to modern scorpions is striking. Nevertheless they may still have been aquatic animals. They appear to be descendants of the eurypterids, which were aquatic, and none of the fossil specimens has revealed the respiratory structures that would prove whether they breathed air or water.

The millipeds have been found only in Wales, where they are associated with eurypterids.

REFERENCES

1. Landes, K. K., G. M. Ehlers, and G. M. Stanley, 1945, Geology of the Mackinac Straits region. *Mich. Geol. Surv. Publication 44*, pp. 1–204.

2. Dellwig, Louis F., 1955, Origin of the Salina Salt of Michigan. *Jour. Sed. Petrology*, vol. 25, pp. 83–110.

3. Seward, A. C., 1931, *Plant Life through the Ages.* Macmillan, New York, p. 110.

Figure 138. Richly fossiliferous Devonian sandstone showing a variety of brachiopods. Chemung sandstone at Glory Hill near Waverly, New York.

Chapter **10. The Devonian Period**

Discovery of the Devonian System. IN GREAT Britain, where historical geology had many of its first devotees and the Early Paleozoic systems were named, the Coal Measures are underlain by a great succession of sandstones and shales known to the pioneer geologists as the "Old Red sandstone." Until Murchison and Sedgwick had defined the Silurian and Cambrian systems, it formed the base of the determined geologic column, and thereafter it was given a place between the Silurian and the Carboniferous.

In 1836 Murchison and Sedgwick began to work in Devonshire and Cornwall, the southwestern provinces of England, which had long been known to be largely covered by a series of gray rocks considered to be Carboniferous because of the presence of fossil plants. They found that only the upper part of these rocks is plant-bearing; the lower part they referred to the Cambrian solely because it was badly deformed and in that respect resembled the rocks of northwest Wales. However, when fossil corals found by local collectors were submitted to the paleontologist Lonsdale, he found them intermediate between corals of the Silurian and those of the Carboniferous, and suggested that these beds might belong to the Old Red. Murchison and Sedgwick were hard to convince, but after two years they accepted Lonsdale's view and proposed the name Devonian for a new system between the Silurian and the Carboniferous. In it they embraced these marine deposits of Devonshire, the Old Red sandstone, and correlative formations elsewhere.

It was eventually found that in Devonshire the system is 10,000 to 12,000 feet thick and consists of graywacke, slates, and limestone, associated with lavas and tuff. The region was an unfortunate one on which to base a system, for the beds are so disturbed by folding, faulting, and intrusions that the detailed succession is still not wholly known. Equivalent but less disturbed beds had already been described in the Rhine Valley in Germany, and these became the actual standard section of the system in Europe. A still finer section in New York State is the standard of reference for America.

PHYSICAL HISTORY OF NORTH AMERICA

The Devonian Cycle of Submergence. Although the close of the Silurian left Europe rugged and mountainous, North America remained low and flat. The Devonian submergence began in the Appalachian Trough, which was soon transformed into a narrow strait reaching from Newfoundland to Mississippi and at times separating Appalachia completely from the mainland (Fig. 139). No marine deposits of Early Devonian time are known in the Cordilleran Trough, though a fresh-water formation bearing fossil fish and land plants is present at Beartooth Butte in Wyoming. During this epoch, probably less than 5 percent of the present continent was submerged.

The beginning of Middle Devonian time was marked by submergence that spread the Appalachian seaway westward to the Mississippi Valley, and soon brought another vast arctic flood creeping southward across western Canada by way of the Mackenzie Valley region in a seaway nearly 1,000 miles wide. This joined the embayment that then occupied the Cordilleran Trough in Utah and Nevada. From this time until late in the period the two great geosynclines were more or less persistently submerged and received a great thickness of sediments; but the Central States were barely awash, or slightly emergent, during much of the time. Figure 139 represents the maximum submergence of Late Devonian time, but should be considered only a temporary stage in an ever-changing scene. Possibly 40 percent of the present continent was submerged at one time or another during both the Middle and Late Devonian epochs, but toward the close of the period emergence was gradual and finally complete.

The Acadian Disturbance. About the middle of the period, uplift was renewed in Appalachia, and the geosyncline was more rapidly depressed. These movements continued with increasing intensity until the close of the period and culminated in the formation of a bold mountain chain that followed the axis of old Appalachia down through the Maritime Provinces of Canada and the New England states and thence southward along the present Piedmont belt to about the latitude of Cape Hatteras (Fig. 139, right). This orogeny was first recognized in the Maritime Provinces—the Land of Acadia—and for this reason it has been named the **Acadian Disturbance.**

The Acadian Mountains were a second generation of Appalachians, much like the Taconian Range of the Late Ordovician and involving nearly

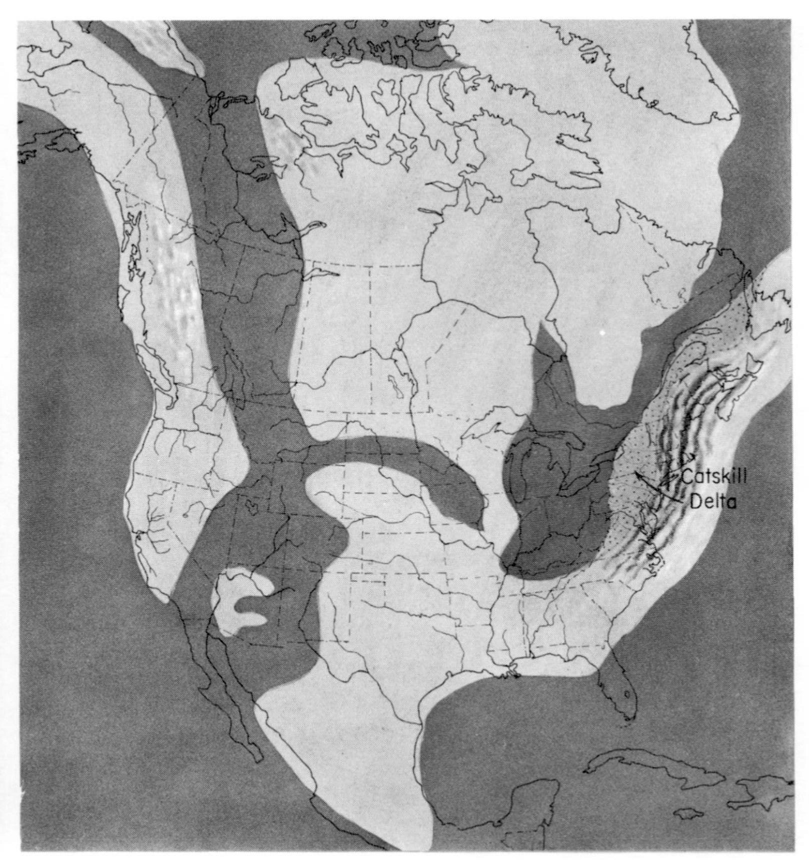

Figure 139. Devonian Paleogeography. Left, Early Devonian; right, Late Devonian lands and seas. In the latter, note the Acadian highlands bordered on the west by the Catskill Delta.

the same region. In Acadia, as in New England, the Devonian and older sedimentary formations of the geosyncline were strongly folded and much disturbed by igneous intrusion. The effect was both profound and permanent, uplifting and folding all the rocks in this part of the Appalachian Trough and destroying its geosynclinal nature so that the seas never again traversed it.

From New England south, the disturbance was east of the present fold belt, in the area of the Piedmont and the Coastal Plain and probably that of the continental shelf. Although the sedimentary rocks have since been destroyed here, and details of the Acadian orogeny cannot be restored, the Devonian formations still preserved in the geosyncline indicate the presence of marked highlands at least as far south as Cape Hatteras.

The volume of the sediments derived from the erosion of Appalachia and preserved in the geosyncline gives some measure of the uplift. The detrital Devonian formations from New York to Virginia, inclusive, have been estimated to measure some 63,000 cubic miles. This is approximately the volume of the modern Sierra Nevada, which exceed 75 miles in width, are 400 miles in length, and rise to nearly 3 miles above sealevel along their crest. Since the deposits laid down in the geosyncline were all derived from the western slope of the Acadian Mountains, it is clear that Appalachia was much more than 100 miles wide or was very lofty or was continuously uplifted during erosion.

The above estimate does not include the deposits in Acadia or those originally laid down along the mountain front between Acadia and New York and subsequently eroded away.

While the Catskill Delta (see p. 181) was forming in New York, a similar great delta was building in Gaspé, and its non-marine beds near Escuminac, at the head of Chaleur Bay, have yielded land plants and many fishes, including the probable forerunner of land vertebrates (Figs. 160 and 164).

Igneous Activity. Much igneous activity accompanied the Acadian disturbance. Great thicknesses of bedded lavas and tuffs in southern Quebec, Gaspé, New Brunswick, and Maine record volcanoes that were active during Devonian time. In most of New England and parts of New Brunswick, such extrusives have been largely eroded away, exposing the related deep-seated plutonic rocks.

The granite core of the White Mountains is an example. Here the intrusions began during the middle of the period and were renewed on a larger scale as the Acadian disturbance came to its climax.[1] Other Devonian batholiths are the granites at St. George and in the Little Megantic Mountains of New Brunswick,[2] the granites that make up most of Nova Scotia, and those that form the cores of such monadnocks as Mt. Katahdin in Maine.

Throughout New England large-scale igneous activity continued intermittently during Mississippian and possibly early Pennsylvanian time, and it is difficult to separate these deep-seated intrusions of Devonian and later age. It now seems probable, on the basis of radioactive dates, that many of these, notably the pegmatites of Central Connecticut, are Mississippian or possibly early Pennsylvanian.[3]

A widespread layer of volcanic ash near the top of the Onondaga limestone in Pennsylvania, West Virginia, and Ohio must have been derived from Mid-Devonian volcanoes in Appalachia.[4]

In Nova Scotia, a thick section of Silurian and Early Devonian formations in Annapolis Valley is intruded by granite that a few miles to the east is unconformably overlain by an early Mississippian formation in which pebbles of the granite are included. Clearly this granite is a Devonian intrusive.[5]

DEVONIAN STRATIGRAPHY

Appalachian Province. The Devonian system reaches the impressive thickness of 12,000 to 15,000 feet in New York and Pennsylvania where it is exceptionally exposed and can be studied in three dimensions; the mountain folds in Pennsylvania expose sections paralleling the axis of the geosyncline, and the north end of the Allegheny Plateau shows an east-west cross section in New York nearly at right angles to the geosyncline. A section along the New York-Pennsylvania boundary (Fig. 140) displays the most significant relations.

The Lower Devonian formations are relatively thin, have their maximum thickness along the Hudson Valley and the mountain front in Pennsylvania,

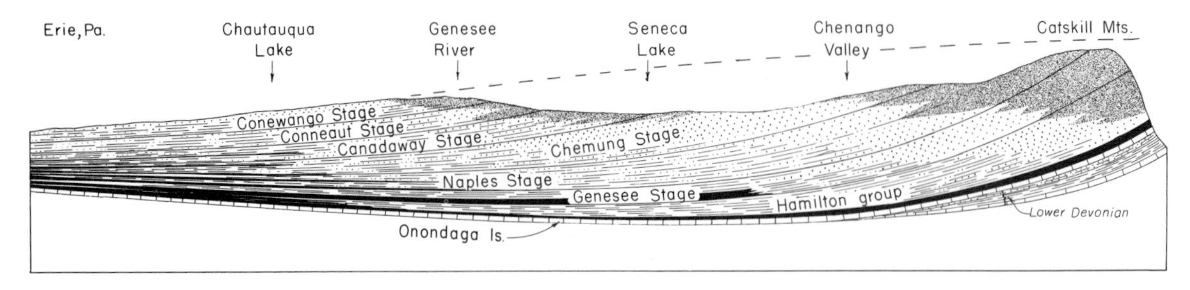

Figure 140. Cross section of the Devonian System from the Hudson Valley in New York to Erie, Pennsylvania. Section about 250 miles long; vertical scale greatly exaggerated. The broken lines above the section indicate the inferred original extent of beds that have been removed by later erosion. Redbeds are shaded; black shales are in solid black; gray shales are in close parallel lines. (Data from Chadwich and from Cooper.)

and thin to a feathered edge in the longitude of Syracuse and Birmingham. During their formation deposition was confined to a narrow seaway along the axis of the geosyncline (Fig. 139, left). At this time Appalachia must have been very low since the Helderbergian formations are chiefly limestones or calcareous shales even in the easternmost outcrops. Locally in Pennsylvania and Virginia it passes into sandstone, probably indicating the position of major streams debouching from Appalachia. The Oriskany sandstone is coarser but is made of nearly pure quartz sand with a calcareous matrix and is generally less than 50 feet thick (locally as much as 250 feet in Pennsylvania).

Chart 4. Correlation of important Devonian sections

Series	Stages	McKenzie Valley	Manitoba	Mont.–Wyo.	Nevada	Mich.	New York (west … east)	Penn.	Stages	Series
Upper	Conn.	?				Antrim black sh.	Connewango Stage	Catskill redbeds	Conn.	Upper
	Cassadaga	Imperial fm.		? Three Forks fm.			Conneaut Stage; Canadaway Stage; Blossurg; redbeds		Cassadaga	
	Chem.			– – ?– –			Angola bl. sh.; Chemung ss.; Montrose; Cattawissa	Wellsburg ss.; Cayuta ss.	Chem.	
	Finger L.			Jefferson ls. ?	Devils Gate ls.; Muddy Pk.; Sultan ls.	Squaw Bay	Enfield f.; Katsburg; Cashaqua sh.; Ithaca fm.; Oneota; West R. bl. sh.; Cornell f.; Sherburne ss.; Unadilla ss.; Onteora redbeds	Brailier sh.; Trimmers Rock; Losh Run ss.; Harrell	Finger L.	
Middle	T.	?				Potters Farm	Tully ls.; Gilboa ss.; Kater-skill	Rush fm.	T.	Middle
	Toughnioga	? Canol fm.				Norway Pt.; Alpina ls.	Windom sh.; Kashong sh.; Portland=Pt.=ls.; Ludlowville f.; Centerfield ls.; Levanna bl. sh.; Panther Mt. ss.; Kiskatom redbeds	Mahantango ss, sh	Toughniog.	
	Cazeno.	? Kee Scarp fm.; Hare Indian fm.	Manitoban; Winnipegosis; Elm Pt. ls.		Nevada ls.	Rogers City; Silica sh.; Dundee ls.	Stafford ls.; Mottville ss.; Cardiff sh.; Oatka Cr. bl. sh.; Chittenango sh.; Ashokan; M. Marion; Bakoven sh	Marcellus sh.	Cazeno.	
	On.	Hume fm.		?		Detroit R.	Onondaga ls.	Needmore sh	On.	
Lower	Dp.	?		Bear Tooth Butte fm.	Nevada ls.	Bois Blanc	Oriskany ss.	Ridgeley ss.	Dp.	Lower
	Helderb.	Bear Rock fm. ?		?			New Scotland ls.; Coeymans ls.	Shriver chert; Mandata sh.; New Scotland ls. ss.	Helderb.	

It therefore appears to represent a sandy mantle that had long been accumulating over the crystalline rocks and at this time was transported into the geosyncline. So thin a sheet of pure quartz sand could hardly be the result of strong uplift or of rapid erosion. It was derived from two distinct sources; a thin sheet of sand (generally not over 10 feet thick) exposed along the Mohawk Valley and locally as far west as Mackinac Strait in Michigan, was derived from the Canadian Shield; the thicker sandstone ranging from Virginia to Maine was limited to the eastern side of the geosyncline and was clearly derived from Appalachia. This formation is extensively used as a source of pure quartz for the manufacture of glass.

The Middle Devonian begins with the Onondaga limestone (Figs. 141 and 142) that extends in a continuous sheet about 100 feet thick across New York State and westward into Ohio where it gradually thins around the Cincinnati Arch. Corals are abundant and patch-reefs of considerable size occur in western New York and Ohio. The most famous of these causes a rapid in the Ohio River at Louisville, Kentucky, commonly known as The Falls of the Ohio.

Obviously Appalachia was still low while the Onondaga limestone was forming, and the sea was shallow and clear as far east as the present Hudson River. But a marked change in regimen followed. The Hamilton group is a great wedge of detrital formations some 2,500 feet thick in eastern New York and about 2,000 feet thick in central Pennsylvania, thinning progressively toward the west. Along the face of the Catskills (and down the strike in Pennsylvania) the Hamilton group begins with dark-gray silty shale bearing marine fossils. This

Figure 141. Onondaga limestone in a quarry one mile south of Stafford, New York. This pure limestone is extensively quarried all across New York State for the manufacture of portland cement, and for crushed stone for construction and road building.

Figure 142. Onondaga limestone disconformably overlying the latest Silurian (Cobleskill limestone) in the Bennett Quarry at north Buffalo, western New York. The Bertie limestone is the source of many of the Silurian eurypterids discussed on page 171. (Charles Schuchert.)

is followed by siltstone and gray sandstone (Fig. 143), also carrying marine fossils, and these in turn by a complex of redbeds alternating with gray, cross-bedded sandstones and conglomerates. In this upper part no marine fossils have been found, but traces of land plants and the imprints of roots are widespread, and stumps of trees, river clams, and fresh-water fishes occur locally. In gray sandstones quarried for the dam at Gilboa reservoir, large stumps occur in abundance at three distinct levels (Fig. 144). Fossils occur chiefly in the gray sandstones while mudcracks are widespread in the red shales.

Quite evidently conditions had changed greatly along the Appalachian Trough during deposition of the Hamilton group. At first this area was a muddy sea floor, then a shallow sandy sea floor and finally a lowland across which streams threaded their way through primeval forests. These streams were choked with sand and gravel now preserved as the gray cross-bedded sandstone and conglomerate. During floods, red mud from the warm humid slopes of Appalachia was spread widely over the interstream lowlands. Rainfall was probably seasonal so that such deposits of fresh mud were dried and cracked before the next flood season. Since conglomerates increase in coarseness toward the top, it is clear that Appalachia was rising.

As these redbeds are traced westward along the strike (Fig. 140), they grade laterally into gray sandstones bearing marine fossils, and, miles farther west, the sandstones grade into siltstones and finally into soft calcareous shales, rich in fossils of many kinds. Still farther west the shales become black. The shoreline of any particular time obviously lay where the plant-bearing redbeds are replaced by gray marine sandstone, and the redbeds here record the exposed surface of a great delta. The westward change to finer and

Figure 143. Evenly bedded marine sandstone (Mount Marion beds) low in the Hamilton group at High Falls, New York. On a bedding plane in this formation a great colony of the primitive starfish (*Devonaster*) was preserved with clams some of which were feeding when overwhelmed by shifting sand. Higher in the face of the Catskills these marine beds are succeeded by some 2,000 feet of non-marine redbeds. (Carl O. Dunbar.)

Figure 144. Stump of a giant tree fern, *Eospermatopteris*, being hoisted from a quarry in the Middle Devonian sandstone at the Gilboa reservoir south of Schoharie, New York. A two-foot ruler lies in the hollow from which the stump was lifted. This is the scene of the Gilboa forests shown in Figure 165.

finer grain proves, of course, that the sediment was coming from Appalachia.

The Upper Devonian formations generally resemble the Hamilton group. Although divided into six stages, each of these grades laterally from redbeds in the east to black shale in the west.[6] The redbed facies is limited to the eastern margin of the Hamilton group, but in successively higher zones in the Upper Devonian it spreads farther west (Fig. 140); obviously the exposed (subaerial) part of the delta was growing, and the shoreline was being crowded back. Late in the period the shore was far out in western New York and in northwestern Pennsylvania. This was probably not the work of a single stream but of several that together built a great compound delta whose subaerial surface formed a wide coastal lowland some 200 miles across, and the subaqueous part extended clear across the geosyncline into Ohio. This was the great **Catskill Delta**, so named for the grand exposure in the Catskill Mountains of New York.

Within the redbed facies occur widespread lenses of gray and locally much cross-bedded sandstone and conglomerate (Figs. 145 and 146). The basal contact of these coarse deposits commonly shows cut and fill relations to the underlying red shales and it is clear that they were deposited in the channels and over the low ground bordering meandering streams; the red shales were laid down over the higher part of broad floodplains during high water and were left exposed during the dry seasons.

West of the redbed facies at each horizon the gray sandstones laid down on a shallow sea floor are richly fossiliferous (Figs. 138 and 147). Still farther west the siltstones and shales are sparsely fossiliferous, probably indicating deeper water.

Figure 145. Lens of gray sandstone in the midst of maroon shales of the Chemung Stage (Catawissa beds) near Parksville, New York, showing cut-and-fill contact at the base. (Carl O. Dunbar.)

Figure 146. Cross-bedding in a gray sandstone unit in the Cattawissa redbeds at Neversink Dam south of the Catskills in New York. This sandstone like the one shown in Figure 145 is in the redbed facies of the Chemung Stage. (Carl O. Dunbar.)

This facies is grandly exposed in the Portage Gorge of Genesee River south of Rochester (Fig. 148). Still further west many of the Devonian units pass into black shale (Fig. 149).

The thickest part of the delta was in Pennsylvania, not far from Harrisburg, where the valley of the Susquehanna exposes about 13,000 feet of Middle and Upper Devonian strata, of which the upper 5,000 feet are red. From central Pennsylvania the system thins to the south and west.

West of the geosyncline, in Ohio, Indiana, and Kentucky, the Devonian is thin, and only parts of the period are represented; the Middle Devonian is chiefly limestone, but the Upper is generally black shale.[7]

Michigan Basin. Michigan was the site of a basinlike depression separated from the geosyncline by a northward extension of the Cincinnati Arch, which was emergent from time to time or at least served as a threshhold to prevent the spread of detrital sediments from Appalachia. Here the Middle Devonian is exceptionally well developed, mostly in limestone facies. Coral reefs are strikingly displayed in some of these beds (Fig. 150). Because of the difference in facies and the partial isolation, the faunas of New York and Michigan are largely different, but a few key horizons can be identified in both and permit the correlation shown in Figure 151.

Cordilleran Province. The Devonian formations of the West are largely calcareous and generally much thinner than those of the East. They are also less well known. In the deeper part of the Cordilleran Geosyncline in eastern Nevada (Eureka district), however, they are 4,000 to 6,000 feet thick and appear to represent nearly all of Middle and Late Devonian time. They are also thick in the Canadian Rockies of Alberta (Fig. 152), and from Jasper National Park northward pass largely into a dark shaly facies. Under the plains of Alberta the Devonian System is thick and complex, including extensive coral reefs as well as thick salt deposits. East of the Cordilleran Geosyncline the Devonian rocks overlapped widely the western part of the Canadian Shield, and here they are much thinner and are chiefly calcareous. Here a widespread sheet of Middle Devonian limestone is distinguished by the striking, large brachiopod, *Stringocephalus* (Fig. 153). This genus is widespread in Eurasia and apparently reached America from the Mackenzie Valley region and migrated southward down the Cordilleran Trough as far as Utah and Nevada, but it failed to reach the Appalachian Province. Another "key horizon," high in the Devonian of the West, is marked by the striking spirifer, *Theodossia hungerfordi* (Fig. 154), another immigrant from Eurasia that spread southward to New Mexico and eastward to Iowa but failed to get into the Appalachian Province.

In the lower part of the Mackenzie Valley the Middle and Upper Devonian formations thicken greatly to the north and pass largely into detrital sediments, indicating local highlands in the far north. In Ellesmere Land, west of northern Greenland, there is also a very thick Devonian section of coarse detritus.

Special interest attaches to the non-marine strata of Central East Greenland, which contain a marvelous record of the earliest known land vertebrates along with abundant fishes and land plants.[8] These deposits include red and gray sandstones and shales and at the base have thick, coarse conglomerates. The series reaches a thickness of at least 3,000 and possibly 10,000 feet, and implies the rather rapid erosion of near-by highlands that lay to the east of the present coast of Greenland.

Figure 147. Chemung sandstones with natural molds of the spiriferoid brachiopod, *Platyrachella*, and a coarse-ribbed *Atrypa*. Glory Hill, 2 miles west of Waverly, New York. (Yale Peabody Museum.)

Figure 148. Upper Devonian shales and flaggy sandstones of the Naples Stage in the gorge of Genesee River near Mount Morris, New York. (New York State Museum.)

THE OLD RED SANDSTONE OF EUROPE

The early Paleozoic systems (Cambrian to Silurian) have yielded abundant remains of marine life, but not until the Devonian do we get the first clear glimpse of the creatures of the land and the streams. There is special fascination, therefore, in the non-marine Devonian rocks which hold the record of the primeval spread of the forests and the coming of air-breathing land vertebrates. The American formations of the Catskill Delta have been noted; in the British Isles similar deposits, long known as the Old Red sandstone, are vastly thicker and more fossiliferous. They lie in a series of five structural basins (Fig. 155) that were formed between the ranges of the old Caledonian Mountains. During Devonian time these basins received the sediments from the rugged mountains just as the California Trough is now being aggraded by the streams from the Sierra Nevada. The several narrow basins subsided as they were filled, so that vast thicknesses (up to 37,000 feet) of sands and muds accumulated without allowing the surface of the basins to sink below sealevel.

The conditions of deposition and the nature of the climate may be inferred from the study of these rocks and their fossils. The sediments were commonly poorly sorted, and they vary greatly from place to place, these features suggesting the work of streams rather than the sea. Conglomerates locally of great thickness, and in places including coarse blocks several feet in diameter, represent fans built where torrential streams debouched into the basins. The purer sandstones are commonly cross-bedded, like the channel sands of streams. The siltstones and shales are marked with mudcracks at many horizons, and in places bear the imprints of Devonian raindrops. Obviously these beds are the deposits of floodplains where the mud spread during the wet season lay exposed during the dry months that followed.

Although red is the dominant color, there are also thick members of greenish-gray sandstone and siltstone and gray shales. The red sediments are completely oxidized; hence they must have come to rest where the drainage permitted good aeration of the soil during the dry seasons. The gray beds, on the contrary, were formed where the ground water stood near the surface, or at times when rainfall was distributed throughout the year so as to prevent deep drying and oxidation. The widely distributed mudcracks bear witness to seasons of drought, but there are no bedded salt or gypsum deposits in the series, and dune sands are lacking or unimportant. Moreover, the abundant fossils show that this was not a desert. Instead, it must have been a region of semiarid climate, one in which the rainfall was largely seasonal, so that periods of plentiful moisture alternated with seasons of drought. This would cause the frequent wetting and drying of the soil so conducive to the formation of red sediments, and would account for the mudcracks on the wide floodplains.

The dominant animals of the Old Red are freshwater fishes, of which there are many kinds. Eurypterids also are common in the lowest beds. Although the earlier eurypterids are generally as-

Figure 149. Black shale of the Naples Stage at Mount Morris dam on Genesee River above Mount Morris, New York. Height of exposure about 175 feet. The Middlesex and Rhinestreet shales are black; the Cashaqua shale is bluish gray. Equivalent beds are more than twice as thick in the Finger Lakes region, 75 miles to the east, where they consist of flaggy sandstone. (Carl O. Dunbar.)

Figure 150. A small coral reef (lighter and non-bedded) in the Alpina limestone at Alpena, Michigan. Larger reefs in this region are as much as 50 feet thick. (Preston E. Cloud.)

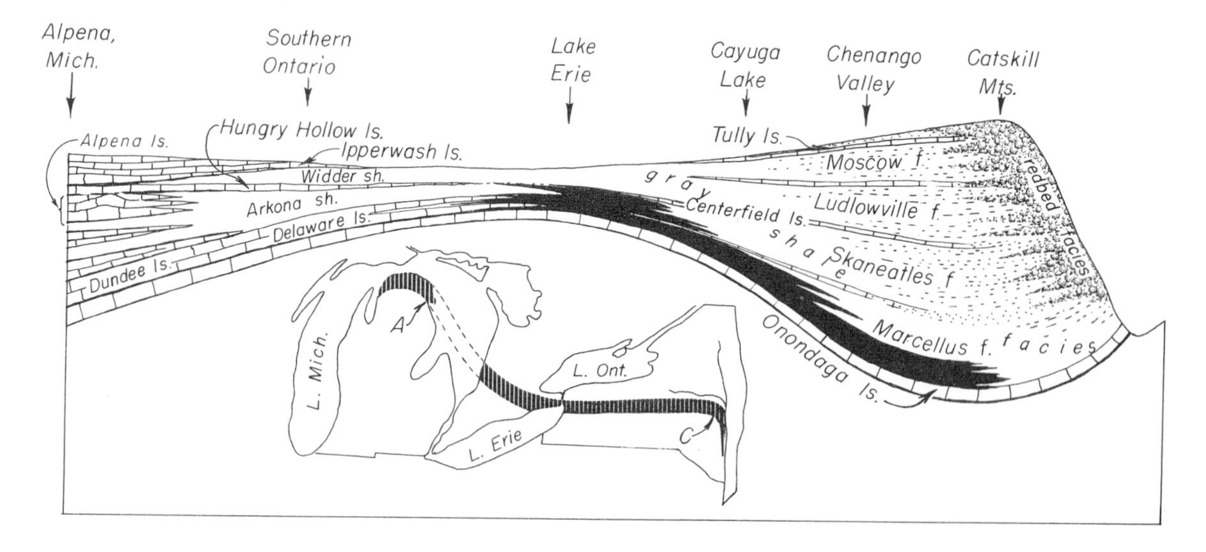

Figure 151. Stratigraphic section from the Catskill Mountains in New York to the Michigan Basin. The inset map shows the outcrop belt followed by the section. Black shale is shown in solid black; gray marine shales are unshaded; the redbed facies is darkly shaded. (Adapted from G. A. Cooper, et al.)

Figure 152. Mount Devon, about 20 miles north of Lake Louise in the Canadian Rockies of Alberta, exposing about 2,000 feet of Devonian limestone. (Charles D. Walcott.)

sociated with marine fossils, those of the Devonian and later times are always found with fresh-water fossils and land plants, indicating that by Devonian time they had invaded the rivers, either to spawn or to make their permanent abode. Plant fossils are locally abundant.

CLIMATE

The climate undoubtedly varied with the topography during Devonian time just as it does today; but there is abundant evidence that climatic belts were not strongly marked as now, and the polar seas could hardly have been icebound. Corals then thrived as far north as Hudson Bay and made extensive reefs in Michigan and in Alberta; and at least three European brachiopod faunas reached the United States by way of the Mackenzie Valley seaway.

This route brought them well within the Arctic Circle and through present polar seas. Examples of this kind are (1) the ***Stringocephalus* fauna** and (2) the ***Hypothyridina* fauna** of the Middle Devonian, and (3) the ***Theodossia hungerfordi* fauna** of the Upper Devonian.

Furthermore, the land plants are much alike in the British Isles, Spitzbergen, East Greenland, and New York. Such distribution of animals and plants would have been impossible if the climatic zones had been strongly marked as they are now.

The redbeds of the Catskill region and East Greenland, like the Old Red of Europe, have been interpreted by some geologists as the deposits of arid basins, but the abundance of fossils, the general lack of wind-blown sands, and other features make this altogether improbable. In the modern world, red soil and red mantle form chiefly where the climate is humid and warm, and where the

Figure 153. *Stringocephalus,* a large brachiopod characterizing a widespread faunal zone in the Devonian of western North America and Eurasia.

Figure 154. *Theodossia hungerfordi,* a distinctly specialized spiriferoid, which marks a widespread faunal zone in the Upper Devonian of western North America and European Russia. From the Lime Creek shale of Cerro Gordo County, Iowa. (Yale Peabody Museum.)

rainfall is seasonal. The warmth and humidity provide ideal conditions for the thorough oxidation of the mantle, so that the iron is changed to a reddish hydroxide. Strong seasonal rainfall in the basins of deposition allows drying and decay of the vegetation, which would otherwise tend to reduce the iron and produce dark colors. It also favors the formation and preservation of mudcracks, a very striking feature of redbeds. Although the Devonian redbeds appear generally to have come from warm humid slopes, there is local evidence of considerable aridity in Montana and Alberta where much anhydrite was precipitated during part of Late Devonian time (the Potlatch anhydrite). In the Michigan Basin, also, thick salt beds occur in the lower part of the Middle Devonian sequence.[9]

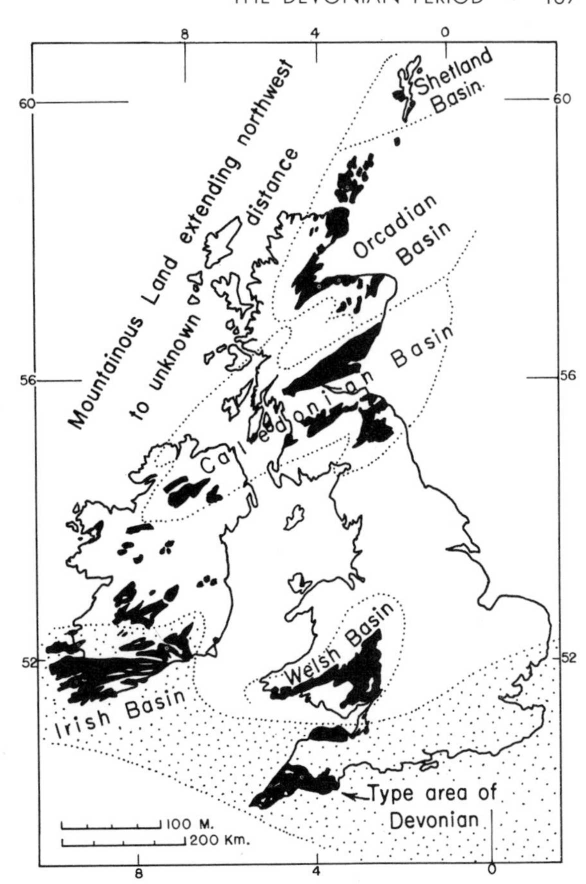

Figure 155. Map showing distribution of the Devonian formations (black) in the British Isles. The stippled area represents the probable extent of marine and brackish water in Devonian time. The other areas, outlined by dotted lines were intermont basins in which the non-marine Old Red sandstone accumulated. (After Barrell.)

DEVONIAN LIFE

Evolution among the Marine Invertebrates. The Devonian seas swarmed with animals of many kinds (Figs. 156, 157). Where the seas were clear, **corals** (Pl. 7, figs. 1–3) made reefs, and some of the species reached large sizes. The greatest of all cup corals, *Siphonophrentis gigantea*, produced individual coralla as much as 3 inches across and 2 feet high. Compound species locally formed "heads" as great as 8 feet across. Among these reefs the honeycomb corals were especially prominent. **Bryozoa** of many kinds, and **crinoids** as well, also lived on the reefs, and hydroid "coral," *Stromatopora*, formed encrusting deposits, cementing other shells together.

Brachiopods (Pl. 7, figs. 6–16) were now at their climax, and the spirifers were particularly varied. No fewer than 700 kinds of Devonian brachiopods are known in North America alone. **Pelecypods** (Pl. 8, figs. 1–6) found the muddy and sandy bottoms of the Middle and Late Devonian seas to their liking and now became more common and more diversified than ever before. Some of these, adapted to burrowing, took on forms much like that of the modern razor clams, whereas others were attached by elastic threads like modern pearl clams, and, like them, became "winged." The **gastropods** (Pl. 8, figs. 13–15) are not as a rule well preserved or highly diversified. **Cephalopods** were varied, although only locally abundant. In some of them the margins of the septa were folded or ruffled so that the sutures between septa and shell show strong flexures (Pl. 8, figs. 9 and 12). These are the primitive forms of the **ammonites**, a tribe of cephalopods that became steadily more important in the Late Paleozoic seas and dominated all other kinds of mollusks during the Mesozoic Era. Their appearance at this time is one of the most significant advances in the marine life of the Devonian Period.

Although trilobites (Pl. 8, figs. 7 and 8) were on the decline and relatively few kinds are found, they were locally abundant, and some among them were of large size, one species of **Dalmanites** reaching a length of 29 inches, probably the record for all time.

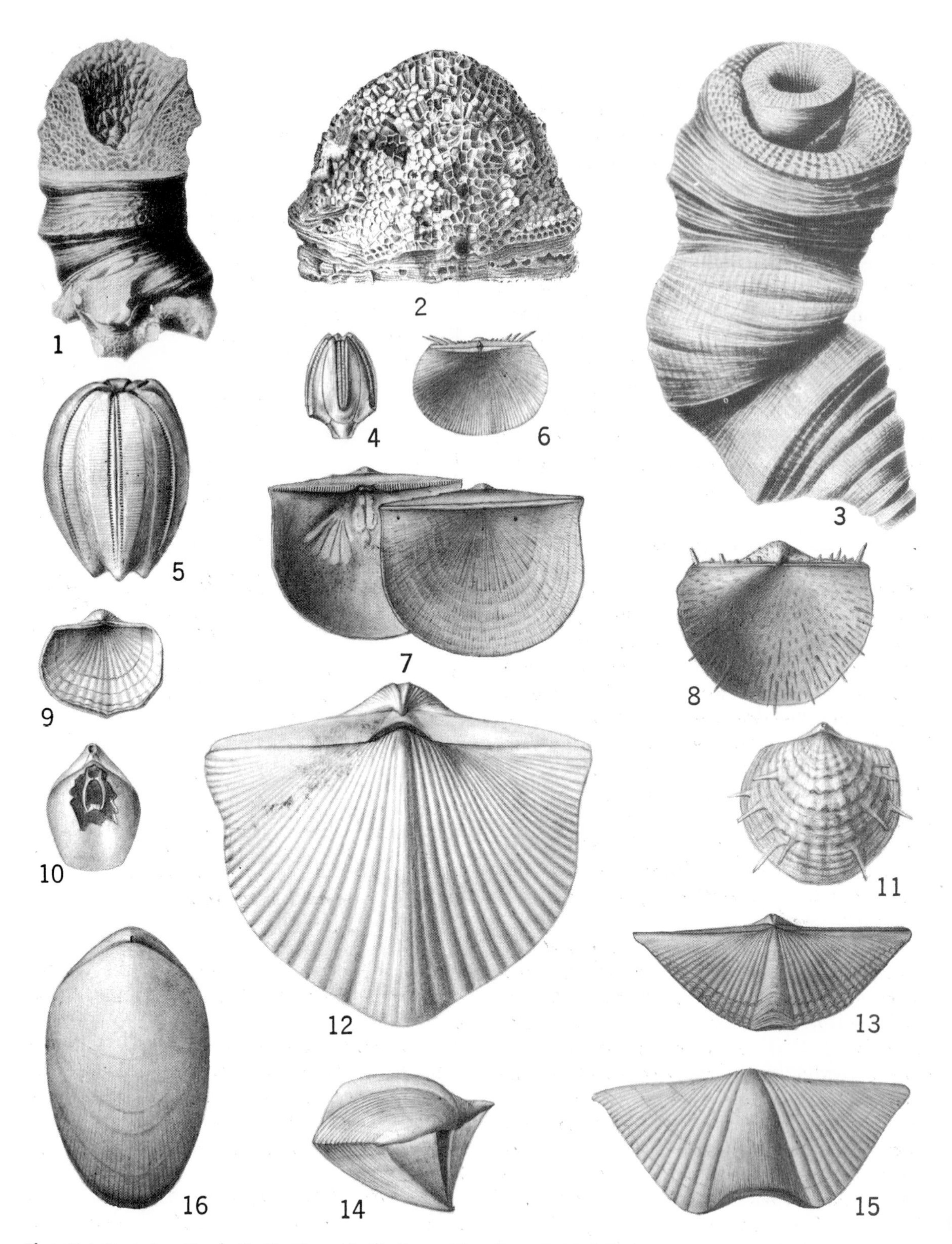

Plate 7. Devonian Corals (1–3), Blastoids (4–5), and Brachiopods (6–16).

Figure 1, *Cystiphyllum vesiculosum;* 2, *Favosites conicus;* 3, *Heliophyllum halli;* 4, *Pentremitidea filosa;* 5, *Nucleocrinus verneuili;* 6, *Chonetes coronatus;* 7, *Stropheodonta demissa* (dorsal view of shell and interior of pedicle valve); 8, *Productella callawayensis;* 9, *Tropidoleptus carinatus;* 10, *Cranaena sullivanti;* 11, *Atrypa rockfordensis;* 12, *Costispirifer arenosus;* 13, *Mucrospirifer mucronatus;* 14, 15, *Platyrachella mesistrialis* (oblique view with ventral beak down, and dorsal view); 16, *Rensselaeria elongata.* All natural size. (Drawn by L. S. Douglass.)

Groups that were less common but on the increase were the **blastoids** (Pl. 7, figs. 4 and 5), **starfishes**, and **echinoids**. A great slab of Hamilton sandstone, found at Mount Marion, New York, and now in the State Museum at Albany, originally preserved the casts of more than 400 starfish, some of which died hovering over clams they were in the act of devouring just as the modern starfish eat oysters. Crinoids were as common and varied as in the Silurian. Siliceous sponges, somewhat like the modern "Venus' flower basket," were locally abundant, especially in the Late Devonian in central New York.

Ascendancy of the Fishes. Although scattered bony plates occur in rocks as old as Middle Ordovician, fish remains are extremely rare until we come to the Devonian, and then they are locally abundant and highly diversified. This must have been a time of rapid evolution for the group, since before the close of the period several of the great orders of fishes were present, and they were widely distributed in the seas and in lakes and streams.

Sharks were common in the seas, but are known chiefly from teeth and fin-spines, since their skeleton is cartilaginous and their scales microscopic.

A distantly related group of fishes, the **Arthrodires**, had the anterior part of the body armored with a cuirass of bony plates. Some of these (Fig. 158) reached a length of about 20 feet and were the largest animals of their time. Although abundant and highly successful in the Late Devonian seas they were destined for a short career and became extinct early in the next period.

Far greater interest attaches to the **Choanichthyes**, a primitive stock of air-breathing fishes that was dominant in Devonian time but is now nearing extinction. The name refers to a feature not found in any other fishes, namely, a pair of openings in the roof of the mouth which communicate with the external nostrils and permit breathing through the nose, as in land animals (Gr. *Choana*, internal nostril + *ichthyos*, fish). This is the stock from which all the higher vertebrates were to develop.[10]

At least five genera of this group are still extant, but unfortunately they occupy remote parts of the

Figure 156. Reconstruction of a bit of a Devonian coral reef with associated seaweeds, sponges, and other marine animals: *a*, crinoid; *b*, seaweed; *c*, corals; *d*, sponges; *e*, snail. About 1/10 natural size. (Buffalo Museum of Natural History.)

Figure 157. Life of a Devonian sea floor, restored. Center, a frilled cephalopod attacking a trilobite; left, a large crinoid, and below it a spiny trilobite; right, other trilobites, shells, and seaweeds. (New York State Museum.)

world and are not commonly known. Perhaps the most remarkable is *Protopterus*, the African lungfish (Fig. 159), which lives in the upper reaches of the Nile, where humid winter seasons alternate with dry summers. During the wet season *Protopterus* swims about and breathes by means of gills like any other fish; but during the summer, when the swamps go dry, it burrows down into the mud and makes a juglike chamber, where it goes into a resting stage like hibernation. Unlike the condition in most fishes, its swim-bladder is connected with the throat, so that air can be inhaled or exhaled at will; furthermore, this organ is supplied with a plexus of blood vessels which have the power to absorb oxygen and discharge carbon dioxide. In short, the swim-bladder in this fish is a

Figure 158. Model of the giant arthrodire, *Dinichthys*. Actual length about 20 feet. (American Museum of Natural History.)

rudimentary lung in both structure and function. As the water disappears during the dry season, *Protopterus* is thus able to breathe air like a land animal; but with the return of the wet season it wriggles out of its mud "cocoon" and swims and breathes again like a normal fish.

A different and perhaps more significant habit is shown by another living lungfish, *Neoceratodus*, which is found in the rivers of arid northern Australia. During the dry seasons it continues to swim about, merely coming to the surface more often for a breath of air, as the water becomes so stagnant that gill-breathing is inadequate. Its rudimentary lung merely supplements the gills at all times, but it permits this fish to live where the water becomes so stagnant and foul that others perish.

In Devonian time the Choanichthyes included two great tribes, the Dipnoi and the Crossopterygii. The living examples described above belong to the Dipnoi, and like all the fossil representatives of that group, they are deficient in having very weak fins, in lacking true teeth, and in other respects which indicate that none of them could be ancestors of the higher animals. The Crossopterygii, on the other hand, show a combination of characters that makes them almost a perfect connecting link between fishes and the lower tetrapods, that is, the four-legged, air-breathing vertebrates.

The *Crossopterygii* (Gr. *crossoi*, a fringe + *pterygion*, a fin) are so named because their fins have a stout muscular basal lobe beyond which the fin rays extend as a fringe. The fleshy basal lobe, lacking in other fish, is the significant thing, for it is the forerunner of the limb of higher animals.

Of Devonian *Crossopterygii* perhaps the best known, and certainly one of the most significant, is *Eusthenopteron* (Fig. 160), remains of which are abundant and exceptionally preserved in Upper Devonian beds near Escuminac, Quebec. Three features are noteworthy: (1) The stout skeleton in the basal lobe of each fin (Fig. 161), (2) the pattern of bony armor plate on the head, and (3) the sharp conical teeth, in which the covering enamel is deeply and intricately infolded.

Emergence of the Tetrapods. It is no accident that the appearance of terrestrial vertebrates followed closely upon the rapid evolution of air-breathing fishes. In 1928 a Danish expedition in Central East Greenland, under the leadership of Lauge Koch, discovered well-preserved skulls and fragmentary skeletons of four-footed animals (tetrapods) in late Devonian formations similar to the Old Red sandstone of Europe. From the skulls alone it was evident that they are closely related to fishes and they were at once recognized as the most primitive known group of land verte-

Figure 159. The African lungfish, *Protopterus*. Left, the fish in its "cocoon" as it was shipped from Africa to Chicago in an open tin can. The shipment was in transit for more than 6 months, during which time the fish lived thus encased in dried mud. Right, the same after being placed in an aquarium when the fish resumed its normal aquatic life. (From *Turtox News* through the courtesy of The General Biological Supply House, Inc.)

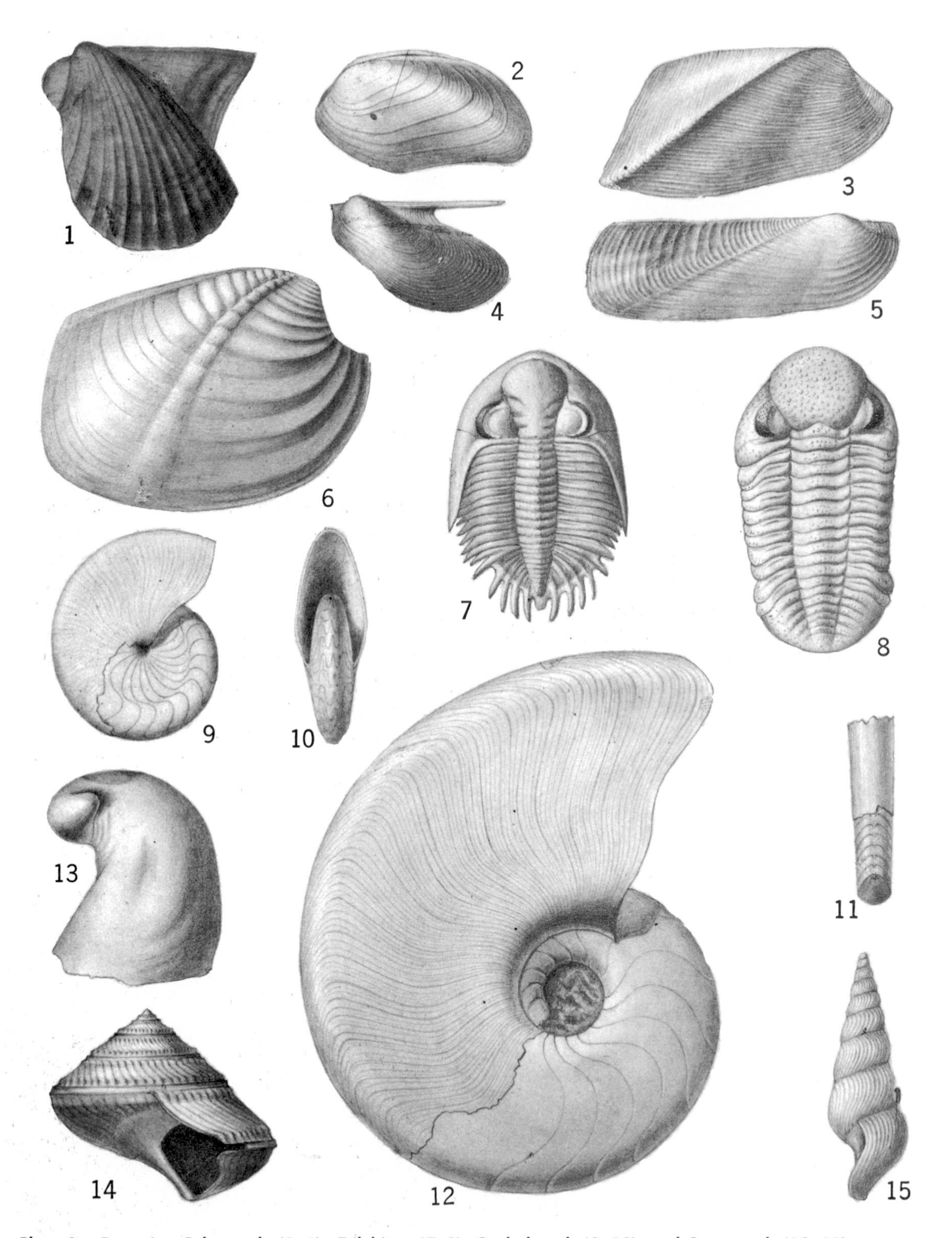

Plate 8. Devonian Pelecypods (1–6), Trilobites (7–8), Cephalopods (9–12), and Gastropods (13–15).

Figure 1, *Cornellites flabellus;* 2, *Nyassa arguta;* 3, *Goniophora hamiltonensis;* 4, *Leptodesma longispinum;* 5, *Orthonota undulata;* 6, *Grammysia bisulcata;* 7, *Greenops boothi;* 8, *Phacops rana;* 9, 10, *Tornoceras uniangulare;* 11, *Bactrites arkonensis* (fragment); 12, *Agoniatites vanuxemi;* 13, *Platyceras reflexum;* 14, *Bembexia sulcomarginata;* 15, *Loxonema hamiltoniae.* All natural size. (Drawn by L. S. Douglass.)

Figure 160. The Devonian crossopterygian, *Eusthenopteron foordi,* from the Upper Devonian beds near Escuminac, Quebec. Length of fish about 2 feet. (A model by George Gaylord Simpson.)

brates. This insight was brilliantly confirmed when a complete tail with one hind limb attached was discovered in 1948 and the tail was found to be scaled and in all respects fishlike.[11] Recently, a large additional collection has revealed all parts of the skeleton except a single toe of the front foot. This rich find is the basis for the reconstruction of the best known genus, *Ichthyostega,* shown in Figure 162.[12] It would be difficult to imagine a more perfect connecting link between fishes and primitive amphibians.

These late Devonian tetrapods belong to the dominant group of Paleozoic amphibia, the *Labyrinthodontia* (Gr. *labyrinthos,* labyrinth + *odons,* a tooth) so named because of the elaborate infolding of the enamel of the teeth (Fig. 163). Their close

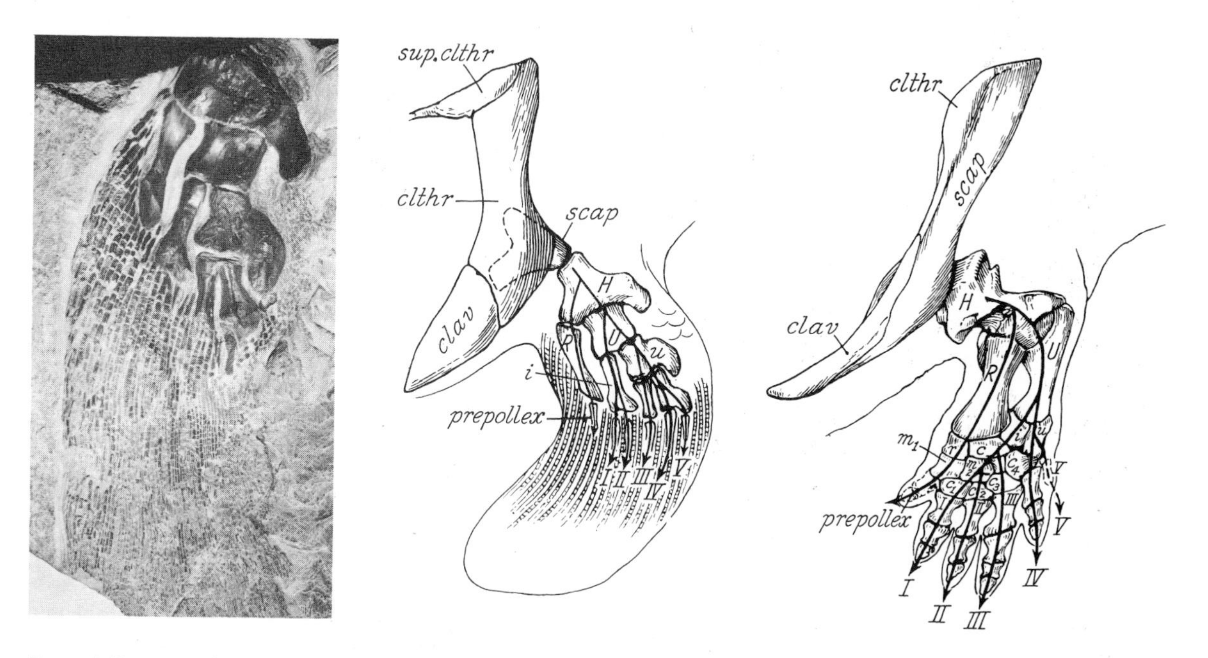

Figure 161. Resemblances between the crossopterygian fin and the limb of a primitive land animal. Left, unretouched photograph of the left front fin of *Eusthenopteron foordi;* center, diagram of the skeletal elements of the same fin; right, the corresponding limb of a late Paleozoic amphibian, *Eryops.* For restoration of *Eryops* see Figure 229. (Photograph from W. L. Bryant; diagrams after W. K. Gregory.)

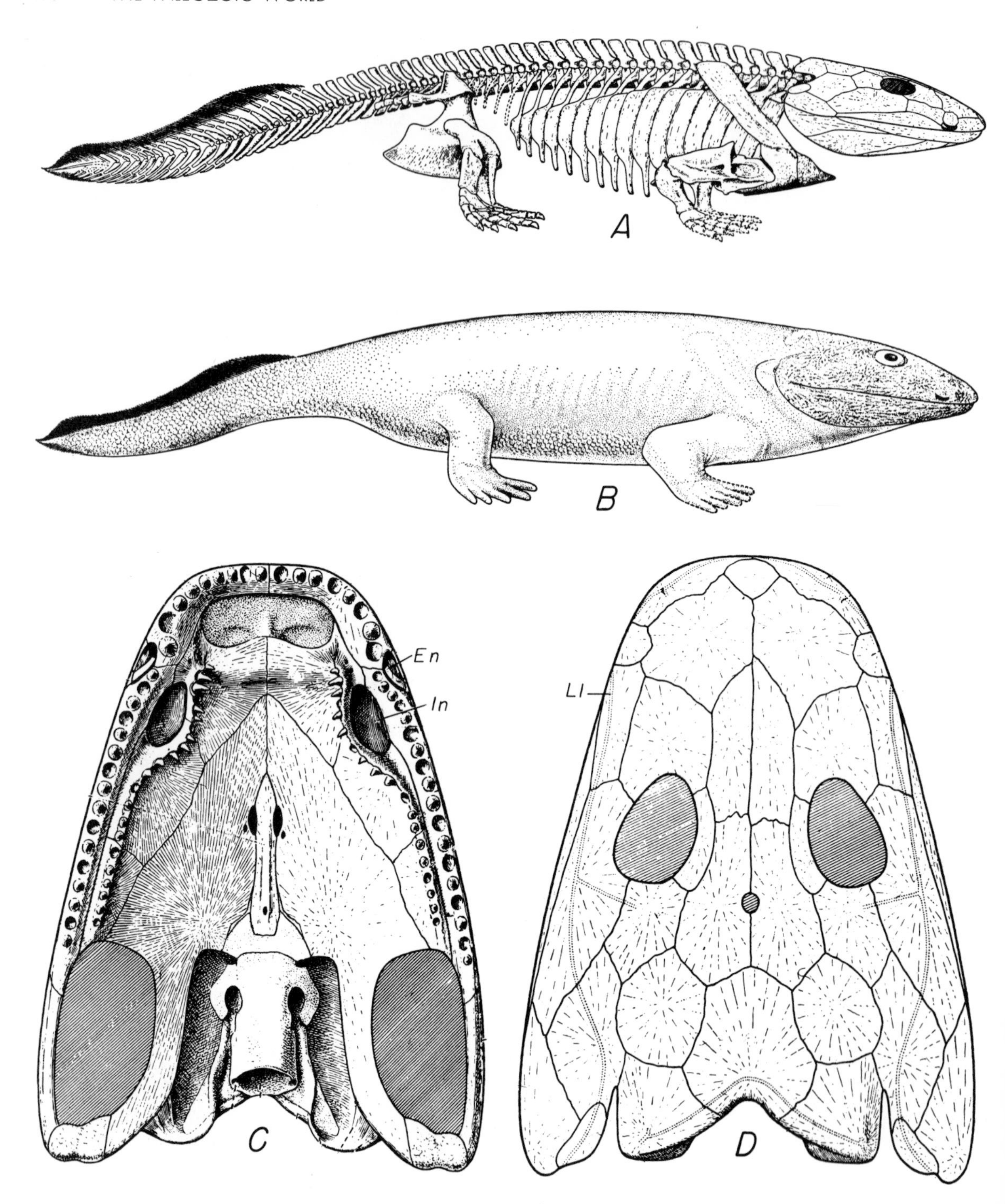

Figure 162. *Ichthyostega*, the oldest known tetrapod. Late Devonian beds of Central East Greenland. *A*, *B*, restoration of skeleton and of complete animal by Jarvik, 1959; C, *D*, ventral and dorsal views of skull after Jarvik, 1952. *En*, external nares; *In*, internal nares; *Ll*, lateral line. (Courtesy Lauge Koch and Erik Jarvik.)

Figure 163. A labyrinthodont tooth, side view and cross section (×6). The creases in the surface result from the enfolding of the surface enamel as revealed in the cross section. Position of the section is indicated by the dashed line across the side of the tooth. (Yale Peabody Museum.)

relation to the crossopteryigian fishes is confirmed not only by the tooth structure, but especially by the arrangement of the dermal bones that form the armor of their massive skulls.

It is now quite clear how the tetrapods evolved from the air-breathing fish and why the first ones were **Amphibia.** Members of that great class, which includes salamanders, toads, and frogs, are still incompletely adapted for life on land. They return to the water to spawn and lay small and simple eggs which, like those of fishes, hatch into tadpoles that breathe by means of gills and are essentially fishlike until partly grown, when legs bud out from their sides, lungs develop from their throat, and the gills are resorbed. Then they leave the water and breathe air. But they still are not quite fully adapted to land life; they must return to the water to spawn, and most of them remain in moist places and spend part of the time in the water. Comparative anatomy and ontogeny both indicate that they evolved from fishes, and the geologic record indicates rather clearly when and under what circumstances the change took place.

The Old Red type of Devonian formations accumulated over basin floors where the rainfall was seasonal. Such conditions persisted throughout much of Devonian time in eastern North America and western Europe, and here for millions of years the fish living in the streams and evanescent lakes had to endure annual seasons of drought. Again and again the shrinking waterholes brought death and destruction—but always there were some that did not go dry, and there the survivors were crowded in stagnant water, starving for oxygen. A great premium was thus placed on ability to gulp air and to use the oxygen straight. Fishes with swim-bladders that could function as lungs were thus at a great advantage and were stimulated to ever greater activity as the oxygen in the water was depleted. Those with stout fins like *Eusthenopteron* could forsake their pools in the cool of the night and flounder about the banks in short forays for food or could migrate overland to other pools. Once the lungs had reached a certain efficiency and the fins had been modified into stubby limbs, land vertebrates had arrived! The environment, of course, had not produced these modifications; it had simply selected ruthlessly those random variants that appeared from time to time and were better adapted to survive under such exacting conditions.

It is almost certain, as Romer has argued, that these late Devonian as well as the Mississippian amphibians lived normally in the water and were not, strictly speaking, land animals, but they had the ability to breath air and to leave the water when necessary.

The transition from fish to tetrapod, as conceived by W. K. Gregory,[13] is shown in Figure 164. It is supported by so many detailed technical facts that the Devonian crossopterygians are now accepted by virtually all zoologists as the ancestors of the tetrapods. For example, if we compare *Eusthenopteron* with an early amphibian, we find correspondence in the head armor, plate for plate; we find the same elaborately intricate infolding of the enamel of the teeth (Fig. 163); and there is a correspondence in other skeletal parts that cannot be attributed to coincidence. In this connection it is significant that the Devonian labyrinthodonts are more primitive than any others yet known in at least two respects, both of which emphasize their close relationship to the fishes. One of these is the submarginal position of the external nasal openings (Fig. 162), and the other is the character of the "lateral line" system (a specialized sense organ)

Figure 164. Stages in the transition of the lung fishes into labyrinthodonts, as reconstructed by W. K. Gregory. Left, the Devonian crossopterygian, *Eusthenopteron,* leaving the water to flounder about on its strong muscular fins; right an early labyrinthodont, *Diplovertebron,* from the Lower Carboniferous beds of Bohemia. (American Museum of Natural History.)

Figure 165. Reconstruction of the Middle Devonian forest at Gilboa, New York. e, a tree fern, *Eospermatopteris;* p, a primitive scale tree, *Protolepidodendron.* *Eospermatopteris* was described as a *seedfern,* whence the name (Gr. eo, dawn + *sperma,* seed + *pteris,* a kind of fern), but later study indicates that the supposed seeds were spore capsules.[16] New York State Museum at Albany.

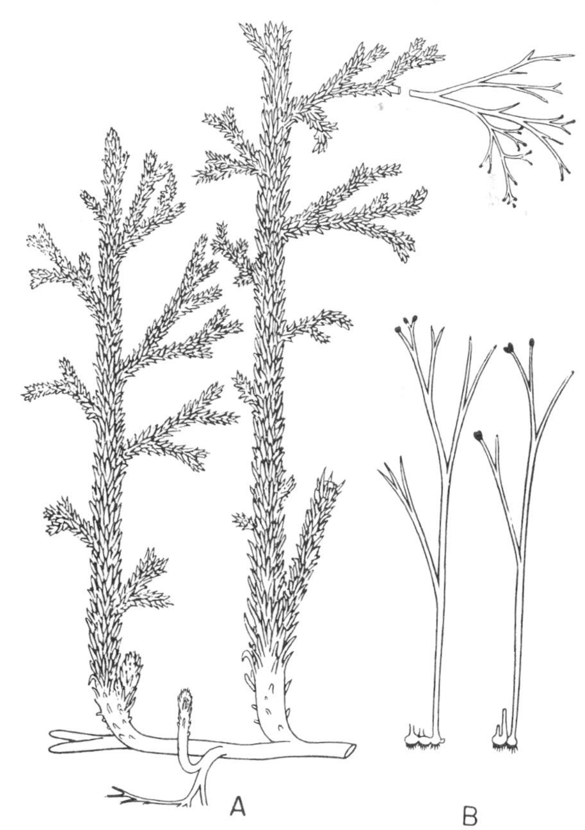

Figure 166. Primitive Devonian land plants from the Lower Devonian beds at Rhynie, Scotland. *A, Asteroxylon mackiei; B, Hornae lignieri.*

that has the form of subsurface canals, as in fishes, whereas in later amphibia it forms only shallow grooves.

Land Plants and the Spread of Forests. Evidence of land plants is very scarce before Devonian time but plentiful thereafter, and by Middle Devonian time there was a considerably diversified flora of primitive trees, some of which have left petrified stumps more than 2 feet in diameter. Among these were tall, slender scale trees (Fig. 165), primitive evergreens with large bladelike instead of needlelike leaves, and abundant ferns. These were the forerunners of the Coal Measures floras of Pennsylvanian time and in general were much like the latter.

Although soft-tissued plants were probably common long before the Devonian, no fossil wood has been found in pre-Devonian rocks. Yet no later age has failed to yield abundant evidence of land plants. We cannot avoid the inference, therefore, that the Devonian possessed the first forests that ever clothed the lands. We need to turn to the treeless barrens of the present world to appreciate what the Early Paleozoic lands looked like and to realize the significance of this great advance in the Devonian.

The oldest known deposit of well-preserved land plants is in rocks of the Old Red series near Rhynie, in the Scottish county of Aberdeen. The wonderfully preserved plants found there represent almost the simplest possible type of structure a land plant could have, and suggest the steps whereby an aquatic alga adapted itself for land life. Two of these earliest of land plants are shown in Figure 166.

Associated with these plants, all of which are herbaceous, are the remains of 3 genera and 18 species of spiders, 1 form of mite, and a primitive wingless insect, showing that the air-breathing arachnids and insects had their rise at least as far back as Early Devonian time.

Primitive land plants have now been found in abundance in the Lower Devonian of Belgium[14] and of Wyoming.[15]

REFERENCES

1. Billings, Marland P., 1945, Mechanics of igneous intrusion in New Hampshire. *Amer. Jour. Sci.*, vol. 243A, pp. 40–68.

2. Rose, Bruce, 1942, Batholith structure in central New Brunswick. *Roy. Soc. Canada, Trans.*, vol. 36, sec. 4, pp. 119–127.

3. Rodgers, John, 1952, Absolute ages of radioactive minerals from the Appalachian region. *Amer. Jour. Sci.*, vol. 250, pp. 411–427.

4. Flowers, Russell R., 1952, Lower Middle Devonian metabentonite in West Virginia. *Amer. Assoc. Petroleum Geol., Bull.*, vol. 36, pp. 2036–2038.

5. Hickox, Charles, Geology of the Central Annapolis Valley. Unpublished thesis.

6. Chadwick, G. H., 1935, Summary of Upper Devonian stratigraphy. *Amer. Midland Naturalist*, vol. 16, pp. 857–862.

7. Haas, W. H., 1956, Age and correlation of the Chattanooga shale and the Maury formation. *U.S. Geol. Surv., Prof. Paper 286*, pp. 1–45.

8. Säve-Soderbergh, G., 1932, Preliminary note on Devonian Stegocephalians from East Greenland. *Meddel. om Grønland*, vol. 94, no. 7, pp. 1–105.

______, 1934, Further contributions to the Devonian stratigraphy in East Greenland. *Ibid.*, vol. 96, no. 2, pp. 1–74.

9. Landes, K. K., G. M. Ehlers, and G. M. Stanley, 1945, Geology of the Mackinac Straits region. *Mich. Geol. Survey, Publ. 44*, pp. 1–204.

10. Romer, A S., 1945, *Vertebrate Paleontology*, 2nd ed. University of Chicago Press, Chicago, pp. 1–687.

11. Jarvik, Erik, 1952, On the fish-like tail in the ichthyostegid Stegocephalians. *Meddel. om Grønland*, vol. 114, no. 12, pp. 1–90.

12. Jarvik, Erik, 1959, De Tigida Fossila Ryggradsdjuren [The early fossil vertebrates]. *Svensk Naturvetenskap*, pp. 5–80.

13. Gregory, W. K., 1928, A tour of the hall of fishes. *Natural History*, vol. 28, p. 5.

14. Stockmans, F., 1940, Vegetaux éodévoniens de la Belgique. *Musée Royal d'Hist. Nat. de Belgique, Mem. 93.*

15. Dorf, Earling, 1934, Lower Devonian flora from Beartooth Butte, Wyoming. *Geol. Soc. Amer., Bull.*, vol. 45, pp. 425–440.

16. Daugherty, L. S., personal communication.

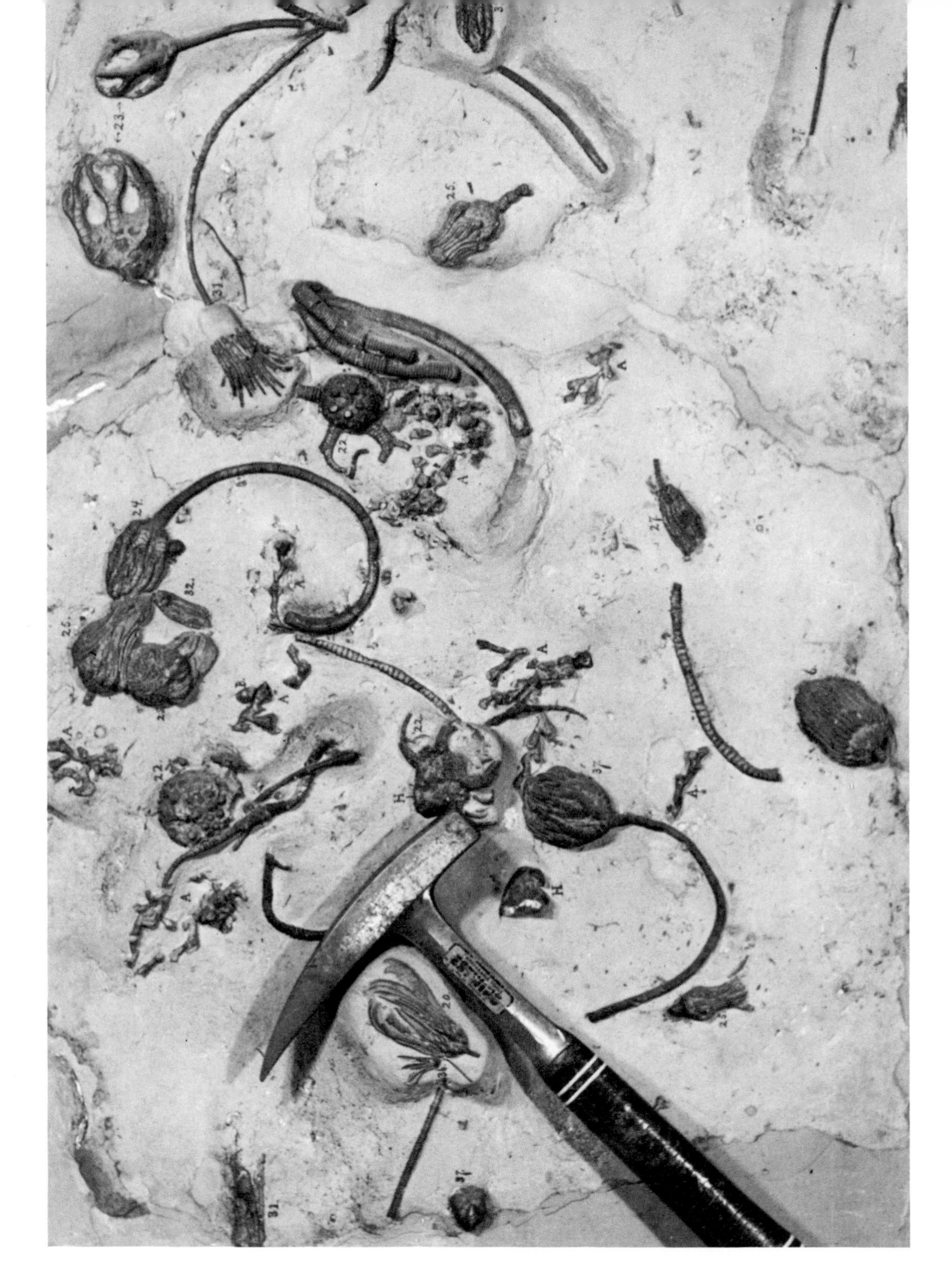

Crinoids on the surface of a shale bed in the Knobstone group (Osagian) at Crawfordsville, Indiana. (Yale Peabody Museum.)

Chapter 11. The Mississippian Period

Subdivision of the "Carboniferous System." The coal-bearing rocks of Europe and eastern North America were among the first to attract the attention of geologists. As early as 1808 the Belgians referred to them as the "bituminous terraine," and in England they were long known as the "Coal Measures." The name **Carboniferous** was introduced by Conybeare and Phillips in 1822, when they attempted the first general account of the geology of England and Wales. The term "system" had not yet come into vogue and they proposed the "Carboniferous Order" to embrace the Coal Measures and three underlying groups of rock: (1) the Millstone grit, (2) the Mountain limestone, and (3) the Old Red sandstone.

The Old Red was transferred to the Devonian System in 1839 and the rest of the Carboniferous Order became the Carboniferous System. Since it seemed to fall naturally into two major subdivisions, the Coal Measures were in time distinguished as **Upper Carboniferous** and the barren groups below as **Lower Carboniferous** or **Subcarboniferous.** This distinction was soon made also in America where the Upper Carboniferous rocks contain practically all the rich Paleozoic coal, and the Lower Carboniferous is generally barren. In 1891 the U.S. Geological Survey recognized these divisions as formal units of series rank and gave each a geographic name, designating the lower the **Mississippian Series** and the upper the **Pennsylvanian Series** of the Carboniferous System.

In 1906 Chamberlin and Salisbury urged that these units be raised to systemic rank, pointing out that they not only differ in lithology over most of this continent, as they do in Europe, but are also separated by a major and very widespread hiatus. This proposal steadily gained favor until it is now universally accepted by North American geologists. European geologists, on the contrary, have been reluctant to follow this lead and still generally recognize Lower and Upper Carboniferous as series of one system.

The Mississippian System in America. As suggested by Figure 167 the region of the Mississippi Valley was almost continuously submerged during this period and here the record is relatively complete and well exposed. The rocks are predominantly marine limestones and most of them are richly fossiliferous. This is the type region for which the system was named and where its major subdivisions were established (Fig. 168). Of course it includes contemporaneous formations of other areas regardless of their nature, but the Mississippi Valley section is the one with which others are correlated.

PHYSICAL HISTORY OF MISSISSIPPIAN TIME

Widespread Submergence. With the exception of Appalachia and Llanoria, North America was generally low and stable until near the close of Mississippian time. The Canadian Shield seems to have been generally above sealevel since no Mississippian formations are known in this vast area, but during much of the period a large part of the United States was submerged. From the Mississippi Valley westward, however, the seas were generally shallow and clear so that continuous deposits of relatively pure, light-colored limestones were laid down over enormous areas, including much of the Rocky Mountain region; the land must have been generally low throughout the western part of the continent as well as the Canadian Shield.

Submergence was greatest during the first half of the period, reaching the maximum limits shown in Figure 167*A* for a time during the Osagian Stage. Marine limestones in the Canadian Rockies and along the Alcan Highway northward to Peace River indicate that for a time the western seaway extended to the Arctic Ocean by way of the Mackenzie Valley as it had during Devonian time. During the latter half of the period, however, the seaways were much less extensive as indicated in Figure 167*B*.

Restless Appalachia. The Acadian disturbance at the close of the Devonian left most of Appalachia a mountainous highland from which mud and sand was shed westward across the Appalachian Geosyncline as far as Indiana, Kentucky, and Tennessee. The strong disturbance in New England had thickened the crust and transformed that part of the old Appalachian Geosyncline into a positive area which was never again crossed by the sea. The northern part of the old geosyncline in Maritime Canada continued to subside locally so that intermont basins in Nova Scotia and southeastern Quebec include a thick section of early

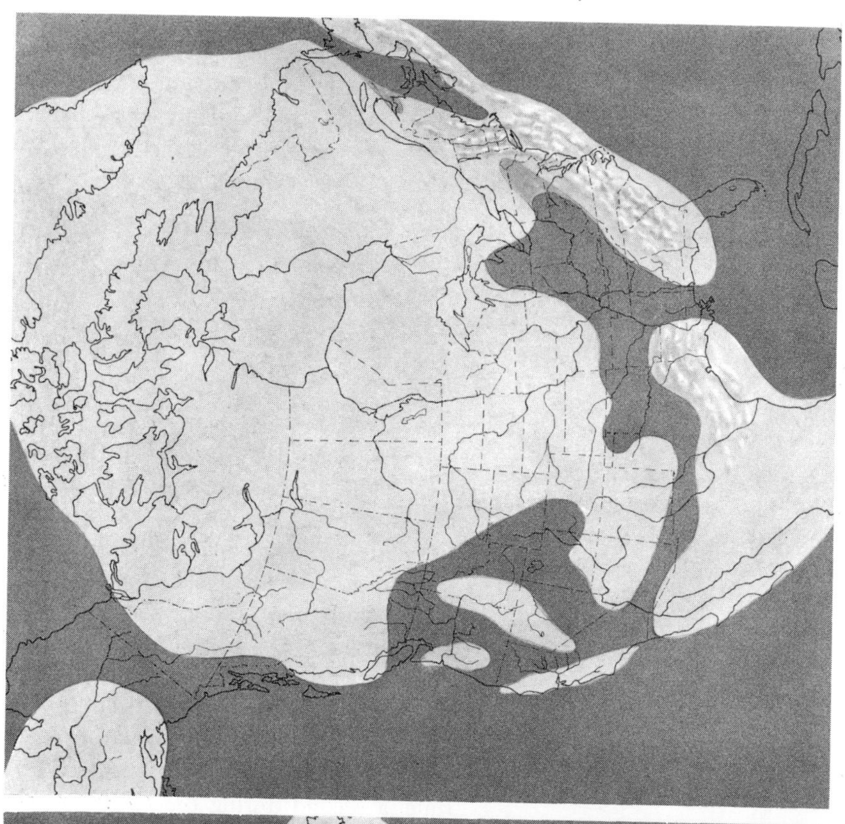

Figure 167*B*. Late Mississippian (Chesterian) paleogeography

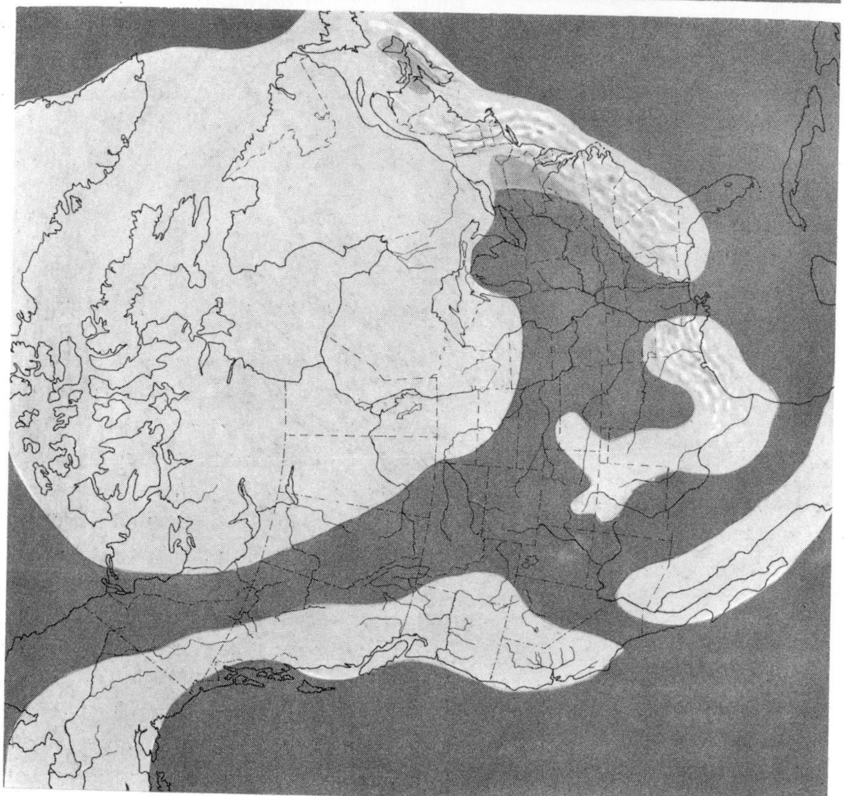

Figure 167*A*. Early Mississippian (Osagian) paleogeography

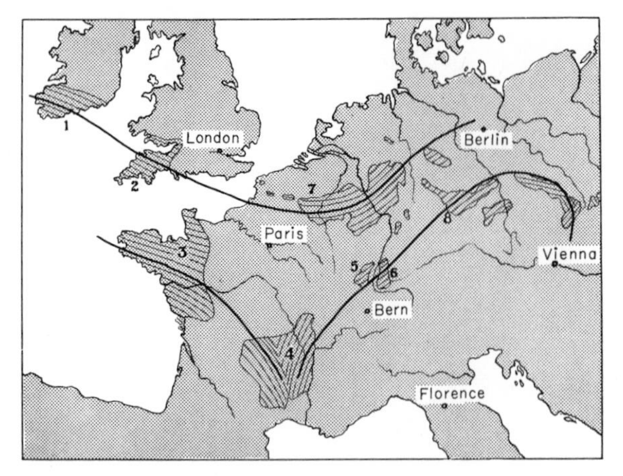

Figure 168. Map showing distribution of the Variscan Mountain System during late Paleozoic time in Europe. The stumps of these ancient mountains are now exposed in the shaded areas. 1, southern Ireland; 2, southwestern England; 3, Armorican Massif, Brittany; 4, Central Massif, France; 5, Vosges Mountains; 6, Black Forest; 7, Ardennes; 8, Erzgebirge. (Adapted from E. Kayser.)

Mississippian non-marine deposits and during the latter half of the period the region was partly submerged.

From New York southward into Alabama the geosyncline subsided steadily throughout the period and here the Mississippian System is as much as 8,000 feet thick but is made largely of sandstones and shales, indicating that Appalachia continued to rise. Indeed, increasing coarseness near the top of the system in Alabama, Tennessee, and Kentucky suggests rather strong uplift in the southern part of Appalachia.

Llanoria shared in this crustal disturbance as the Ouachita Geosyncline was deeply depressed in Arkansas and Oklahoma and was filled with detrital sediments that are largely non-marine on the south side of the trough.

Closing Episodes of Uplift and Orogeny. In North America the final stage of the Mississippian Period was marked by more widespread crustal disturbance than any previous part of the Paleozoic Era. Mountains were then rising not only in Appalachia and Llanoria, but in Colorado as well. These movements were forerunners of others to follow intermittently during the rest of the Paleozoic Era and to culminate in the Appalachian revolution late in Permian time. These far-reaching changes account for the general contrast in the lithology of the Mississippian and Pennsylvanian systems over most of the central and western part of the United States, the Mississippian rocks being predominantly calcareous and the Pennsylvanian and Permian overwhelmingly detrital.

Variscan Mountains of Europe. Much of Europe was also undergoing profound change during the last three periods of the Paleozoic Era. Orogenic movements began there during Mississippian (Lower Carboniferous) time and were repeated during the next two periods. This resulted in a great chain of mountains (Fig. 168) that ran southeastward across southern Ireland and England to southern France and then curved northeastward across Switzerland and southern Germany into Bohemia and Austria. These were the Variscan Mountains.

The growth of these ranges involved folding and faulting of the early Paleozoic formations over much of western Europe and was accompanied by large-scale igneous activity both in England and on the Continent. This was the result of three chief movements, one at the end of Mississippian time, a second during the middle of the Pennsylvanian Period and a third late in the Permian. It was this orogeny that so badly deformed the Devonian rocks in their type region in Devonshire. There is evidence also of late Mississippian orogeny in the region of the Kuen-Lun Range north of the Himalayas.

STRATIGRAPHY OF THE MISSISSIPPIAN SYSTEM

Mississippi Valley Region. Here (in Illinois, western Kentucky, and parts of Missouri and Iowa) the Mississippian System ranges from 2,000 to 2,500 feet in thickness, is almost entirely marine, and consists largely of limestones some of which extend as a continuous and fairly uniform sheet all the way from Iowa to central Kentucky. A somewhat generalized section for this region is represented in Figure 169.

The **Kinderhookian Series**, laid down while the invading seas were still relatively small, is less widespread than succeeding horizons, and varies lithologically from place to place because of the local influence of the adjacent land masses. It is therefore subdivided into several more or less local formations.

The **Osagian Series** reflects clearing of the waters as the region was more widely submerged. It consists largely of limestones, but is remarkable for the large amount of bedded chert, which commonly occurs as nodules or lenses in the limestone but locally forms thick units of well-bedded chert. In the Tri-State area of Missouri, Kansas, and Oklahoma it appears as a single formation and is known as the **Boone chert.** Here it carries the lead and zinc ores of the Joplin District.

The **Meramec Series** consists of purer and less cherty limestones which locally pass into oölites on a scale unequaled at any other horizon in America. The Salem limestone of Indiana, known to the building trades as **Indiana limestone,** is the most extensively quarried building stone in the United States. Being soft and uniform in texture, it tools easily and is therefore much used for copings and exterior trim as well as for marble finish in lavatories. There are probably few cities east of the Rocky Mountains that do not have some public buildings trimmed with this stone. Most of it is supplied by the enormous quarries about Bedford (Fig. 170), which place Indiana far in the lead among the states producing finish building stone. In the last two decades the annual output from these quarries has ranged between 1,000,000 and 1,500,000 tons.

The most widespread member of the Meramec Series is the **St. Louis limestone,** a purer and more compact stone which forms the conspicuous bluffs of the Mississippi River near St. Louis, and stretches continuously from Iowa to Alabama as one of the greatest sheets of limestone in this country.

The **Ste. Genevieve limestone,** next younger than

Chart 5. Correlation of important Mississippian sections

Series	Arizona	Utah	Mont.	Colo.	Okla.-Ark. (Ouachita)	Mo.-Ark. (Ozarks)	Illinois	Indiana	Va.-WVa.	Pa.
Chesterian	Paradise fm.	Manning Canyon sh.; Great Blue ls.	Big Snowy group		?; Jackfork ss.; - - ?- -; Stanley sh.	Pitkin ls.; Fayetteville sh.; Batesville ss.	Elvira: Kinkaid ls., Degonia ss., Clore fm., Palestine ss., Menard ls., Waltersburg ss., Vienna ls., Tar Springs ss.; Homberg: Glen Dean ls., Hardinsburg ss., Golconda ls., Cypress ss.; New Design: Paint Creek ls., Bethel ss., Renault ls., Aux Vases ss.		Bluestone gr.; Hinton gr.; Bluefield gr.; Greenbrier ls.; Mauch Chunk fm.	Mauch Chunk fm.
Meramec.	Paradise fm.	Humbug ls.; Deseret ls.	Big Snowy group		Stanley sh.	Moorefield	Meramecian: Ste. Genevieve ls., St. Louis ls., Salem ls., Warsaw ls.		Greenbrier ls.	
Osagian	Redwall ls.	Madison ls.	Madison ls.; Mission Canyon	Leadville ls.	?	Boone chert; St. Joe ls.	Osagian: Keokuk ls., Burlington l., Fern Glen l.	Borden gr.: Edward., Floyds, Carwood, Locust P., New Provid. sh.	Maccrady ss.; Grainger ss.; Pocono ss.	Pocono ss.
Kinderhook.	Redwall ls. ?	Madison ls. ?	Madison ls.; Lodge-pole ls. ?	Leadville ls. ?			Kinderhook: Gilmore City, Sedalia ls., Choteau ls., Maple Hill sh, Louisiana ls., Saverton sh.	Rockford l.; New Albany sh.	Pocono ss.; Bigstone Gap sh; Olinger; Cumberl. Gap	Pocono ss.

Formations	Groups	Stages
Kinkaid ls.	Elvira	Chesterian
Degonia ss.		
Clore sh.		
Palestine ss.		
Menard ls.		
Watersburg ss.		
Vienna ls.		
Tar Spring ss.		
Glen Dean ls.	Homberg	
Hardinsburg ss.		
Golconda ls.		
Cypress ss.		
Paint Creek sh.	New Design	
Bethel ss.		
Renault fm.		
Aux Vases ss.		
Ohara oolite	Ste. Genevieve ls.	Meramacian
Roseclaire ss.		
Fredonia oolite		
St. Louis ls.		
Salem oolite		
Warsaw fm.		
Keokuk ls.		Osagian
Burlington ls.		
Fern Glen ls.		
Choteau ls.	Easley group	Kinder-hookian
Hannibal ss.		
Lousiana ls.	Fabius group	
Saverton sh.		

Figure 169. Type section of the Mississippian System showing the classification used.

the St. Louis, is likewise pure but inclined to be oölitic. It has suffered much underground solution where it floors large areas in the Ohio Valley. Mammoth Cave and thousands of others in the "Land of Ten Thousand Sink Holes" in Kentucky are excavated in this formation.

The **Chester Series** is formed of alternating sandstones, shales, and limestones that have a combined thickness of 1,000 to 1,500 feet and are grouped into more than a dozen formations in western Kentucky and Illinois. The spread of much sand and mud over the Mississippi Basin at this time reflects, of course, uplift in southern Appalachia and Llanoria.

Ouachita Trough. In Oklahoma and Arkansas the Mississippian rocks are deeply buried by Pennsylvanian formations along the axis of the Ouachita Trough, but they crop out on both the north and south flanks. On the north side, flanking the Ozark Dome, they are some 1,200 feet thick, are largely if not entirely marine, and consist of shale with interbedded chert, limestone, and sandstone (Fig. 171). The faunas here indicate that all the major divisions of the period are represented. On the south side of the trough the section is totally different (Fig. 171). Here a wedge of detrital deposits more than 12,000 feet thick appears to represent part of a vast delta built northward from Llanoria into the Ouachita Trough. The Stanley "shale" consists largely of siltstone and sandy shale, and the Jackfork sandstone is rather fine grained and muddy. The lower part of the Stanley shale includes at least five beds of volcanic ash, one of which reaches the impressive thickness of 85 feet. The volcanoes from which this ash was derived could only have existed in Llanoria.

Both the Stanley and the Jackfork formations are so sparingly fossiliferous that their age has long been a subject of controversy. On the basis of conodonts, however, the lower part of the Stanley shale is now correlated with the Meramec Stage of the Mississippian,[1] and cumulative but somewhat indirect evidence now indicates that the Jackfork formation is also of Mississippian age.[2]

Evidently the shales and sandstones of the north side of the Ouachita Trough are tongues of detrital sediment transported across the basin while the Stanley-Jackfork Delta was forming on its southern margin. The Mississippian formations farther north, both on the west and east flanks of the Ozarks are almost entirely limestones. Evidently

Figure 170. Quarry of the Indiana Limestone Company in the Salem limestone (Bedford oölite) near Bedford, Indiana. (Indiana Limestone Company.)

Llanoria was a highland of considerable magnitude and for a time bore active volcanoes.

Appalachian Province. This whole province, as far west as the Cincinnati Arch was dominated by detrital sediments poured into the geosyncline from Appalachia. In Pennsylvania and parts of Maryland and Virginia the deposits are non-marine and were probably spread over a broad low coastal plain. Here two thick formations are recognized, the **Pocono sandstone** below, followed by the **Mauch Chunk redbeds.** The Pocono reaches a thickness of 2,000 feet or more and consists of gray sandstones and siltstones with scattered fossil land plants, and locally, near Roanoke, Virginia, it includes coal beds. Fuel for the *Merrimac* in her historic battle with the *Monitor* was derived from this Mississippian coal. In the anthracite basins of eastern Pennsylvania, the lower part of the Pocono formation includes massive beds of coarse conglomerate. Here the formation is an important ridge-maker. The Mauch Chunk is composed of dull red sandstone alternating with bright red siltstone and shale, and reaches a thickness of about 3,000 feet in Pennsylvania. Many bedding surfaces in the shales show fossil mudcracks. This formation represents the subaerial surface of a low delta plain and probably accumulated under a climate of abundant but markedly seasonal rainfall.

In the central part of the geosyncline, along the Virginia-West Virginia border, the Mississippian System thickens to more than 8,000 feet and here

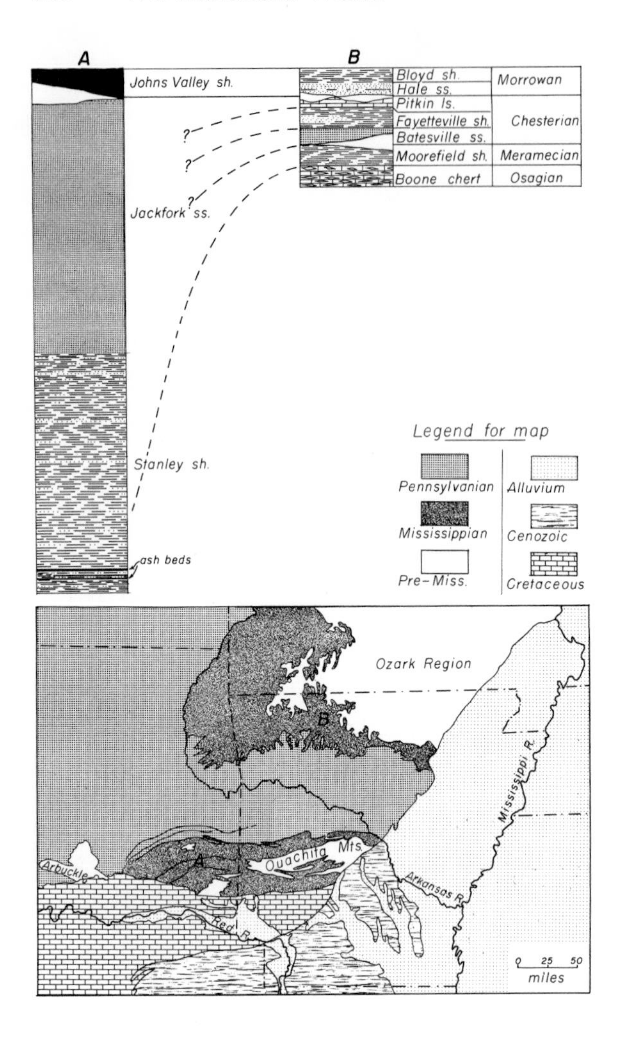

Figure 171. Sections of the Mississippian formations on north and south flanks of the Ouachita Geosyncline in Arkansas.

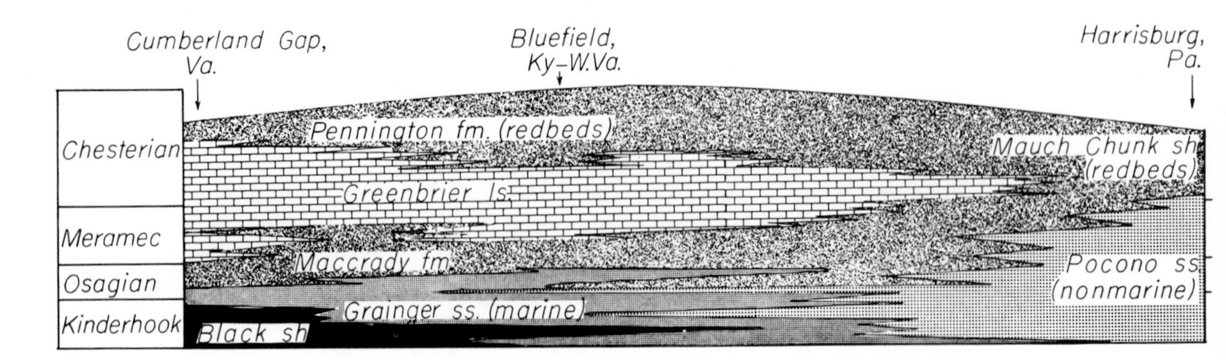

Figure 172. Stratigraphic diagram to show complex facies of the Mississippian System in the Appalachian Trough. (After Byron Cooper.)

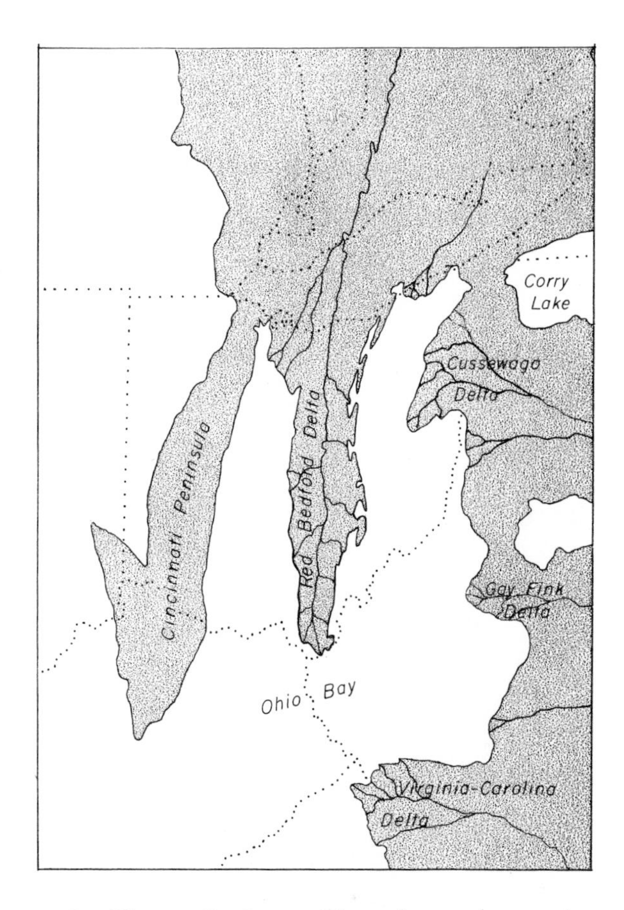

Figure 173. Early Mississippian paleogeography in Ohio. (After Pepper, de Witt, and Demarest.)

the subsidence was rapid enough to permit submergence part of the time and the stratigraphy is complicated by rapid facies changes (Fig. 172).

The Pocono equivalents thin rapidly in western Pennsylvania and become finer of grain and at least partially marine. A magnificent recent study of these deposits in Ohio (the Bedford shale and Berea sandstone) has revealed the paleogeography represented in Figure 173.[3] During deposition of the Bedford shale a large but very shallow and irregular bay (Ohio Bay) of the interior sea covered parts of Ohio, West Virginia, and eastern Kentucky; streams heading in Appalachia and flowing westward across the Pocono coastal plain were building deltas along the east side of the bay while another stream, heading in the Canadian Shield was building the Bedford Red Delta southward. The Cincinnati Arch then stood as a low peninsula, **Cincinnatia.**

Only fine mud got beyond the Cincinnati Arch into Indiana, and in Illinois the sea floor was covered only with lime mud.

Cordilleran Region. Throughout the Rocky Mountain region the Mississippian System is represented by limestone, commonly massive and cliff-forming. Although it bears local names in different areas, it must originally have been a vast sheet of limestone strata stretching continuously from Nevada to the Black Hills, Yellowstone Park, and the Canadian Rockies. It is the cliff-forming **Redwall limestone** of the Grand Canyon (Figs. 54 and 174), and the **Madison limestone** of the northern Rockies (Fig. 110). It reaches a thickness of 1,200 feet in the vicinity of Yellowstone National Park and continues far north into Canada. This limestone is all of Early Mississippian age (Kinderhook-Osage).

The upper part of the Mississippian System is less well developed and less well known, but in parts of Utah, Nevada, and Idaho, and locally farther west, it is represented by thick masses of limestone. In the Oquirrh Range south of Great Salt Lake, for example, the Mississippian formations, mostly calcareous, are approximately 6,000 feet thick, and of this nearly 4,000 feet is be-

Figure 174. Redwall limestone overlooking Bright Angel Trail in the south wall of the Grand Canyon. (Carl O. Dunbar.)

lieved to be of Chesterian age. Local formation names are used throughout the West, and a satisfactory synthesis is not yet possible.

CLIMATE

In North America evidence of climatic conditions is rather limited. In the intermont basins of Nova Scotia and Newfoundland, the Windsor redbeds of the Upper Mississippian contain extensive deposits of gypsum and some salt, recording rather severe but probably local aridity in the rainshadow of the mountains. In Michigan also red shales of Mississippian age are rich in brines that have been the source of salt manufactured in the Saginaw Valley, but since the underlying Silurian and Devonian rocks in Michigan contain enormous deposits of salt, the Mississippian brines may have been derived from these older formations around the margins of the basin during deposition.

The western slope of the Appalachian highlands appears to have received plentiful rainfall and the gray color of the Pocono sandstone suggests that during early Mississippian time the surface of the coastal plain was humid throughout the year. In contrast, the red color and abundant mudcracks of the overlying Mauch Chunk formation clearly indicate a change of regimen. The red mud formed on humid uplands could have remained red if deposited on well-drained slopes or if deposited under conditions of marked seasonal rainfall. The good preservation of mudcracks at many horizons would be favored by dry seasons alternating with rainy seasons.

The great amount of limestone deposited in the shallow seas across the central and western part of the United States indicates that the water was warm.

In contrast to these indications of mild climate in North America, extensive glaciation in eastern Australia is indicated by the Seaham tillites of the Kuttung Series.[4]

LIFE OF MISSISSIPPIAN TIME

Marine Invertebrates. Marine animals are still much better known than the land life of this period, for the continental sediments accumulated under conditions poorly suited to the preservation of fossils, whereas the shallow, limy sea floors harbored, and preserved, life of the greatest luxuriance.

Although clearly evolved from Devonian life, the Mississippian faunas were given a distinctive character by the decline of such groups as the corals and trilobites and the great expansion of others such as the echinoderms, the lacy bryozoa, and the spiny brachiopods.

Echinoderms flourished as never before. **Crinoids** (Pl. 9, figs. 6–10) grew in such luxuriance that their dismembered plates contributed largely to the making of thick crinoidal limestones, some of which have a large areal extent. No other geologic system has yielded such a variety or such numbers of well-preserved specimens of this class (Fig. 175). **Blastoids** (Pl. 9, figs. 4 and 5) were also at a climax, the typical bud-shaped species (genus *Pentremites*) being particularly characteristic of this time (Fig. 176). Starfishes appear to have been rare, but sea-urchins of a few kinds were locally abundant. The most striking of these were large melon-shaped echinoids (*Melonechinus*, Fig. 177) found chiefly in the St. Louis limestone.

The **Foraminifera** for the first time assumed an important role as rock-makers (Fig. 178). A single genus, *Endothyra*, occurs so abundantly in the Salem (Bedford) oölite that the formation locally takes on the character of a formaminiferal limestone.

Corals persisted throughout the period but gen-

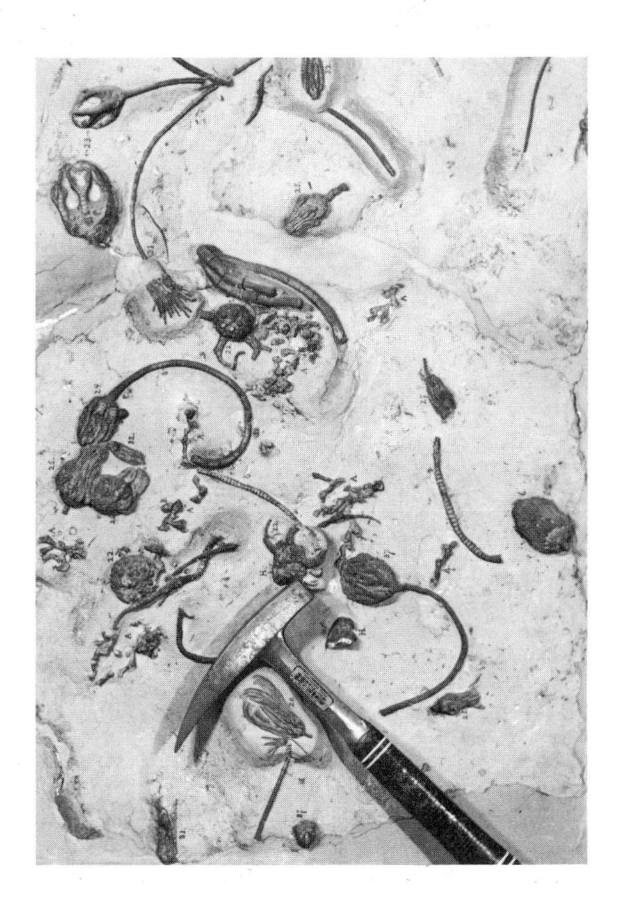

Figure 175 and chapter opening. Crinoids on the surface of a shale bed in the Knobstone group (Osagian) at Crawfordsville, Indiana. (Yale Peabody Museum.)

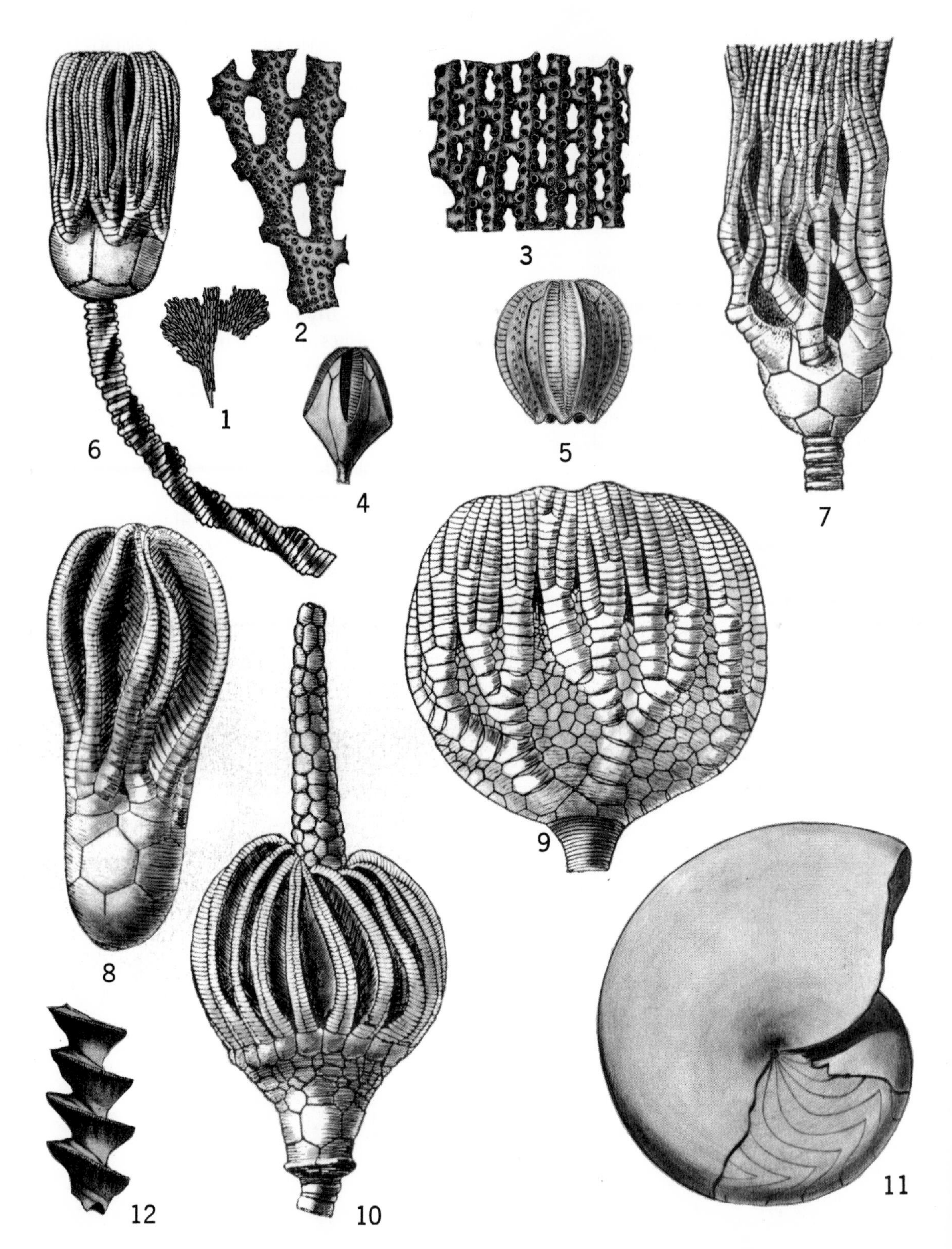

Plate 9. Mississippian Bryozoa (1–3, 12), Blastoids (4, 5), Crinoids (6–10), and Ammonite (11).

Figures 1, 2, *Polypora cestriensis* (× ⅔ and × 6); 3, *Fenestella cingulata* (× 6); 12, *Archimedes wortheni*, the screw-like axis of a colony; 4, *Pentremites pyriformis;* 5, *Cryptoblastus pisum;* 6, *Platycrinites hemisphericus;* 7, *Cyathocrinus multibrachiatus;* 8, *Agassizocrinus dactyliformis;* 9, *Forbesiocrinus wortheni;* 10, *Batocrinus pyriformis;* 11, *Imitoceras rotatorius.* All natural size except Figures 1–3. (Drawn by R. G. Creadick.)

erally were neither varied, reef-making, nor especially common. The most conspicuous type in the interior seaways was a compound tetracoral (*Lithostrotionella*) that, during the deposition of the St. Louis limestone, formed "heads" as much as 2 feet across. On the other hand, we must note the complete absence of the honeycomb coral (*Favosites*), which was so conspicuous in the Devonian reefs.

Byrozoa were again very numerous (Fig. 179), and the lacy types (fenestellids) now reached their greatest variety. Among these the genus *Archimedes*, with its thickened and spirally twisted axis, is most distinctive (Pl. 9, fig. 12).

Brachiopods continued to be the dominant "shellfish," and many of them were much like the Devonian forms, differing only in specific details. The spiny brachiopods (**Productidae**) evolved so rapidly that they dominated many of the faunas as they continued to do from the beginning of Mississippian time till the end of the Paleozoic Era.

Molluscs continued in considerable variety, and in the sandy sediments of the Pocono group small clams and gastropods are locally more common than any other fossils. The Salem oölite includes a large number of tiny snails. Perhaps the most significant molluscan advance is among the **goniatites** (Pl. 9, fig. 11); these primitive ammonites were much more common in Europe, however, than in America.

Figure 176. *Pentremites* from the Chester formation.

Figure 177. Surface of a layer of St. Louis limestone covered with the cantaloupe-shaped sea urchin, *Melonechinus*.

Figure 178. Shells of the small foraminifer, *Endothyra,* from the Salem oölite near Salem, Illinois. In places the "oölite" is largely made of such shells. Enlarged × 15.

Trilobites had already declined almost to extinction, and the remaining species were small and rather rare. No trace of insects has yet been found, though the high development of that group in the next period suggests strongly that they were actually present in Mississippian time.

Vertebrate animals. Fishes were undoubtedly abundant but are not nearly so well recorded as they were in the Devonian rocks. The great armored arthrodires survived for a time but became extinct during this period. The lungfish (Choanichthes) seem to have passed their heyday and are not common fossils in the Mississippian rocks. The best recorded group of fishes is a tribe of sharks (cestracionts) commonly known as **shell-crushers** because they were specialized for feeding on crustaceans and small clams, and had their jaws paved with blunt teeth suitable for crushing the shells of such prey. Since the shark skeleton is cartilaginous it is rarely preserved, but the spines and the distinctive blunt teeth of these fish are common in the marine formations of this period—more common than at any other time. Some 300 species of shell-crusher sharks have been described from Mississippian rocks as compared with 39 in the Devonian and 55 in the Pennsylvanian. A few of the shell-crushers are still living, the best known being the Port Jackson shark of Australia (Fig. 180), and these afford direct evidence of the

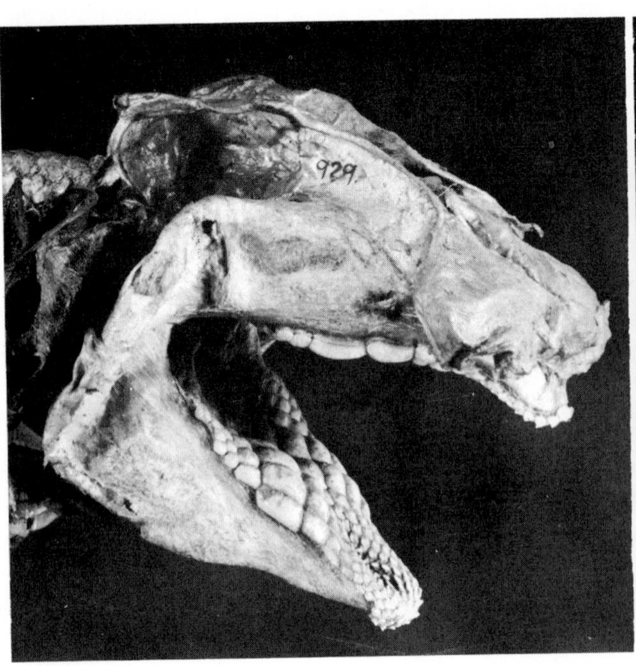

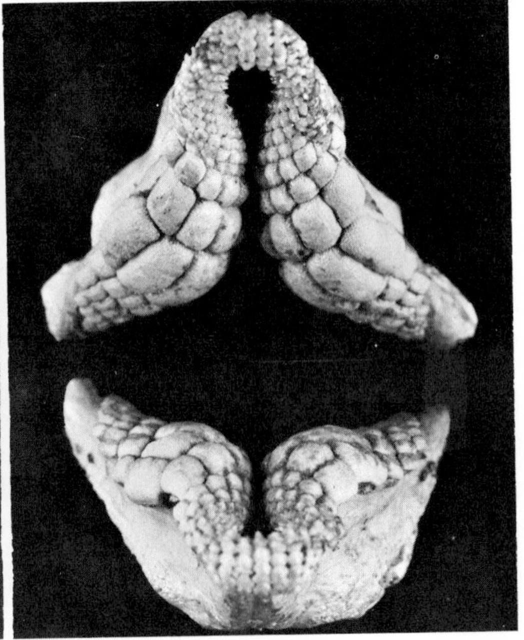

specialized feeding habits of their Paleozoic ancestors. The appearance of this group of fishes in the Devonian Period and their great expansion in the Mississippian may have contributed to the decline of the trilobites.

Land animals left an indisputable record in the form of numerous footprints, and in 1941 actual skeletal remains were found in the Mauch Chunk beds in West Virginia. In Europe, also, the skeletons of small, salamanderlike amphibia have been found. The footprints are most common in the Mauch Chunk redbeds, where they are associated with mudcracks and rain imprints. Doubtless many of these record the tragic search for water as the vanishing mudholes gave way to barren flats during the summer droughts. Yet among them there may be the hallmarks of destiny, for some of these restless creatures, driven by their extremity, were to develop agility and freedom from the water that would enable them in the coming ages literally to inherit the Earth.

Land Plants. Land plants were, of course, as abundant as in the Late Devonian, but their remains are lamentably broken and macerated in the deposits available to us. So far as is known, they were much like those of the Pennsylvanian, which will be described in Chapter 12.

REFERENCES

1. Hass, W. H., 1950, Age of the lower part of the Stanley shale. *Amer. Assoc. Petroleum Geol., Bull.*, vol. 34, pp. 1578–1584.

———, 1956, Conodonts from the Arkansas novaculite, Stanley shale, and Jackfork sandstone. *Guidebook to Field Conference in the Ouachita Mountains*, Ardmore Geological Society, pp. 25–33.

2. Cline, L. M., and O. B. Shelburne, 1959, *Late Mississippian–Early Pennsylvanian stratigraphy of the Ouachita Mountains.* Dallas Geological Society and Ardmore Geological Society, pp. 175–208.

I am indebted to Dr. Thomas A. Hendricks for data and confirmation of the Mississippian age of the Jackfork sandstone.

3. Pepper, J. F., Wallace de Witt, Jr., and D. F. Demarest, 1954, Geology of the Bedford shale and Beria sandstone in the Appalachian Basin. *U.S. Geol. Surv., Prof. Paper* 259, pp. 1–111.

4. Süssmilch, C. A., 1935, The Carboniferous period in eastern Australia. *Assoc. Adv. Sci. of Australia and New Zealand, Report*, vol. 22, pp. 83–118.

Osborne, G. D., and W. R. Browne, 1921, Note on a glacially striated pavement in the Kuttung Series of the Maitland District. *Linnean Soc. New South Wales, Proc.*, vol. 46, pp. 259–262.

Figure 179 (top). Surface of a limestone layer largely made of lacy bryozoans of the tribe of *Fenestella*. A small spiriferoid brachiopod appears to the right of the center.

Figure 180 (bottom). Skull of Port Jackson shark, a modern relative of the "shell crushers" that were so common in Mississippian time. Left, a side view of the skull with jaws agape; right, oral view with jaws wide open to show their complete armor of blunt teeth. Yale Peabody Museum.

Pennsylvanian landscape in the swampy lowlands showing characteristic vegetation and sprawling amphibians. Part of a great mural by Rudolph F. Zallinger. Plants: 1, a tree fern; 2, *Lepidodendron*, a scale tree; 3, *Sigillaria*, a scale tree; 4, *Cordaites*, a precursor of the conifers; 5, *Calamites*, a scouring rush. Animals: 6, *Diplovertebron*, a primitive amphibian; 7, *Eryops*, a large amphibian; 8, *Eogyrinus*, one of the largest of amphibians; 9, *Seymouria*, a primitive reptile; 10, *Limnoscelis*, a reptile; 11, *Varanosaurus*, a reptile; 12, *Meganeuron*, a giant dragonflylike insect. (Yale Peabody Museum.)

Chapter 12. The Pennsylvanian Period

IT IS FITTING THAT THIS GREAT COAL-BEARING system should be named for the state of Pennsylvania where it was first comprehensively studied and where it is fabulously rich in the black fuel.

PHYSICAL HISTORY

Inland Seas and Vast Swamps

At the beginning of this period a mountainous rim extended all along the eastern margin of the continent from Newfoundland to Alabama and thence across the Gulf border into northern Mexico (Fig. 181, left). So far as known, the whole of Canada was emergent, though low and stable, and between it and the mountainous border a broad basin was forming that soon involved much of the interior of the United States. Shallow sea spread widely over the Rocky Mountain states and eastward into Texas and Oklahoma, but from there eastward mud and sand from the mountainous borderland filled the basins as fast as they sank, holding back the sea and transforming vast areas into lowlands covered with lush forests and dotted with great swamps in which the fallen vegetation accumulated to form coal.

Submergence became more widespread toward the middle of the period (Desmoinesian Epoch) when the inland seas reached the limits shown in Figure 181, right. East of the present Mississippi River, filling by detrital sediment from Appalachia kept approximate pace with subsidence, at times lagging enough to let the sea creep eastward even as far as western Pennsylvania, and then exceeding subsidence enough to push the shoreline westward into Kansas and Nebraska. During much of the rest of the period this delicate balance was maintained as the shoreline crept back and forth across the Eastern Interior producing an alternation of marine and non-marine formations. In the vast paralic (seaside) swamps thus maintained, the coal beds of Kansas, Oklahoma, Illinois, Indiana, Kentucky, West Virginia, and Pennsylvania were formed.

West of the hundredth meridian where the sea was dominant the record is quite different and highly varied. Over much of this region marine limestones predominate, as in southern Nevada; but in basins adjacent to the rising mountains of Colorado (described below) thick detrital formations of highly varied lithology were laid down.

Growing Crustal Unrest

In spite of persistent erosion, the mountains in Appalachia and Llanoria remained high throughout this period; they must have been repeatedly uplifted to supply the enormous volume of detrital sediments, which reached a thickness of 9,000 feet in Alabama, 20,000 feet in Arkansas, 15,000 feet in Oklahoma and 13,000 feet in Nova Scotia.

In the Maritime Provinces of Canada the basins of deposition were intermont fault troughs, and here the thick sequence of Pennsylvanian formations includes five important unconformities indicating as many episodes of disturbance.

Oklahoma Mountains. As noted in the previous chapter, strong uplift was underway along the Gulf border during the latter half of the Mississippian Period. The early phases of this movement were confined to Llanoria, the marginal land south of of the geosyncline; but early in Pennsylvanian time deformation reached farther north, and the crust buckled along the northern margin of the geosyncline to form a chain of domed mountains along the southern border of Oklahoma and across the Panhandle of Texas (Fig. 182). These were the **Oklahoma Mountains.** The eroded stumps of these ancient ranges now form the Arbuckle and Wichita Mountains of Oklahoma and the buried Amarillo Range of Panhandle Texas. As these ranges rose out of the sea, or out of a wide alluvial plain, synclinal basins on both flanks trapped the debris supplied by their erosion. Meanwhile sediment was converging into the broad surrounding basin from distant Appalachia on the east and from Llanoria on the south. The Oklahoma Mountains must then have resembled the modern Shantung Highland which rises in the midst of the great Hwang-Ho Delta in China.

The Oklahoma Mountains probably did not attain great elevation, for they were rising in the midst of a subsiding region and the sediment eroded from their summits accumulated on their flanks and in adjacent basins until, eventually, they were almost buried in their own debris. The Pennsylvanian formations are at least 12,000 feet thick in the Ardmore Basin south of the Arbuckles

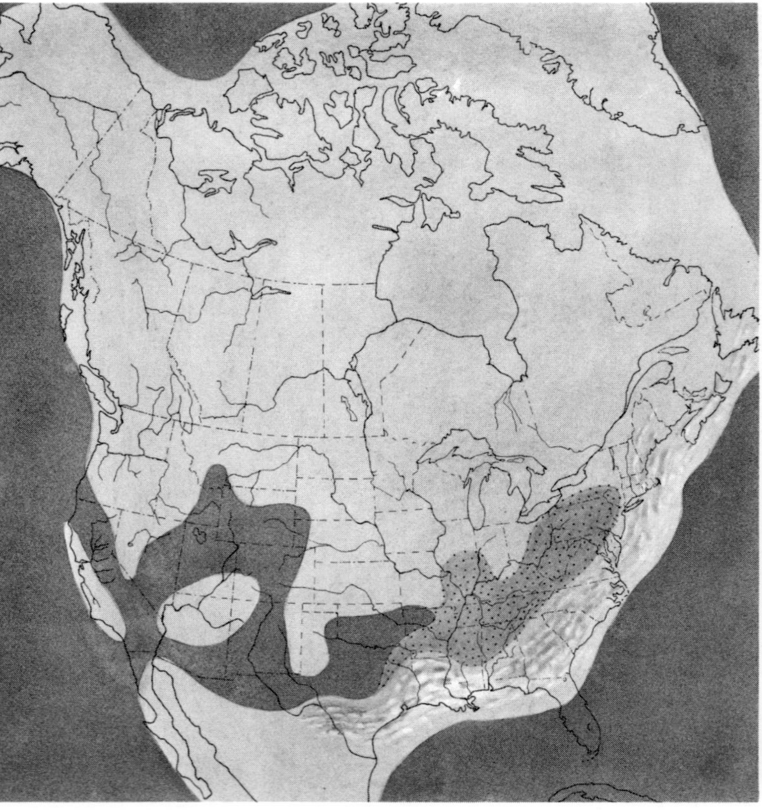

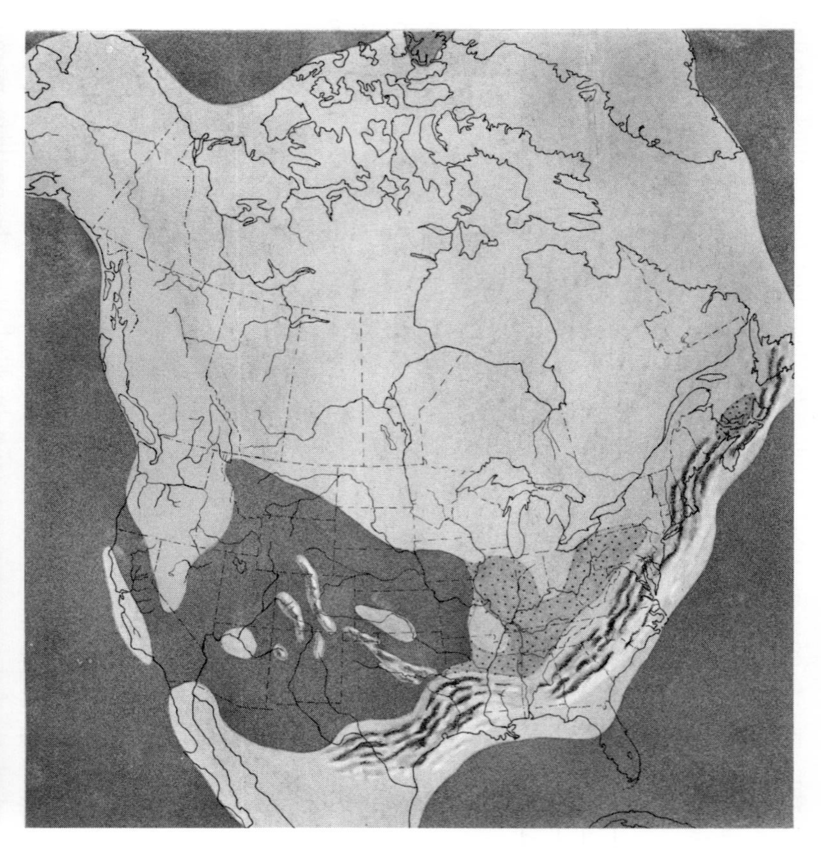

Figure 181. Paleogeography of North America in Pennsylvanian time. Left, Early Pennsylvanian (Morrowan) time; right, Middle Pennsylvanian (Desmoinesian) time showing the maximum inundation of the period. The stippled shading indicates areas of non-marine deposition.

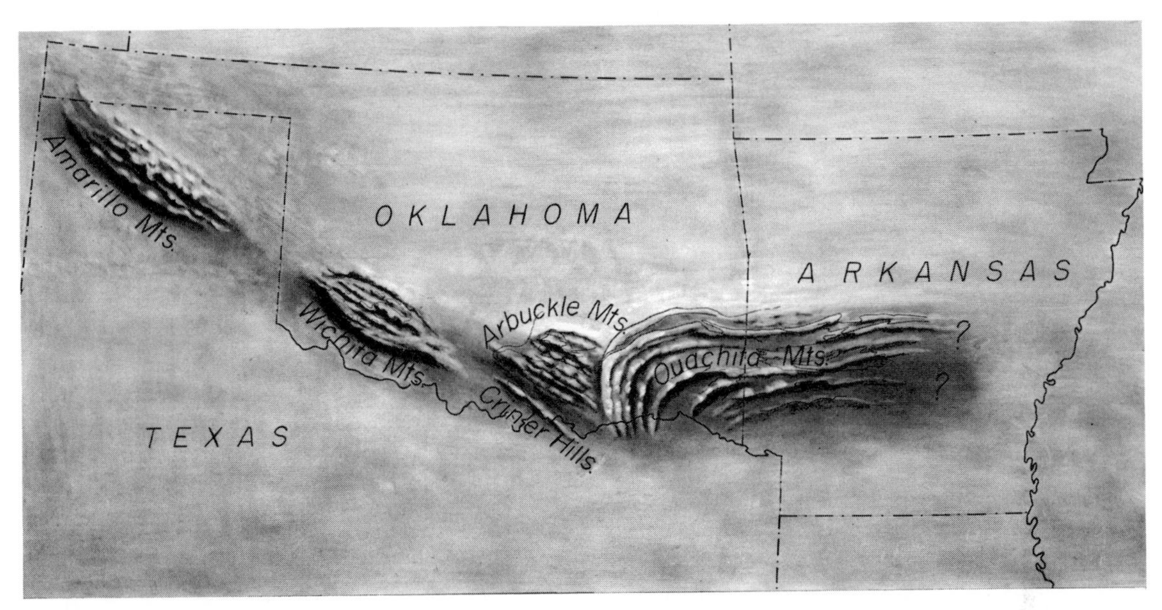

Figure 182. The Oklahoma Mountains of Pennsylvanian and Permian time. The Amarillo, Wichita, and Arbuckle Mountains were active in Pennsylvanian time; the Ouachita Mountains were thrust into this area in Permian time, overriding the eastern end of the Arbuckle Mountains.

and in the Anadarko Basin to the north of the Arbuckles and Wichitas, and in both basins they include much conglomerate derived from the cores of the local ranges. If these strata were to be stripped away, the Arbuckles would tower above their base as a range of mountains more than 2 miles high. Unconformities about the borders of the Arbuckles indicate at least two major episodes of uplift, one early and one near the middle of the period.

Colorado Mountains. Late in the Mississippian Period, or at the beginning of the Pennsylvanian, two major uplifts began in Colorado and a smaller one in the northwest corner of New Mexico (Figs. 183*A*, 183*B*). As they continued to rise during the period, synclinal basins formed between and to the west of them trapping much of the detrital sediment eroded from the ranges, and in these basins the Pennsylvanian System is exceptionally thick and nearly all detrital.

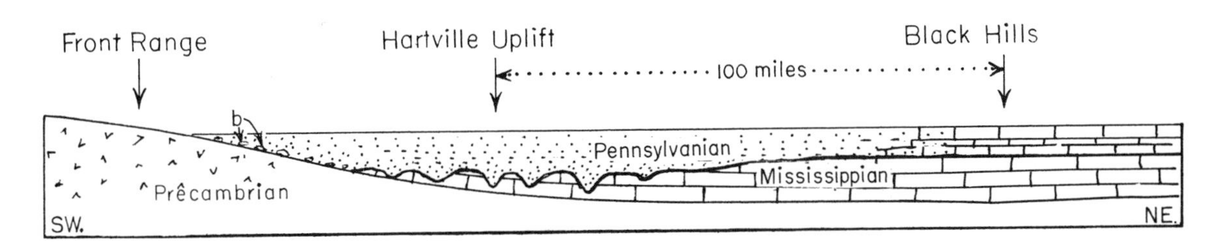

Figure 183A. Idealized section from the Front Range at Ingleside, Colorado, to the Black Hills in South Dakota. Mississippian limestone originally extended unbroken across the region but, following the uplift of the Colorado Mountains, they were eroded from the area of the present Front Range and the Precambrian granite floor was laid bare. Here the early Pennsylvanian redbeds (Fountain arkose) overlap the Mississippian and come to rest on granite. Farther east these nonmarine redbeds grade laterally into fossiliferous limestone. Obviously the detrital Pennsylvanian sediments of this area were coming from the Colorado Mountains, which then occupied approximately the same area as the present Front Range. At their base the overlapping Pennsylvanian strata include pebbles of fossiliferous Mississippian chert (*b*).

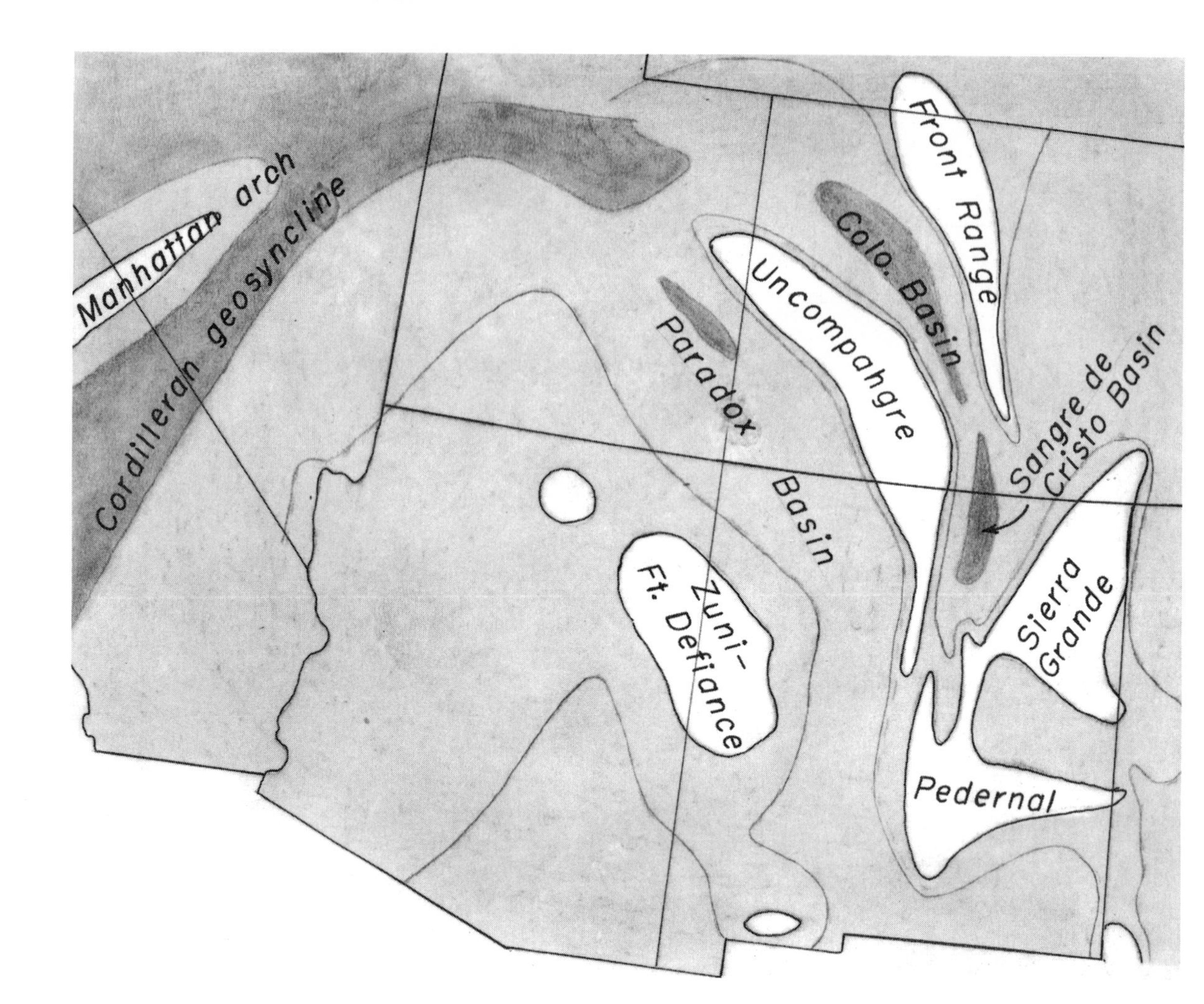

Figure 183*B*. Colorado Mountains and basins of PennysIvanian time, adapted from Wanless and Patterson, 1951. The chief uplifts are unshaded and are named; light shaded areas are underlain by Pennsylvanian formations. The contour line marks a thickness of 1,000 feet of Pennsylvanian deposits. Deep shading indicates deeper structural basins where the Pennsylvanian formations exceed 5,000 feet in thickness.

The **Colorado Mountains** were structurally aligned with those in Oklahoma and appear to have been part of one system. Since Precambrian time this broad region had been stable and was repeatedly submerged beneath shallow seas. During Mississippian time, for example, a thick sheet of limestone spread widely across the region proving the absence of highlands. The rise of mountains during Pennsylvanian time therefore marked an important change in the paleogeography of the western states.

Since the mountains in Colorado roughly coincided in position with the modern Rockies, Lee once proposed to call them the "Ancestral Rocky Mountains." This now seems to be a misleading name, however, since the alignment of the Paleozoic ranges from eastern Oklahoma across Colorado diverges widely from that of the present system, which did not begin to form until near the close of the Mesozoic Era some 200,000,000 years later.

The Grand Canyon region was a low island during most of the period and here Permian redbeds rest paraconformably on Mississippian limestones, but farther west, in southern Nevada and southern California, the Pennsylvanian System is represented by a succession of limestones approximately half a mile thick.

Marathon Disturbance of Trans-Pecos Texas. Near the close of the period a range of fold mountains was thrust up out of the sea in Trans-Pecos Texas, accompanied by northward thrusting that carried Devonian and Ordovician formations up over the Pennsylvanian. These structures are now clearly exposed in the Marathon Basin (Fig. 184) and the disturbance has been named for this region.

The axis of the Ouachita Geosyncline ran through the Marathon region, and here the Pennsylvanian formations are very thick and mostly detrital, formed largely of sediment derived from the highlands of Llanoria immediately to the south. Repeated uplift in Llanoria during the period is indicated by the thick sandstones and local conglomerates of the basin. It was not until near the close of the period, however, that compressive forces from the south crushed the geosyncline and threw the Paleozoic formations into close folds and northward thrusts that were later truncated by erosion and then overlapped with profound unconformity by the Permian. The disturbance was gentler to the north and west, but some angular discordance is common at the Pennsylvanian-Permian boundary as far west as El Paso. Most of the disturbed area in Texas is now covered by Cretaceous rocks.

At one locality in the Marathon Basin a wedge of the early Permian (**Wolfcamp formation**) is involved in the folding, proving that movement had not completely ceased at the end of the Pennsylvanian Period.

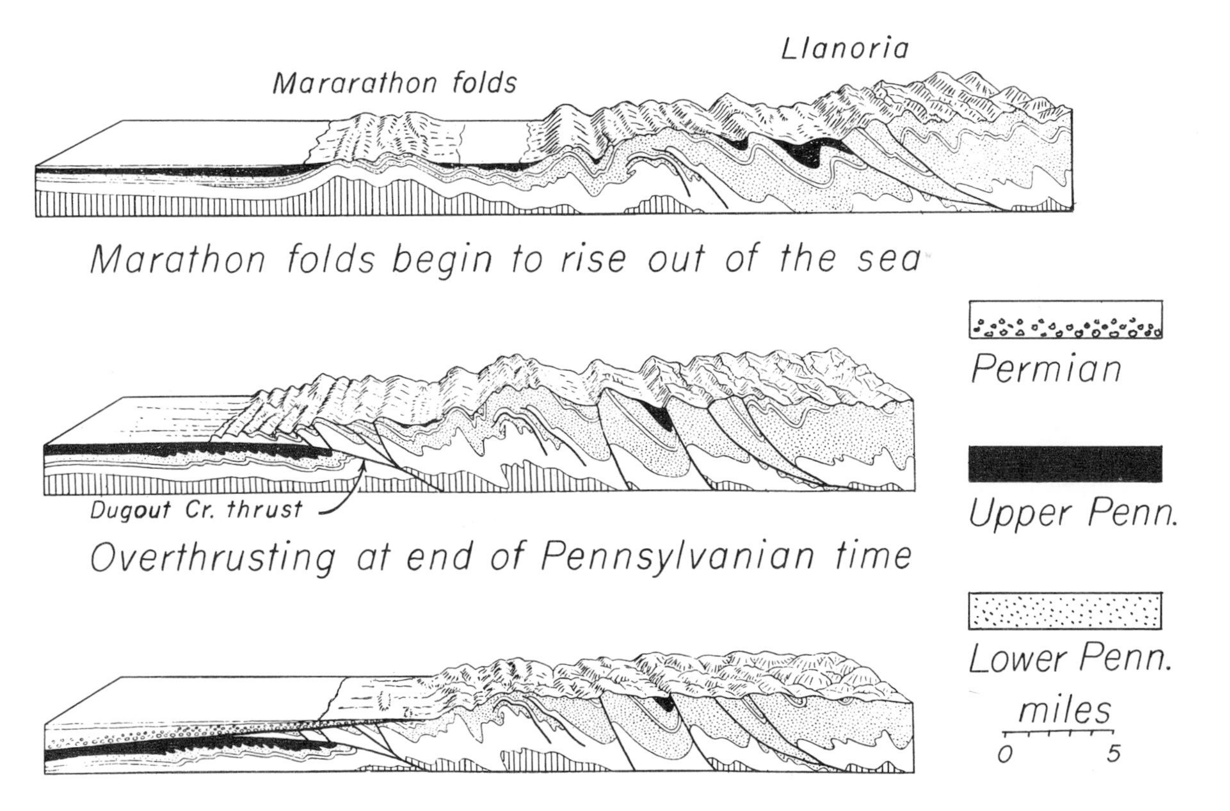

Figure 184. Three stages in the history of the Marathon orogeny. The section runs from northwest to southeast across the Marathon fold belt and includes the edge of Llanoria at the extreme right. (Adapted from P. B. King.)

Chart 6. Correlation of important Pennsylvanian sections

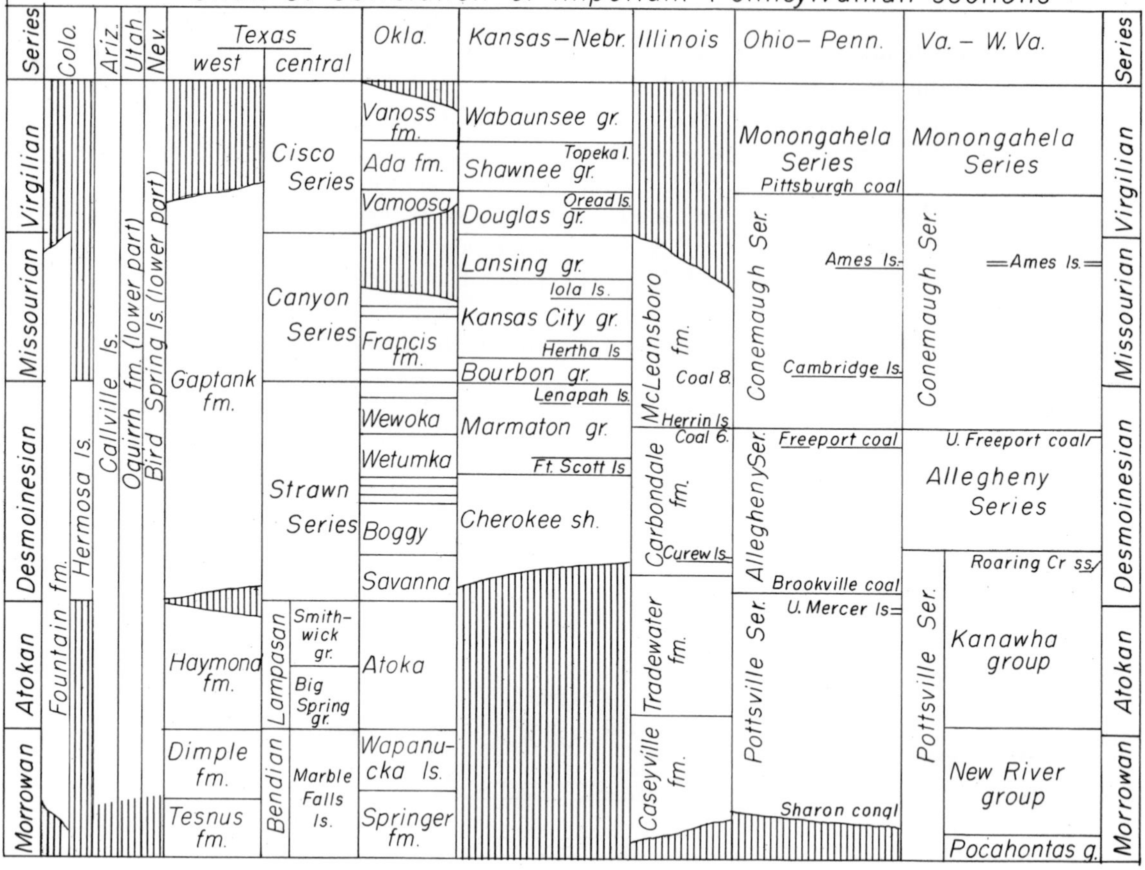

Series	Colo.	Ariz.	Utah	Nev.	Texas west	Texas central	Okla.	Kansas–Nebr.	Illinois	Ohio–Penn.	Va. – W. Va.	Series
Virgilian						Cisco Series	Vanoss fm.; Ada fm.; Vamoosa	Wabaunsee gr.; Topeka l.; Shawnee gr.; Oread ls.; Douglas gr.		Monongahela Series; Pittsburgh coal	Monongahela Series	Virgilian
Missourian	Fountain fm.	Callville ls.	Oquirrh fm. (lower part)	Bird Spring ls. (lower part)	Gaptank fm.	Canyon Series	Francis fm.	Lansing gr.; Iola ls.; Kansas City gr.; Hertha ls.; Bourbon gr.	McLeansboro fm.; Coal 8	Conemaugh Ser.; Ames ls.; Cambridge ls.	Conemaugh Ser.; Ames ls.	Missourian
Desmoinesian	Fountain fm.; Hermosa ls.	Callville ls.	Oquirrh fm. (lower part)	Bird Spring ls. (lower part)	Gaptank fm.	Strawn Series	Wewoka; Wetumka; Boggy; Savanna	Lenapah ls.; Marmaton gr.; Ft. Scott ls; Cherokee sh.	Herrin ls; Coal 6; Carbondale fm.; Curew ls.	Allegheny Ser.; Freeport coal; Brookville coal	U. Freeport coal; Allegheny Series; Roaring Cr ss.	Desmoinesian
Atokan	Fountain fm.; Hermosa ls.	Callville ls.	Oquirrh fm. (lower part)	Bird Spring ls. (lower part)	Haymond fm.	Lampasan: Smithwick gr.; Big Spring gr.	Atoka		Tradewater fm.	Pottsville Ser.; U. Mercer ls.	Pottsville Ser.; Kanawha group	Atokan
Morrowan	Fountain fm.	Callville ls.	Oquirrh fm. (lower part)	Bird Spring ls. (lower part)	Dimple fm.; Tesnus fm.	Bendian: Marble Falls ls.	Wapanucka ls.; Springer fm.		Caseyville fm.	Pottsville Ser.; Sharon congl	Pottsville Ser.; New River group; Pocahontas g.	Morrowan

Close of the Period

The seas retreated gradually during the latter part of the period and at its close the continent was largely if not completely emergent. This was due to a world-like lowering of sealevel, or to gentle continental uplift in North America, and over large parts of the interior of the United States Permian formations rest with apparent conformity on the Pennsylvanian.

In several other parts of the world, however, extensive orogeny occurred about the end of the Pennsylvanian Period (Fig. 168, p. 204). The Armorican ranges of Europe, initiated at the end of the Mississippian, experienced marked rejuvenation during and at the close of the Pennsylvanian. In fact, the culmination of Late Paleozoic mountain-making occurred at this time and during the Early Permian. The effects of this orogeny are to be seen in the stumps of the ancient mountains in southern Wales and England, in the central plateau of France, in the Harz and Black Forest regions of Germany, and in Bohemia; likewise in the Spanish Meseta, Corsica, and Sardinia. In the Himalaya region, this was a time of great mountain-making, "a great revolution in the physical geography of India," which during Pennsylvanian time blotted out the inland (Tethyan) sea. In the Urals also, as in eastern Australia and the Andean region, there was disturbance at this time. In most parts of the world, however, the areas of Late Pennsylvanian orogeny suffered even greater disturbance during or at the close of the Permian.

STRATIGRAPHY

Appalachian Coal Fields. From the front of the Allegheny Plateau westward across Ohio, Indiana, Kentucky, and Illinois, Pennsylvanian rocks are at the surface and comprise one of the great coal fields

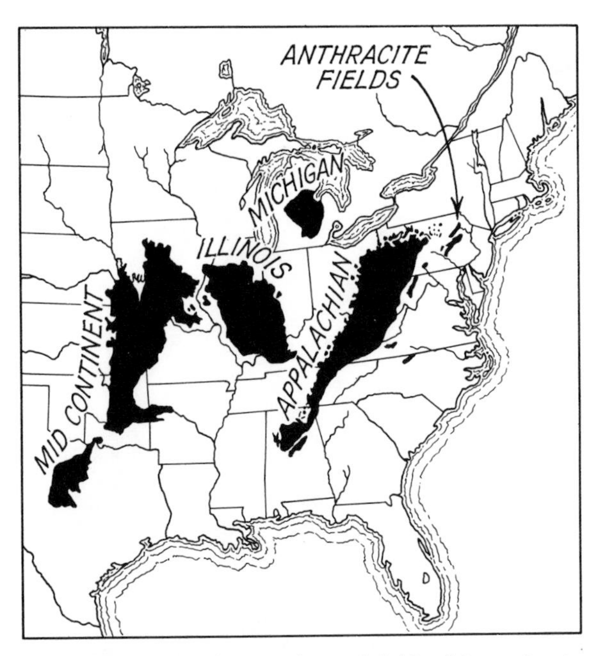

Figure 185. Map showing the coal fields of Pennsylvania age in the eastern United States.

of the world (Fig. 185). A generalized columnar section of the system in eastern Ohio will serve well to illustrate the nature and classification of these rocks (Fig. 186). In this area, well out in the center of the basin of deposition, it presents a long and rather monotonous succession of shales, sandstones, thin marine limestones, and coal beds. About three-fifths of the total thickness is made up of shales and siltstones, mostly gray or dark gray in color. The sandstones are commonly irregularly bedded and cross-stratified; they vary in thickness and coarseness and in places show cut and fill relations and commonly grade laterally into siltstones and shales. Generally the only fossils to be found in either the shales or sandstones are land plants, and these are locally abundant and well preserved. In short, these formations were laid down by streams that built an aggraded plain across the lowlands west of Appalachia. The coal beds are formed of plant tissue that accumulated under standing water in great swamps. Some of these are thin and lenticular,

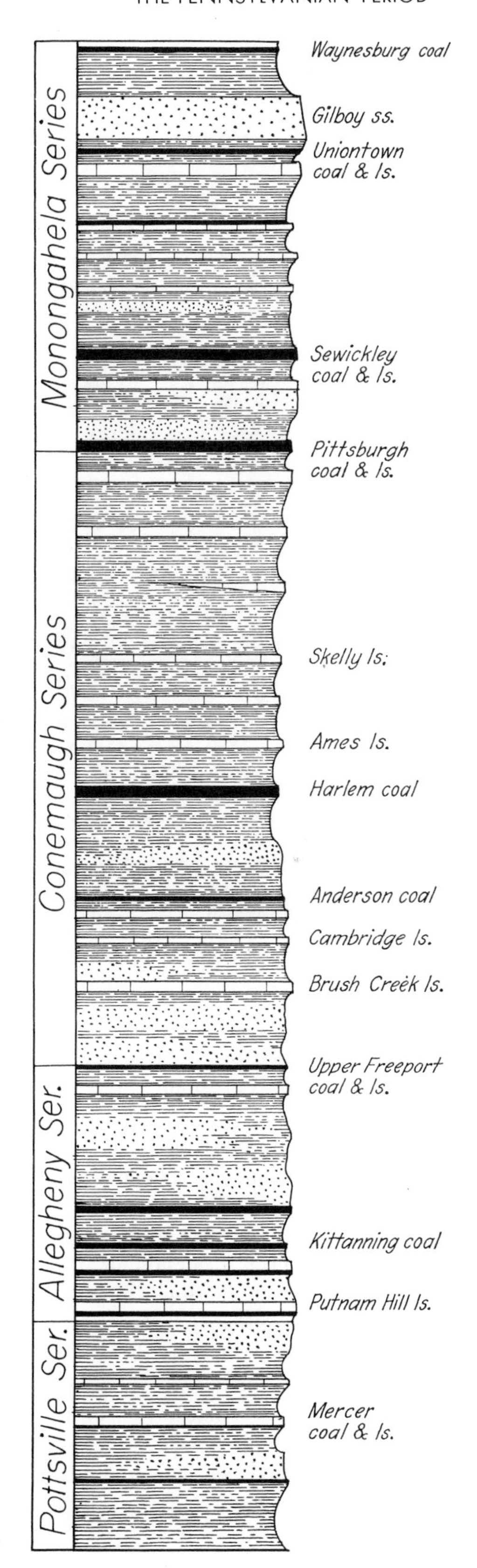

Figure 186. Columnar section of the Pennsylvanian System in eastern Ohio, showing repeated alternations of sandstone, shale, and coal with thin interbedded marine limestone. Vertical scale 150 feet to the inch.

Figure 187A. Natural outcrop of the Pittsburgh coal near Riverside, Pennsylvania. (Carl O. Dunbar.)

recording disconnected and rather transient swamps, but a few, such as the Pittsburgh coal (Fig. 187), cover hundreds of square miles and are several feet thick.

The limestones are thin, most of them less than 10 feet thick, but they commonly extend over great areas with little change in thickness, and all of them bear marine fossils. In short, each of the limestones records a brief incursion of the sea which for a relatively short time drowned the whole region and then retreated to the west.

Such thin but persistent units as the limestones and coal beds make it possible to subdivide the system into many formations that have been named and can be traced and mapped over a large region. For convenience these have been grouped into four series, as indicated in Figure 186. These are widely recognized throughout the Appalachian Province. Where first defined, in western Pennsylvania, the Allegheny and Monongahela series are rich in coal, whereas the Pottsville and Conemaugh series are relatively barren. In a broader regional view these distinctions do not hold, however, the Pottsville Series being the chief coal-producing horizon in West Virginia and Alabama. In actual practice the boundaries between the series are determined by tracing or identifying key beds such as the Pittsburgh coal at the base of the Monongahela or the Upper Freeport coal at the top of the Allegheny Series. Further afield the equivalents of each series can be recognized by distinctive assemblages of fossil plants.

Traced eastward into Pennsylvania or West Virginia the limestones all thin out to feathered edges and disappear, and in much of West Virginia and Alabama the entire Pennsylvanian section is non-marine; but toward the west, in Indiana and Illinois, the limestones are thicker, more numerous, and more persistent.

In the coal fields of Nova Scotia and New Brunswick where the Pennsylvanian System is as much as 13,000 feet thick, deposition was in intermont basins and the entire system is non-marine. The section exposed in the sea cliffs at The Joggins near the head of the Bay of Fundy is of special interest because of the stumps and trunks of trees buried in the position of their growth (Fig. 188). Here erect trunks are recorded at 20 horizons distributed at intervals through about 2,500 feet of beds. Many of the preserved trunks are several feet high, some exceeding 20 feet. They show clearly how rapid the deposition of individual beds must have been, since they were in each case buried before the stumps had time to decay. It is evident, however, that deposition at any locality was intermittent, since these trees, some of them as much as 4 feet in diameter, must have grown unhindered before their burial. Deposition appears to have been by sluggish, meandering streams that frequently deserted their sediment-choked channels to burst out

Figure 187*B*. Open mine in the Pittsburgh coal near Pittsburgh, Pennsylvania. (U.S. Bureau of Mines.)

Figure 188. Fossil tree trunks preserved in position of growth. Specimen at the left in sea cliffs at "The Joggins," Nova Scotia; that at the right, showing an 8-foot trunk, is from Table Head, Great Bras d'Or, Cape Breton. (W. A. Bell, Geological Survey of Canada.)

in new courses over timbered lowlands. (Compare Fig. 33, p. 44.)

Illinois Coal Fields. The Illinois field is closely allied to that of the Appalachian Basin. The two were originally continuous in the southern part and shared in common deposition, but have since been isolated by later uplift and erosion along the Cincinnati Arch. In general, the sediments are finer of grain in Illinois, and marine shales assume much greater importance than in the East. There are a number of widespread coal beds, however, some of which appear to have extended over most of the state and eastward into Indiana. A limestone "cap rock" occurs a short distance above nearly every one of the coals; these vary in thickness from several inches to a few feet and are as widely persistent as the coal beds, the repeated occurrence of these marine horizons above the coals emphasizing the cyclic nature of the deposition in this region. Each coal is the residue of vegetation that grew here while the region stood as a swampy lowland. The cap rock of limestone shows that the sea followed, inundating the swamp. Marine shales follow the limestone, grading up into non-marine shales and sandstone that were formed as the sea was filled up and driven back. Local unconformities occur at the horizon of the transition, marking places where the extended streams cut channels in the shale and filled them with sand.

Mid-Continent Region. The coal fields of Missouri and Kansas, like those of adjacent parts of Nebraska and Iowa, present a section of 2,000 to 3,000 feet of beds in which limestones and shales alternate repeatedly, while sandstones and siltstones occur at greater intervals. Here the limestones comprise about 25 percent of the section and sandstones generally less than 10 percent. Many of the shales and siltstones bear no fossils except fragments of land plants, and were probably deposited on low delta plains. The limestones, on the contrary, like certain of the shales, have abundant marine fossils. In this region many of the thin units persist with little change over great distances, bearing witness to uniform conditions of deposition over great areas. Repeated alternations of marine and non-marine beds indicate that deposition was approximately at sealevel, and suggest that the marine waters were extremely shallow.

Traced southward into Oklahoma and Arkansas, the entire system changes gradually but profoundly as we enter the Ouachita Geosyncline and approach Llanoria (Fig. 189). There the section thickens to 12,000 or even 23,000 feet; sandstones and siltstones assume great prominence, while the limestones thin and in many cases grade laterally into sandstone or shale. In short, the thickness of the Coal Measures in the Ouachita Geosyncline is fully five times that of the northern Mid-Continent fields. This has resulted in part from the more rapid deposition in the geosyncline where subsidence allowed the sediment to come to rest, in part from the nearness to Llanoria which was supplying much of this material, and in part from the fact that deposition began first in the geosyncline and gradually overlapped northward.

In central and western Texas the Pennsylvanian formations are several thousands of feet thick, and here also the influence of Llanoria may be seen.

Deep drilling has shown that Pennsylvanian formations extend west of their outcrop under nearly all of the Great Plains. They are exposed in the Black Hills and in the hogbacks flanking the front of the Rockies, as well as about many of the ranges farther west.

Cordilleran Region. Throughout the Cordilleran region there is so much local variation that brief description is impossible. Along the front of the Rockies, in Wyoming and Colorado, where these formations overlap on Precambrian granite, the lower part (**Fountain formation**) is arkosic and red. In the vicinity of Colorado Springs these rocks are much cross-bedded, unfossiliferous, and wholly non-marine, but toward the northeast they grade into marine limestones (e.g., the Minnelusa limestone of the Black Hills). In the basins associated with the Colorado Mountains, the Pennsylvanian System varies rapidly in thickness and in lithology, but farther south and west it is predominantly marine limestone, which in southern Nevada and adjacent parts of southern California is half a mile thick.

ECONOMIC RESOURCES

Coal. It is no accident that in both Europe and North America the Pennsylvanian rocks are known as the **Coal Measures.** No other geologic system contains so much **high-rank coal.** In these formations lie the great coal fields of the British Isles, of the Saar Basin in France, of the Ruhr Basin in Germany, of Belgium, and of the Donetz Basin in Russia; in America it includes the coal fields that stretch from Oklahoma and Kansas to the Appalachian Mountains. These fields together produce

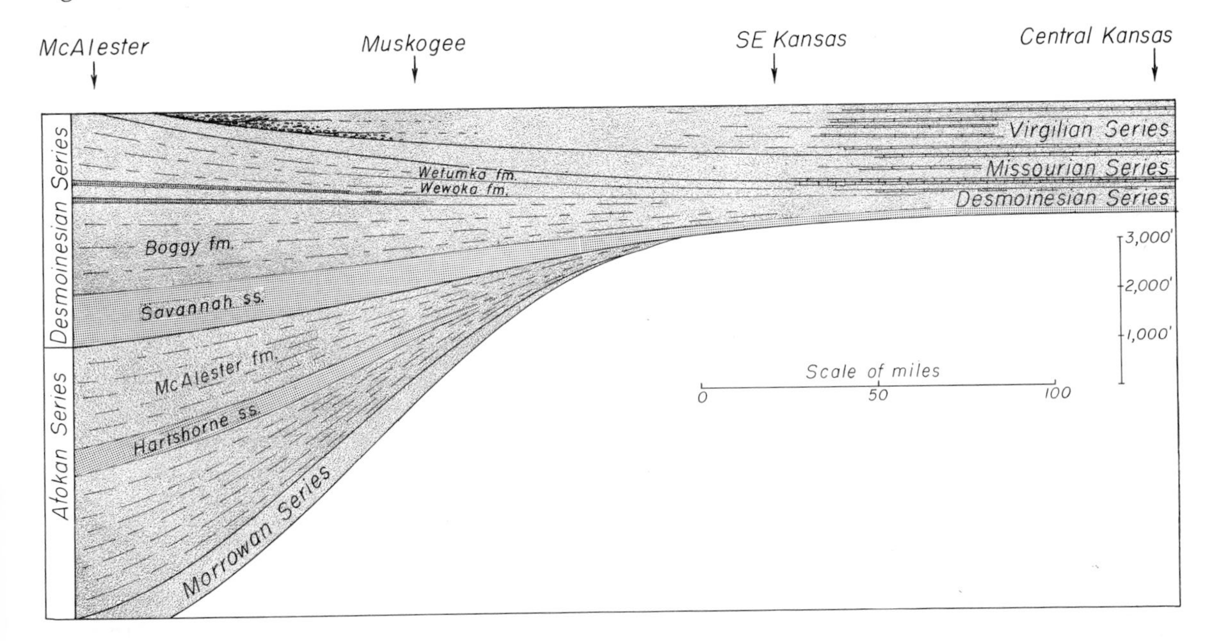

Figure 189. Stratigraphic section of Pennsylvanian System from Iowa to southern Oklahoma.

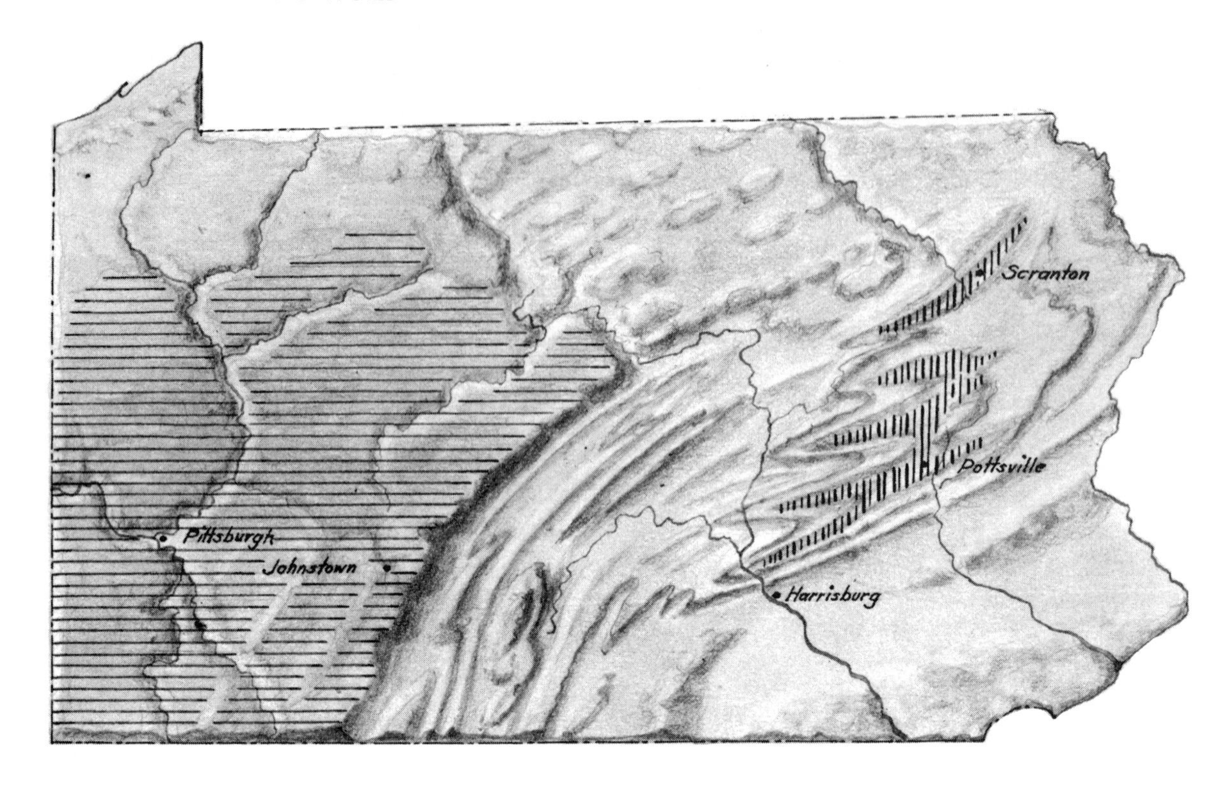

Figure 190. Coal fields of Pennsylvania. The Anthracite fields (vertically shaded) are synclines in the folded belt; the bituminous fields (horizontally lined) are in the flat-lying beds of the Allegheny Plateau.

more than 80 percent of the world's coal. Some of the younger systems also include much coal but it is mostly of low rank and less suitable for industrial uses.

In America the coal fields of Pennsylvanian age occupy an area estimated to exceed 250,000 square miles, a figure considerably greater than that of the coal fields of any other continent. They lie almost entirely in the eastern half of the United States, the chief exception being the small Acadian Basin of the Maritime Provinces of Canada.

Of the five well-defined fields shown in Figure 185, the **Anthracite field** of eastern Pennsylvania is in some respects the most interesting. Although less than 500 square miles in area, it has produced to date almost one-fourth of the total output of coal in North America. Its production reached a peak of 93,000,000 tons in 1923 and has averaged over 85,000,000 yearly for the last quarter-century. Unfortunately more than half of the coal has already been mined, and the supply of anthracite bids fair to be exhausted during the life of the present generation.

The anthracite field is in reality but an eastern part of the vast Appalachian basin that was caught in the Permian folding and isolated from the rest by later erosion, which destroyed all the Coal Measures in eastern Pennsylvania except those parts preserved in deep synclinal folds (Figs. 190 and 191). This folding and the resulting pressure converted the bituminous coal into the hard anthracite by eliminating the volatile matter. The thickness of some of the anthracite beds is noteworthy. The most remarkable bed is the Mammoth, which extends throughout the field, with an average thickness of 35 to 40 feet and in one place has a thickness of 114 feet due to overfolding.

The **Appalachian field** is the second largest, and much the greatest producer of the several coal regions. It underlies the Allegheny Plateau and extends from northern Pennsylvania to Alabama. Pennsylvania and West Virginia are the heaviest producers, but Ohio, Kentucky, and Alabama also yield much coal. This field alone furnishes almost one-fourth of the world's coal supply.

Throughout most of this area the strata lie quite flat, and the coal is bituminous, occurring at many levels. About 60 beds are recognized in Pennsylvania, but of these only 10 are widely mined, the rest being too thin to work profitably. The most remarkable of these beds is the Pittsburgh coal (Fig. 187), which is more than 13 feet thick about Pittsburgh and is known to be workable over an area of 6,000 square miles in western Pennsylvania, eastern Ohio, and northwestern West Virginia, where it is estimated to contain more than 22,000,000,000 tons of coal. Up to 1926 it had yielded approximately 3,500,000,000 tons of coal, with a value at the mines more than 20 times that of the gold produced by the greatest gold mine in the United States.[1]

The **Illinois field** is a shallow structural basin extending into southwestern Indiana and western Kentucky. It includes ten or more important producing horizons and ranks second to the Appalachian field, far outstripping the much larger Mid-Continent region in production. The coal beds here do not attain so great a thickness as they do farther east, but some of them, notably the Herrin coal, persist with remarkable uniformity over much of the state of Illinois.

The **Mid-Continent field** embraces the coal fields of Missouri, Iowa, Kansas, Oklahoma, and northern Texas. Although the area exceeds that of the Appalachian field, the output of coal has been less than one-tenth as great. Here the beds are commonly less than 4 feet thick, and the best producing horizons are in the lower part of the system. There are extensive areas where the surface is flat and the coal so near the surface that it is mined by stripping with steam shovels.

The remaining fields are relatively small producers, together supplying less than 1 percent of the world's coal. In the tiny Rhode Island Basin extreme metamorphism has reduced the coal to graphite, or so nearly so that it has little fuel value.

Most of the Pennsylvanian coals of the United States include sulphur as an impurity. This is believed to indicate that the coal swamps bordered the inland seas and were brackish, since sulphur-depositing bacteria live in the sea but do not thrive in fresh-water lakes and swamps. Conversely, the

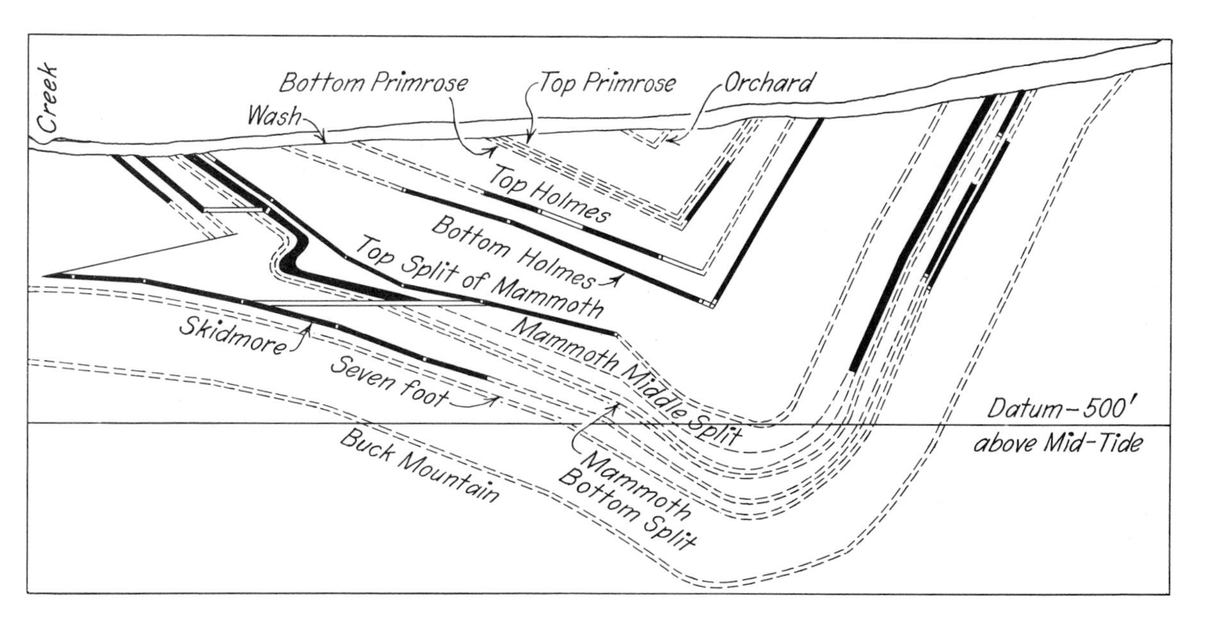

Figure 191. Cross section of the South Anthracite coal basin. The Mammoth coal, which attains a thickness of over 100 feet, is separated by interbeds of shale into 3 distinct beds, each known as a "split" of the Mammoth coal.

slight amount of sulphur in the anthracite of eastern Pennsylvania and in the coals of the Acadian Basin indicates that in these regions swamps were entirely of fresh water.

Petroleum and Natural Gas. Pennsylvanian rocks have been an important source of petroleum and natural gas in the Mid-Continent oil fields, and for a number of years, from the discovery of these fields in the 1890's until about 1925, constituted their only important producing horizon. During that time Kansas and Oklahoma produced from these beds over 2,000,000,000 barrels of oil. Subsequently, however, production has been found at greater depths in the Ordovician "sands," which have given rise to the spectacular developments of recent years in those two states and in north-central Texas.

CLIMATE

The terrestrial sediments with their plant remains speak eloquently of warm, moist climate during the chief coal-producing stages of the Pennsylvanian in many parts of the world. The vegetation of the coal beds clearly grew in swamps, where it accumulated under standing water, as evidenced by the spreading root systems still preserved in the fire clays that underlie the coals in many places. Moreover, the structural types of the foliage so well preserved in the roofing shales at many places indicate marked humidity. Swamp waters are required to protect the fallen vegetation from the air and thus save it from decay. The wide distribution and the repeated occurrence of coals therefore assure us that there was a persistently moist climate over vast regions of the Pennsylvanian landscape.

This does not prove, of course, that no parts of the Earth were arid. It is well to remember that at present the dripping jungles of the Amazon Valley are separated only by the narrow Andean chain from the desert coast of western Peru. Similar extremes probably existed on the continents during Pennsylvanian time, for lofty mountains must have been accompanied, then as now, by a leeward rain shadow of deficient rainfall. The salt deposits of the Paradox formation in eastern Utah and western Colorado, like the red arkose of the Fountain formation of central Colorado, may indicate such local aridity about the Colorado Mountains. On the contrary, the coal swamps of the eastern interior were formed where the warm, moist winds were rising up the long western slope of Appalachia. In general, it appears that humid climatic conditions were exceptionally widespread during Pennsylvanian time.

There is also much evidence that the climate was warm, even in high latitudes, during much of the period. The mere presence of abundant vegetation is no evidence, for it is well known that the most extensive modern accumulation of peat is in subarctic regions where slow growth is more than counterbalanced by slow decay; but the *character* of the Carboniferous vegetation indicates a lack of freezing winters, at least in the lowlands where the plants are preserved. The trees, whether tree ferns, seed ferns, cordaites, or the great scale trees, bore succulent foliage of almost unprecedented luxuriance. Not merely were the leaves large, but their texture indicates rapid growth under warm, humid conditions. For example, the very large size of the individual cells, the arrangment of the stomata (breathing pores), the smoothness and thickness of the bark, the presence of aerial roots, and the absence of growth rings in the woody trunks are all features of significance. One of the foremost paleobotanists of our times concluded that "the climate of the principal coal-forming intervals of the Pennsylvanian was mild, probably nearly tropical or subtropical, generally humid, and equable."[2]

The animal life of the time also seems to support this view. Insects, for example, attained an extraordinary size and, so far as known, averaged larger than in any other period of Earth history. Since it is well known that the modern orders of insects have their large representatives in the tropics, with smaller and smaller species in regions of more rigorous climate, the significance of the Pennsylvanian insects is obvious. To this may be added the fact that at certain times during the period corals were able to thrive in great abundance and to form reefs as far north as the arctic islands of Spitzbergen (lat. 78° N.). The presence of these ancient reefs in the sea cliffs of a land now treeless and ice-covered speaks eloquently of the climatic contrast between the Present and the Pennsylvanian ages in this region. The exceptional abundance of the large fusulines in the limestones of the northern hemisphere, and even as far north as Spitzbergen, seems to have a significance like that of the insects.

The extensive continental glaciation of India, South Africa, South America, and Australia, which some geologists attribute to Late Pennsylvanian time, we regard as of Permian age. This is discussed in Chapter 13.

Without a doubt the polar regions were cooler than those of low latitudes, and it may well be that the mild climate of Spitzbergen was due to the local influence of a warm ocean current which then streamed into the Arctic. It is not to be assumed that all parts of the Earth were warm or that any parts were uniformly warm and moist throughout the period. Nevertheless, the evidence for mild climate is so widespread that we cannot avoid the belief that in general the Pennsylvanian was an exceptional period in the climatic history of the Earth.

Figure 192 and chapter opening. Pennsylvanian landscape in the swampy lowlands showing characteristic vegetation and sprawling amphibians. Part of a great mural by Rudolph F. Zallinger. Plants: 1, a tree fern; 2, *Lepidodendron*, a scale tree; 3, *Sigillaria*, a scale tree; 4, *Cordaites*, a precursor of the conifers; 5, *Calamites*, a scouring rush. Animals: 6, *Diplovertebron*, a primitive amphibian; 7, *Eryops*, a large amphibian; 8, *Eogyrinus*, one of the largest of amphibians; 9, *Seymouria*, a primitive reptile; 10, *Limnoscelis*, a reptile; 11, *Varanosaurus*, a reptile; 12, *Meganeuron*, a giant dragonflylike insect. (Yale Peabody Museum.)

LIFE OF THE PENNSYLVANIAN PERIOD

Forests of the Swamp Lands

Forests of fast-growing, soft-tissued trees, spread over the moist lowlands of the Pennsylvanian landscape. Among these were none of the deciduous forms like those of our modern forests, for they had not yet evolved. The giants of the time were strange, spore-bearing trees which today are represented only by insignificant, herbaceous descendants like the ground pines and scouring rushes (Fig. 192).

Under the moist and perpetual summer of the coal swamps, shades of green must have been dominant. It is likely that the monotonous verdure was rarely enlivened by bright colors, for the primitive flowers of the time were simple and small. There was probably no honey to lure the insects and no sweet perfumes to scent the air, only fresh resinous odors such as pervade the living conifer forests.

Although seed-bearing plants were common, spore-bearing trees were even more abundant and at certain seasons must have covered the forests with a greenish yellow or brownish dust of spores, since some of the coals (cannel coals) are composed almost entirely of spore cases.

Ferns of many kinds were common, and they alone gave a modern aspect to the dells of these ancient forests. The leaves of some species attained huge proportions, single fronds reaching a length of 5 or 6 feet; and the slender, unbranched trunks grew to be as high as 50 feet.

Seed ferns resembled the true ferns in every respect save one: they bore small nutlike seeds instead of spores appended to their fronds. They may have descended from ferns and in turn may have given rise to all the higher, seed-bearing plants. They were more common than the true ferns in Pennsylvanian time and have often been confused with them, since the two groups can be distinguished only when fruiting fronds are found.

Scouring rushes of giant size grew in solid stands like "cane brakes" in portions of the swamps. Like their humbler modern descendant, *Equisetum*, they are easily recognized by their vertically ribbed and regularly jointed stems (Fig. 193*D*). The Paleozoic forms bore at each joint a whorl of slender simple leaves which in modern rushes are

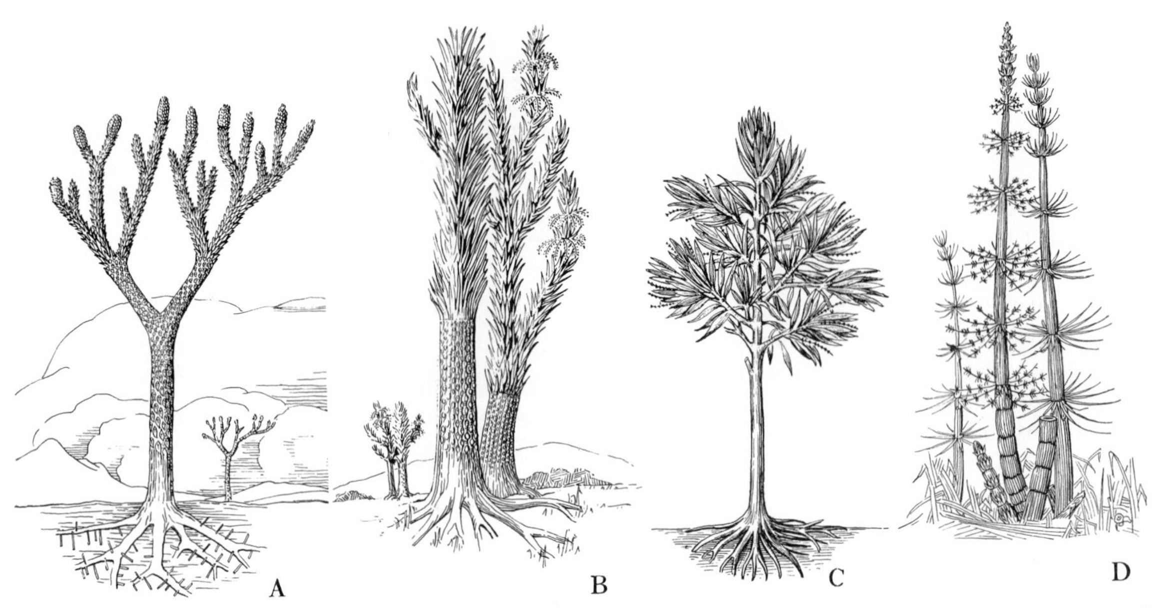

Figure 193. Four of the dominant types of forest trees during Pennsylvanian time. *A, Lepidodendron; B, Sigillaria; C, Cordaites; D, Calamites.*

represented only by bractlike vestiges. The leaf whorls, known as *Annularia*, commonly present a false resemblance to flowers. The largest of the Pennsylvanian rushes belonged to the genus *Calamites.* Some of these exceeded 12 inches in diameter and had a height of 30 or more feet. Their trunks were not solid woody stems, but rather thin woody cylinders filled with a core of pith and surrounded by thick bark, the woody layer rarely having a thickness of 2 inches.

The **scale trees** were the most imposing plants of the forests and in many places the most common. Their name is derived from the fact that their close-set leaves left permanent leaf scars over the trunk and limbs that make them appear scaled (Fig. 193*A,B*). So striking is this deception that twigs have been mistaken by amateur fossil hunters for petrified snake skins. The scale trees grew to a large size, their stumps reaching a diameter of 4 to 6 feet and their slowly tapering trunks an extreme height of more than 100 feet. Most of them belonged to one of two well-defined genera, *Lepidodendron* or *Sigillaria.*

Lepidodendron (Fig. 193*A*) grew a tall slender trunk branching repeatedly near the top to present a spreading crown of stubby twigs covered with slender straplike leaves. These leaves, like immensely overgrown pine needles, in some species were 6 to 8 inches long and ½ inch wide. The older leaves were shed as new ones formed at the tips of the branches, leaving sharply defined diamond-shaped leaf scars which were normally arranged in spiral rows about the limbs and the trunk (Fig. 194). The branching was normally dichotomous (with equal forks). Spore cases were borne as cones at the tips of the limbs.

Sigillaria (Figs. 193 and 194) possessed a thicker trunk which rarely branched and was clothed for several feet from the top with large bladelike leaves, resembling those of *Lepidodendron* but larger. In these trees the bark was vertically ribbed, and the leaf scars were normally in vertical rows. Trunks have been found with a diameter, just above the roots, of 6 feet, and one specimen is known to be 100 feet long without a branch.

About 100 species each of *Sigillaria* and *Lepidodendron* have been described. Although many of them were large trees, some were relatively small. In all of them the structure of the trunk and limbs was peculiar in that they had a relatively large center of pith surrounded by a woody cylinder, and this in turn by two very thick layers of corklike bark. The leaf scars are impressed only on the bark. The root system likewise was peculiar, the main trunk roots spreading almost horizontally without a tap root; moreover, they branched but a few times and so were stubby and thick. The real rootlets sprang directly from the sides of these trunk roots, radiating thickly away to a distance of several inches. Such root stocks, known as **stigmaria**, are common in the fire clays under coal beds and not infrequently appear in the coal.

The **cordaites** (named after the Bohemian botanist Corda) were the forerunners of the modern conifers, which they resembled in their sturdy softwood trunks and their parallel-veined leaves (Fig. 193*C*). They differed from true conifers chiefly in two ways: (1) their leaves were not needlelike but bladelike, attaining a length of several inches to 5 or 6 feet, and (2) their seeds were borne in racemes instead of being crowded into cones. Many of them were tall, graceful trees, some attaining a height of 120 feet and a diameter as great as 3 feet. In such trees fully two-thirds of the trunk was without branches, though the top was a dense crown of branches and large simple leaves. The wood of the cordaites was much like that of modern pines, but the pith at the center was larger. They appear to have been one of the chief contributors to the vegetation that made the Pennsylvanian coal.

True conifers appeared during the period but have been found in only a few localities, probably because they lived on the uplands where they were not commonly preserved. It is obvious that our knowledge of the Pennsylvanian land plants relates almost wholly to the swampy lowlands. Possibly the most rapid advances were being made in the uplands, where the climate was more rigorous and more stimulating but where the chances for preservation were slight.

One of the striking features of the Pennsylvanian floras is the marked similarity of the species in different parts of the world. They were as nearly cosmopolitan as any in the Earth's history. This may be attributed to their habit of reproduction by spores that are easily carried by the wind, but it also suggests the absence of well-marked climatic zones.

Animal Conquest of the Lands

Through the dank forests of Pennsylvanian time droned clumsy, primitive insects, while centipedes,

Figure 194. Pieces of the bark of "scale trees" showing characteristic arrangement of the leaf scars. Right, *Lepidodendron;* left, *Sigillaria.* (Yale Peabody Museum.)

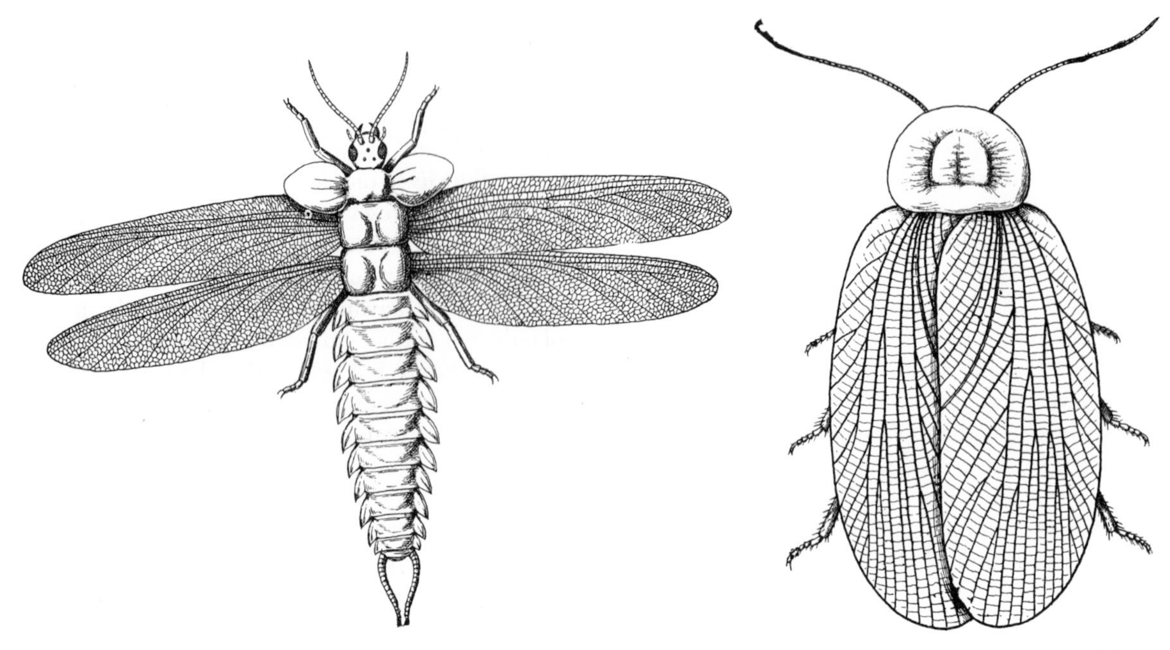

Figure 195. Primitive insects of the Pennsylvanian Period. Left, a primitive and generalized type, *Stenodictya,* right, a primitive cockroach.

spiders, and scorpions scurried about over the fallen logs in search of food. Small land snails worked their tedious way in the trees, and in the swamps a hundred or more kinds of sprawling Amphibia lolled about as do crocodiles or giant salamanders (Fig. 192). Before the close of the period the more adventurous of these amphibians had left the water permanently to establish the dynasty of reptiles. Now for the first time we find the record of varied and abundant land animals; henceforth their dominion over the lands is never for a moment in doubt.

Figure 196. Spiders preserved in concretions in mid-Pennsylvanian shale at Mazon Creek, Illinois. Both are seen in ventral view. Right, *Architarbus rotundatus;* left, *Architarbus carbonarius.* (After Petrunkevitch.)

The **insects** of this time were truly remarkable for their great size. Out of four hundred forms known from Lower and Middle Pennsylvanian strata, more than a score exceeded 4 inches in length, six attained nearly 8 inches, and three exceeded a foot, the average length being about 2 inches. The largest of all was a dragonflylike type found in the Coal Measures of Belgium, which had a wing spread of 29 inches (Fig. 192). No period since has produced insects so large. Most of these insects were of strange primitive stocks not exactly like any of the modern orders. Cockroaches, however, were very like the living ones, only larger, and so common that the period has sometimes been called the **Age of Cockroaches** (Fig. 195). Several of the Pennsylvanian species achieved a length of 3 or 4 inches.

The presence of several hundred species of insects in the Pennsylvanian makes their sudden appearance at this time the more remarkable. The

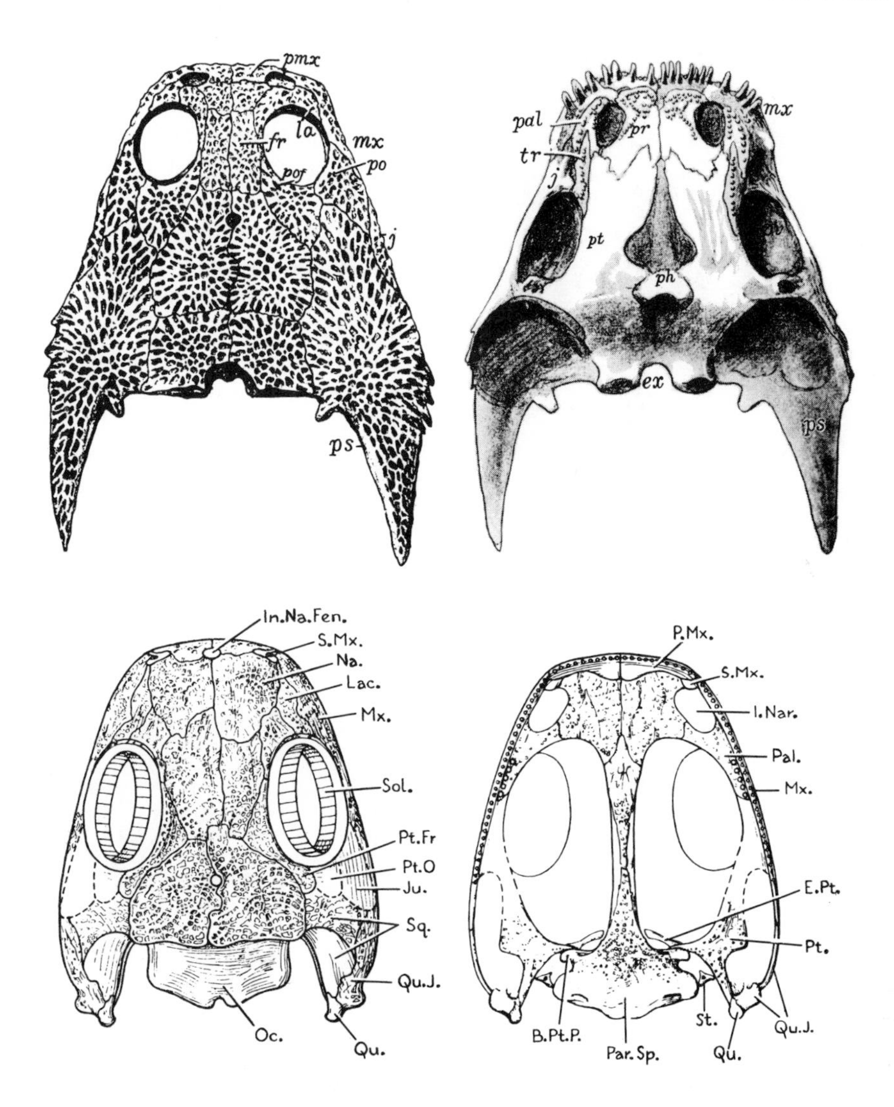

Figure 197. Pennsylvanian amphibians. 1, 2, Upper and under surfaces of the skull of *Diceratosaurus*, from Linton, Ohio (slightly enlarged); 3, 4, dorsal and ventral views of the skull of *Miobatrachus*, from Mazon Creek, Illinois (× 3). *Miobatrachus* is considered a possible representative of the ancestral line from which the frogs evolved at a later time. (After Roy Moodie and D. M. S. Watson, respectively.)

Figure 198. One of the oldest known reptiles, *Eosauravus copei*, from mid-Pennsylvanian beds at Linton, Ohio. Slightly enlarged. The hind legs and most of the backbone are preserved but the head is missing. (Roy L. Moodie, U.S. National Museum.)

diversity of the forms represented implies a long antecedent evolution whose record may yet be found in Mississippian if not in Devonian rocks.

Scorpions, remarkably like modern ones in size and structure, occur with the insect fossils. **Spiders** (Fig. 196) likewise occur, though none of the fossils shows clear evidence of spinnerets, and it may be that these early forms did not make webs. **Centipedes** (or myriapods) of several kinds are known, the largest of which, found at Mazon Creek, Illinois, had a length of 12 inches.

Land snails were first discovered in the famous Joggins section of Nova Scotia, where they were associated with the skeletons of Amphibia. Both had taken refuge in standing hollow stumps that were overwhelmed by floods and buried by sand and mud. Land snails are extremely rare fossils in the Paleozoic rocks, however, and all are small.

Small **fresh-water clams** of several kinds (*Carbonicola, Anthracomya*, etc.) occur abundantly in the dark shales of certain of the coal fields, especially in Nova Scotia and Europe.

Vertebrate animals are represented by abundant skeletal remains of **Amphibia.** From the Coal Measures of North America alone no fewer than 7 orders, 19 families, 46 genera, and 88 species are known. Such great diversity suggests that these animals were common in spite of the fact that they are still the rarest of fossils. The most remarkable single locality for such remains is at Linton, Ohio, at the base of the Freeport coal, where abundant ganoid fishes and no fewer than 50 species of Amphibia have been found (Figs. 192 and 197).

The Pennsylvanian Amphibia were labyrinthodonts, and nearly all were small (Fig. 197). Many of them were only a few inches long, and large ones, scarcely 10 feet over-all, would not be bigger than a large Florida alligator. The greatest of all is known only from its tracks, deeply impressed in Mid-Pennsylvanian sandstone near Lawrence, Kansas. This animal (*Onychopus*

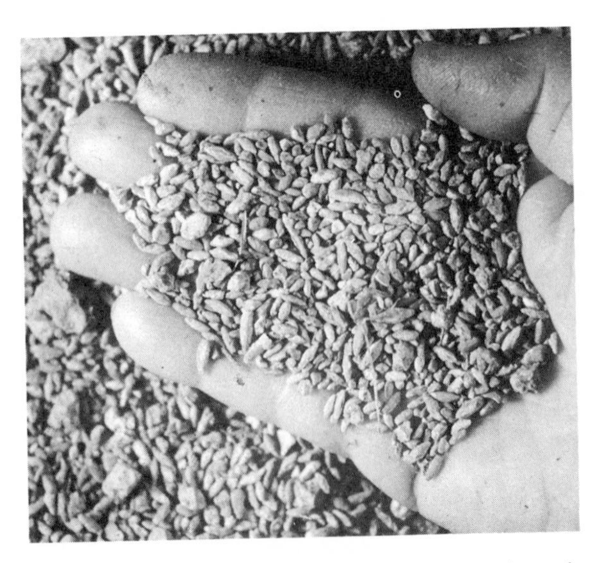

Figure 199. Fusuline foraminifera weathered from the rock.

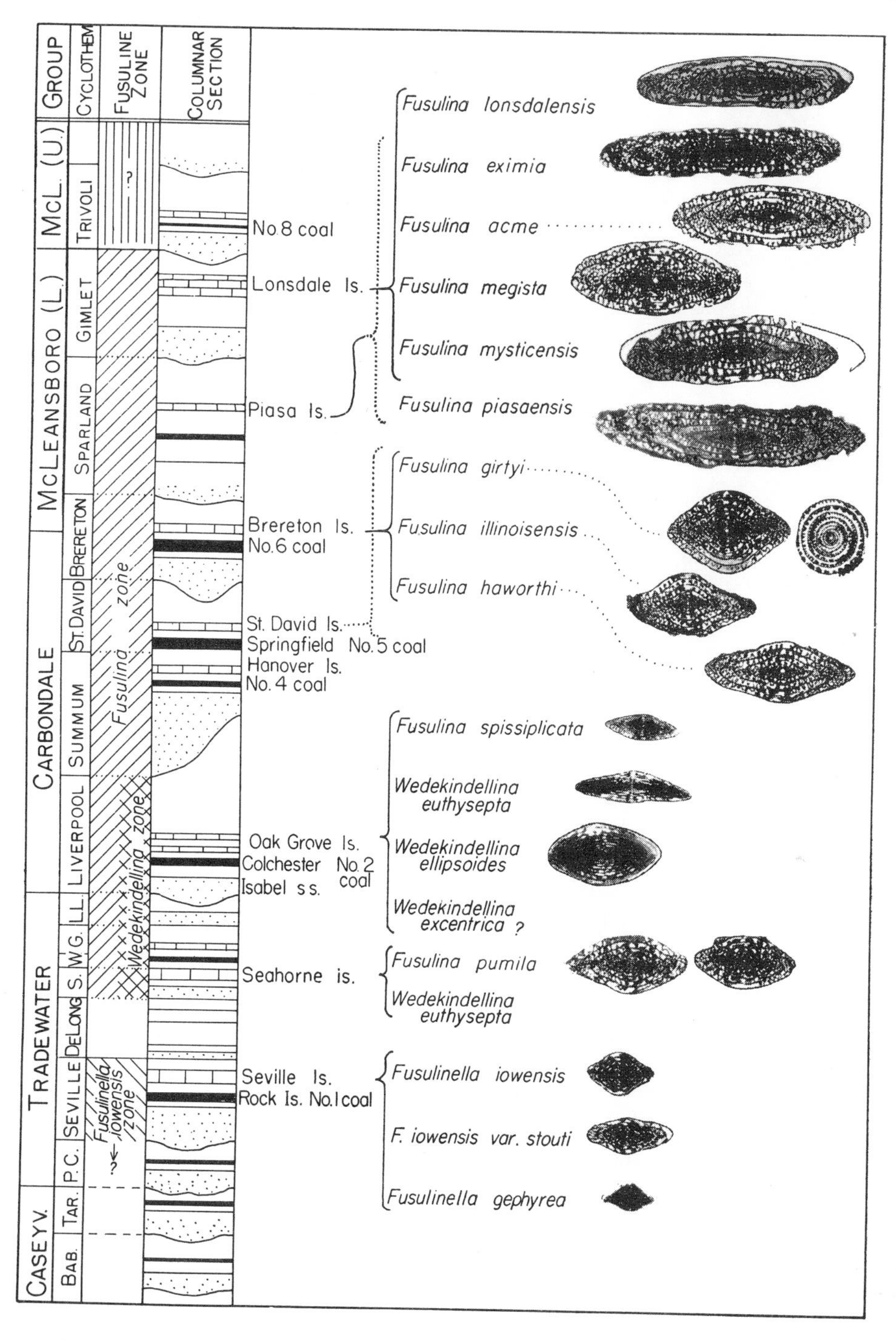

Figure 200. Fusulines as zone fossils. The columnar section of the lower half of the Pennsylvanian System in Illinois shows an alternation of sandstones, shales, and coal beds, with several thin but widespread limestones each of which bears fusulines. The fusuline faunas are shown at the right by an axial section of each species enlarged four diameters. Obviously the faunas of the Lonsdale and Piasa limestones are almost identical but are very different from those of the Braerton and St. David limestones and the faunas of the three lower limestones are quite distinctive. Each of these zones could be easily identified in a well core.

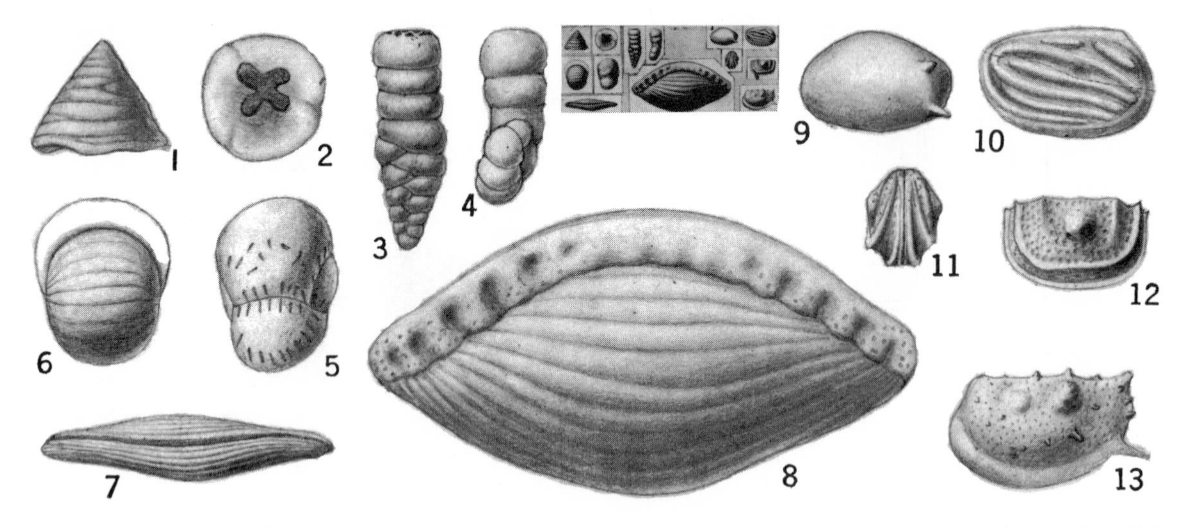

Figure 201. Microfossils from the Pennsylvanian, greatly enlarged. Foraminifera: 1, 2, *Tetrataxis palaeotrochus* (side and dorsal views); 3, *Climacammina cylindrica;* 4, *Ammobaculites stormi;* 5, *Bradyina magna;* 6, *Staffella keytei;* 7, *Wedekindellina euthysepta;* 8, *Triticites ventricosus.* Ostracoda: 9, *Healdia limacoidea;* 10, *Glyptopleura menardensis;* 11, 12, *Amphiscites centronotus* (end and side views); 13, *Hollinella kelletae.* The insert at center top shows the specimens about twice natural size.

gigas) had blunt, stubby feet over 5 inches long, and although its stride was only about 30 inches, the right and left treads were wide apart, indicating a short but very heavy-bodied animal estimated to weigh not less than 500 or 600 pounds. There is some evidence that the feet were webbed like those of a crocodile.

A few **reptiles** of small size appeared during the later half of the period, but their remains are very rare. (Fig. 198).

Résumé of the Marine Animals

The invertebrate life of the Pennsylvanian seas was not only prolific but also varied. Moreover, it was a cosmopolitan assemblage, presenting much the same aspect in various parts of the world.

Brachiopods (Pl. 10, figs. 1–6, 8–12) and **lacy bryozoa** continued in great profusion. The spiny productids exceeded all other brachiopods and gave a distinctive aspect to all the faunas.

The muddy and sandy sea floors seem to have been especially suitable for **pelecypods** (Pl. 10, figs. 18–22) and **gastropods** (Pl. 10, figs. 14–17), which were represented by hundreds of species. In general, these were still small, however, few of the shells exceeding a length of 1 or 2 inches. **Cephalopods** were much less numerous and generally are poorly preserved, though in some regions, especially the coal fields of Europe, they are not so rare and are of great value in stratigraphic correlation. Of these, the nautiloids were rather on the decline, but the goniatites were rapidly changing into a variety of forms and developing more complicated sutures, foreshadowing the expansion of the typical ammonites during the next period.

Corals (Pl. 10, fig. 7) of a few kinds, mostly solitary types, persisted, but only locally assumed importance. Echinodermata are represented by abundant **crinoidal** fragments and the plates and spines of **sea-urchins**, but well-preserved skeletons of both groups are not common because the shallow sea floors were wave-swept enough to break apart the echinoderm bodies. **Blastoids** made their last stand in the earliest part of the period and are never found above the lowermost Pennsylvanian formations (Wapanucka and Morrow), except in the East Indies, where several genera appear in the Permian.

One of the most striking groups of Pennsylvanian fossils is the **fusulines**, a family of relatively large bottom-dwelling Foraminifera. They built multichambered limy shells of globular or fusiform shape, whence the name Fusulinidae, meaning

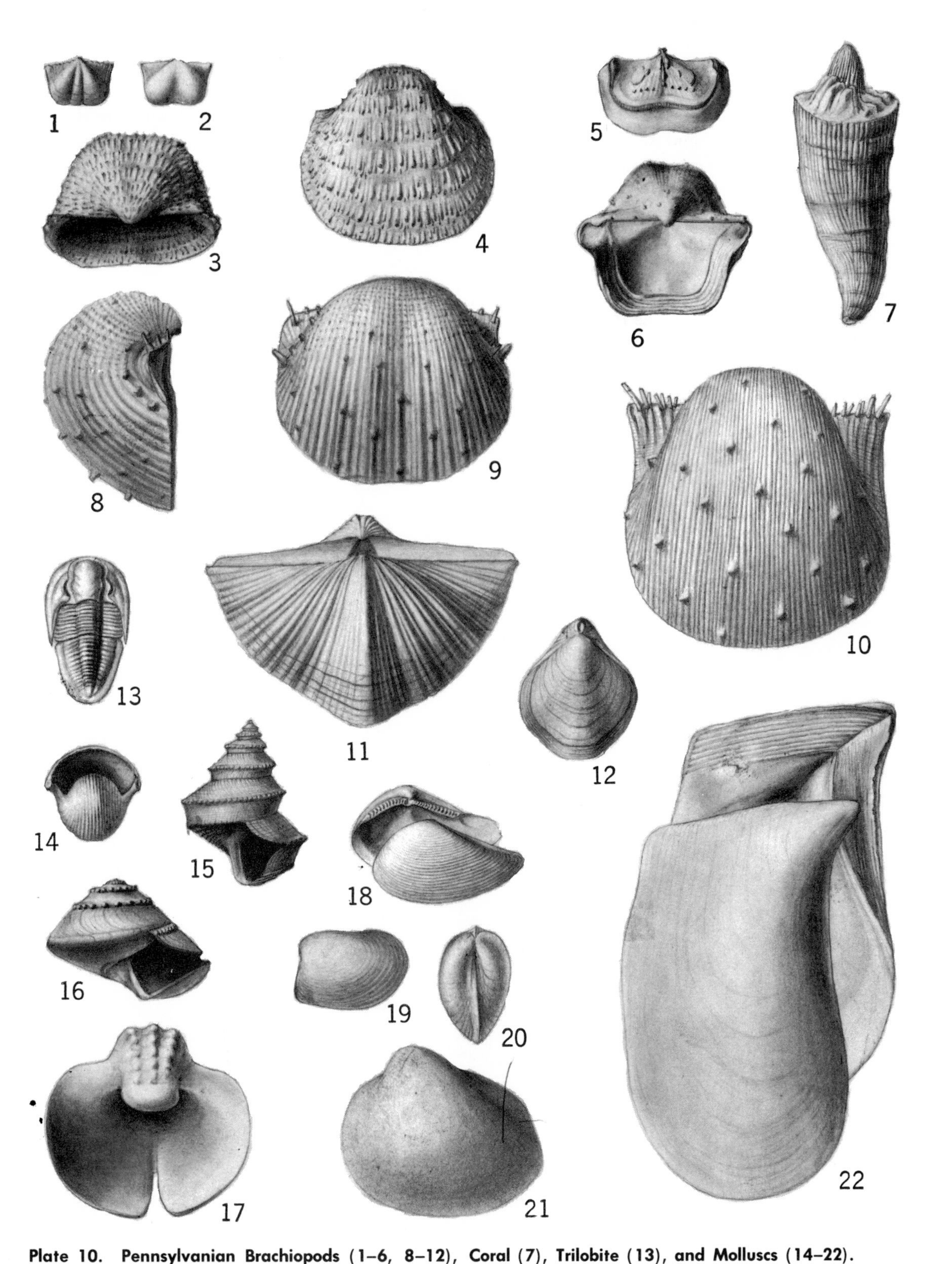

Plate 10. Pennsylvanian Brachiopods (1–6, 8–12), Coral (7), Trilobite (13), and Molluscs (14–22).

Figure 1, *Mesolobus mesolobus;* 2, *Lissochonetes geinitzianus;* 3, 4, *Juresania nebrascensis;* 5, 6, *Marginifera splendens* (5, interior view of dorsal valve); 7, *Lophophyllum profundum;* 8, 9, *Dictyoclostus portlockianus;* 10, *Linoproductus prattenianus;* 11, *Neospirifer dunbari;* 12, *Composita subtilita;* 13, *Phillipsia major,* one of the very last of the trilobites; 14, *Euphemites carbonarius;* 15, *Worthenia tabulata;* 16, *Trepospira sphaerulata;* 17, *Pharkidonotus tricarinatus;* 18, *Nuculana arata;* 19, 20, *Nuculopsis ventricosa;* 21, *Schizodus wheeleri;* 22, *Myalina subquadrata.* All natural size. (Drawn by L. S. Douglass.)

spindle-shaped. Commonly they resemble grains of wheat or oats in size and shape. They were important rock-makers in many parts of the Northern Hemisphere, where fusuline limestones are widely spread (Fig. 199).

Small foraminifers were also common and varied in the Pennsylvanian seas. Ostracods were still numerous though nearly all very small.

Minute types of fossils, such as foraminifers and ostracods, have proved to be very useful in subsurface correlation in the oil fields, since they can be recovered from the drill cuttings and, when studied, serve to identify the formation through which the drill is passing (Fig. 200). Because of their small size they are commonly spoken of as **microfossils** (Fig. 201), and their study has become a specialized science known as micropaleontology.

REFERENCES

1. Ashley, George H., 1928, Bituminous coal fields of Pennsylvania. *Topogr. and Geol. Surv. Pennsylvania, Bull. M16.*

2. White, David, and R. Thiessen, 1913, The origin of coal. *U.S. Bureau of Mines, Bull. 38,* pp. 67–75.

Chapter 13. *The Permian Period: A Crisis in Earth History*

Figure 202. Guadalupe Mountains of west Texas carved from the great Capitan reef complex. Aerial view from southwest of Guadalupe Peak. The Delaware Basin is to the right of the reef front and the platform with its lagoonal deposits stretches away to the left. BC Brushy Canyon formation; BS, Bone Spring limestone; C, Capitan limestone; CC, Cherry Canyon formation.

MOMENTOUS CHANGES USHERED THE PALEOZOIC Era to its close. As the mobile borderlands continued to rise, several of the great Paleozoic geosynclines were uplifted and transformed into ranges of folded mountains. While the Appalachians were forming in eastern America, the Urals were rising out of a great geosyncline in eastern Europe and other ranges were growing across southern Europe and southern Asia. By the close of Permian time all the continents were completely emergent, deserts were widespread, and the world had experienced its most severe and widespread glaciation. For the Paleozoic forms of life, both animal and plant, it was a time of reckoning and many of the dominant groups failed to survive. Judged by the changes that occurred, the end of the Paleozoic Era was one of the great crises in the history of life on the Earth.

Founding of the Permian System. Almost as soon as the early Paleozoic systems were defined, Murchison and Sedgwick were concerned to know whether they would be recognizable in other regions. Travel in Germany, the Alps, and Belgium confirmed their hopes that they would. In all these regions, however, the rocks are much disturbed; hence, when rumors were brought back that Paleozoic strata were flat-lying over great areas in Russia, Murchison determined to extend his exploration in that direction. The publication of his great classic, *Siluria*, had brought him such renown that it was easily arranged for his expedition to proceed under the royal patronage of the Czar. He was joined in this undertaking by two friends, the Russian geologist, Count Keyserling, and his French colleague, De Verneuil.

In western England and Wales, where so many of the systems had been named, the Coal Measures are succeeded by redbeds that are in the main unfossiliferous. In Russia, on the contrary, Murchison found the Coal Measures to be overlain by a widely distributed series of highly fossiliferous rocks, partly terrestrial but largely marine. These he first studied in the province of Perm on the western flank of the Urals, and from these exposures he called them the **Permian System**. Later work has shown that the system can be recognized in many other regions and that the older part of the redbeds overlying the Coal Measures of England and Germany is of the same age, though deposited under different conditions. The extensive development of Permian rocks in America was not recognized until after 1900, when the thick and richly fossiliferous sections of western Texas and New Mexico were discovered; but it is now clear that we have a Permian section unexcelled in any part of the world.

PHYSICAL HISTORY OF A CHANGING WORLD

Final Emergence of the Appalachian Geosyncline. Over eastern North America the change from Pennsylvanian to Permian conditions was transitional rather than abrupt. A mountainous borderland stretched from Newfoundland to Mexico, and the region of the Appalachian Geosyncline remained a broad alluvial plain crossed by sediment-laden streams flowing westward toward the retreating sea. Deposition continued for a time across the central part of the geosyncline, as shown by the **Dunkard group** in southeastern Ohio and northwestern West Virginia (Fig. 208). Probably these formations were originally more extensive along the trough and were largely destroyed by erosion later in the period.

Before Middle Permian time the uplift had become general over the whole of the eastern United States, so that the streams carried their burdens through to the basin which then occupied the Mid-Continent region, and deposition ceased over the Appalachian Trough, which later in the period was folded into an anticlinorium and destroyed forever as a geosyncline. Thus with the close of the Paleozoic Era came an end to one of the grandest features of ancient North America. Since earliest Cambrian time the Appalachian Trough had subsided intermittently during every period, and had been the site of the most persistent interior seaways, trapping some 50,000 feet of strata. With the Permian came a change so profound that the region has never since been crossed by the sea!

The Dunkard group of Ohio and West Virginia is almost wholly non-marine, including plant and insect fossils and many thin coal beds. One thin zone has yielded, in addition, the brachiopod **Lingula** and a few shark spines, indicating that for a very brief time the sea reached this far eastward. Otherwise no marine Permian is known east of Kansas.

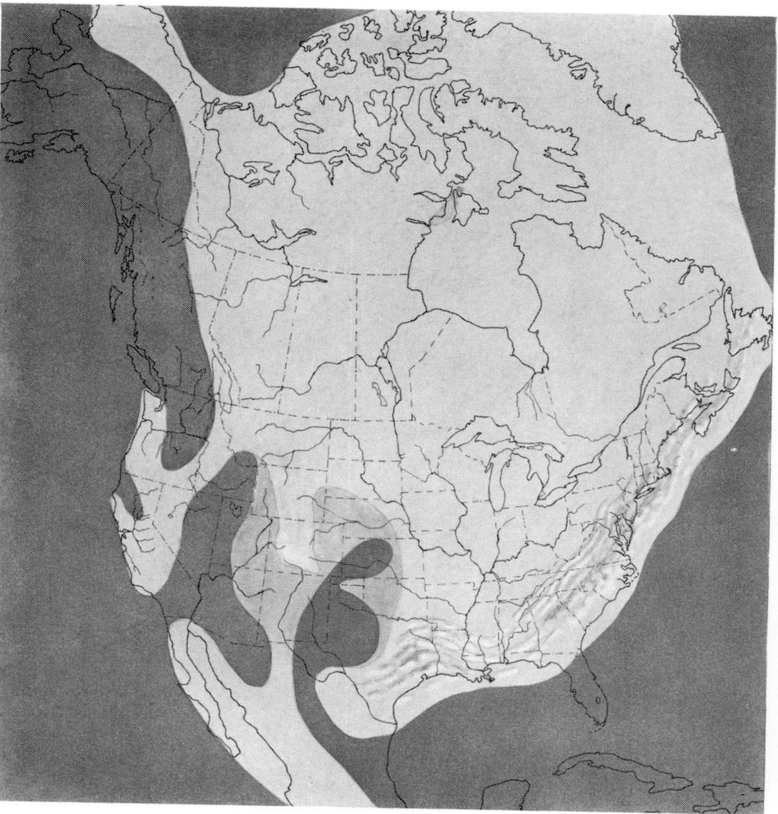

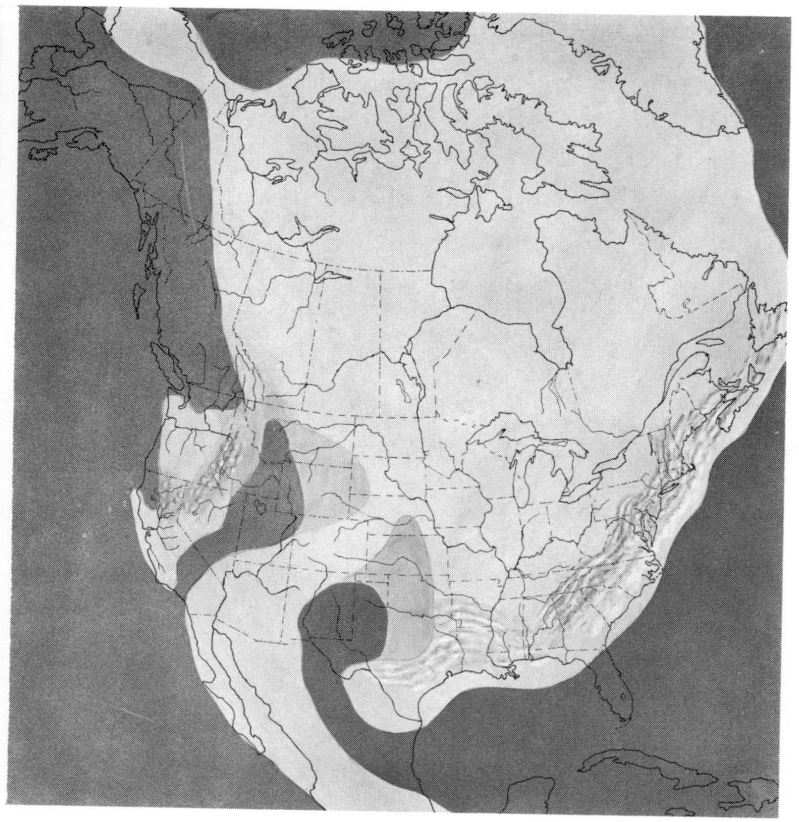

Figure 203. Permian paleogeography. Left, Early Permian (Wolfcampian) time; right, late Middle Permian (Guadalupian) time.

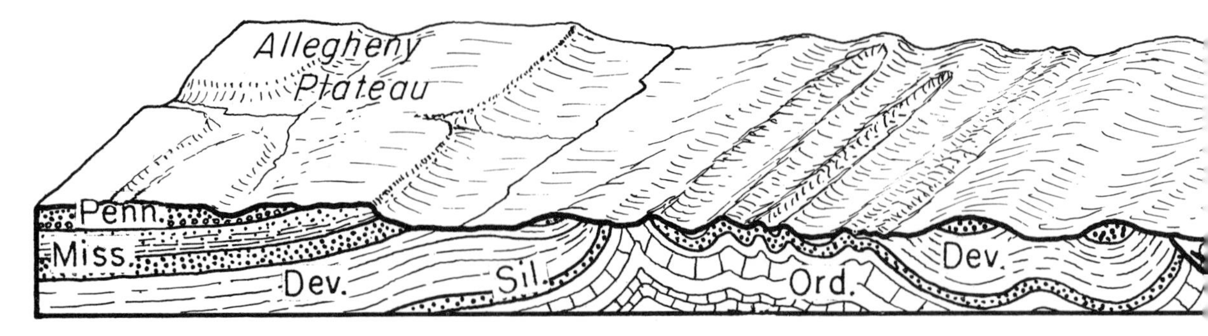

Figure 204. Section across the Appalachian System in central Virginia from the edge of the Allegheny Plateau to the Piedmont slope near Richmond. Length of the section, about 100 miles; vertical scale about 2½ times the horizontal. All the deformation was produced by the Appalachian revolution.

Vanishing of the Mid-Continent Seaway. The Mid-Continent region, from Kansas and Nebraska southward across Texas, remained a vast basin of deposition, as it had been in the previous period, and here, too, the change from Pennsylvanian to Permian conditions was transitional, though ultimately profound (Fig. 203).

Early in the period a shallow sea reached northward to southeastern Nebraska and eastern Kansas. In the extensive area of outcrops across Texas, Oklahoma, and Kansas, early Permian formations consist of alternating shales and thin limestones generally similar to those below. Ascending in the section, however, a gradual though profound change is seen. In successive marine horizons the fossils are reduced to fewer and fewer kinds, as corals and echinoderms drop out and finally bryozoans and brachiopods also disappear. Above several hundreds of feet of such beds lies a thick gray shale (**Wellington shale**) bearing the great salt deposits of Kansas, succeeded in turn by red sandstones and maroon shales without fossils.

From this record we may infer that at the beginning of the period an extensive epeiric sea occupied the region of the western Great Plains; it doubtless spread far east of the present outcrops and at one time reached temporarily to Ohio; its outlet to the south across Oklahoma was closed by the growth of a great delta from Llanoria, which surrounded the Arbuckle and Wichita mountains as the modern delta of the Hwang-Ho surrounds the Shantung Peninsula in China. Deltas were also growing eastward from the Colorado Mountains in New Mexico. The climate gradually became so arid that evaporation exceeded precipitation, and eventually a vast dead sea occupied the middle of the basin which centered over Kansas and Oklahoma. One group after another of the marine animals died out, and eventually the water became a brine from which salt was precipitated. Across Mexico and the Gulf region a connection with the ocean was maintained through which more salt water was supplied as evaporation proceeded. Eventually the waters disappeared, either because the basin was filled to sealevel, or because of regional warping. Then, streams, converging into the basin, spread over its desert floor hundreds of feet of red mud and sands. For a time, extensive dunes covered parts of Oklahoma, where they are preserved in the Whitehorse sandstone.

The **Kansas dead sea** marks the last stand of the Paleozoic epeiric seas east of the Cordilleran region. Even this sea had vanished before the close of the period, and we must turn to the far Southwest for a record of Late Permian time.

Permian Basin of West Texas and New Mexico. The grandest Permian record in America, if not in the world, occurs in western Texas and southeastern New Mexico, where Permian strata total about 14,000 feet in thickness. This was a basin, occupied much of the time by a seaway that entered through Mexico, and toward which the drainage converged from the Eastern Interior. Out of the midst of it now rise the Guadalupe Mountains with a superb display of Permian rocks (Fig. 202), and for these the entire depression of

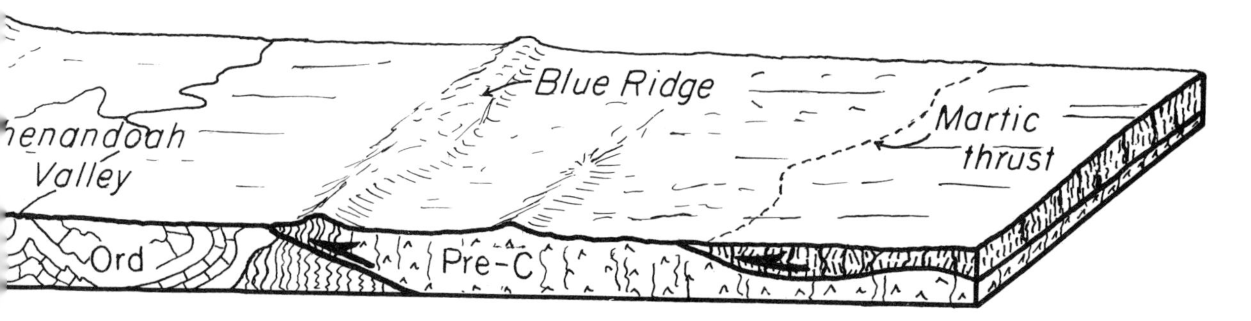

Permian date may be called the **Guadalupe Basin** (Fig. 211). Within this major depression there were three subsidiary and rapidly sinking areas, the **Delaware Basin** in Trans-Pecos Texas and southeastern New Mexico, the **Marfa Basin** farther southwest, and the **Midland Basin** of central-western Texas.

As the rest of the Mid-Continent region emerged into lowland and the climate turned increasingly arid, local conditions, in the Guadalupe Basin gave rise to exceptional Permian deposits. Evaporation was matched by a steady flow of the marine water from the basin to its bordering shallow fringe. This caused deposition of limestone along the margins of the basins where the water was warmed, producing reeflike, limy banks between the deeper basins and vast marginal lagoons (Fig. 215). The lagoons become salt pans in which the red muds from the surrounding lands settled, to intertongue with deposits of gypsum and anhydrite and salt; while nearly pure limestone was accumulating over the reefy areas, and dark shales, dark limestone and siltstone were deposited in the deeper water of the basins. In the lagoon, life was sparse or limited in variety; the reefs were inhabited by numerous highly specialized brachiopods and by other invertebrates which preferred this environment; and the sea floors of the basin included a varied and more normal population.

Finally, during the last epoch of the period, the marine water shrank into the deeper part of the basin to form a dead sea (Fig. 203), in which phenomenal deposits of salt and anhydrite were precipitated. These are discussed on page 258.

Changes in the Cordilleran Region. In the Far West, also, important changes were taking place. During early Permian time a shallow sea covered eastern Nevada and much of Utah, and another covered northern California. Thick and nearly pure limestones of this age in southern Nevada and in northern California imply that the near-by lands were still low. During the middle part of the period, however, volcanoes were active in California, western Nevada and Idaho, and eastern Oregon (Fig. 203). This was the forerunner of the great igneous activity that was to characterize the Pacific border during Mesozoic time. Near the middle of the period a new trough occupied the central part of British Columbia, extending southward into Washington and Oregon and bearing an oriental fauna not known farther south in America.

Permian rocks are also widely distributed in arctic America, notably in Alaska and in the Arctic Archipelago. These northern outcrops bear fossils indicating a common connection across the northern margin of the continent from Alaska to East Greenland and thence, via Spitzbergen and Novaya Zemlya, to the Ural region of the USSR.

FAR-REACHING OROGENY AND CONTINENTAL UPLIFT

Appalachian Revolution. During or at the close of this period Appalachia was thrust westward against the geosyncline, folding and thrusting the thick Paleozoic formations into a great mountain chain that extended unbroken from Newfoundland to Alabama. Practically all the folds and faults south of New England date from this disturbance. In New England and Maritime Canada the earlier disturbances (Taconian, Acadian, etc.) had more or less strongly deformed the rocks of the geosyncline, and there the effects of these several movements are compounded and difficult to separate; but south of New England the earlier movements had been east of the geosyncline where the crystalline belt and the Piedmont

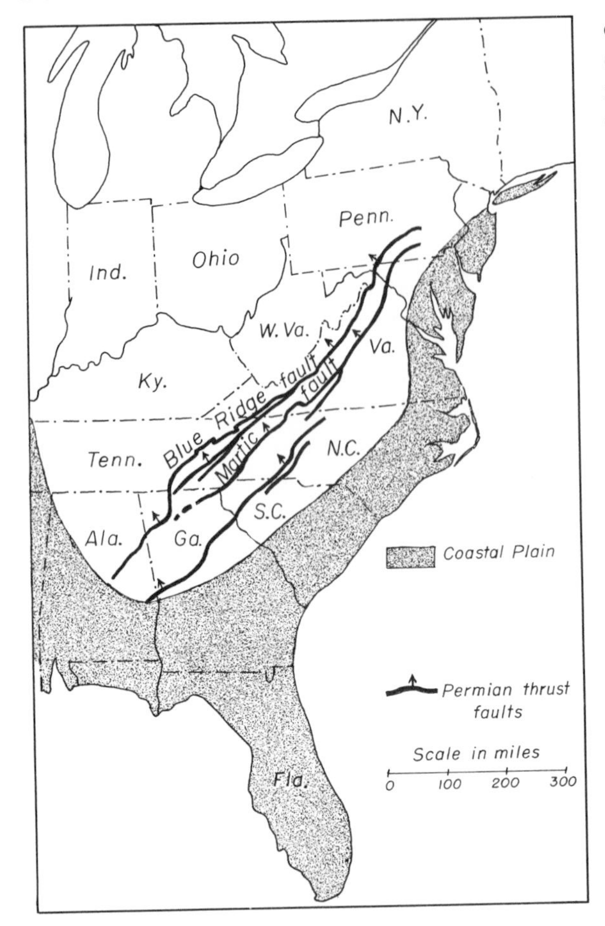

Figure 205. Sketch map showing traces of the major thrust faults in the southern Appalachians. Overlapping Mesozoic and Cenozoic deposits of the Coastal Plain are shaded.

now lie, and the great mountain folds of the Valley and the Ridge Province date entirely from the Appalachian Revolution.

The folding was clearly later than the Early Permian, since the Dunkard group is gently deformed along with the older strata; and it was long before the middle of the Triassic, since the folds had been locally peneplaned before deposition of the Newark group began in Late Triassic time. In the absence of late Permian and early Triassic formations the movement cannot be more precisely dated, though it probably culminated at the end of the Permian Period.

A cross-section of the Appalachian Province (Fig. 204) shows clearly that the moving force was from the southeast. For example, along the eastern margin of the geosyncline a series of thrusts of great magnitude carried Cambrian and younger rocks westward until in places they rested upon the Coal Measures. Figure 205 shows the position of the greatest of these faults. The Martic thrust can be traced from Georgia to Pennsylvania, a distance of more than 500 miles, and the Blue Ridge fault extends over 700 miles, from Alabama into Pennsylvania. Westward movement of as much as 12 miles has been recorded on a single thrust.

In the belt of thrust faults the softer rocks are strongly crumpled (Fig. 206), and the folds are generally overturned to the northwest. The intensity of deformation dies out to the westward, however, and the folds are more and more open until the beds lie nearly horizontal in the Allegheny Plateau. The effect of the folding and faulting has been to reduce greatly the original width of the folded belt. It has been estimated that the section between Philadelphia and Altoona, Pennsylvania, was shortened by 100 miles,[1] and that the entire geosyncline, with an original width of 500 miles, is now reduced to 270 miles.

It is impossible to determine how high the mountains stood at any given time during the Permian, but they probably rivaled the modern Alps in grandeur. The amplitude of some of the folds in Pennsylvania (Fig. 207) would suggest a height of 5 miles, but this is probably too great, since the highest peaks must have suffered rapid erosion as they slowly rose; moreover, we do not know how much regional uplift went along with the folding.

Ouachita Disturbance. The structures of the Ouachita Mountains of Arkansas and Oklahoma appear also to have been formed in the Permian. They present a northward-facing arc of intensely folded Paleozoic formations, lying in a series of great imbricated thrust sheets (Fig. 182, p. 221). The whole mass of the mountains has been thrust northwestward, probably tens of miles, over the eastern end of the older Arbuckle Range. There is still some uncertainty as to the exact time of the thrusting. It involves thick Lower Pennsylvanian formations and is, of course, younger than these. Moreover, the Ouachita thrusts override the Arbuckle Mountain structures, which in turn were uplifted during Pennsylvanian time. It appears probable, therefore, that the Ouachita structures were formed by Permian thrusting.[2]

Volcanic Activity in the West. During the latter half of Permian time volcanoes were active on a grand scale in eastern California, western Nevada, eastern Oregon, and western Idaho (Fig. 203, right). This marks the beginning of igneous activity that was to become increasingly important in the western part of the continent during Mesozoic time and culminated in the formation of the Columbia Plateau and the Cascade Range in Cenozoic time. In the Humboldt Range of Central Nevada, as in the Seven Devils region of western Idaho and the region about Baker in eastern Oregon, volcanic agglomerates, tuffs, and flows of Permian (and in part Triassic) age, exceed a mile in thickness. For the most part these are, of course, unfossiliferous, and it is still impossible in many places to draw the boundary between Permian and Triassic volcanics. In several sections, however, lenses of interbedded sedimentary rocks contain Permian marine fossils indicating that the volcanoes were in part submarine.

In northern California the Lower Permian rocks are calcareous (McCloud limestone) but are succeeded by thick dark shales of late Middle Permian age (**Nosoni formation**) which is overlain by thick volcanics. Here the interbedding of sediments and lava at the top of the Nosoni formation dates rather precisely the beginning of volcanic activity. Other important areas of volcanism were the southern half of Alaska and central Mexico.

Permian formations are locally thick and are widely distributed in British Columbia and northward into Alaska but have not yet been sufficiently studied to permit a clear understanding of the Permian history of this region.

Permian Mountains of Eurasia. Crustal instability seems to have been as great in Europe as it was in North America during Pennsylvanian

Figure 206. Folds in thin-bedded Silurian strata produced during Permian time. The surface here visible is due to erosion and is not the original surface due to the folding. "Fluted rocks" on Great Cacapon River, West Virginia. (G. W. Stose, U.S. Geological Survey.)

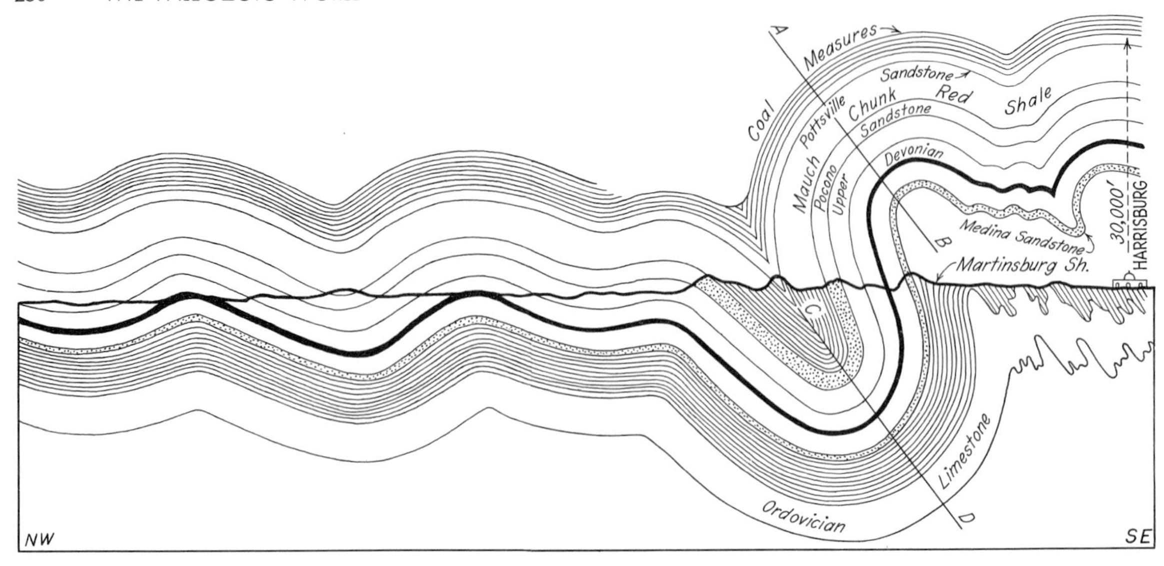

Figure 207. Reconstruction of the eroded folds near Harrisburg, Pennsylvania. Length of section about 15 miles; vertical scale not exaggerated. The portion of the section still remaining lies below the heavy line near the middle of the diagram, the rest having been lost by post-Paleozoic erosion. Adapted from a diagram by George Ashley.

and Permian time. The Urals, which closely parallel the Appalachians in structure as in history, were folded during the Permian, while the Variscan chains were completed across southern England, Germany, and northern France.

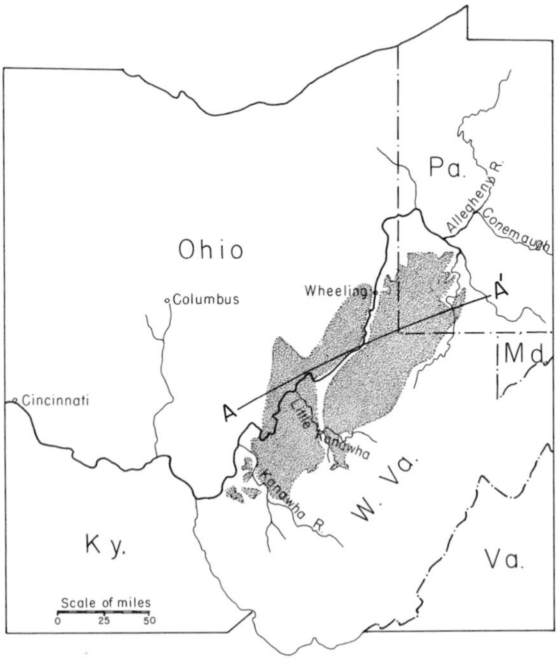

Figure 208. The Dunkard Basin.

THE STRATIGRAPHIC RECORD

Dunkard Group of the Appalachian Region. The only Permian rocks preserved in the Appalachian Province in the United States comprise the Dunkard group which underlies an oval area of about 30,000 square miles in southwestern Pennsylvania and adjacent parts of Ohio and West Virginia. They lie west of the folded belt and are still nearly horizontal.

The character of these beds in the southeastern part of the basin contrasts strikingly with that on the northwest side, though the two facies deeply intertongue in the middle of the basin and are certainly contemporaneous. To the southeast of line *A–A′* of Figure 208 they consist of red shales and siltstones with numerous interbedded sandstones. The sandstones are lenticular, vary rapidly in thickness, and are generally cross-stratified (Fig. 209). In many places they fill shallow valleys that had been cut in the underlying shales. Clearly the sandstones were deposited in and along the channels of aggrading streams and the redbeds are the deposits spread over the higher ground at times of flood. Contemporaneous deposits in the northwestern side of the basin are dark gray shales and siltstones with many local and lenticular coal beds and interbedded fresh-water limestones (Fig. 210). The coal beds record swamps choked with vegetation, the limestones mark shallow open lakes, and the gray shales imply poorly drained lowland in which much organic matter was buried with the sediment.

The transition zone, where these strikingly different facies of the Dunkard group intertongue, marks the boundary where the low, well-graded piedmont west of the Appalachian highlands met the poorly drained humid lowlands. As the streams, heavily laden with red mud and sand from the warm, moist slope of Appalachia, meandered over the region, the sands were deposited chiefly in and near the channels, whereas the finer muds settled over higher ground during floods. Wherever the slopes were well drained during the season the muds remained red, but in the swampy lowland decaying organic matter destroyed the red pigment and turned the muds gray. Most of the sand was dropped on the lower slope and failed to reach the center of the basin.

By the end of Early Permian time deposition ceased here as the region began to rise, and the streams from Appalachia flowed through to spread their red muds farther west, in Kansas and Nebraska and Oklahoma and Texas.

Permian Basin of West Texas. The most complete development of Permian System known anywhere occupies a basin that includes most of western Texas and southeastern New Mexico (Figs. 203 and 211). Here the system is nearly 3 miles thick, is nearly all marine, and is richly fossiliferous. It has therefore become the standard section for the American Permian with which deposits in other areas are correlated. Here the Permian is divided into four series, as follows, in descending order:

Ochoan Series
Guadalupian Series
Leonardian Series
Wolfcampian Series

Chart 7. Correlation of important Permian sections

Series	Calif.	Ariz.	Utah	N. Mex.	West Texas — Guadalupes (lagoon … basin)	Glass Mts.	Central Texas	Kansas–Nebraska	Ohio W. Va.	Series
Ochoan	Dekkas volcan.				Dewey L. redbeds; Rustler fm.; Salado halite; Castile anh.	Tessey ls.		Day Cr. dol.		Ochoan
Guadalupian	Nosoni sh.		Park City group; Phosphoria fm.		Tansill fm.; Yates fm.; Seven R.; Queen fm.; Grayburg ls.; Goat Seep; San Andres ls.; Capitan ls. (reef); Lamar ls.; Radler ls.; Hegler ls.; Bell Can. ss.; Cherry Canyon ss.; Brushy Canyon s.; Delaware Mt. ss.	Gilliam dol.; Capitan ls.; Altuda; Vidrio ls.; Word ls.	Pease River: Whitehorse; Dog Cr. dol.; Blaine fm.; Flowerpot; San Angelo	Quarterm.: Whitehorse ss.; Marlow fm. Salt Fork gr.: Dog Cr. dol.; Blaine fm.; Flowerpot; Cedar Hills		Guadalupian
Leonardian	McCloud ls.	Kaibab.; Toro.; Coco.; Her.	Diamond Cr. ss.; Kirkman	Yeso fm.	Victorio Peak ls.; Bone Spring ls.	Leonard fm.; Hess facies	Clear Fk.: Choza fm.; Vale fm.; Arroyo fm. Wichita gr.: Lueders fm.; Clyde fm.; Belle Plains	Salt Plain f.; Harper ss.; Ninnescah sh.; Wellington sh.		Leonardian
Wolfcampian	McCloud ls.	Supai fm.	Oquirrh fm.	Abo redbeds; Bursum fm.	Hueco ls.	Wolfcamp fm.	Wichita gr.: Admiral fm.; Putnam fm.; Moran fm.; Pueblo fm.	Chase gr.; Council Grove gr.; Admire gr.	Dunkard gr.	Wolfcamp.

The Wolfcamp Series was named for exposures in the Glass Mountains on the south rim of the Guadalupe Basin. Here the early Permian sea was lapping up against the foothills of Llanoria and present exposures, extending for some 40 miles along the face of the Glass Mountains, roughly parallel the old shoreline. As a result the Wolfcamp beds in their type region thicken and thin irregularly and show complex facies changes with thick masses of coarse limestone conglomerate grading laterally into shales. No individual bed or unit can be traced with certainty for more than a few miles along the strike. Deep wells in the basin northeast of the Glass Mountains indicate a much greater thickness of beds with Wolfcamp faunas, suggesting that the present outcrop displays a very incomplete record of Early Permian time. In spite of all this, the Wolfcamp area affords a useful standard section because it is richly fossiliferous and carries a very distinctive assemblage of fusulines (Fig. 212) by which equivalent deposits can be recognized in other widely separated regions. The most distinctive of the Lower Permian fusulines is the strongly inflated genus *Pseudoschwagerina*.

In the Hueco Mountains, which are near the western side of the Guadalupe Basin, the Wolfcamp equivalents consist of more evenly bedded limestones with interbedded shales, and reach a total thickness of about 1,600 feet. Here they are known as the **Hueco formation.** Deep wells reveal that in the center of the Delaware Basin the Wolfcamp equivalents are dark shales.

The Leonard Series also is based upon the Glass Mountains where it exceeds 2,000 feet in thickness and consists of gray silty shales with interbedded light gray limestones (Fig. 213). Dipping eastward under cover in the Staked Plains, the Leonard Series reappears in central Texas as a complex of redbeds with channel sands and local units of gray shale and several thin but widespread limestones. Here it constitutes the upper part of the Wichita group and the Clear Fork group. The channel sands and gray shales of this region have

Figure 209. Lenticular gray sandstones alternating with red shales and siltstones in the Dunkard group near Marietta, Ohio. (Carl O. Dunbar.)

Figure 210. Fresh-water limestones and dark shales at the base of the Dunkard group (Fishpot limestone) west of Bridgeport, West Virginia. (Carl O. Dunbar.)

yielded a large fauna of primitive reptiles and labyrinthodont amphibians (Figs. 226 and 229).

Along the northwest rim of the Delaware Basin the Leonard Series is extensively exposed in the face of the Sierra Diablo and in the west face of the Guadalupe Mountains, where it is wholly marine but lithologically unlike the type section in the Glass Mountains. Here it appears in two strikingly different facies, the Victorio Peak white limestone and the thin-bedded Bone Spring black limestone (see p. 255). Around the margins of the basin the two facies intertongue.

The Guadalupe Series has its type section in the great Permian reef complex of the Guadalupe Mountains (Figs. 202 and 216).

During the Leonardian Epoch the Marfa, Delaware, and Midland basins had taken form, subsiding faster than they were filled so that the water here was several hundred feet deep while the surrounding area to the northwest, north, and east

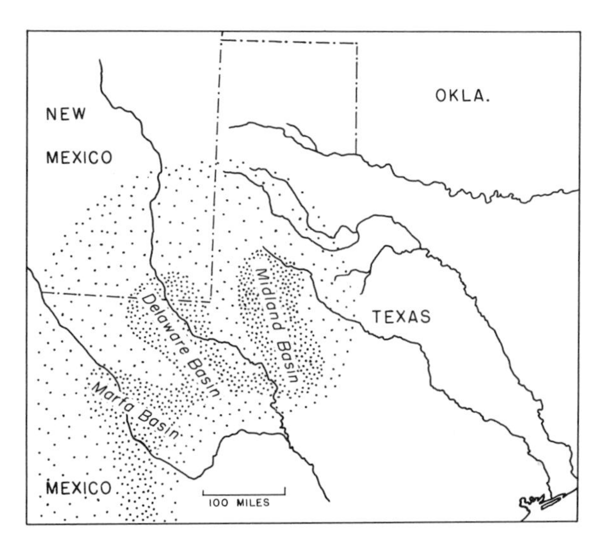

Figure 211. Sketch map of the Guadalupe region and its three basins of thick Permian deposits. (After P. B. King.)

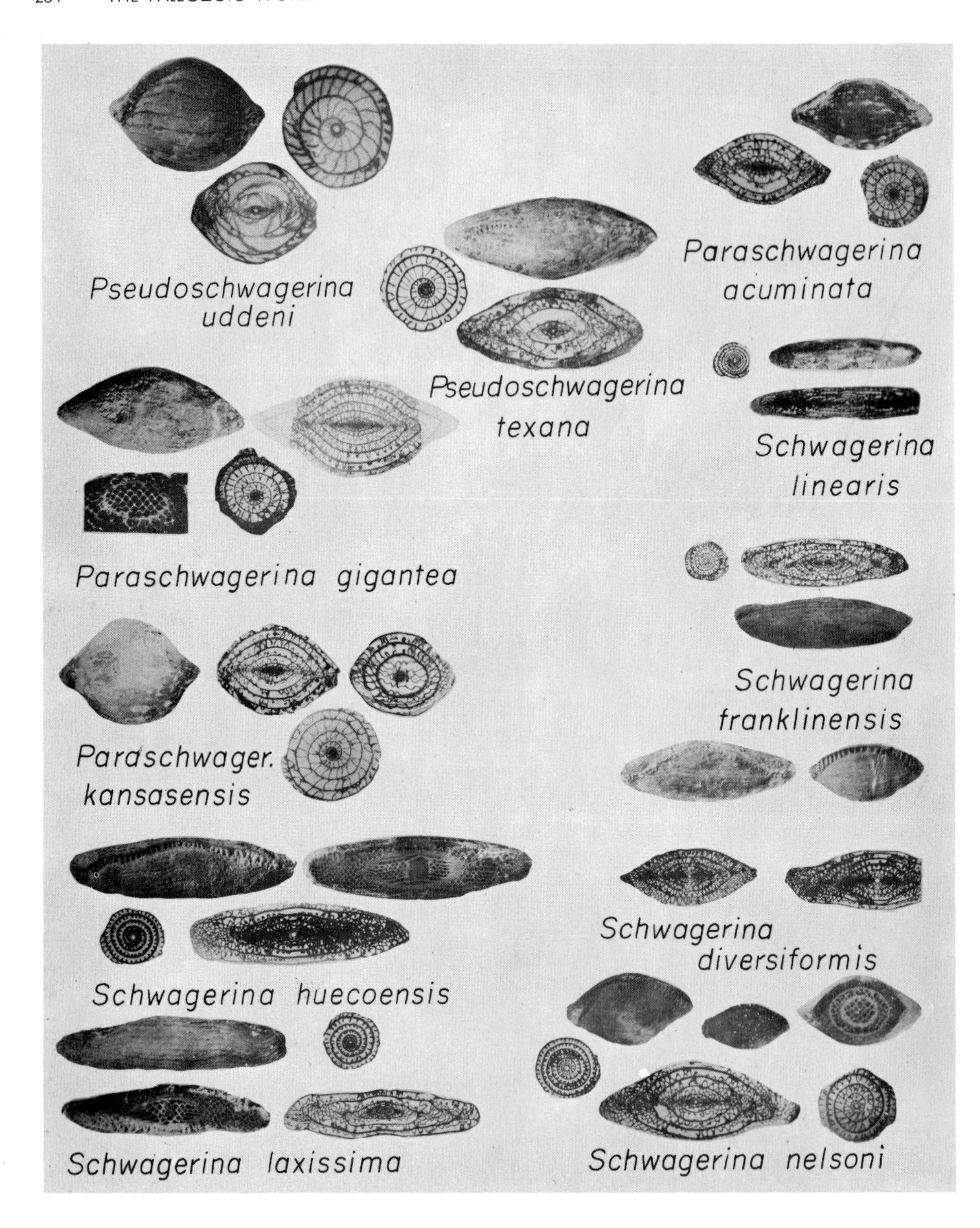

Figure 212. Wolfcampian fusulines.

Figure 213. Typical outcrop of the Leonard Series in the Lennox Hills in the western part of the Glass Mountains. (Carl O. Dunbar.)

subsided more slowly and remained as a broad platform only partly awash with the sea. The submerged portion of the platform was covered by broad and extremely shallow lagoons within a vast lowland over which streams from far to the east and north were spreading red mud and sand. Over the seaward margin of the shelf the Victorio Peak white limestone accumulated in the form of broad shallow limy banks. In the meantime the basins had subsided faster than the threshold in Mexico, over which water from the ocean flowed in to replace evaporation. As a result, the deeper water became stagnant and so deficient in oxygen that bottom-dwelling organisms died out. Thereafter organic matter settling from above accumulated with the sediment to produce a dark pigment of carbon and hydrocarbons. Over these foul and stagnant bottoms the Bone Spring black limestone accumulated (Fig. 214).

Figure 214. Bone Spring black limestone in a road cut on Highway 62 below Guadalupe Peak. (Carl O. Dunbar.)

The regional climate had become strongly arid by the beginning of Leonardian time and, in a great lagoon that for a time stretched across Kansas, enormous deposits of salt were precipitated **(Wellington formation).**

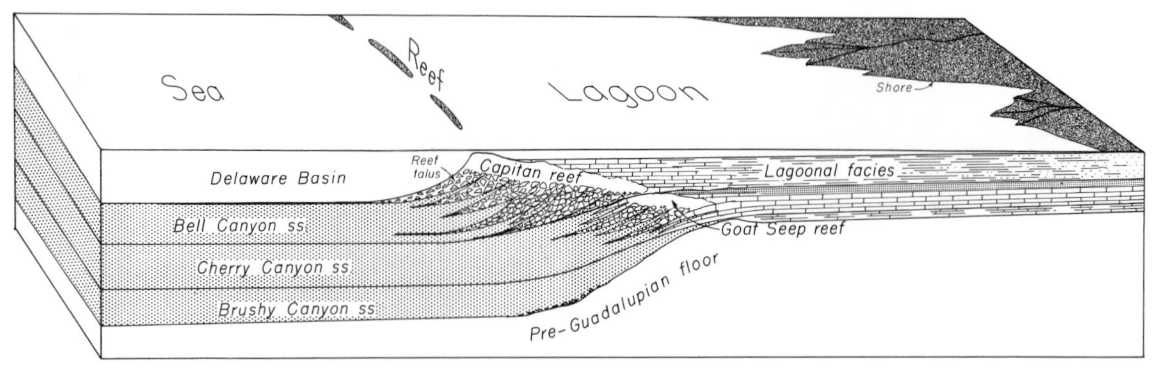

Figure 215. Block diagram to show relations as they existed along the northern margin of the Delaware Basin near the close of Middle Permian (Guadalupian) time. The front face of the block shows a section through the Capitan reef with deeper water in the basin at the left and very shallow water in the lagoon behind the reef. A low delta plain stretches away in the distance at the right. Length of section along the front of the block about 12 miles; vertical scale exaggerated.

By the beginning of Guadalupian time calcareous reefs had begun to form along the rim of the deeper basins, almost separating them from the wide shallow lagoons of the platform (Fig. 215). To replace the water lost by evaporation in the shallow lagoons, a sheet of water flowed in from the basins bringing fresh oxygen, food, and lime salts required by the organisms (chiefly calcareous algae, sponges, bryozoans, and brachiopods) that were the chief reef-builders. As a result, growth was chiefly along the seaward face of the reef and here debris broken loose by storm waves rolled down to form a slope of fore-reef talus (Figs. 216 and 217). The talus becomes finer of grade down the slope and grades out into a series of tongues of dark arenaceous limestones interbedded with the basin deposits. By this time the threshold to the basins had been deepened so that the bottom water was well aerated and normal marine faunas were thriving, to be entombed in the gray siltstones and fine sandstones that make up the Delaware Mountain group (Brushy Canyon, Cherry Canyon, and Bell Canyon formations).

Within a few miles back of the reef, on the contrary, the water had been concentrated to brine from which much gypsum and anhydrite was pre-

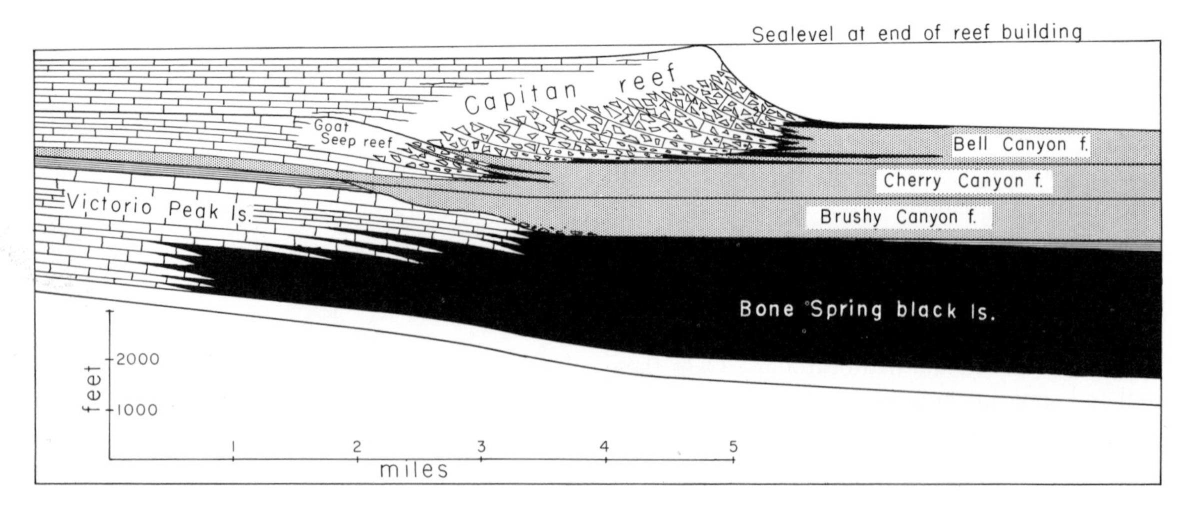

Figure 216. Permian reef complex. A section across the Capitan reef complex at the end of Guadalupian deposition. The view is east across the northern margin of the Delaware Basin. Stippling denotes sandstone; black indicates deep-water basinal limestone; triangles mark reef talus. (After P. B. King, 1948.)

Figure 217. Front of the Capitan reef (massive) built out over the steeply dipping reef talus (foreground). East wall of McKittrick Canyon. (Carl O. Dunbar.)

cipitated along with gray shales. Marine organisms could not endure these conditions and the back-reef formations are generally unfossiliferous. At the shoreline these gray, gypsiferous shales pass laterally into redbeds that were accumulating over the lowland that still stretched away into central Texas, Oklahoma, and Kansas.

Thus at each horizon in the Guadalupian Series three very different facies were accumulating simultaneously—(1) the back-reef facies of gypsiferous shales, thin dolostones, and sandstones of the shallow lagoons on the platform, (2) the reef and reef talus at the margins of the basins, and (3) the normal marine deposits on the floor of the basins. By the end of Guadalupian time the water in the basins was probably as much as 1,000 feet deep.[3]

The reef complex, so grandly exposed in the Guadalupe Mountains, has been exposed by post-Cretaceous uplift. It slopes downward to the northeast and passes below the surface near Carlsbad, New Mexico, but is known from deep wells to continue around the Delaware and Midland basins. It reappears in the Glass Mountains on the south side of the Delaware Basin.

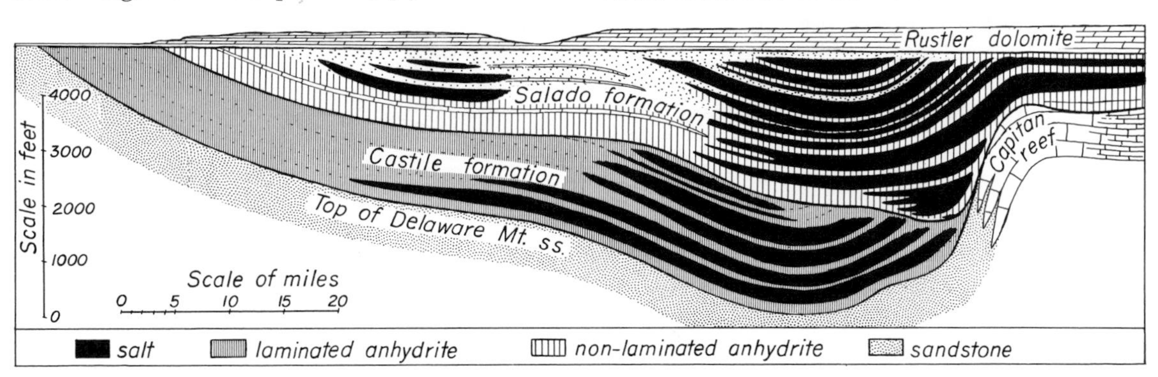

Figure 218. Cross section of the Ochoan Series in the Delaware Basin. (Adapted from George A. Kroenlein.)

Figure 219. Section of a deep well core (natural size) showing the laminated anhydrite of the Castile formation. From Gresham well No. 1 in Culbertson Country, Texas. This is the core on which Udden's study was based. (Yale Peabody Museum.)

The Ochoan Epoch witnessed a profound change in the regimen of this region. As a result of regional warping the water level fell below the rim of the deep basins leaving the reef exposed and the platform emergent. Under the intense aridity but little detrital sediment now reached the Delaware and Midland basins and, as evaporation continued, each became a dead sea in which colossal amounts of anhydrite and salt were precipitated (Fig. 218). The Castile formation, as much as 2,000 feet thick in the east-central part of the Delaware Basin, consists largely of laminated anhydrite (Fig. 219) in which a number of thick salt beds are interstratified. The Salado formation, as much as 2,400 feet thick in the eastern part of the basin, is largely made of salt (halite) with interbeds of anhydrite and, in its middle portion, it includes lenses of potash salts, the chief of which are:

Sylvite (KCl)
Carnallite ($KCl{\cdot}Mg\ Cl_2{\cdot}6H_2O$)
Polyhalite ($CaSO_4{\cdot}Mg\ SO_4{\cdot}K_2SO_4{\cdot}2H_2O$)

Figure 220. Permian section in the wall of the Grand Canyon from a point at the top of the Redwall limestone on Bright Angel Trail. Here Permian formations totaling slightly more than 2,600 feet thick rest paraconformably on the Redwall limestone (Mississippian). C, Coconino sandstone; K, Kaibab limestone; R, Redwall limestone; S, Supai formation; To, Toroweap formation. (Carl O. Dunbar.)

Figure 221. Cross-bedded Coconino sandstone with Toroweap and Kaibab formations above it. Hermit Basin, Grand Canyon. (National Park Service, U.S. Department of the Interior.)

This formation includes one of the world's great deposits of potassium salts.

After final deposition of the salts a brief influx of normal sea water produced the **Rustler dolostone** and introduced a limited fauna of marine organisms. With this exception the Ochoan Series is entirely unfossiliferous. It is therefore a very unsatisfactory standard section for the youngest epoch of the Permian Period.

The lamination so common in the Castile gypsum is well shown in Figure 219. The light layers are nearly pure anhydrite, and the thin, dark layers have considerable organic matter and microscopic crystals of calcite. The well from which this core was taken passed through more than 1,200 feet of such laminated material. Udden[4] gave reasons to suspect that these are seasonal precipitates, the purer layers representing the drier season and the darker layers a more humid season. On this assumption, and from a count of the laminae in this well core, Udden estimated that it required 306,000 years to deposit the Castile and Salado formations.

The total evaporation implied by so much salt is colossal. King has recently estimated that, if the salt were precipitated from normal sea water which constantly flowed into the basin to replenish the loss, an average evaporation of about 9½ feet per year over the 10,000 square miles of the basin would be required for a period of 300,000 years.[5] Since the average evaporation in Death Valley is only about 11½ feet, this is a striking commentary on the Late Permian climate of this region.

Cordilleran Region. As indicated in Figure 203, the southern part of the Cordilleran Trough was occupied by a shallow sea during much of Permian time. This left an imposing marine record in southern and eastern Nevada, most of Utah, southeastern Idaho, and extreme western Wyoming.

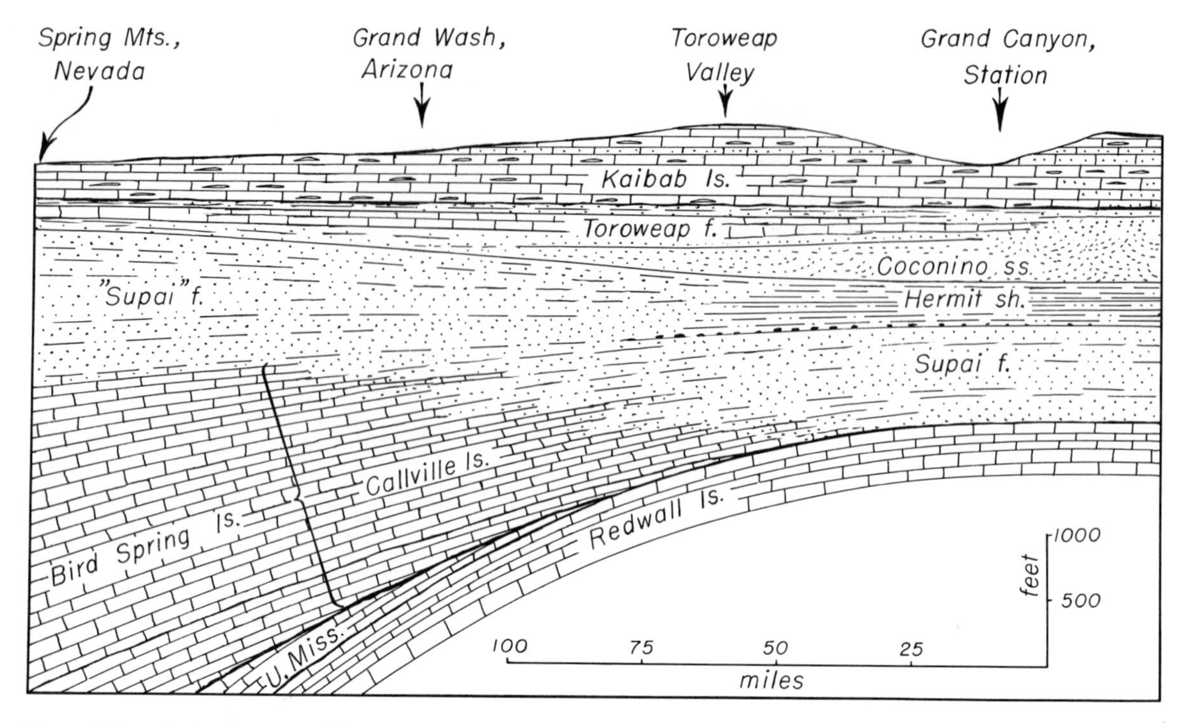

Figure 222. Idealized section of the Permian formations in the Grand Canyon region showing the westward thickening and change of facies. Figure 220 shows the section below Grand Canyon Station. (Data from Edwin D. McKee.)

Farther east, redbeds accumulated over a great area surrounding the Colorado Mountains.

Grand exposures of these Permian formations of the Far West are to be seen in the walls of the Grand Canyon (Figs. 220, 221), where the lateral change of facies from redbeds to marine sediments may be studied. The general relations are suggested by Figure 222. The Kaibab limestone is a key horizon rimming the inner gorge of the canyon in unscalable cliffs from 500 to 600 feet in height. It persists as a marine horizon from southern Nevada to northeast Utah, but in southeast and east-central Utah grades laterally into sandstone like the Coconino. The Toroweap formation (until recently included in the Kaibab) consists of a marine limestone with redbed members both above and below it. The limestone thickens and largely replaces the redbeds in southern Nevada, but thins toward the east and is replaced first by redbeds and then by the massive, cliff-forming, light gray Coconino sandstone. Farther east, massive wind-blown sands (De Chelly sandstone) accumulated to a thickness of hundreds of feet (Fig. 223).

In the familiar Bass Trail section, in the eastern part of the Grand Canyon, the Coconino sandstone rests on soft red Hermit shale, and that in turn on the Supai formation of red sandstone, siltstone, and shale (Fig 222). The Supai rests disconformably on the Redwall limestone of Mississippian age. Traced westward, the Hermit shale becomes sandy and takes on the character of the Supai formation. At the same time the typical Supai redbeds become calcareous toward the west and grade over into the upper part of a great mass of marine limestone, which has been called the Callville formation just west of the Grand Canyon and the Bird Spring limestone still farther west. In southern Nevada the lower part of that great mass of limestone, which exceeds 5,000 feet in thickness, is Pennsylvanian, while the upper part is Permian. The pre-Permian beds lap out against the underlying Redwall limestone near the western end of the Grand Canyon, and the Permian part alone grades eastward into the Supai redbeds (Fig. 222).

Throughout this province marine limestone, fluvial redbeds, and wind-blown sands were deposited simultaneously according to local conditions, and, as these conditions shifted geographically during the period, complex changes of facies occurred.

A great area of Mesozoic rocks separates the exposures of the Grand Canyon region from those of northern Utah and southeastern Idaho, where the Phosphoria formation is the most widely distributed and best known Permian deposit. Where typically developed, it includes a basal member of black phosphatic shale and a thicker, upper member of cherty limestone, but toward the northeast it intertongues with, and is finally replaced by, red shales (lower part of the Chugwater formation) that extend across Wyoming and into the rim of the Black Hills of South Dakota. Its marine fossils indicate that the Phosphoria formation is younger than the Kaibab. Marine fossils indicate that the Kaibab limestone is of Leonard age and the Phosphoria is Guadalupian. In the Confusion Range of western Utah and in the Provo region southeast of Salt Lake City, Kaibab equivalents are now known to underlie the Phosphoria complex.

CLIMATE

It was a natural sequel to the great changes in the physical geography described above that climatic extremes were introduced. The extensive withdrawal of all the epeiric seas during Permian time removed one of the chief agents in stabilizing the temperature and providing moisture to the winds that crossed the interiors of the continents. The enlarged lands must have interfered greatly with the spread of warm ocean currents toward the poles. At the same time each lofty mountain range which stood athwart a prevailing wind belt must have increased precipitation on the windward side and reduced it on the lee. The extensive highlands were chilled by their altitude. Under these conditions local extremes of climate are not paradoxical but natural.

Deserts. During the Permian period, deserts were probably more widespread than at any other time save the present. The dune sands and the widespread deposits of salt and gypsum in the central and western United States indicate a vast

Figure 223. Massive De Chelly sandstone some 800 feet thick, made of wind blown sands. Canyon De Chelly, about 150 miles east of Grand Canyon Station, Arizona. (Spence Air Photos.)

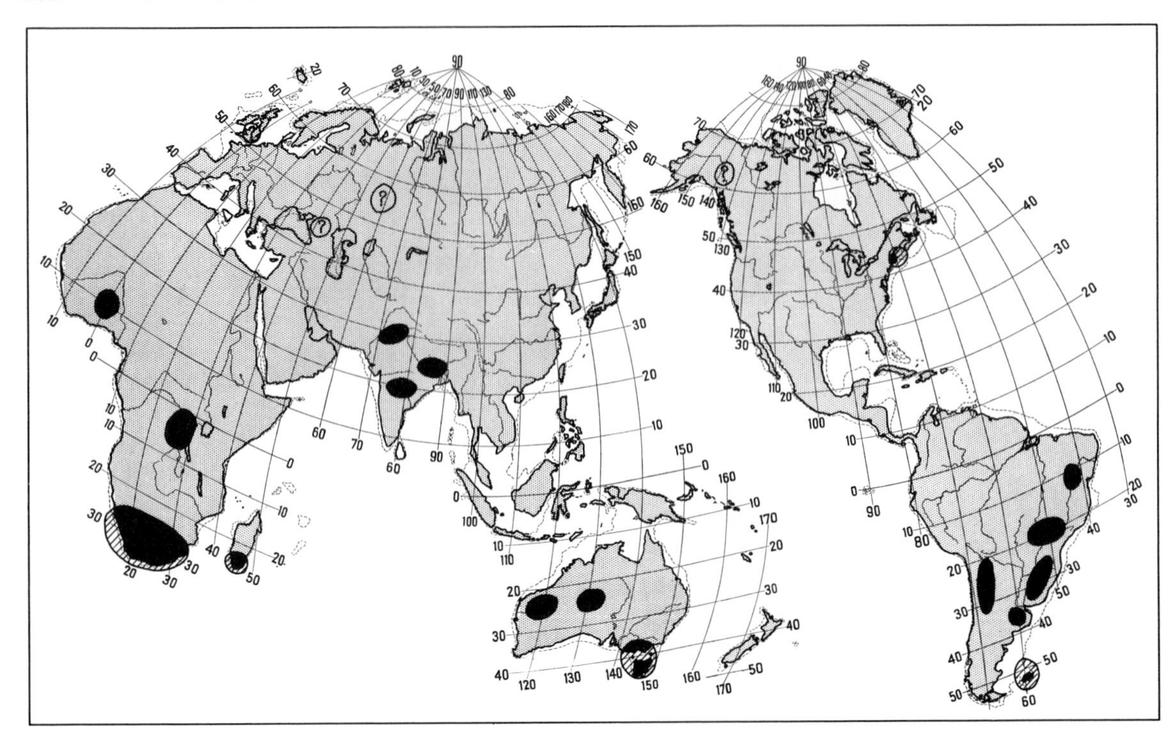

Figure 224. Distribution of Permian glacial deposits (black). (Base map courtesy of the American Museum of Natural History.)

interior more arid than the present Great Basin. The salt beds that stretch from Kansas to New Mexico have been estimated to include 30,000 billion tons of salt and would require the evaporation of more than 22,000 cubic miles of sea water with a salinity like that of the modern oceans. The salt is not all of one age; in Kansas it is in early Middle Permian strata, and in western Texas the chief deposits are in the latest Permian formations.

Central and western Europe were also strongly arid during a part of Permian time. In Soviet Russia the Uralian Geosyncline was then a great trough lying just west of the modern Ural Mountains. For a time shortly before the middle of the period it included a dead sea in the midst of a vast desert basin in which the Kungurian Series formed. In the deepest part of this basin, about Solikamsk, these deposits exceed 4,500 feet in thickness, are largely formed of salt and anhydrite, and include probably the world's largest accumulation of potash salts. The Stassfurt region of Germany has another of the great deposits of salt, one which until recently has been the world's chief producer of potassium. Thus three areas—one in southwestern United States, one in the USSR, and one in Germany—include the world's three greatest salt deposits, and all are of the Permian date.

In South Africa the Permian deposits are largely non-marine redbeds, though there they are not associated with salts or dune sand, and, on the contrary, include a wonderful assemblage of fossil reptiles.

Although aridity seems to have prevailed over much of the United States and central Europe, there was abundant rainfall in some regions, notably northern China and eastern Australia, where important coal fields lie in the Permian rocks.

Permian Ice Age. At times during the Permian period great areas in the southern continents were covered with ice sheets (Fig. 224). South Africa has the most spectacular evidence of glaciation, for there the ancient Dwyka tillite at the base of the Permian sequence includes large faceted boulders and rests upon the heavily scored and polished floor over which the ice moved (Fig. 225). The ice cap covered practically all of southern Africa up to at least latitude 22° S. and also spread to Madagascar (which was then part of the continent). There were three or four centers of movement, but the greatest seems to have been in the Transvaal, which then was a plateau from which the ice moved southwestward for a distance of at least 700 miles. The tillite reaches a thickness of less than 100 feet in the northeast but increases to 2,000 feet in southern Karroo. Australia was likewise the scene of extensive and repeated glaciations, the ice apparently moving northward across Tasmania, Victoria, and New South Wales. Here five sheets of tillite are interbedded in some 2,000 feet of Permian strata which have at least one horizon of commercial coal. South America bears evidence of glaciation in Argentina and southeastern Brazil, even within 10° of the equator. In the northern hemisphere, peninsular India, within 20° of the equator, was the chief scene of glaciation, with the ice flowing north; in the Salt Range on the southern flank of the Himalayas, the thick Talchir tillite underlies the marine Permian.

Aside from India there is no certain evidence of Permian glaciation in the northern hemisphere.

It is almost certain that the Permian ice age, like the recent one of Pleistocene time, was a relatively brief episode in a long geologic period. The three widely spaced repetitions of glacial beds in the thick Australian sequence may indicate recurring glaciation in that continent. In any event, the main glacial deposits are in each region confined to a limited horizon of the older Permian rocks. The presence of large reptiles in the higher Permian redbeds of South Africa and of northern Russia would suggest a mild-temperate climate without freezing winters at the time when they lived.

The exact *time of the ice age* is difficult to prove in most of the glaciated regions. In the Salt Range of India and in western Australia, however, it is fairly certainly dated as early in the Leonardian Epoch.

The most remarkable feature of the Permian glaciation is its distribution. It was chiefly in the southern land masses and in regions which now lie within 20° to 35° of the equator. This circumstance, more than any other, has made attractive the belief in **continental drift**. If the southern continents were united to Antarctica until after

Figure 225. Glaciated floor beneath the Dwyka tillite near Kimberley, South Africa. (A. P. Coleman.)

Figure 226. A Permian landscape showing characteristic animals and plants. 1, a fin-back reptile, *Edaphosaurus;* 2, another fin-back, *Dimetrodon;* 3, *Sphenacodon;* 4, a pelycosaur, *Ophiacodon;* 5, another primitive reptile, *Araeoscelis;* 6, ferns; 7, *Lepidodendron;* 8, *Sigillaria;* 9, a conifer, *Walchia.* Part of a great mural by Rudolph F. Zallinger in Yale Peabody Museum.

Permian time, the glaciation may not have spread into low latitudes. A later "drift" of these continents toward the north would account, far more easily than any other means yet postulated, for the present distribution of the glacial deposits. But this premise itself is still in the realm of speculation!

PERMIAN LIFE

Decline of the Carboniferous Floras. In the northern hemisphere the dominant types of Pennsylvanian plants lived on into Permian time. Lepidodendrons, sigillarias, calamites, cordaites, and seed ferns were the common forest types during the early part of the period. These swamp-dwelling plants were ill adapted to the oncoming aridity and to winter cold. With the passing of the period, therefore, hardier stocks with reduced foliage evolved, or came to the fore, as the Pennsylvanian types declined (Fig. 226). By the close of the period the great scale trees were almost extinct. The cordaites were likewise nearly gone, having first given rise to the conifers. Seed ferns were rare after the close of the period, and the race died out in the Jurassic.

True conifers rapidly sprang into the lead as the dominant type of woody trees, while primitive cycadeoids (allies of the sago palm) foreshadowed the expansion of higher plants in the Mesozoic.

The *Glossopteris* Flora of the Glaciated Regions. Throughout the glaciated regions of the southern hemisphere the most distinctive group of plants were the **tongue-ferns** of the genera *Glossopteris* and *Gangamopteris*. These bore clusters of simple, spatulate leaves that apparently arose from creeping stolons. They produced winged spores, and some have been found with the reproductive organs attached to individual leaves by a slender petiole[6] (Fig. 227), but uncertainty still exists as to whether these were spore cases or seed vessicles. Accordingly the position of these strange plants in the plant kingdom is still a subject of controversy.

Gangamopteris has been reported by DuToit "jammed in between the boulder beds [of the Dwyka tillite] and the glaciated floor beneath it" near Strydenburg and at Vereening in South Africa.[7] Elsewhere the characteristic winged spores have been found at several places in the tillite. The common association of the *Glossopteris* flora with glacial deposits may indicate that these strange plants were especially adapted to a cold environment.

By Middle Permian time some members of the flora had migrated as far as northern Russia and the Altai Mountains of Siberia, but none ever reached western Europe or North America. Along with the *Glossopteris* flora there lived in the southern hemisphere many ferns, conifers, calamites, etc., but none of the great scale trees. After the passing of the glacial climates, however, both *Lepidodendron* and *Sigillaria* succeeded in reestablishing themselves to a limited extent during the latter half of the period.

Insects. Insects (Fig. 228) were abundant and extremely varied at this time, though rarely preserved because of their delicate structure. However, a small locality near Elmo, Kansas, has yielded many thousands of specimens from a single thin bed in the Lower Permian, and other finds have been made in nearly equivalent beds in Oklahoma, in the Dunkard Series in Ohio, in the Lower Permian of Russia, and in the Upper Permian of Australia. All these show great changes from the Pennsylvanian insect types. Although a few were still large in the Early Permian, the majority were small and many were minute, showing thereby a striking contrast with the giants of the previous age. Moreover, many new orders were now arising, foreshadowing the modern groups. Mayflies were common, true dragonflies were present, and in the Late Permian, beetles lived in Australia.

Figure 227. Glossopteris leaf and attached reproductive organ. (Adapted from Plumstead.)

Cockroaches persisted, but then, as ever afterward, played a minor role in the insect world.

Sprawling Reptiles and Labyrinthodonts. Even in the semiarid regions the old labyrinthodonts clung to the stream courses with surprising success. Their heavily armored skulls are locally abundant in old stream-channel deposits in the redbeds of Texas and Oklahoma and in the fluvial deposits of Germany, South Africa, and the USSR. Nearly all of them had broad heads, thick bodies, and short, feeble legs. As Huxley once said, they "pottered with much belly and little leg, like Falstaff in his old age" (Fig. 229). Few reached a length of 10 feet.

Reptiles increased greatly in variety during the Permian. The older forms are known chiefly from the redbeds of Texas and Oklahoma and from the USSR, where conditions of preservation happened to be good, whereas the later kinds come from South Africa, India, northern Russia, and Brazil. Before the close of the period they had undoubtedly mastered all the lands, and some even reverted to aquatic life, both in the rivers and in the sea.

The great range of specialization displayed by the Permian reptiles emphasizes the rapidity of their evolution. Most of them had long bodies,

Figure 228. A primitive Permian insect, *Dunbaria*, with color pattern of its wings preserved. Photograph not retouched. The wingspread of this genus is only about 1.5 inches, but an associated form, *Megatypus*, had a wingspread of about 15 inches. Early Permian near Elmo, Kansas. (Yale Peabody Museum.)

Figure 229. A characteristic Permian labyrinthodont amphibian, *Eryops*. Lower Permian of Texas. Length about 5 feet. (After a model by Dwight Franklin.)

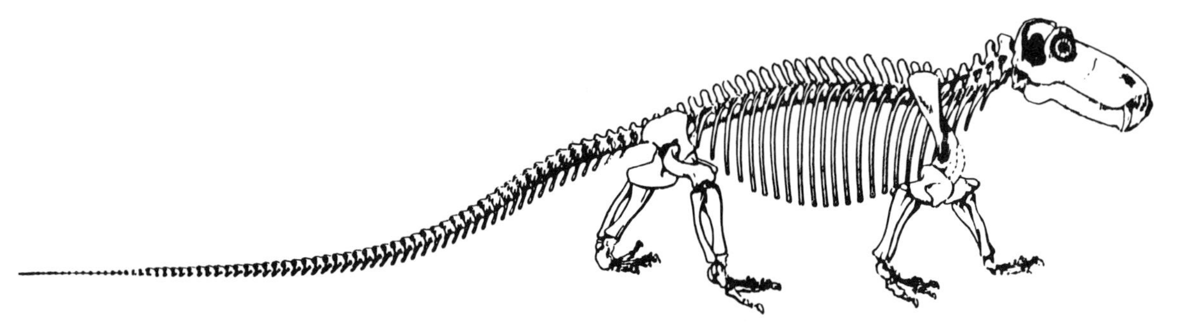

Figure 230. Skeleton of a theriodont reptile, *Titanophoneus*, from the Upper Permian (Kazanian) near Icheevo on the Volga River south of Kazan, USSR. The animal was about 11 feet long. (After U. A. Orlov.)

long tails, and short legs. While some were agile and lizard-like (*Varanops*), others were sluggish and semiaquatic like alligators (*Limnoscelis*), and yet others were thick-bodied and had stubby tails and short, thick legs. Many had sharp holding teeth and were certainly carnivorous; some had blunt teeth adapted to crushing shelled molluscs or crustaceans; and others, with toothless jaws like those of turtles, may have been herbivorous (*Endothiodon*). They had already deployed into several orders, but none of these corresponds to any of the living groups. Two features the Permian reptiles possessed in common: (1) none was very large, about 15 feet being a maximum length; (2) all were four-legged creatures and most of them sprawled.

The most bizarre of them all were the **fin-backs**, so called because of their greatly extended neural spines. The reason for such extraordinary specialization is entirely problematical.

Far greater significance attaches to a group of stout-bodied flesh-eating reptiles known as **theriodonts**, which foreshadow the coming of the mammals. These are known chiefly from the middle Karroo formation (Upper Permian and Triassic) in South Africa and from equivalent formations in the Permian Basin of the USSR.

A well-known and typical theriodont is *Titanophoneus* (Figs. 230 and 231, from the Upper Permian (Kazanian) in the USSR,[8] whose carriage and differentiated teeth offer striking resemblances to a primitive mammal. Unlike other reptiles, they had teeth differentiated into incisors, canines, and molars as do the mammals. Moreover, they carried their bodies off the ground instead of sprawling, and numerous details of skull and jaws confirm their ancestral relation to the mammals.

Specializations and Extinctions among the Marine Invertebrates. The marine invertebrates of the Permian evolved gradually out of the Pennsylvanian faunas. As some groups advanced steadily into progressive types, others assumed extravagant specializations which led shortly to their extinction; yet others, already on the decline, gradually died out.

The **cephalopods** (Pl. 11, figs. 5–9) showed the most significant gains, as goniatites with more and more complex sutures gave rise to typical ammonites. The rapid evolution of this group fore-

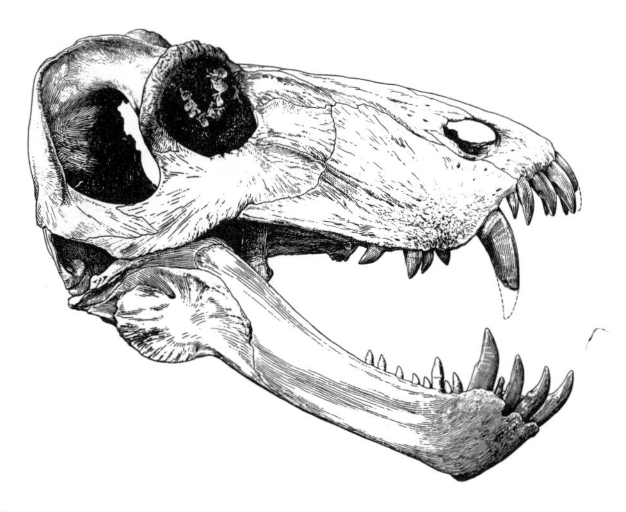

Figure 231. Skull of *Titanophoneus*, showing mammal-like differentiation of the teeth. Same locality as Figure 230. (After U. A. Orlov.)

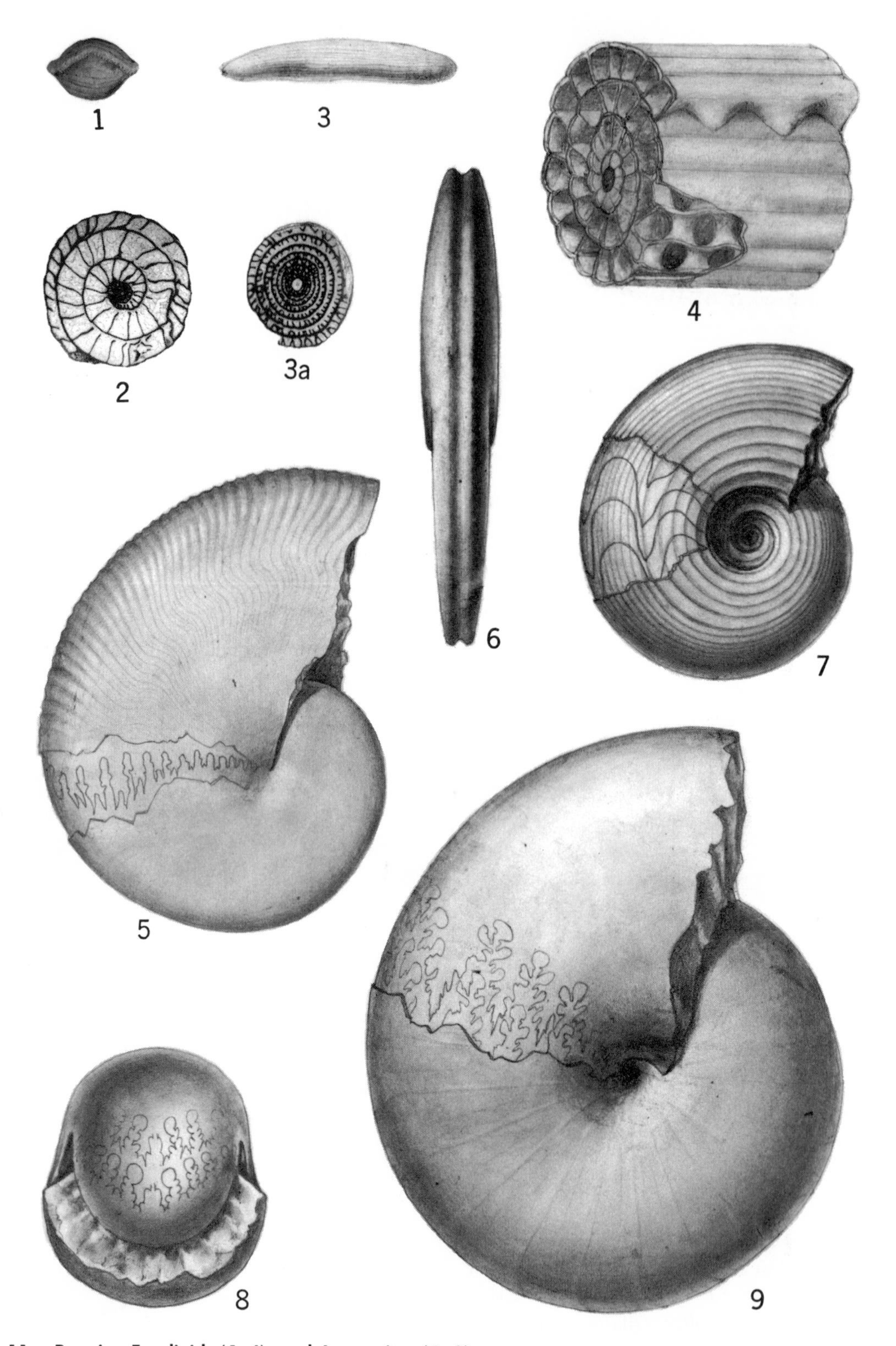

Plate 11. Permian Fusulinids (1–4), and Ammonites (5–9).

Figure 1, *Pseudoschwagerina uddeni;* 2, enlarged section of same; 3, *Parafusulina wordensis;* 3a, enlarged section of same; 4, model of portion of a shell showing septa; 5, 6, *Medlicottia whitneyi* (lateral and edge views); 7, *Gastrioceras roadense;* 8, *Waagenoceras dieneri;* 9, *Perrinites vidriensis.* All natural size except 2 and 4. (Drawn by L. S. Douglass.)

Marine Brachipods - Climate was changing so fast that they became extent

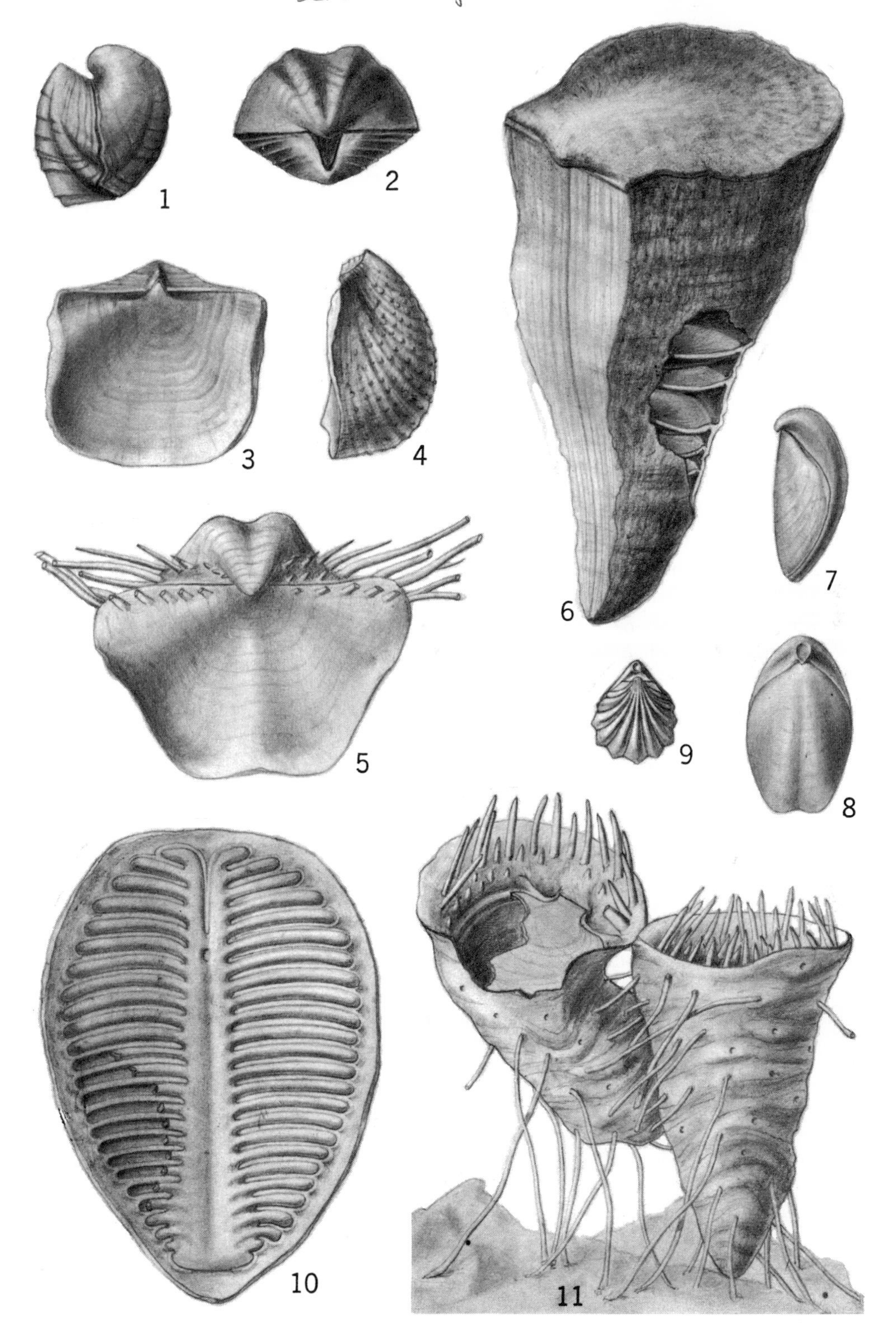

Plate 12. Permian Brachiopods.

Figures 1, 2, *Parenteletes latesinuatus;* 3, 4, *Aulosteges medlicottianus;* 5, *Horridonia horrida;* 6, *Scacchinella gigantea* (with break in conical ventral valve showing internal septa); 7, 8, *Dielasma angulatum;* 9, *Hustedia meekana;* 10, *Leptodus americanus* (showing skeletonized dorsal valve and corresponding flanges in spoon-shaped ventral valve); 11, *Prorichthofenia permiana* (two specimens in position of growth, that at the left broken at the front margin to show the operculiform dorsal valve on its seat below the overarching spines; the dorsal valve also broken). All natural size. (Drawn by L. S. Douglass.)

shadowed their spectacular rise to dominance among the marine invertebrates of the next era. Yet, strangely, they came near to extinction at the close of the Permian, and of 13 families that thrived in this period only 2 survived into the Triassic, one of these dying out early in that period while the other gave rise to a second great burst of evolution that repopulated the seas with ammonites.

Pelecypods and **gastropods** progressed steadily but more conservatively. Among the **brachiopods** (Pl. 12), which generally make up the bulk of the faunas, the productids remained the dominant group, while several new genera, growing fast to the bottom, developed into most extraordinary types, and some of them even grew conical shells mimicking corals (Pl. 12, fig. 11). Before the close of the period, however, all the productids and most of the other groups of brachiopods died out. The **fusulines** (Pl. 11, figs. 1–4) continued as important rock-makers and attained their maximum size near the close of the period, though none survived the end of it. The trilobites, already nearly extinct, died out, as did all the honeycomb corals and the tetracorals; likewise most of the groups of crinoids, all the blastoids, and two of the orders of bryozoa.

Partly because of the great differences between the Late Paleozoic and Triassic life of the seas, and partly because in many regions (Germany and Russia especially) the Permian rocks have limited faunas, the misconception has arisen that the Permian was a time of great organic restriction and that the oceans may then have contained relatively few kinds of life. Such is, however, far from the truth. More species are now known from Permian than from Pennsylvanian rocks. The rich marine Permian faunas of the East Indies, especially on the island of Timor, contain not less than 600 species in 285 genera, and in the Salt Range (Punjab) of India there are 325 forms. Southwestern Texas has in its Permian rocks probably more than 500 species.

This was a time of rapid evolution, great specialization, and constant change. The net result was the disappearance of many of the characteristic groups of the Paleozoic life, but the change was orderly and gradual, not cataclysmic.

REFERENCES

1. Shand, S. J., 1938, *Earth-lore: geology without jargon*, 2nd ed. E. P. Dutton, New York, p. 95.
2. Van der Gracht, W. A. J. M., 1937, the Permo-Carboniferous orogeny in the south central United States. *Amer. Assoc. Petroleum Geol., Bull.*, vol. 15, pp. 991–1057.
3. King, Philip B., 1948, Geology of the southern Guadalupe Mountains, Texas. *U.S. Geol. Surv., Prof. Paper 215*, pp. 1–183.
4. Udden, J. A., 1924, Laminated anhydrite in Texas. *Geol. Soc. Amer., Bull.*, vol. 35, pp. 347–354.
5. King, Ralph, 1947, Sedimentation in Permian Castile Sea. *Amer. Assoc. Petroleum Geol., Bull.*, vol., 31, pp. 470–477.
6. Plumbstead, Edna P., 1952, Description of two new genera and six new species of fructifications borne on *Glossopteris* leaves. *Geol. Soc. South Africa, Trans.*, vol. 55, pp. 281–318.
7. Du Toit, A. L., 1953, *Geology of South Africa*, 3rd ed. Hafner Publishing Co., New York, p. 279.
8. Orlov, V. A., 1958, Predaceous Deinocephalan fauna of Icheeva. *Studies of the Paleontological Institute, Academy of Sciences, USSR*, vol. 72, pp. 1–112. [In Russian.]

PART III

PART III

THE MESOZOIC WORLD

Figure 232. Glimpse into a Triassic landscape early in the Mesozoic Era. Part of a great mural by Rudolph Zallinger. Plants: 1, a broadleafed fern, *Macrotaeniopteris;* 2, a primitive cycadeoid, *Wielandiella;* 3, a conifer, *Voltzia.* Animals: 4, a primitive reptile ancestral to the dinosaurs, *Saltopsuchus;* 5, one of the smallest dinosaurs, *Podokesaurus* (about 3 feet long); 6, one of the largest Triassic dinosaurs, *Plateosaurus,* a probable ancestor of the great sauropods of the next period (length about 20 feet); 7, a mammal-like reptile, *Cynognathus.* (Yale Peabody Museum.)

Chapter 14. The Triassic Period

The Mesozoic Era. AFTER THE CLOSE OF THE Paleozoic Era reptiles came into their own. While dinosaurs ruled the lands, marine reptiles splashed and slithered through the seas and winged dragons took to the air. Fourteen distinct orders of reptiles then thrived (there are but four in the modern world), and for more than a hundred million years they held complete sway over the Earth. The founders of geology considered this the middle of three great ruling dynasties on Earth, preceded by that of the invertebrate animals and followed by that of the mammals, and they named it, accordingly, the **Mesozoic Era** (Gr. *mesos*, middle + *zoon*, life).

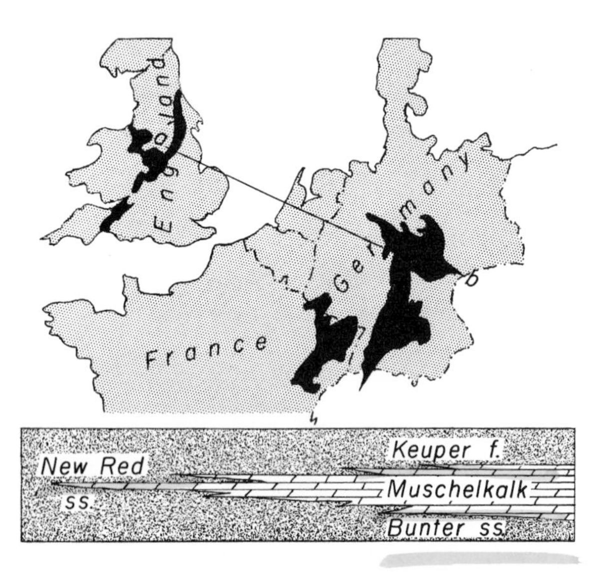

Figure 233. Map and idealized section to show the relations of the Triassic System in its type region.

The Triassic Period. In Great Britain, where so many of the geologic periods were named, the Coal Measures are overlain by a thick sequence of redbeds. At first these were called the **New Red sandstone,** in contradistinction to the **Old Red sandstone** which underlies the Carboniferous. Here they form a natural unit, but in Germany, where a marine sequence intervenes, a three-fold subdivision is natural, and for this region Alberti in 1834 named this the Triassic System (Fig. 233). Such a three-fold division does not hold in most other parts of the world, and modern usage would call for a geographic rather than a descriptive name, but Triassic soon became so deeply entrenched in the literature that it is not likely ever to be replaced. This system represents the first period of the Mesozoic Era.

PHYSICAL HISTORY OF NORTH AMERICA

Newark Fault Troughs of the East

After the Appalachian Revolution the eastern half of North America, including the present continental shelf, was fully emergent for two long geologic periods. Erosion was in progress throughout the whole region during Early Triassic time, as the Appalachian Mountains were being reduced and the debris transported beyond the present margins of the continent (Fig. 234, left). For the first half of the period there is no record save that of erosion. Then, as though the compressive stresses had relaxed, the axis of the Appalachian chain began to be riven by great normal faults that produced a narrow chain of block mountains bordered by downfaulted troughs (Fig. 234, right). The height and extent of the new block mountains are conjectural, but the structural troughs, which were filled as they sank, still retain a rich record of the time. The northernmost basin lies in Nova Scotia, and others are distributed southward into North Carolina, a distance of about 1,000 miles. The Triassic strata formed in these troughs have been named the **Newark group** (Fig. 235) for the exposures near Newark, New Jersey, where they probably exceed 20,000 feet in thickness; and the structural troughs are known as the Newark basins. Deep wells in the Panhandle of Florida and adjacent corners of Georgia and Alabama have penetrated redbeds with diabase flows and dikes so similar to the Newark rocks that they are believed to be contemporaneous.[1] Here the redbeds dip westward suggesting that they also occupy a fault trough similar to the Newark basins farther north.

The Connecticut Trough as a Type. The Triassic Trough of central Connecticut stands near the middle of this chain of basins and will serve well for further description. It extends northward from New Haven across Connecticut and most of Massachusetts, its length nearly 100 miles and its greatest breadth about 25 miles.

The Triassic beds dip eastward 15° to 30° against a great fault that bounds the basin on the east and

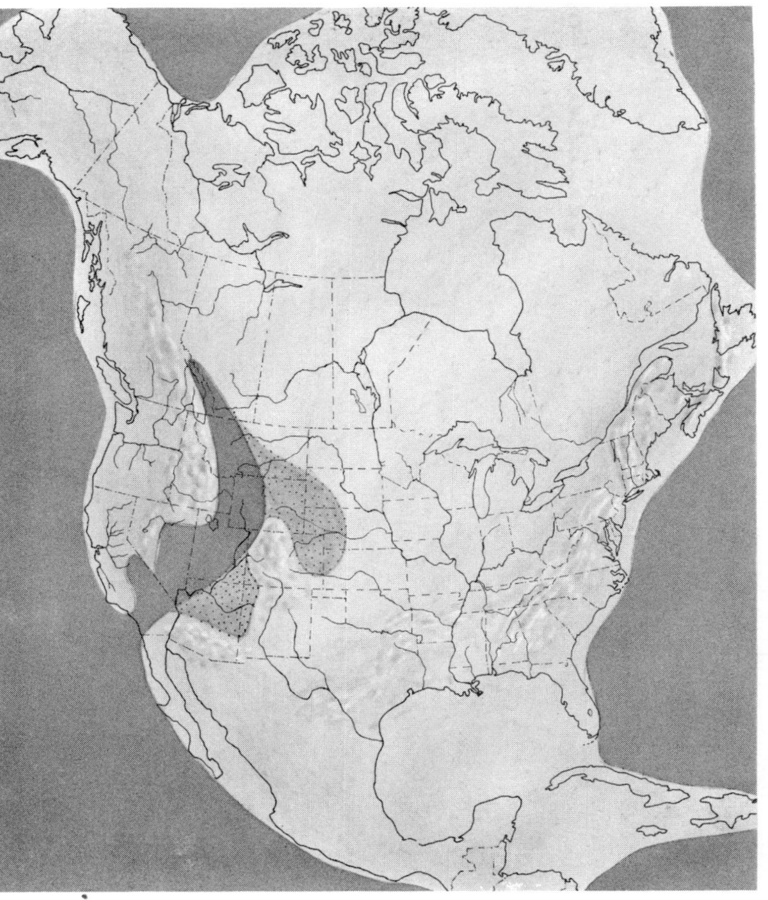

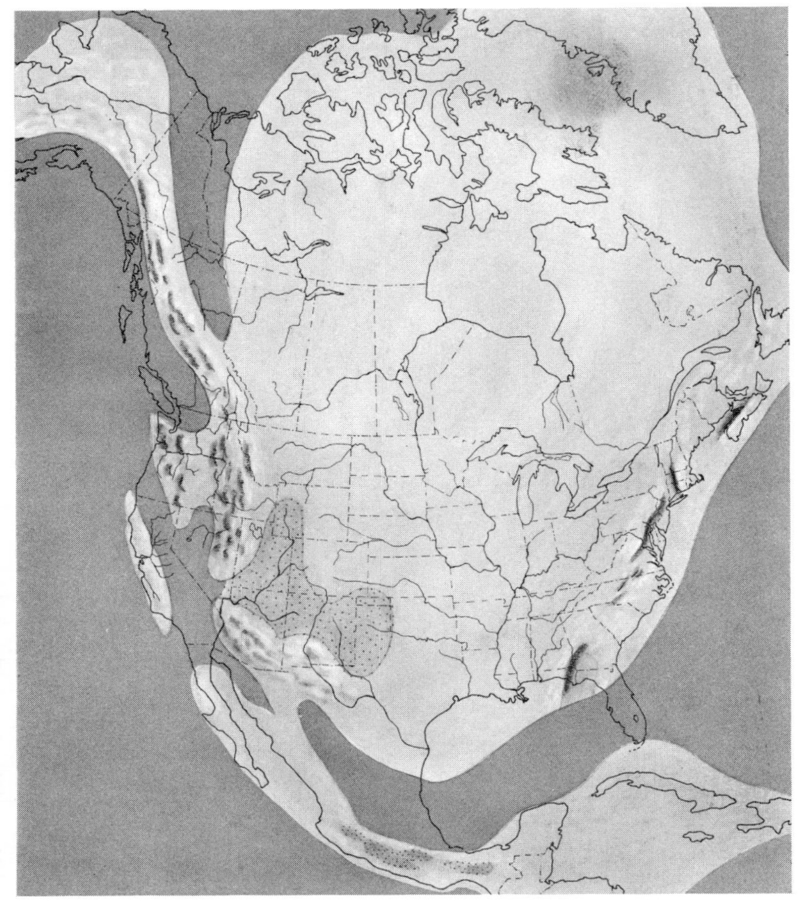

Figure 234. Triassic paleogeography of North America. Left, Early Triassic time; right, Late Triassic time. Darker shading marks seas; lighter shading marks basins of non-marine deposition.

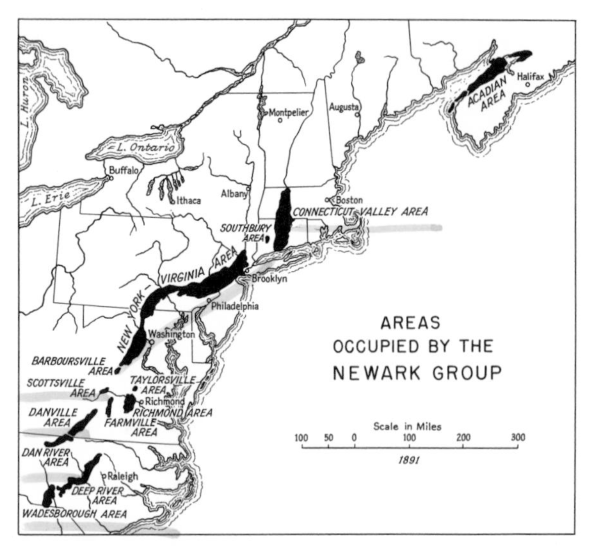

Figure 235. Map showing Triassic fault troughs of the Appalachian region in which the Newark group is preserved. (After I. C. Russell, U.S. Geological Survey.)

must have a maximum throw of about 3 miles (Fig. 236).

The Triassic rocks of the basin are conglomerates, sandstones, siltstones, and shales, with interbedded flows of basic lava. Perhaps half of the sediments are gray, but the most prominently exposed beds are red, and these give the impression that the whole group consists of redbeds.

The sediments are poorly sorted and irregularly bedded, sandstones grading laterally into siltstones or conglomerate. All the coarse deposits are arkosic, and much of the feldspar is remarkably fresh. The conglomerates are thickest and coarsest along the eastern margin of the basin and clearly represent fans built where torrential streams debouched from the highlands to the east. In Connecticut the Newark group has an estimated thickness of 10,000 to 15,000 feet, and in New Jersey it may reach more than 20,000 feet, but it diminishes to 2,000 or 3,000 feet in the southern basins.

Three extensive trap sheets lie near the middle of the sequence in Connecticut, each separated from the next by several hundred feet of sedimentary beds (Fig. 236). The middle sheet attains a thickness of about 500 feet and now forms conspicuous ridges such as The Hanging Hills of Meriden. Each of the trap sheets has a scoriaceous and amygdaloidal upper surface; the underlying redbeds are bleached near the contact as a result of the heat from the lava; but the overlying redbeds show no similar effect and, on the contrary, include fragments of the scoriaceous lava. It is clear therefore that these are surface flows rather than sills — they represent lavas that welled out to flood the Triassic Basin. The eruptions were remarkably

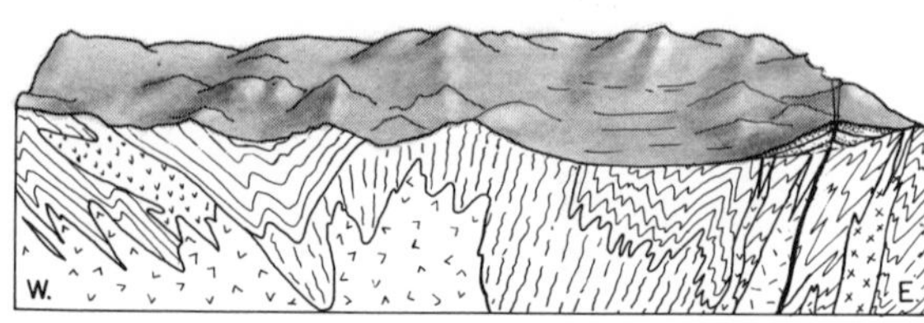

A Mountains at the beginning of Triassic time

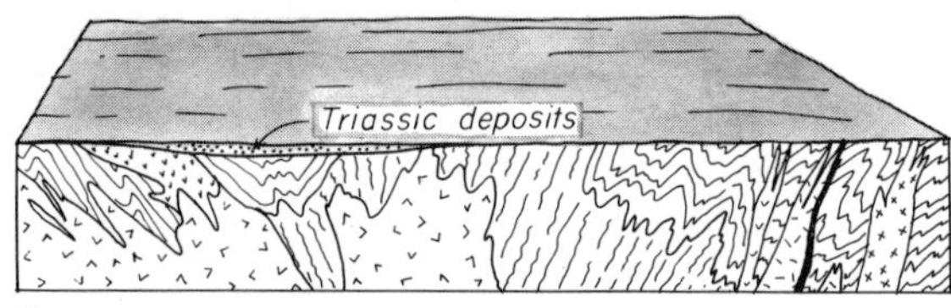

B Mid-Triassic peneplane on which deposition began

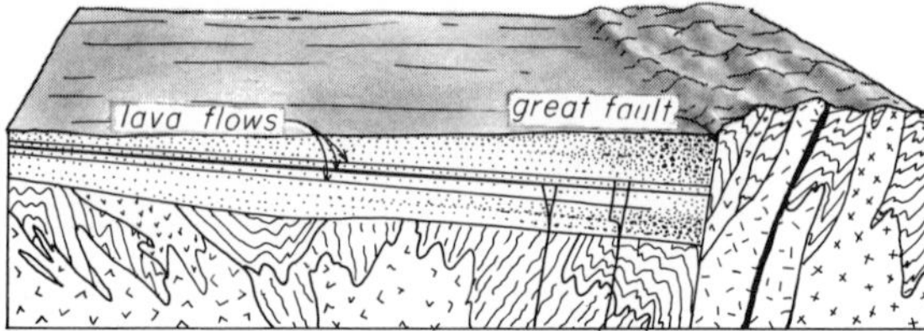

C The close of deposition in the Connecticut fault trough

D Block mountains formed by the Palisade disturbance

Figure 236. Four stages in the development of the Triassic basin of central Connecticut. Length of sections about 30 miles. Block *A* shows the complex structure and rugged topography inherited from the Appalachian revolution; block *B* shows the beginning of Newark deposition after the region was largely peneplaned; block *C* shows the Newark fault trough fully developed through subsidence along the great fault; block *D* shows the final stage with the Newark deposits complexly faulted during the Palisade disturbance. The modern structure of the region dates from this time. Triassic strata stippled. (Modified from Joseph Barrell.)

Figure 237. Slabs of Newark sandstone from Turners Falls, Massachusetts, bearing dinosaur tracks. These are photographed from the under side of the beds so that the tracks stand in relief; they are natural molds of the tracks which were made in the underlying mud. The lower slab shows molds of the imprints of raindrops. (Yale Peabody Museum.)

free of explosive violence, however, for ash and bombs are known in only one small area (near the Holyoke Range in Massachusetts). The lava must have been very fluid to spread in such flat and extensive sheets. Many dikes cut the underlying strata.

The middle third of the Newark group, associated with the lava flows, is generally finer grained than the rest, and is predominantly gray in color, whereas the higher and lower beds are chiefly red.

No marine fossils have been found anywhere in the Newark group, but land plants and fresh-water fishes are locally abundant in the darker gray beds, and dinosaur tracks in the redbeds are more plentiful than anywhere else in the world. Ripple marks are common, and mudcracks cover many of the bedding planes. The imprints of Triassic raindrops are in places associated with the footprints and mudcracks (Fig. 237).

With these facts in mind, it is not difficult to reconstruct the events that transpired here during the latter part of Triassic time. The Connecticut Basin was then a fault trough similar to the California Trough which now lies between the Coast Ranges and the Sierra Nevada. A range of block mountains bordered it on the east, with a fault scarp facing the basin. Repeated movement along the great fault depressed the basin and elevated the mountains. Meanwhile the streams that reached the basin from the uplands dropped most of their sediment here, building fans along the eastern border and fluvial deposits over the floor. Before the igneous activity began, the basin was well drained by through-flowing streams, and much of the mud was carried away, while gravel, sand, and silt were dropped. The uplands must have had plentiful rainfall to develop such a quantity of red mantle as is represented in these sediments, but the rains were probably seasonal. Thus the mud that spread over the floodplains during wet seasons lay exposed to the sun during the dry months. Dinosaurs crossed and recrossed, leaving their tracks in the mud. The last spatter of passing showers also left imprints of raindrops where the mud was exposed and still soft. During the dry season the mud shrank and cracked and then was sunbaked and hardened so that it could hold these surface features until they were buried by a new layer of sediment.

Where the drainage was good and the ground water not close to the surface, the iron-stained sediments remained red. After the first lava flow, however, the drainage was impounded, and for a considerable time swampy conditions obtained over much of the lowland[2]; during that time vegetation accumulated with the sediments, and in its decay reduced the iron oxide, producing gray or dark colors. Such conditions held until after the last flow, and then, with better drainage, redbeds again accumulated over the basin.

Other Newark Basins. The geology of the other Triassic fault troughs is, in general, like that sketched above. In the Acadian area the sediments are predominantly red, and include one large trap sheet. The dip here is northwest, and the bounding fault is on the west side. In the New York-Virginia and Danville areas also the dip is westward, whereas in the Deep River and Wadesboro areas it is to the east. As we follow the basins southward from New Jersey, more and more of the sandstones and shales are greenish-gray instead of red and, finally, in the Danville area, there are interbedded coals that locally reach a thickness of 26 feet. This may imply that the rainfall was more evenly distributed through the year in the southern basins, or that it was greater, or that the basins were not so well drained.

In the New York-New Jersey area there are three great lava flows that may be equivalent to those in the Connecticut Trough. A thick sill of dolerite occurs near the base of the group and its eroded margin now forms the Palisades of the Hudson River from New York City northward, for a distance of nearly 50 miles. A few great dikes which cut across the margins of the area and extend out into the older rocks of the piedmont in southeastern Pennsylvania and central Maryland suggest that the volcanic activity was not confined to the structural troughs, but for the most part the Triassic volcanics are preserved only in the basins whose subsidence protected them from later erosion.

Age of the Newark Group. The fishes and plants of the Newark beds indicate that the entire group belongs to the upper half of the Triassic System. In other words, at least half a period had elapsed after the folding of the Appalachians before the Newark basins began to form. Herein lies the explanation of the remarkable unconformity at the base of the Triassic. Wherever the basal contact has been seen, the Newark beds rest upon a surface of slight relief cut across the complex structures of the older rocks. In Nova Scotia truncated folds of Pennsylvanian and older strata are overlain by the Triassic; in eastern Pennsylvania the strongly crumpled Ordovician limestones are in contact with the gently tilted redbeds in places where all the later Paleozoic rocks had been removed before the beginning of Newark deposition. In short, the Appalachian folds had been worn down and the region was at least partially peneplaned during the late Permian and the earlier half of the Triassic Period.

The Arid Cordilleran Basin

Triassic rocks are widely distributed through the Rocky Mountain region from Idaho and Wyoming southward across Utah, Colorado, Arizona, New Mexico, and western Texas. This is the greatest area of continental Triassic deposits in North America (Fig. 234 and 238). Here redbeds predominate, though marine members of the older Triassic interfinger from the west. Bright red or maroon shales and cross-bedded red sandstones make colorful landscapes such as the Painted Desert of Arizona and the Great Red Valley in the rim of the Black Hills.

North of the Colorado highlands, the redbeds are mostly Lower Triassic, whereas farther south and west they are Upper Triassic, no clear evidence of Middle Triassic being yet known in this whole region.

In Utah and Arizona the Triassic redbeds attain a thickness of more than 4,000 feet and are divisible into four widespread units, the Moenkopi, Chinle, Wingate and Moenave formations.

The **Moenkopi** (mō-ĕn-kō-pē) is generally a weak formation of reddish-brown siltstone and muddy

Chart 8. Correlation of important Triassic sections

Series	European Stages	California: Shasta C.	California: Inyo Mts.	Nevada (central)	Idaho	Wyoming	Ariz.–Utah	New Mexico	West Texas	Conn.–N.J.	Series
Upper Tiassic	Rhaetic	Modin fm.		Gabbs fm.			Moenave fm. Wingate fm.				Upper Triassic
	Noric	---?--- Brock sh.			Ankareh fm.					Newark group	
	Karnic	Hosselkus ls.		Luning fm.	Higham grit		Chinle fm. Shinarump congl.	Chinle fm.	Dockum group		
Middle Triassic	Ladinian	Pit sh.	volcanics								Middle Triassic
	Anisian			Excelsior fm.							
L. Triassic	Scythian	Bully Hill rhyolite	unnamed ls. & sh.	Candelaria fm.	Thaynes fm. Dinwoody fm.	Chugwater fm. Dinwoody fm.	Moen-kopi fm.				L. Triassic

Figure 238. West Temple of the Virgin, Zion National Park, Utah. A 4,000-foot wall of Triassic and Jurassic rocks carved out of the edge of the Colorado Plateau by the Rio Virgin. Triassic rocks extend up to the base of the Navajo sandstone. The ranch houses at the bottom indicate the scale. (Union Pacific System.)

sandstone (Figs. 238 and 239). In northern Arizona and eastern Utah it is commonly about 1,000 feet thick, but it thins eastward and laps out against the old highlands of Colorado. Toward the west, on the contrary, it intertongues with, and grades laterally into, a marine facies in southern Nevada where it consists largely of gray shale and thin bedded limestone, only the upper part remaining red. One marine tongue reaches as far east as south-central Utah, thinning gradually to about 10 feet of limestone in the San Rafael swell where it is known as the **Sinbad limestone.** The marine facies carries the **Meekoceras** fauna, proving that the Moenkopi formation is Lower Triassic.

In its typical development in northeastern Arizona and southern Utah, the Moenkopi formation shows abundant evidence of deposition by aggrading streams meandering over a low alluvial plain. Cut and fill by channel sands is common, many of the layers are marked by mudcracks, and locally some of the bedding surfaces bear abundant tracks of sprawling reptiles and large amphibians that then lived along the stream courses as alligators now do in subtropical regions.[3]

The **Chinle** (chĭn·leé) formation is a complex of variegated and highly colored shales and siltstones well exposed in the Painted Desert of eastern Arizona (Figs. 240 and 241). Its colors range from red to pink and yellow, and locally to ashen gray and white. It contains much volcanic ash derived from volcanoes in California and Nevada. It reaches a maximum thickness of 3,000 feet, but like the Moenkopi, thins eastward to a feathered edge in western Colorado.

A basal member of the Chinle, known as the **Shinarump conglomerate,** is persistent over a great area though generally less than 150 feet thick. It includes well-rounded pebbles of older rocks commonly as large as door knobs. Maximum coarseness occurs along the Mogollon Rim in central Arizona, where cobbles range up to 6 inches in diameter; but the coarseness decreases generally toward the north and east, and in Monument Valley in southeastern Utah, the conglomerate grades into sandstone. This suggests that the gravel was coming largely from the west or southwest. The contact of the Shinarump member with the underlying Moenkopi formation is an erosion surface with considerable relief, and the conglomerate is thickest where it fills old valleys. Evidently the hiatus between it and the Moenkopi was of considerable duration.

Animal fossils are extremely rare in the Chinle formation, but fossil wood is abundant in its lower part in the Petrified Forest area in eastern Arizona.

The **Wingate** formation includes nearly a thousand feet of redbeds in northeastern Arizona where it consists of two members, the lower of well-bedded reddish-brown siltstone and sandstone (Fig. 241) and the upper of cliff-forming deep red dune sand.[4] Only the upper member is present at the type locality, Old Ft. Wingate, New Mexico. The lower member has yielded teeth and fragmentary bones of phytosaurs in some of the old channel gravels, but the upper member is unfossiliferous. The Wingate formation thins westward and is absent, for example, in Zion Canyon where the Navajo sandstone rests directly on the Chinle formation (Fig. 238).

The **Moenave** formation is a complex of red sandstones somewhat like the Wingate but generally more irregularly bedded.

Marine Triassic of the Far West

During Early Triassic time a sea covered much of southern California, spreading northeastward across Nevada and Utah, and then northward into Alberta (Fig. 234). In this seaway a thick and richly fossiliferous sequence of gray shales and limestones was formed, carrying all the major faunal zones of the Lower Triassic Series of the world. Meanwhile non-marine redbeds were accumulating over a large lowland to the east of it in eastern Montana and Wyoming and adjacent parts of South Dakota, Nebraska, Kansas, and Colorado, just as they had been forming during Permian time. In these redbeds it is commonly difficult to draw the boundary between Permian and Triassic deposits.

Figure 239. Moenkopi formation in the edge of Paria Plateau near Navajo bridge over the Colorado River. (Carl O. Dunbar.)

Figure 240. Chinle formation in Petrified Forest National Monument, Arizona. Petrified logs in the foreground. (Joseph Muench.)

By middle Triassic time an axis of uplift was forming in eastern Nevada and western Utah, and thence northward across western Montana and Idaho and far into Canada. This was the beginning of the **Mesocordilleran Geanticline** that would remain a major structural feature of the continent throughout the rest of the Mesozoic Era, rising as a mountainous highland in late Jurassic and Cretaceous time. Meanwhile, a new geosyncline was forming along the western margin of the continent from southern California to Alaska. This was the **Pacific Coast Geosyncline** that would remain a major basin of deposition throughout the Mesozoic Era. Simultaneously a trough was beginning to subside along the east side of the Mesocordilleran Geanticline in Canada, in which a Triassic sea crept southward from the Arctic as far as central Alberta. This was a forerunner of the great **Rocky Mountain Geosyncline** that would grow in importance during the Jurassic and Cretaceous periods. In short, a major paleogeographic and structural realignment was developing in the Far West during Triassic time that would dominate the rest of the Mesozoic Era.

In western Nevada and southern California thick marine sections of the whole of the Triassic System are present, and sections of Middle and Upper Triassic are known in many places from northern California through western British Columbia and in southern Alaska. This marginal seaway was the scene of much volcanic activity during Late Triassic time. In Vancouver Island and the Queen Charlotte Islands, for example, the Upper Triassic is some 13,000 feet thick, about nine-tenths of it being comprised of submarine eruptives—lava flows, volcanic breccias, and tuffs—in which fossiliferous slaty shales and quartzites are interbedded. Volcanics occur also in southern Alaska where thick formations of Triassic limestone are capped by an extensive black shale.

The Triassic deposits along the north side of the Brooks Range in northern Alaska, on the contrary, are free of volcanics. These thicken eastward toward the Canadian border and were undoubtedly continuous with those formed east of the Mesocordilleran Geanticline.

In northern Sonora, southern California, and parts of Nevada deposition appears to have continued without a break from Late Triassic into early Jurassic time.

Palisade Disturbance and the Close of the Period

In the Appalachian region, faulting occurred repeatedly along a few great rifts, but the Newark group, with its interbedded lavas, accumulated with no more disturbance than a very slight eastward tilt due to the unequal depression of the floor.

At the close of the period, however, general uplift began, accompanied by complex normal faulting that tilted the Triassic beds more steeply and broke them into fault blocks, as suggested in Figure 236. Subsequent erosion has beveled these tilted blocks and etched out the resistant trap sheets into the prominent ridges of today, such as the Palisades of New York, the Hanging Hills of Meriden in Connecticut, and the Holyoke Range in Massachusetts. All the structures involved, however, date from the faulting at the close of the Triassic, an orogeny known as the **Palisade disturbance.** The regional uplift that accompanied the faulting brought an end to deposition in eastern North America until after Jurassic time.

It is worthy of note that, although the Palisade disturbance followed the axis of the Appalachian System, the forces involved, as well as the struc-

Figure 241. Chinle formation overlain by Wingate sandstone in the face of Paria Plateau west of Navajo bridge, Arizona. (Carl O. Dunbar.)

tures produced, were almost the antithesis of those of the earlier deformation. The horizontal compression that made the Appalachians had apparently relaxed, to give way to normal faulting and broad uplift.

In the western part of the continent, general emergence is inferred, since latest Triassic and most of early Jurassic time are not represented there, but no pronounced disturbance is known.

TRIASSIC HISTORY OF OTHER COUNTRIES

In a general view of the Earth, one of the most remarkable features of the Triassic is the almost universally emergent condition of the continents, and the extensive spread of non-marine deposits, largely redbeds.

South Africa. Here non-marine formations of great thickness (upper Karroo) are overlain by volcanics and shot through with basic intrusions of extraordinary magnitude (Drakensberg volcanics). The lower part of the series includes gray sandstones, siltstones, and shales with thin beds of coal and abundant plant remains, but the middle part consists of thick redbeds with mudcracks and a very interesting reptilian fauna. Overlying the redbeds come purer, wind-blown sands varying in thickness up to 800 feet. The succession of formations is interpreted to imply a growing aridity that resulted in desert conditions over a considerable area in South Africa before the close of the Triassic.[5] The basic igneous rocks intruded into this series have a present area of fully 220,000 square miles, and before their erosion covered at least 330,000 square miles in a great belt between latitudes 26° and 33° S. that extended from the east coast probably to the Atlantic. With a volume estimated as between 50,000 and 100,000 cubic miles, this constitutes one of the greatest known masses of basic intrusives. The time of its intrusion is either late Triassic or more probably early Jurassic.

USSR. The Permian Basin west of the Urals in the USSR also includes a vast area of redbeds (upper part of the Tatarian Series) that have yielded striking vertebrate fossils.

Brazil. In the Paraná Basin of southern Brazil, late Triassic redbeds with reptiles similar to those of Africa are also overlain by enormous lava flows which still cover an area of some 300,000 square miles to a depth ranging from 400 to 2,000 feet.[6] These lavas, like those of South Africa, may be dated as either late Triassic or early Jurassic.

England, Germany, and France. In these countries the Triassic is represented chiefly by redbeds of non-marine origin. In France these are salt-bearing, and those in Germany have gypsum. On the other hand, southern Europe was covered by a vast epeiric sea in the Tethyan Geosyncline, which continued eastward through the Himalayan region and thence southward into the East Indian arc. Throughout this vast area, there is a fine development of marine Triassic, which is nowhere better displayed than in the dolostone peaks of the Tyrolean Alps. The dolostones of the South Tyrol are in places over 3,000 feet thick and were largely built by marine reef-making algae.

CLIMATE

We have noted the evidence of widespread semiarid climate in North America, South America, South Africa, and western Europe. On the whole, semiarid climate seems to have been remarkably widespread during the Triassic. Perhaps this was partly due to the size of the emergent land masses, since the interiors of the continents—dependent for their moisture upon evaporation from the seas—include the chief deserts of the world. At the same time, parts of the Triassic lands were well watered, just as parts of the present continents are humid.

In view of the widespread Permian glaciation, it is noteworthy that no glacial deposits have been found in the Triassic rocks.° The temperature had become mild long before the close of the Permian. This we may infer from the distribution of late Permian and Triassic vertebrates, all of which were cold-blooded, that is, without a device to keep their bodily warmth above the temperature of their environment. Modern reptiles and amphibians, without exception, become torpid and helpless

°Triassic or Jura-Triassic tillites are reported in equatorial Africa west of Lake Tanganyika. The tillites occur in the Lubilache formation. Valves of *Estheria* occur. It is not proved that this formation is of Triassic age, and it may after all be of Permian time. See A. P. Coleman, *Ice Ages,* The Macmillan Co., New York, 1926, p. 86.

Figure 242. Petrified logs in Petrified Forest National Monument, Arizona. (Joseph Muench.)

when the temperature drops to near freezing. Small species may take refuge in holes and hibernate, but all large species are confined to regions without frost. For example, the alligators and crocodiles, the great land tortoises, the large lizards and boas, all live in the tropics or subtropics. It is therefore highly probable that the dinosaurs as well as the sprawling reptiles and the large labyrinthodonts of the Triassic could not endure freezing weather. By Middle Triassic time corals had re-established themselves and were making small reefs in the seaways along the Pacific coast of America as far north as Alaska. However, since these are of few kinds and the reefs are small, it is probably not safe to infer that the water was subtropical so far north.

LIFE OF TRIASSIC TIME

Land Plants. The plants of this time are still imperfectly known, for less than 400 species have been described from all the world, and these are chiefly from the Upper Triassic formations. This may be due to an actual impoverishment of plant life because of the harsh climates, but is more probably due to the unfavorable conditions for preservation where redbeds were forming.

In America we get two glimpses of the Triassic flora, one in the foliage preserved in the dark shales of the Newark group, particularly in the southern areas (Virginia and the Carolinas), the other in the petrified logs of the western redbeds, as at Petrified Forest, Arizona.

Figure 243. A living cycad. The short trunks heavily armored by leaf bases, and the graceful pinnate leaves are characteristic of the cycads. (Yale Peabody Museum.)

The first is a swamp flora of ferns and scouring rushes, to which are added, where streams entered the swamps, the transported leaves of conifers and cycads that formed the forests on the uplands and slopes.

The Petrified Forest of Arizona, on the contrary, has yielded chiefly petrified logs, although foliage has been found in several places,[7] recording cycadeoids and ferns that grew along the stream courses. The logs are of conifers, not unlike the great pines that now stand in stately grandeur upon the rim of the Colorado Plateau. Many of the logs are of noble size, some attaining a diameter of 10 feet at the base and a length exceeding 100 feet. It has been estimated that some of these trees stood nearly 200 feet high (Fig. 242). They now lie imbedded in the Chinle shale, petrified as agate.

These two occurrences give a fair representation

of what we know of Triassic land plants of the world as a whole. The forests (Fig. 232) were then predominantly of conifers much like our modern evergreens, and of cycads (Fig. 243). The undergrowth consisted of ferns, tree ferns, and scouring rushes. The chief groups of Paleozoic plants were extinct, or nearly so. The seed ferns, so characteristic of the Coal Measures, had largely vanished, and the great scale trees are known only from rare specimens of *Sigillaria* in the early Triassic and a few other doubtful representatives. *Lepidodendron* is not represented, and cordaites were no longer conspicuous.

In 1953 and 1954 leaves believed to be of a primitive palm (Fig. 244) were discovered in the Triassic redbeds of southwestern Colorado.[8] If true, this is the earliest known angiospermous flowering plant.

The Beginning of a Reptilian Dynasty. The vertebrates of the lands were now varied and evolving rapidly. While the labyrinthodonts attained their culmination in size and variety, they were already far surpassed by the **reptiles**, which adapted themselves to all conditions of life on the lands, and early in the period began to invade the seas and compete with the fishes as do the modern seals and whales. **Phytosaurs** (Fig. 245) were common in the streams, and several other orders of reptiles, now extinct, were adapted to life on the lands. The phytosaurs resembled the modern gavials in appearance and habits but were not closely related to crocodiles. Their bones are found in association with river clams and lungfishes. One species from western Texas had a length of 25 feet. All the phytosaurs were confined to the Triassic Period.

Dinosaurs (Gr. *deinos*, terrible + *sauros*, reptile) made their appearance in the Triassic (Fig. 232) and before the close of the period outnumbered other kinds of reptiles and held complete sway over the lands—a dominion they were destined to hold until the close of the Mesozoic Era. Unlike other reptiles, they were adapted to a running locomotion, carrying their bodies up off the ground as mammals do, with the legs under the body rather than at its sides. Other reptiles sprawl. This is the only obvious feature that ties the diverse types of dinosaurs together as a natural group, for they vary by the widest extremes in size, bodily form, and habits. Indeed, they constitute, as we now know, not a single great order of reptiles but two that are only remotely related, having had very different origins (Fig. 260, p. 305).

Compared with the giants of later Mesozoic ages, the Triassic dinosaurs were hardly "terrible reptiles," for nearly all of them were slender of build and few reached a length of more than 10 or 15 feet. Almost all the known Triassic species were bipedal (Fig. 232) and shaped somewhat like a kangaroo, with powerful hind legs and a thick, powerful tail which aided in balancing the body as they ran. Abundant trackways prove that they ran like an ostrich instead of leaping.

The side toes on the hind feet were already vestigial in most of the Triassic species, so that they made three-toed footprints that were for a long time mistaken for bird tracks. Although the dinosaurs were very numerous in the eastern

Figure 244. Leaves of a Late Triassic plant (*Sanmiguelia lewisi*), interpreted by R. W. Brown to be a palm and the oldest known angiosperm foliage. From the Dolores formation near Fall Creek Post Office, southwestern Colorado. 1/5 natural size. (After R. W. Brown, U.S. Geological Survey.)

Figure 245. A Triassic phytosaur, *Rutiodon*. These reptiles closely mimicked the crocodiles and had similar habits. Length 10 to 12 feet or more. (After S. W. Willison.)

United States, skeletal remains are extremely rare, because the redbeds were a poor environment for the preservation of bones. As the dinosaurs crossed and recrossed the mud flats of the Connecticut Trough, however, they left an amazing record, not of dead but of living creatures, now hurrying in search of food or water and again stopping to rest and to leave in the soft mud an impression of the body and the tiny front feet. The best-known American form is *Anchisaurus*, a slender, graceful animal that reached a length, over-all, of probably 5 to 8 feet; its birdlike tracks have a length of 3 or 4 inches. Some of the similar tracks 5 or 6 inches long indicate larger species. The largest track of all (*Otozoum*) is that of a ponderous type, probably larger than an elephant, for its foot was more than 18 inches long and almost half as broad.

In 1947 a rich deposit of small Triassic dinosaur skeletons was discovered near Abiquiu, New Mexico.[9] Dinosaurs similar to those of America were also present in Europe, and nearly complete articulated skeletons of prosauropod dinosaurs were discovered in the Upper Triassic of China in 1940.[10]

The mammal-like reptiles (Order Theriodonta) continued from the Permian through the Triassic, and became extinct in early Jurassic time, meanwhile having given rise to true mammals. This group is best known from the Triassic of South Africa and from European USSR where many different kinds occur. Figure 246 shows the skeleton of a well-preserved form from near the base of the Triassic in South Africa, and a reconstruction of a similar form from the same region is shown in Figure 247. Another (*Cynognathus*) appears in the foreground of Figure 232.

A remarkable occurrence was discovered near the base of the Chinle formation at St. Johns, which is southeast of Petrified Forest in eastern Arizona.[11] Here, from a single layer, some 1,600 bones were collected representing at least 39 individuals of a single species, *Placerias gigas* (Fig. 248) along with fragments of five other kinds of reptiles. The carcasses had been dismembered

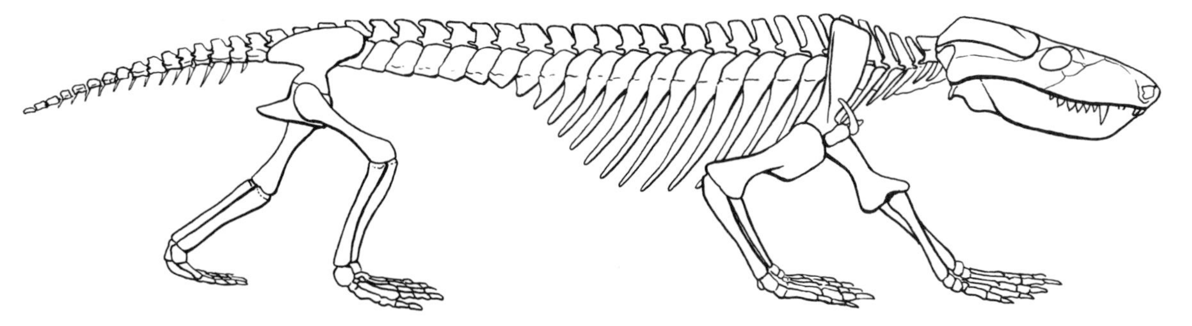

Figure 246. A mammal-like reptile, *Thrinacodon*, from a zone low in the Triassic part of the Karoo group of South Africa. (After Brink.)

by carnivorous reptiles before burial, but they had not been concentrated by currents. The reason for such mass mortality at a single spot remains an enigma.

The First Mammals. Fragmentary remains of small mammals occur in the Rhaetic formation of western Europe. This is a deposit of fluvial sands and muds at the Triassic-Jurassic boundary, and there is still some uncertainty as to whether it belongs at the top of the Triassic or the base of the Jurassic. Since present opinion favors a late Triassic age, the mammals are briefly mentioned here.

The chief finds have been made since World War II in southern Wales and across the Bristol Channel in Somerset where the fossils are concentrated in fillings of crevices in the Lower Carboniferous limestone.[12] The field relations suggest that these tiny mammals lived in crevices and crannies in the rocky uplands where they could evade their reptilian enemies. The remains are chiefly isolated teeth and fragments of jaws, but they represent three distinct mammalian orders. Since they are better known in the late Jurassic rocks further discussion of them will be postponed until the next chapter.

Return of Reptiles to the Sea. Marine reptiles are known in the Lower Permian rocks of South America and South Africa, but they did not become common until late in Triassic time. Dolphin-like reptiles called **ichthyosaurs** (Gr. *ichthys*, fish) appeared in the late Triassic seas and developed rapidly into one of the dominant groups of marine animals of the Mesozoic Era. They were already abundant in the late Triassic of California and Oregon, where the largest species was about 60 feet long, and they were probably the largest animals in the world at that time. The ichthyosaurs had a fishlike contour with a laterally com-

Figure 247. A mammal-like reptile, *Cynognathus*, from the Triassic beds of South Africa. (From a painting by F. L. Jaques under the direction of W. K. Gregory, American Museum of Natural History.)

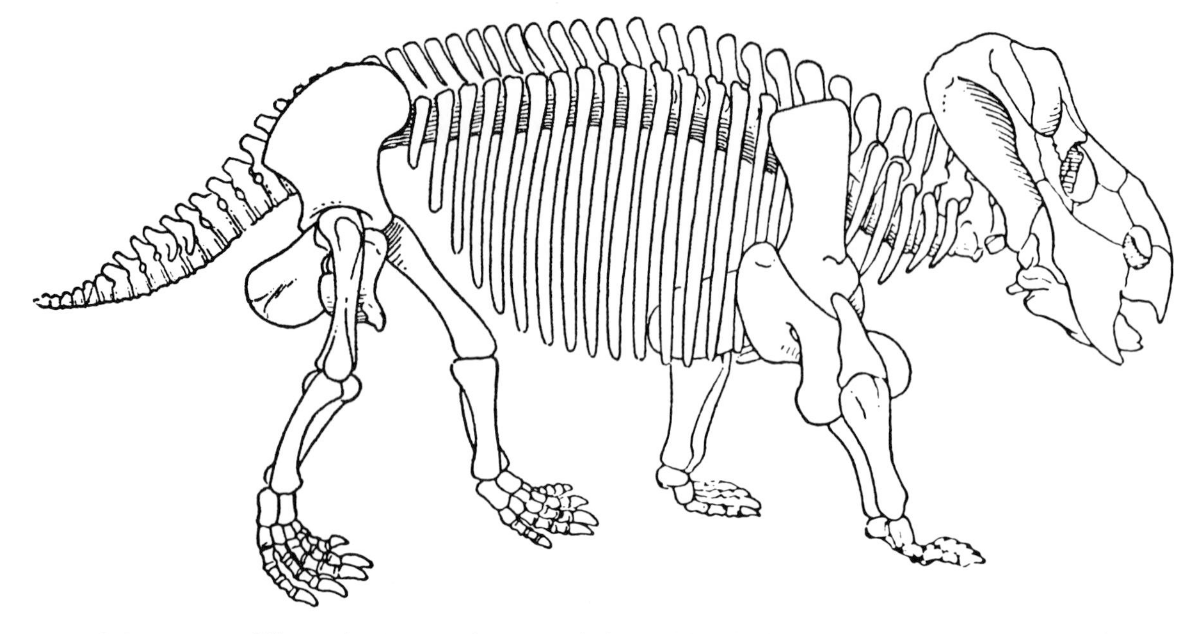

Figure 248. A mammal-like reptile, *Placerias*, from near the base of the Chinle formation at St. Johns, eastern Arizona. (After C. L. Camp.)

pressed tail and flipperlike limbs (Fig. 265, p. 309). They were undoubtedly fast swimmers, able to capture fish or the ancient squids (belemnites) and ammonites of their time.

The structure of their limbs indicates clearly that they had descended from terrestrial ancestors, their legs being modified into flippers similar to those of a seal.

Marine Invertebrates. The seas now swarmed with **ammonites** (Pl. 13, figs. 6–14) of many kinds, some far larger than any in the Permian. They were not only the most beautiful and characteristic shelled animals of the Mesozoic seas, but also the highest expression of invertebrate evolution in agility and strength. The rapid expansion of the group during the Triassic continued nearly to the close of the period, when a very rapid dying out almost caused their extinction. However, one genus (*Phylloceras*) with several species managed to survive into the Jurassic and to give rise to another great evolution of forms in that period.

The decline of so great and adaptive a group is difficult to explain. The ammonites suffered this fate three times, first at the end of the Devonian Period, again at the end of the Permian, and finally at the end of the Triassic Period. Each time a few survived to start another great evolution; they failed to survive a fourth great decline and at the close of the Cretaceous Period were totally extinct.

The belemnites (cousins of the squids) now, for the first time, became common but were to see their heyday in the next period. In Triassic time they seem to have inhabited the open seas but avoided interior seaways. Among other molluscs, both clams and gastropods were varied and common and several modern tribes were clearly differentiated. The oyster, for example, was present before the close of the Triassic Period.

Reef-building corals related to living stocks appeared in Middle Triassic time and contributed to the thick dolostones and limestones of the Alps and the Himalayas. They were widely distributed through the Tethyan geosyncline of Eurasia and also spread along the Pacific coast of North America from California to Alaska. **Brachiopods** (Pl. 13, figs. 1–3). though still common in Tethys, had suffered a very great decline elsewhere from which they failed to recover. They were never afterward common in America.

REFERENCES

1. Applin, Paul L., 1951, Preliminary report on buried pre-Mesozoic rocks in Florida and adjacent states. *U.S. Geol. Surv., Circular 91*, pp. 1–27.

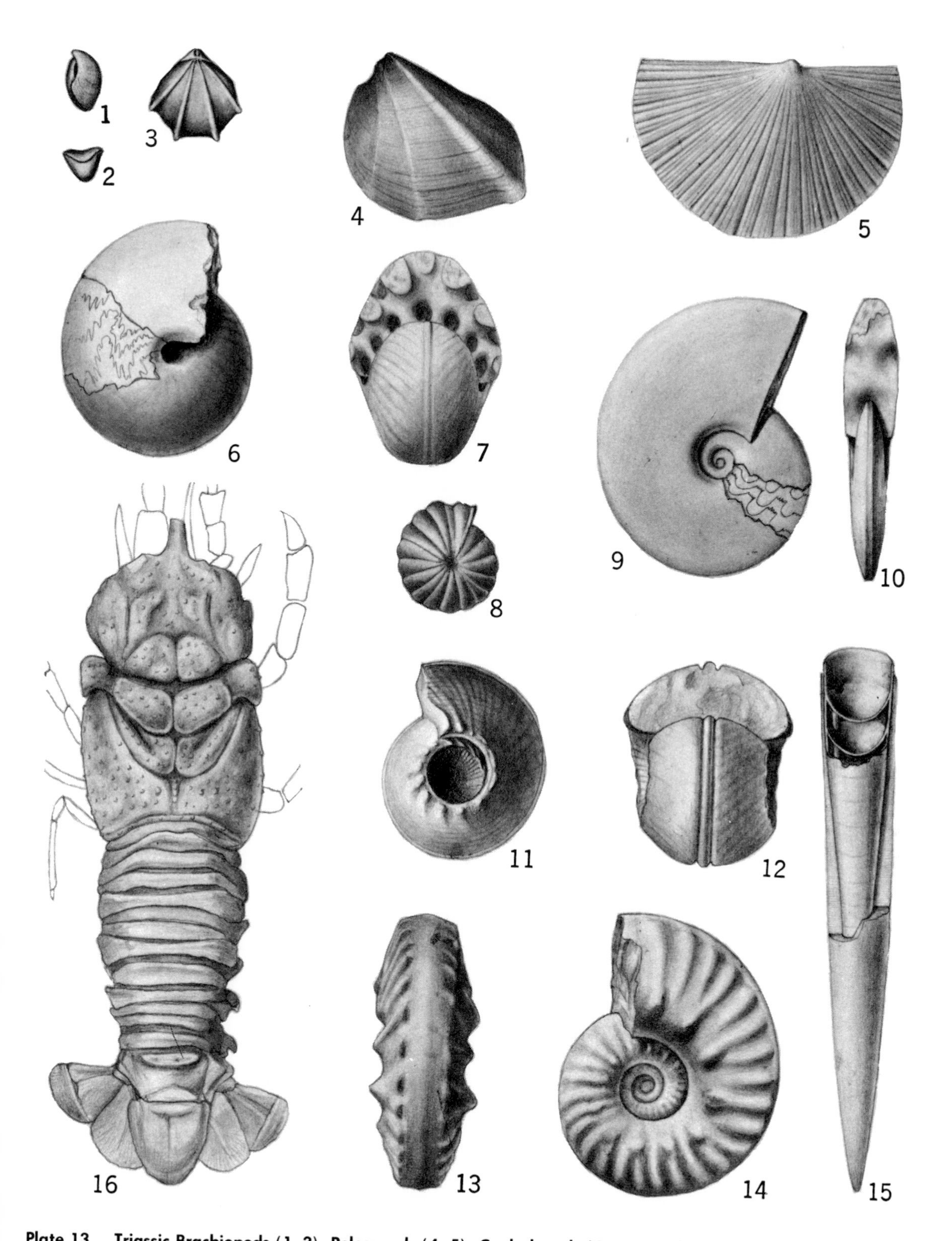

Plate 13. Triassic Brachiopods (1–3), Pelecypods (4, 5), Cephalopods (6–15), and Crustacea (16).
Figures 1, 2, *Aulacothyris angusta* (side and front views); 3, *Tetractonella trigonella;* 4, *Myophoria kefersteini,* a forerunner of the Trigonias; 5, *Daonella americana;* 6, 7, *Paratropites arnoldi;* 8, *Leconteiceras californicum;* 9, 10, *Meekoceras gracilitatis;* 11, 12, *Tropites subbullatus;* 13, 14, *Ceratites spinifer;* 15, *Atractites macilentus,* the shell of a primitive belemnite broken to show internal chambered portion; 16, *Pemphix sueuri,* the oldest known lobster. All natural size. (Drawn by L. S. Douglass.)

2. Krynine, Paul D., 1950, Petrology, stratigraphy, and origin of the Triassic sedimentary rocks of Connecticut. *Conn. State Geol. and Nat. Hist. Survey, Bull. 73,* pp. 1–247.

3. Peabody, Frank E., 1948, Reptile and Amphibian Trackways from the Lower Triassic Moenkopi Formation of Arizona and Utah. *Univ. of California, Bull., Dept. Geol. Sciences,* vol. 27, no. 8, pp. 295–467.

4. Harshbarger, J. W., C. A. Repenning, and J. H. Irwin, 1957, Stratigraphy of the uppermost Triassic and the Jurassic rocks of the Navajo Country. *U.S. Geol. Surv., Prof. Paper 291,* pp. 1–74.

5. Du Toit, A. L., 1953, *Geology of South Africa,* 3rd ed. Hafner Publishing Co., New York, p. 566.

6. Baker, C. L., 1923, The lava field of the Paraná Basin, South America. *Jour. Geol.,* vol. 31, pp. 66–79.

7. Daugherty, L. H., 1941, Upper Triassic flora of Arizona. *Carnegie Institution of Washington, Publ. 526.*

8. Brown, Rowland W., 1956, Palmlike plants from the Dolores Formation (Triassic), southwestern Colorado. *U.S. Geol. Surv., Prof. Paper 274–H.,* pp. 205–209.

9. Colbert, Edwin H., 1947, Little dinosaurs of Ghost Ranch. *Natural History,* vol. 56, pp. 392–399, 427–428.

10. Young, C. C., 1940, Preliminary note on the Lufeng vertebrate fossils. *Geol. Soc. China, Bull.,* vol. 20, pp. 237–239.

———, 1941, *Gyposaurus sinensis* Young (sp. nov.), a new prosauropod from the Upper Triassic beds at Lufeng, China. *Geol. Soc. China, Bull.,* vol. 21, pp. 206–252.

11. Camp, C. L. and S. P. Welles, 1956, Triassic dicynodont reptiles, Part 1: The North American genus *Placerias. Univ. Calif. Mem.,* vol. 13, no. 4, pp. 255–348.

12. Robinson, Pamela L., 1957, The Mesozoic fissures of the Bristol Channel area and their vertebrate faunas. *Linnean Soc., Jour. Zoology,* vol. 43, pp. 260–282.

Chapter 15. The Jurassic Period

Figure 249. Jurassic dinosaur skeletons against a background of the great mural in Peabody Museum. *Brontosaurus* (middle) was 67 feet long and 18 feet high.

Shallow seas spread widely over Europe during the Jurassic Period, bearing a rich and varied marine fauna, and the record they left is uncommonly clear. Formations of limestone and shale succeed one another, "like slices of bread and butter" over large areas in England and France, where they now dip gently and crop out in low scarps that are easily traced. They were the training ground for many of the pioneer geologists and have given us an understanding of some of the fundamental principles of geology.

Figure 250. William Smith (1769–1839), the father of English geology.

It was here, for example, that William Smith (Fig. 250) first discovered the use of fossils in dating and correlating the rocks. As a surveyor he was concerned with mapping estates, draining swamps, and laying out routes for canals across southern England where the Jurassic rocks are so well exposed. The limestones were extensively quarried for use in construction and were well known to Smith. Indeed, he gave names that are still in use to many of the formations.

As a hobby he collected fossils, not with any idea of their significance, but merely because they were interesting curios. One day in 1798, however, as he was cataloguing these treasures, he suddenly realized that each rock formation yielded a distinctive assemblage of species wherever encountered. This being true, he reasoned, it should be possible to recognize a formation in any outcrop by its fossils. With this insight he visited a friend, Rev. Richardson, also a collector of fossils, and amazed the latter by identifying the source of each lot of his fossils. Mr. Richardson broadcast the idea by writing to a number of the prominent geologists of the day, and it soon became common knowledge. Thus was born the idea of using fossils to date and correlate rock formations. It was, of course, an open sesame, permitting synthesis of local studies into regional interpretation. It is no accident that within the next few decades all the geologic systems had been worked out and named, and a geologic time scale for the entire Earth had been established. Such rapid advances would have been impossible without the principle discovered by William Smith, who has justly been called the father of English geology.

Study of the rich ammonite faunas of these Jurassic rocks also led later to the first clear ideas of climatic zones in the geologic past and of world paleogeography.

Jurassic History of North America

Erosion Prevailed in the East. In marked contrast with its fine development in Europe, the Jurassic is the least widespread system in North America, not a trace of Jurassic rocks being known in the eastern half of the continent except where deeply buried along the central Gulf border (Fig. 251). Undoubtedly the Appalachian region had considerable relief after the Palisade disturbance. Although this was gradually reduced during Jurassic time, the shoreline remained east of the present continental shelf and no basins of deposition are recorded east of the Great Plains.

From deep wells in the Gulf Coastal Plain late Jurassic formations are known to underlie a large crescent-shaped area from Alabama to southern Texas (Fig. 251). Their greatest thickness, exceeding 7,000 feet, is in Louisiana, whence they

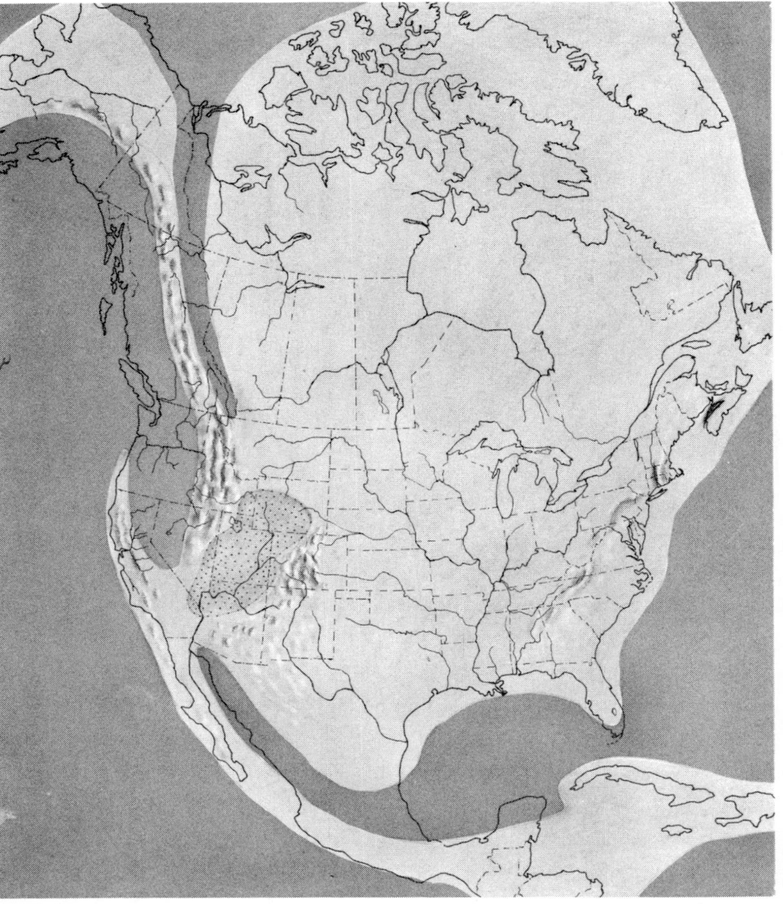

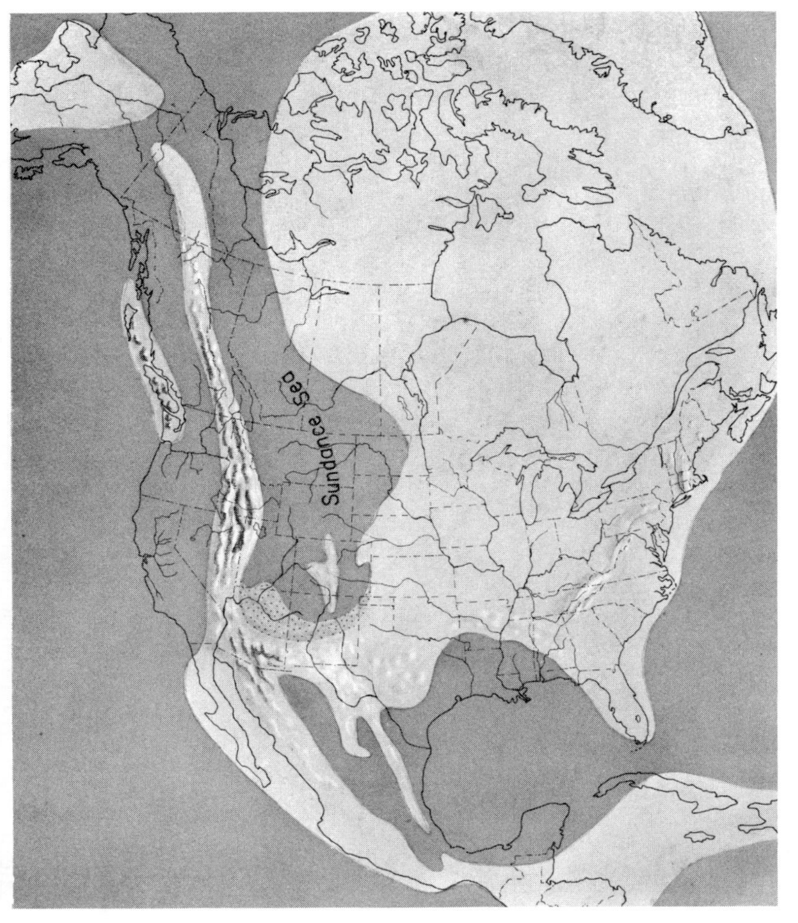

Figure 251. Jurassic paleogeography of North America. A (left), Early Jurassic time; B (right), middle Late Jurassic time. Stippled areas were above sealevel and were covered with wind-blown sand.

thin inland to a feathered edge in southern Arkansas and in central Texas and are overlapped by Createaceous strata (Fig. 252). In Louisiana and eastern Texas these rocks are locally oil-bearing and include large deposits of salt and anhydrite, probably formed in nearly landlocked coastal lagoons.

Development of the Rocky Mountain Geosyncline. An early Jurassic seaway crept southward across Canada along the east side of the Mesocordilleran Geanticline, following the pattern established in Triassic time. Further south a subsiding lowland centering over Utah and Wyoming (Fig. 251) was covered by wind-blown sand (now the Navajo sandstone of the Colorado Plateau and the Nugget sandstone of Idaho and Wyoming).

During Middle Jurassic time the sea spread southward into Idaho and western Wyoming and for a very brief time reached into central Utah. Along its western margin thick limestones were laid down in Idaho (Fig. 253) while lagoons along its shallow eastern border were the site of precipitation of extensive deposits of gypsum (the Gypsum Spring formation).

Early in the Late Jurassic Epoch this northern sea reached the maximum limits indicated in Figure 251. Because it was the site of deposition of the widespread Sundance formation of the northern Great Plains, this has long been known as the Sundance Sea. It fluctuated widely across Utah and western Colorado while non-marine mud and sand accumulated over the bordering lowlands. The resulting San Rafael group (Fig. 256) of the Colorado Plateau is a complex of marine and non-marine formations showing rapid changes of facies as gray limestones grade laterally into redbeds and these, in turn, grade locally into thick masses of wind-blown sand.

Later in the period the sea withdrew and then streams, flowing eastward from the rising Mesocordilleran Geanticline, spread a vast sheet of fluvial mud, sand, and gravel across the interior lowland to form the Morrison formation, entombing an amazing record of the land life of the time.

The Pacific Coast Geosyncline. The region west of the Mesocordilleran Geanticline was even more widely submerged than in the Triassic Period, and here detrital formations of great thickness accumulated throughout most of Jurassic time, generally accompanied by volcanics which came in part from the Mesocordilleran Geanticline but even more from submarine flows and volcanic islands. In British Columbia submarine volcanics range up to 3,000 feet in thickness and in California immense flows of basic lava occur in the Mariposa formation.

This region has been intensely deformed since Jurassic time and its early history and paleography are still very imperfectly known. The Jurassic rocks now crop out in relatively small and disconnected areas and are structurally involved and in large part strongly metamorphased. In several places thick sequences of fossiliferous strata indicate submergence throughout much of Jurassic time, but only local details are generally known.

Nevadian Disturbance. Growing crustal unrest west of the Rocky Mountain Geosyncline was evident during Triassic and Jurassic time in the deep subsidence of the Pacific Coast Geosyncline, the progressive rise of the Mesocordilleran Geanticline, and the immense amount of volcanic activity. About the close of the Jurassic Period this culminated in the first really great paroxysms of orogeny in the western part of North America since Precambrian time. As ranges of fold mountains arose, the deposits of the Pacific Coast Geosyncline were crushed and in places isoclinally folded and complexly faulted. Shales were metamorphosed into slate and limestones into marble.

Intense deformation of the older rocks at this time spread eastward across nearly all of Nevada and Idaho.

The precise date of the Nevadian disturbance is still uncertain. Fossils of Kimmeridgian age (next to youngest stage in the Jurassic of Europe) have been found in the strongly deformed Mariposa formation of California; and the supposedly equivalent Galice formation in Oregon is more deformed than the overlying Franciscan formation which bears fossils of Portlandian age (latest Jurassic). Here the main movement clearly occurred before the close of the period. In any event it is unlikely that the disturbance was of short duration or was contemporaneous over a region extending from southern California to Alaska. The main pulse may have come before the end of the Jurassic in some areas and after it in others. As indicated symbolically in Figure 8 (p.

15), the Nevadian disturbance was only the precursor of movements that occurred intermittently during Cretaceous time and culminated in the formation of the Rocky Mountain System near the end of the Mesozoic Era. Better evidence for dating the Nevadian disturbance will undoubtedly be secured as more fossils are found in the metamorphosed Jurassic and Cretaceous rocks of California.

JURASSIC STRATIGRAPHY

The Gulf Coast Overlap. By the beginning of Middle Jurassic time a sea occupying the present site of the Gulf of Mexico began to encroach on the coastal belt, gradually spreading during later Jurassic time to the limits indicated in Figure 251. The deposits formed here are now deeply buried but are known from many wells and have been subdivided into five formations whose relations are indicated in Figure 252. The Eagle Mills formation is of interest because it includes an immence body of salt. The basin in which it was precipitated must have been nearly landlocked and the climate at the time must have been rather severely arid in the Gulf region. The Smackover formation contains marine fossils indicating open connection to the sea, but an extensive deposit of anhydrite in the Buckner formation suggest a return to the conditions of a nearly landlocked lagoon. The Marly limestone of the Cotton Valley formation, on the contrary, implies a wide spread of shallow marine water well into Arkansas.

Marine Sequence of the Sundance Sea (Fig. 253). The **Sundance formation** of the older literature is a widespread and conspicuous marine unit between the Triassic redbeds of the Wyoming region and the overlying non-marine Morrison formation. In recent years it has been subdivided

Chart 9. Correlation of important Jurassic sections

Series	European Stages	Calif.	Oregon	Nevada	Utah	N. Mexico	Idaho	Wyoming	La.-Ark.	Series
Upper Jurassic	Purbeck / Portlandian	Knoxville fm. / Franciscan	Dothan fm.		Zuni ss. / Morrison fm.	Morrison fm.		Morrison fm.	Cotten Valley ls.	Upper Jurassic
	Kimmeridgian									
	Oxfordian	Mariposa slate	Galice fm.		Summerville fm. / Curtis fm	Wangakah fm. / Todilto ls.	Stump ss.	Sundance fm.	Buckner / Smackov'r / Eagle Mills fm.	
	Callovian	Amador gr.	Trow-bridge g.		Entrada / Preuss	Entrada ss.	Preuss ss			
Middle	Bathonian	volcanics			Carmel fm. / Twin Cr. ls.	Carmel fm.	Twin Creek ls.	Gypsum Spring fm.		Middle
	Bajocian	Mormon / Thompson	Izee gr. / Colpitts g							
Lower Jurassic	Toarcian	Fant andesite	Mowich gr.	Dunlap fm. / Navajo ss.	Navajo ss.	Navajo ss.	Nugget ss.	Nugget ss.		Lower Jurassic
	Pliensbachian	Hardgrave ss.	Donovan fm.	Sunrise fm						
	Sinemurian	Trail fm.								
	Hettangian									

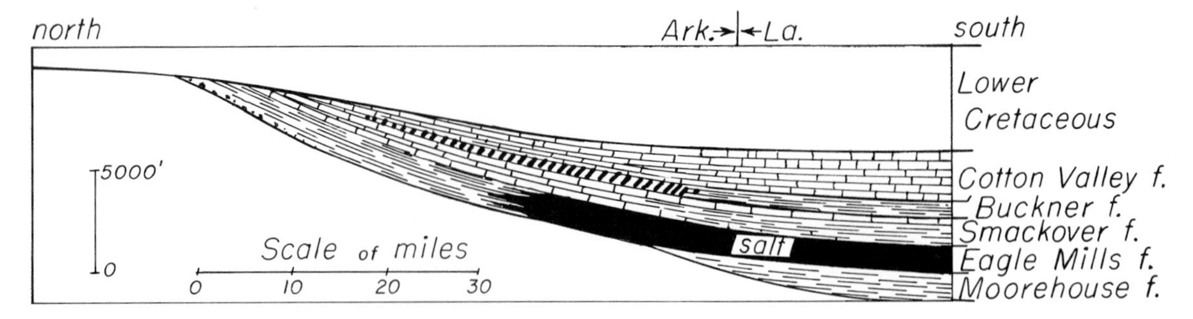

Figure 252. Section of the deeply buried Jurassic formations under the Gulf Coastal Plain in Arkansas and northern Louisiana.

into two major units, the Gypsum Spring formation of Middle Jurassic age and the Sundance formation (restricted) of early Late Jurassic age. Both consist of interbedded shale and sandstone with rather thin limy zones that are filled with belemnites, oysters and other clams, and a considerable variety of ammonites. Rare fragments of ichthyosaur skeletons have also been found. The water was evidently shallow and the extensive beds of gypsum in the Gypsum Spring formation must have been precipitated in lagoons that were largely landlocked. The combined thickness of the Gypsum Spring and Sundance formations is generally less than 300 feet but near the western border of Wyoming the Gypsum Spring formation thickens rapidly and grades into the Twin Creek limestone of Idaho and north central Utah which is 5,000 to 6,000 feet thick and represents Middle Jurassic and early Late Jurassic time. Here, in the center of the growing Rocky Mountain Geosyncline subsidence was more rapid and the sea more persistent than it was farther east.

The Colorado Plateau. Here the Jurassic rocks are several thousands of feet thick and are very largely non-marine. At the base is the widespread **Navajo sandstone** (Figs. 254 and 255) that generally forms plateaus bounded by unscalable cliffs several hundreds of feet high. It is formed of fine sand so evenly size-graded that bedding is generally ob-

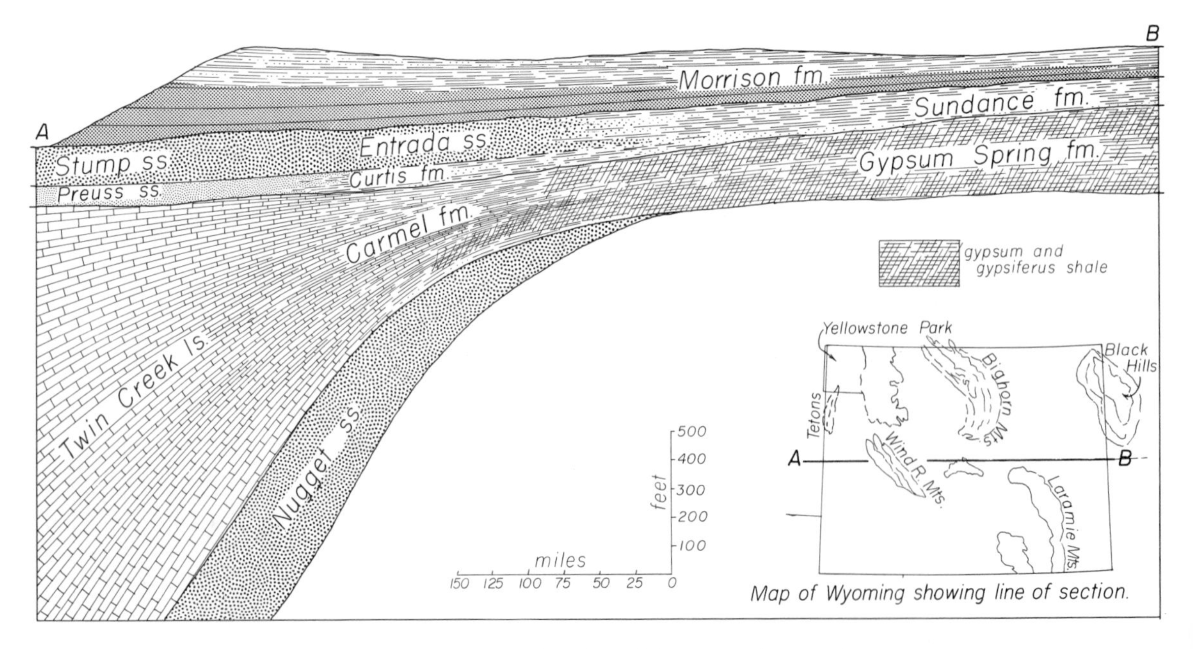

Figure 253. Section of the Jurassic formations in Wyoming.

scure, but in many places it shows the large-scale cross-bedding characteristic of dunes. For the most part it is light gray in color, thus contrasting with the underlying red sandstones of the Triassic, but in places it also is red or variegated, the color boundaries commonly not following the bedding. This is the formation spectacularly displayed in the walls of Zion Canyon, in Glen Canyon of the Colorado River, in Natural Bridge National Monument, and in Monument Valley.

The Navajo sandstone proper has yielded but few fossils (fragments of two dinosaurs and rare dinosaur tracks), and its position in the Jurassic System is still uncertain. The thin-bedded and somewhat calcareous Kayenta formation at its base, however, has yielded remains of a dinosaur (*Megalosaurus*) from which the age is inferred to be Early Jurassic (though possibly basal Middle Jurassic).[1] This unit has also yielded remains of small mammal-like reptiles, the first to be found in America.

The **San Rafael group** overlying the Navajo sandstone is a complex of variable deposits some 1,500 feet thick divided into several formations (Fig. 256), two of which are marine and the others non-marine redbeds. The marine units represent tongues of the thick marine sequence of Idaho and Wyoming and were formed during temporary advances of the Sundance Sea across Utah. However, since non-marine muds and sands were accumulating over the lowlands bordering these seas, marine deposits in part grade laterally into non-marine and the named formations overlap more or less in age. Furthermore, all of them thin eastward to feathered edges as they approach the old highlands of Colorado.

Marine fossils clearly show that the Carmel formation is of Middle Jurassic age and correlates with part of the Twin Creek formation of Idaho and Wyoming, whereas the Curtis formation is early Upper Jurassic and correlates with the Sundance formation of Wyoming.

Morrison Formation and Its Dinosaurs. All the gigantic dinosaurs of the American Jurassic have come from a single formation (Figs. 257 and 258) that was deposited as a blanket of fluvial sediments over the rest of the Jurassic formations in the Cordilleran region. It was named for exposures at Morrison, near Denver, but extends far to the north into Montana, west into Utah, and south into New Mexico, originally having covered more than 100,000 square miles of the Rocky Mountain region. In spite of this great extent, it is generally less than 400 feet thick.

The Morrison formation consists of shales, siltstones, and sandstones with local conglomerates, all of which intergrade laterally, as is the habit of fluvial deposits, so that it is impossible to follow a single bed over a considerable distance. The coarser sediments are commonly irregularly bedded and cross-laminated. The color varies locally from greenish-gray to black or lavender or pink or even white. No marine fossils have ever been found, but more than 150 kinds of terrestrial animals and land plants are known from these beds. These include the greatest of all dinosaurs. Sixty-nine of the species are dinosaurs, 25 are tiny primitive mammals, 3 are crocodiles, 24 are river clams and land snails, and 23 are plants.

From these facts we can picture the region at the time of deposition in a setting not unlike that of the present basins of the Amazon or Paraná rivers. It was a low alluvial plain crossed by sluggish streams heading in the distant highlands to the west, whence came heavy loads of mud and sand. Here and there swamps or small lakes interrupted the courses of the braided streams. The shifting sands and gravel bars along the channels gave rise to deposits of cross-bedded sandstone and conglomerate, while the finer mud and silt settled over the floodplains to produce the varicolored shales. The climate had become more humid with slight emergence of the whole region from the sea, so that vegetation spread over the landscape and animal life was abundant.

The precise geologic date of this formation is difficult to prove. It overlies beds (Sundance) dated certainly as early Late Jurassic and is in turn overlapped (in Oklahoma and southeastern Colorado) by beds of late Early Cretaceous age (Washita). So far as the stratigraphic evidence goes, therefore, the Morrison may be Late Jurassic or Early Cretaceous. The fauna, though abundant, cannot be compared with anything in the standard marine sections of the world, and we still know little about the land life of the Late Jurassic and Early Cretaceous of America except what is recorded in this formation. A comparison of the dinosaurs of the Morrison with those of the Jurassic

Figure 254. Towering cliffs of Navajo sandstone in Zion National Park, Utah. In the distance at the left, The Great White Throne, also made of the Navajo sandstone. (Carl O. Dunbar.)

and Cretaceous of Europe, however, brings out rather convincing evidence of Jurassic affinities (especially among the Stegosauria), and this is supported also by a comparison of the mammals.

Curiously, the best evidence on the age of the Morrison is found nearly halfway around the Earth, in East Africa, where beds bearing dinosaurs much like those of the Morrison are interbedded with marine zones carrying undoubted Jurassic ammonites. Although it is possible that the Morrison and the East Africa (Tendaguru) formations are not strictly equivalent, the balance of the evidence favors the assignment of the Morrison to the Late Jurassic.

Rocks of the Pacific Coast Geosyncline. Jurassic rocks are extensively exposed in California but in widely separated areas where they have escaped the several later periods of uplift and deep erosion. In most places they are deformed and metamorphosed to such an extent that fossils are obscure. With these fragments of the record, it is impossible to restore a complete picture of the Jurassic history of California. Suffice it to say that the sediments were very thick and almost entirely detrital, proving that the bordering lands were sufficiently elevated to be undergoing extensive erosion.

In eastern California the **Mariposa slates** and interbedded volcanics reach a thickness of possibly 10,000 feet. Mount Jura at the northern end of the Sierra Nevada presents a very complete Jurassic section, with 15 formations ranging from Lower to Upper Jurassic and containing volcanic tuffs and agglomerates of various ages throughout the period; and recently a still finer and more complete section was discovered in eastern Oregon. In Shasta County, California, the Jurassic is represented by the **Knoxville sandstone and shale,** which may total 10,000 feet in thickness, and includes continental beds with land plants, as well as marine zones with the peculiar arctic clam, *Aucella* (Pl. 14, fig. 6). The **Franciscan series,** which is widely spread in the Coast Ranges both north and south of San Francisco, contains radiolarian cherts and interbedded sandstones of late Jurassic age, with an estimated thickness of 15,000 feet. These sediments become coarser toward the west, suggesting their origin from the marginal land, Cascadia. In the vicinity of Vancouver Island, also, thick detrital Jurassic formations are found.

The great thickness and the detrital nature of all these western formations show that the disturbance culminating in the Nevadian mountains was already being felt during Late Jurassic time, and that the Pacific Coast Geosyncline was profoundly depressed as the bordering geanticline arose.

Southern Alaska has a great development of Jurassic rocks, though they have not been studied in detail. Marine formations of Early, Middle, and Late Jurassic age are known, and much volcanic material is associated with these, especially in the lower and upper portions.

CLIMATE

As we have seen, desert conditions continued in the southern part of the Cordilleran region, where the Navajo sandstone is one of the greatest dune-sand formations of the entire Earth. This, however, was apparently a local condition, because the region was low and in the "rain shadow" of the

Figure 255. "Frozen dunes" in the Navajo sandstone near the entrance to Zion National Park, Utah. (Carl O. Dunbar.)

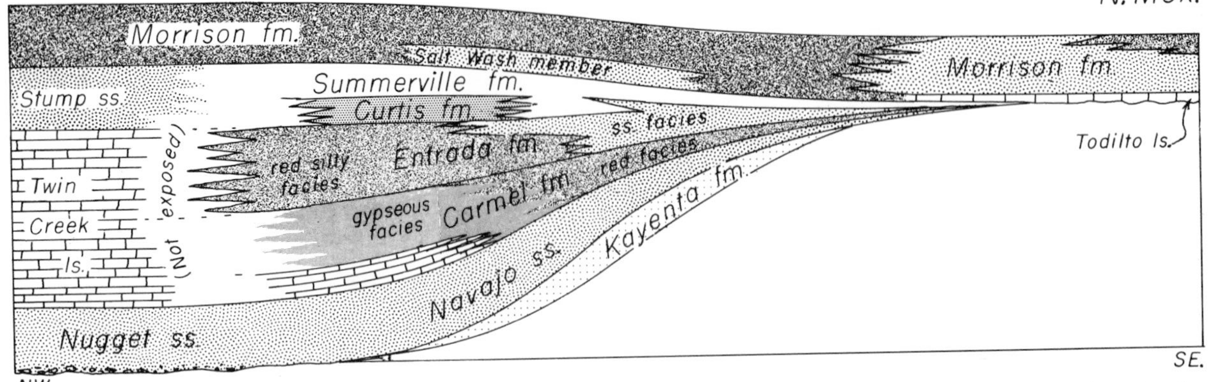

Figure 256. Stratigraphic section of the Jurassic System from north-central Utah to northwestern New Mexico, showing complex facies relations in the San Rafael group. In the Fort Douglas area of northern Utah the Twin Creek limestone is the marine equivalent of the entire San Rafael group. Twice the sea spread southward into the desert basin where the San Rafael group was accumulating, first during deposition of the Carmel formation and later during deposition of the Curtis formation. (After Baker, Dane, and Reeside, 1936.)

Mesocordilleran highland. Extensive deposits of gypsum in Wyoming and of salt and gypsum in Louisiana also suggest local aridity. In many other parts of the world, the climate was decidedly more humid than it had been in the Triassic, and gray or dark sediments with coal beds accumulated in the lowlands. For example, the Middle Jurassic is coal-bearing in Mexico, California, Alaska, Greenland, Spitzbergen, Europe, Siberia, India, China, Australia, South Africa, and Antarctica.

Figure 257. Upper part of the Morrison formation near Cisco, Utah, comprised of variegated shale and sandstone. (C. H. Dane, U.S. Geological Survey.)

Figure 258. Excavating a dinosaur skeleton in the Morrison formation near Shell, Wyoming. (Barnum Brown, American Museum of Natural History.)

There was nothing like the wide distribution of redbeds that we observed in the Triassic. Outside of North America the epeiric seas were again very extensive, and with this spread of marine water went, apparently, milder and moister climate.

The temperature appears to have declined somewhat at the close of the Triassic, though not enough to bring on glaciation. The middle and later parts of the Jurassic, on the contrary, were marked by very mild climate even in high latitudes, and probably by subtropical conditions over most of the United States and southern Europe.

The lowering of the temperature at the end of the Triassic is inferred from the dwarfing of the Early Jurassic insects, a decided reduction and geographic restriction of the reef corals of Early Jurassic time, the marked development of growth rings in the woods of that time in temperature latitudes, and the great decline of the ammonites.

That the Middle and Late Jurassic climates were

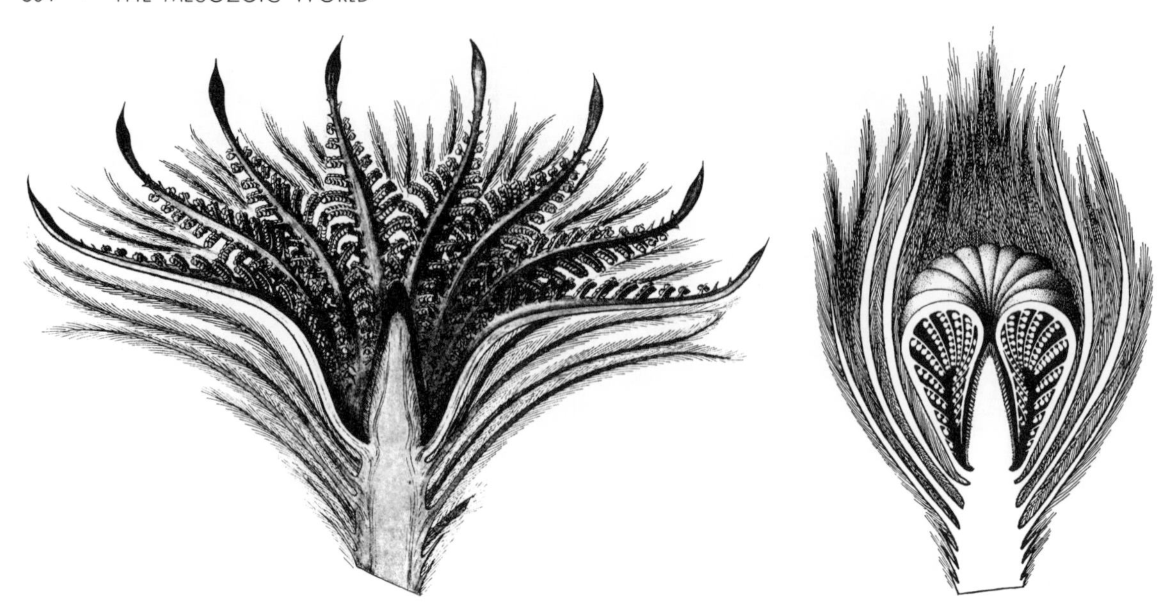

Figure 259. Flower of a cycadeoid. Median section of a full-blown blossom and an unopened bud of *Cycadeoidea ingens*, about ½ natural size. (G. R. Wieland.)

milder and more equable than the present ones must be inferred from the distribution of both animals and plants. Toward the close of the period the greatest of all dinosaurs ranged over the western United States at least as far north as Montana, and in Asia they were at home in Mongolia, where winter temperatures now fall far below zero. Yet the dinosaurs very probably could not endure freezing weather. Reefs of corals, sponges, and bryozoa abound in the Jurassic rocks, corals occurring some 2,000 miles north of the present range of similar forms. The distribution and character of the Mid-Jurassic land plants are thought also to indicate a warm, moist climate over much of the Earth. Furthermore, the insects of the early Upper Jurassic formations are much larger than those of the Lower Jurassic.

ECONOMIC RESOURCES

Coal. The Jurassic is an important coal-producing system, if we consider the world at large. Extensive areas in Siberia are underlain by Jurassic coal of economic importance, and in Tasmania and Australia the chief coal measures are the Jurassic rocks. There are also important coals in Spitzbergen and smaller deposits in various parts of Europe and southern Asia. In North America, however, there is no workable Jurassic coal except that of eastern Greenland.

Gold. The gold that attracted the "Forty-Niners" and led to the rapid settlement of California has its source in the gold-quartz veins formed in the Jurassic slates along the western slope of the Sierra Nevada. The placer gold that the early settlers panned from the streams was concentrated in the river gravels during Cenozoic times, but it came originally from the Jurassic veins and was freed during their erosion. A long, narrow belt of Jurassic rocks containing gold veins and extending for 120 miles along the western foothills of the Sierra Nevada is called the "Mother Lode" belt.

In the century following the Gold Rush of 1849, California produced more than one-third of the nation's gold—slightly over 103,000,000 ounces valued at almost $3,300,000,000. Production declined to an all time low of 170,000 ounces, valued at $5,950,000 in 1957, yet California still ranks fourth among the states in gold production.

Uranium. In recent years the largest source of uranium ore in the United States has been in the Triassic and Jurassic rocks of the Colorado Plateau, but the lead-uranium ratios indicate that the ores were introduced between 60,000,000 and

75,000,000 years ago, near the end of the Mesozoic Era, and are not related to Jurassic history.

LIFE OF THE JURASSIC PERIOD

Forests of Evergreens. The Jurassic forests consisted of pines and other conifers with a mingling of gingkos and tree ferns and an undergrowth of herbaceous ferns and scouring rushes. No grasses were yet present and the drier slopes and plains must have supported an open growth of ferns and cycadeoids.

Spores of waterlilies (*Nelubium* and *Castalia*) and of *Magnolia* have been reported from Jurassic deposits at Brora, Scotland,[2] but no other evidence of angiosperms is yet known.

The cycadeoids were an important and characteristic group of Mesozoic plants, widely distributed over the world in both Jurassic and Cretacous periods. Like their modern descend-

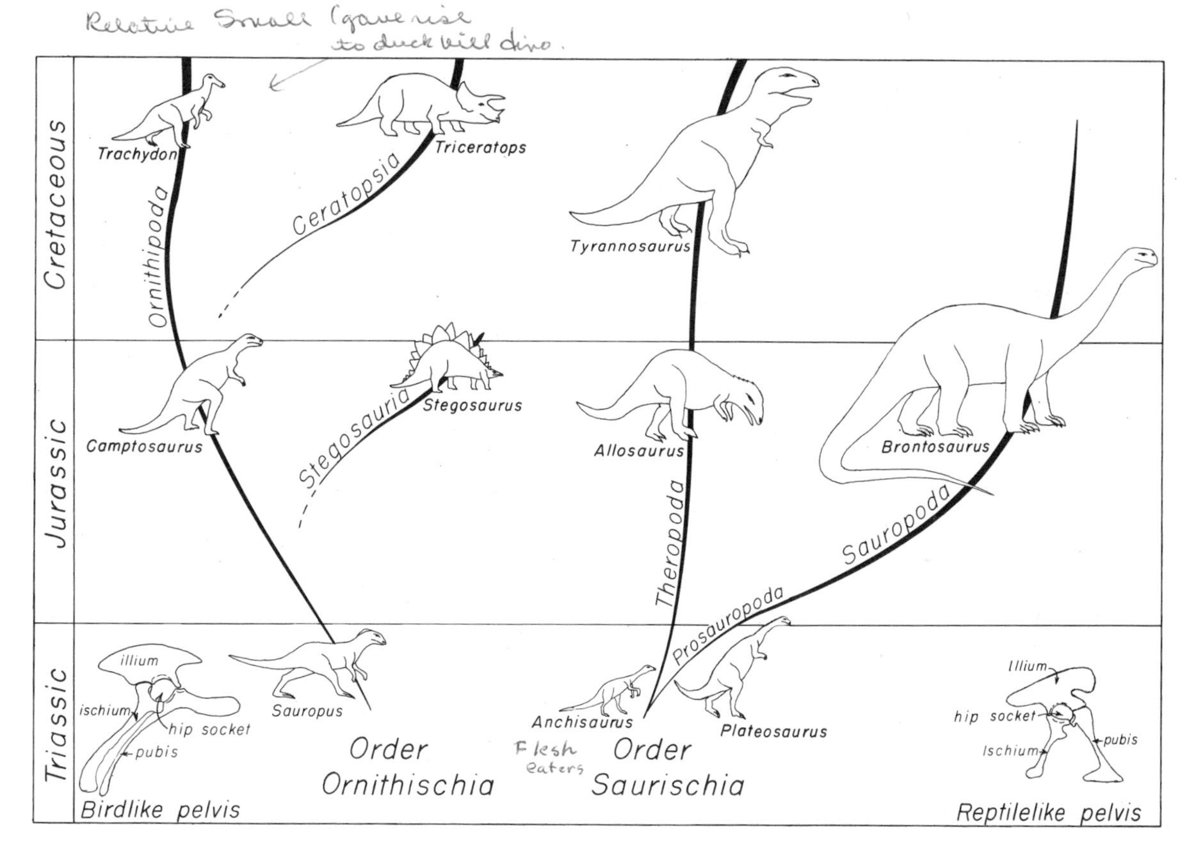

Figure 260. Diagram to show the relations and geologic range of the main groups of dinosaurs. The two orders were independent from their appearance late in Triassic time. The Saurischia (Gr. *sauros*, reptile + *ischios*, hip) had a triradiate pelvis such as is normal for reptiles. Originally they were bipedal and carnivorous, but before the close of Triassic time they were diverging into 2 suborders.

The Theropoda remained bipedal and carnivorous and culminated in the great carnivore, *Tyrannosaurus*, late in the Cretaceous Period. The Sauropoda became ponderous before their front limbs had been greatly reduced and during Jurassic time they reverted to a quadrupedal habit and a herbivorous diet, culminating in the greatest of all dinosaurs such as Brontosaurus.

The Ornithischia (Gr. *ornithes*, bird + *ischios*, hip) had a bird-like pelvis in which the pubis lay nearly parallel to the ischium. They were small, bipedal, and herbivorous in Triassic time. The main line, the Ornithopoda, increased in size but remained bipedal, culminating in the duck-bill dinosaur, Trachydon. During Jurassic time an offshoot of this line returned to a quadrupedal habit and developed armor plate along the back, culminating in forms such as Stegosaurus. Early in Cretaceous, another branch reverted to a quadrupedal habit and developed bony horns. These were the Ceratopsia. All of the Ornithischians were herbivorous.

Figure 261. *Stegosaurus*, a herbivorous dinosaur with large, erect bony plates along its back.

ants, the true cycads (Fig. 243), they had short trunks heavily armored with leaf bases (Fig. 284, p. 334), and their leaves were large and pinnate; but unlike the modern cycads, the cycadeoids of the Mesozoic bore large and showy flowers (Fig. 259).

Medieval Insects. About a thousand kinds of insects are known from the Jurassic rocks, and among these we note representatives of most of the modern orders. Caddis-flies, scorpion-flies, dragonflies, and beetles were common; grasshoppers, cockroaches, and termites or white ants were also present; moths and flies (Diptera) made their appearance at this time; and even the social ants were represented. Since the last three groups represent the most highly specialized stocks of the insects, it is clear that the significant features of insect evolution had already appeared by the middle of the Mesozoic Era.

Reptile Hordes. By Jurassic time the **Age of Reptiles** was in full swing. Not content with a complete domination of the lands, some of the reptiles anticipated the birds in flight, and others excelled the fishes in the sea. The dinosaurs had attained their greatest size in ponderous sauropods so enormous that a circus parade of 60 to 75 individuals would have been a mile long. Never before or since has the Earth been so completely under the sway of reptilian hordes.

Dinosaurs were now in their heyday, and four of the five great tribes of these reptiles were represented (Fig. 260). **Sauropods** were the largest and most distinctive. ***Brontosaurus*** (Fig. 249), one of the best known American forms, reached a length of about 65 feet, but the more slender ***Diplodocus*** was nearly 85 feet long; the brain of each of these huge animals, however, weighed less than a pound. In spite of their great size the sauropods were probably inoffensive creatures, for they were all herbivorous.

It has been argued that they were too large to support their own weight on the land and must have inhabited swamps where they were largely supported by water as they devoured the lush aquatic vegetation, and they have commonly been restored in such a setting. This, however, is almost certainly unjustified. Their skeletons are commonly found along with those of smaller dinosaurs that would have drowned in water deep enough to support a sauropod. Furthermore, a remarkable bedding surface in the basal Cretaceous beds at Glen Rose, Texas, bears abundant tracks of sauropods along with those of smaller dinosaurs (including carnivorous forms).[3] Here again, if the water had been deep enough to support the sauropods the smaller types could not have touched bottom.

Until after 1940 the huge sauropods were known only from Jurassic rocks but they have since been found in the Lower Cretaceous of Wyoming and in the Upper Cretaceous of New Mexico, Utah, and Texas.

The plated dinosaur, **Stegosaurus** (Fig. 261), with a 2½-ounce brain for 10 tons of weight, was equally distinctive of this time. In addition, there were bipedal carnivores of large and small size, one of which, **Compsognathus,** must have been as agile and slender as a small kangaroo, for it was only 2½ feet long. Of the larger carnivores of this period, **Allosaurus** (Fig. 262) was perhaps the greatest, having a length over-all of more than 30 feet. Still larger species lived in the Late Cretaceous.

The herbivorous bipedal dinosaurs (ornithopods) (Fig. 262) are known in several genera, but were less common here than in the Cretaceous.

Among the most bizarre animals of the Mesozoic were the **pterosaurs** (Fig. 263) or winged reptiles which "laid claim to the empire of the air in those medieval times." With leather wings and naked bodies, they must have presented a batlike appearance, though the structure of their wings shows

Figure 262. Jurassic dinosaurs and associated plants. At the center, *Allosaurus* feeding on the carcass of one of the sauropods. Another individual appears in the distance at the left. Lower right a small plant-feeding dinosaur, *Camptosaurus*. Extreme lower right, a cycadeoid plant with leaves and blossoms. *Allosaurus* was about 35 feet long. Part of a great mural by Rudolph F. Zallinger. (Yale Peabody Museum.)

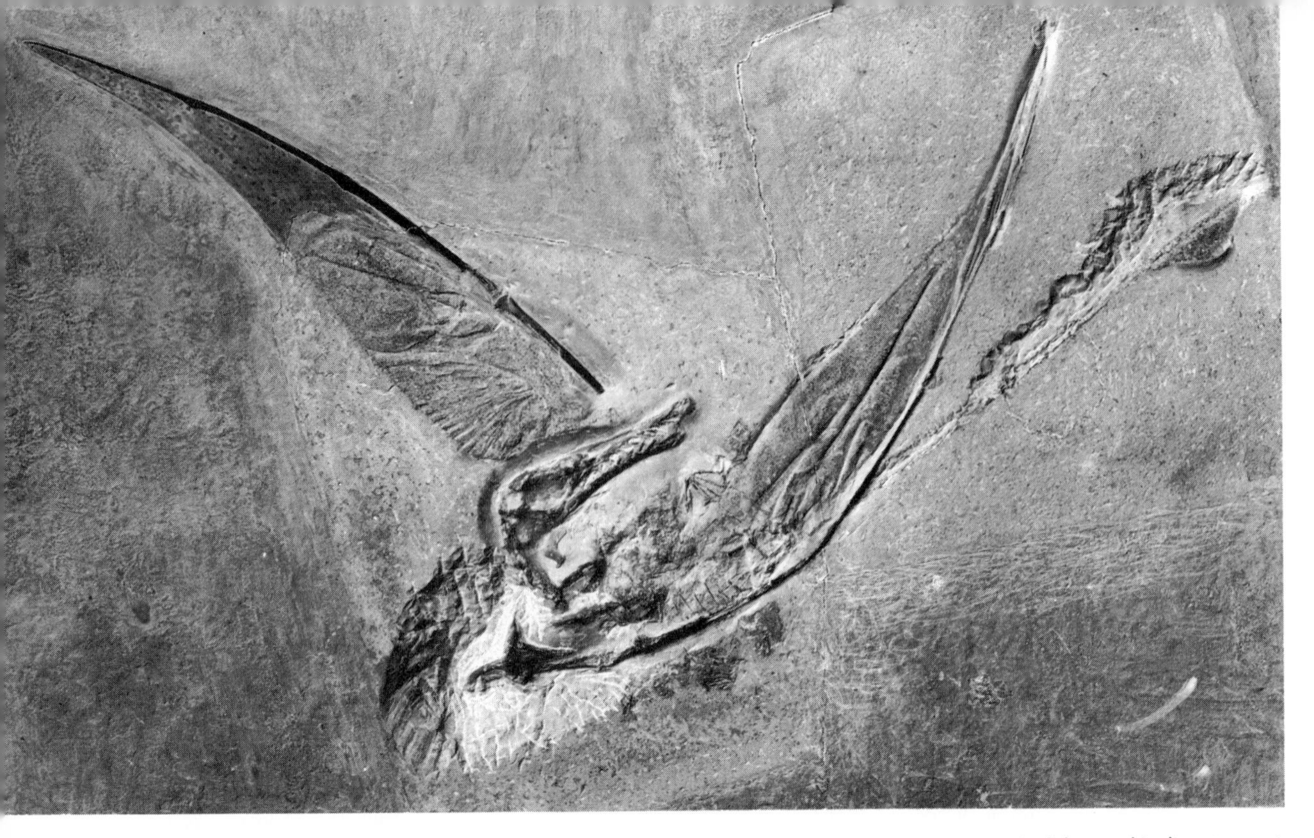

Figure 263. A batlike flying reptile, a pterosaur, *Rhamphorhynchus*, from the Upper Jurassic lithographic limestone at Solenhofen, Bavaria. The delicate wing membranes and the tail fluke are preserved as an impression in the rock. (Yale Peabody Museum.)

this resemblance to be superficial. The bat is a warm-blooded animal allied to the other mammals, but the pterosaur was a reptile. The bat has all its digits extended to bear the weblike wing membrane, whereas the pterosaur had only the fourth finger greatly extended to support the wing, leaving the other digits free to serve as claws. The Jurassic species had sharp, slender teeth, and heads that were decidely reptilian. Some had long tails with flukes, which probably aided in keeping the balance during flight, but other forms were tailless. In the Jurassic pterosaurs the front and hind limbs were not greatly disproportionate in size, and it is clear that these winged dragons developed from

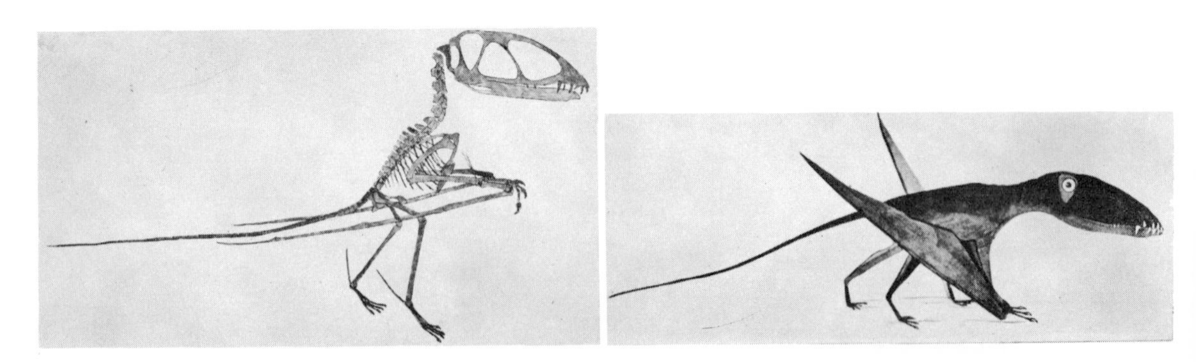

Figure 264. A small pterosaur, *Dimorphodon*, skeleton at the left and restoration at the right in a walking position. From the Lower Jurassic shales at Lyme Regis, England. This animal was slightly more than 3 feet long from nose to tip of tail. (From H. G. Seeley, *Dragons of the Air*, D. Appleton and Company, 1901.)

quadrupedal land reptiles. Upon alighting, they certainly walked on all fours (see Fig. 264). Indeed, their tracks have recently been identified.[4]

During the Jurassic period, the pterosaurs ranged in size from minute species with a wingspread equal to that of a sparrow up to others with a wingspread of 3 or 4 feet. The greater and more highly specialized forms followed in the Cretaceous Period.

In the seas, both **ichthyosaurs** and **plesiosaurs** were at the zenith of their development. The former, with their streamlined contour and powerful fluked tail, must have been efficient swimmers (Fig. 265). They certainly resembled the modern porpoise to a remarkable degree, except that their tail flukes were in the vertical plane, so that they swam by a lateral instead of a vertical motion. The resemblance is purely superficial, however, for the porpoise is a warm-blooded animal and a mammal.

In the Lower Jurassic black shales of Germany, remarkable preserved specimens of ichthyosaurs

Figure 265. The marine reptile, *Ichthyosaurus*, with a brood of young. The adult was about 10 feet long. See also Figure 21. (From a painting by Charles R. Knight, American Museum of Natural History.)

Figure 266. The marine reptile, *Plesiosaurus*. A pair of plesiosaurs in the foreground with ichthyosaurs in the right background and fish in the left foreground. (After E. Fraas, Stuttgart Museum.)

are found with the entire skeletons articulated and surrounded by a carbonized film that outlines the contour of the flesh (Fig. 21, p. 35). Some of these, moreover, have been found with unborn young inside the rib case, proving that they were viviparous. In this respect the ichthyosaurs show a more perfect adaptation to aquatic life than any other known reptiles, for even the great marine turtles come ashore to lay their eggs. The Jurassic species were rather smaller than some of the Triassic forms, rarely attaining a length of 25 feet. Many were mature at a length of 5 to 10 feet. They fed on fish and cephalopods. A remarkable skeleton found with some 200 belemnite shells inside suggests that they were especially fond of these squidlike animals.

Plesiosaurs (Fig. 266) are also best known from the Jurassic rocks. In these reptiles the tail was not fluked, and propulsion was by means of the paddlelike flippers, as in the marine turtles. The largest Jurassic species scarcely exceeded 20 feet in length.

Slender-snouted **crocodiles** much like the modern gavial of India were abundant in the seas as well as in the rivers. Marine turtles also were present, though less common than the groups of reptiles already mentioned.

First Birds. Birds appear as fossils for the first time in Upper Jurassic rocks and represent one of the most remarkable advances in the life of this period. As yet only three specimens are known, and these are from the famous lithographic stone quarries about Solenhofen, Bavaria. Two of these are fine skeletons with impressions of the feathers. The third specimen is the impression of a single feather.*

To the first-discovered bird was given the appropriate name ***Archaeopteryx*** (Gr. *archaios,* ancient, + *pteron,* wing). It was a strange creature, more reptile than bird, and yet because of its feathers distinctly to be classed as a bird. It would be difficult to find a more perfect "connecting link" between two great groups of animals, or more cogent proof of the reptilian ancestory of the birds.

* For some years it was believed that the skeletons represent distinct genera but restudy by DeBeer indicates that they are congeneric if not con-specific.[5]

Archaeopteryx (Fig. 267) was about the size of a crow. Three remarkable features strike one at the first glance: (1) The jaws were set with a row of small teeth. These were not mere serrations on a horny beak but true conical teeth set in individual sockets like those of many reptiles. (2) In the wings the digits were not completely fused, and the first three still functioned as claws. (3) The tail

Figure 267A. The skeleton of *Archeopteryx*, the earliest known bird, as it lies in the rock with impressions of the feathers clearly preserved. From lithographic limestone of Late Jurassic age at Solenhofen, Bavaria. This specimen is preserved in the Museum in Berlin.

Figure 267B. Reconstruction of the dead bird in the position in which it was preserved. Note the toothed jaws and the claws of three digits at the front edge of the wings. (Drawing by Shirley Glaser under the direction of Joseph Gregory.)

was long and slender, with the feathers diverging pinnately from its axis and not fanwise as in modern birds. The plumage was thoroughly bird-like, but the teeth, clawed wings, and long tail betray reptilian affinities.

The Mesozoic Mammals. In the previous chapter it was noted that three distinct orders of mammals made their appearance in the Rhaetic formation of Europe either very late in the Triassic Period or very early in the Jurassic. These three

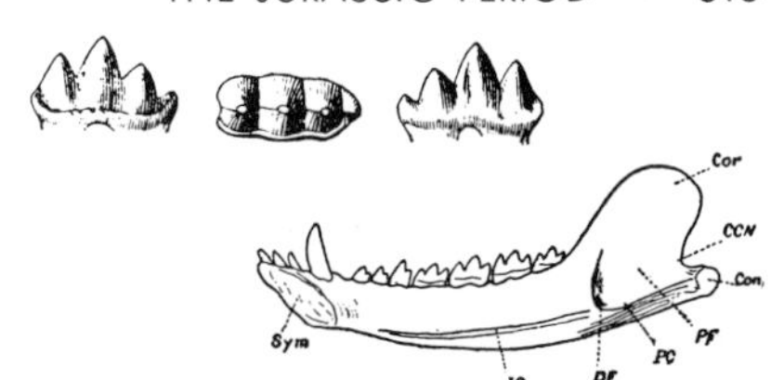

Triconodonta

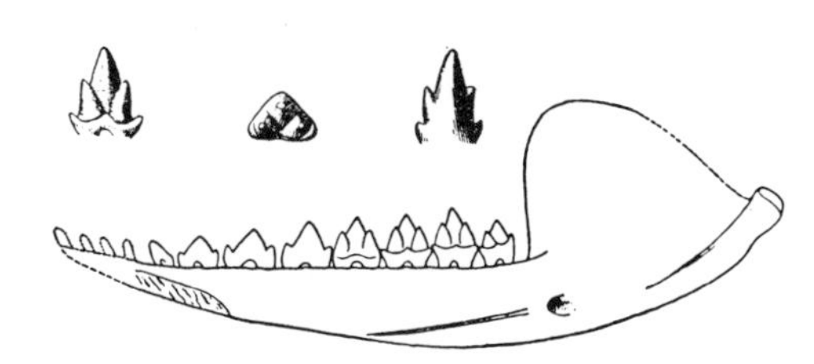

Symmetridonta

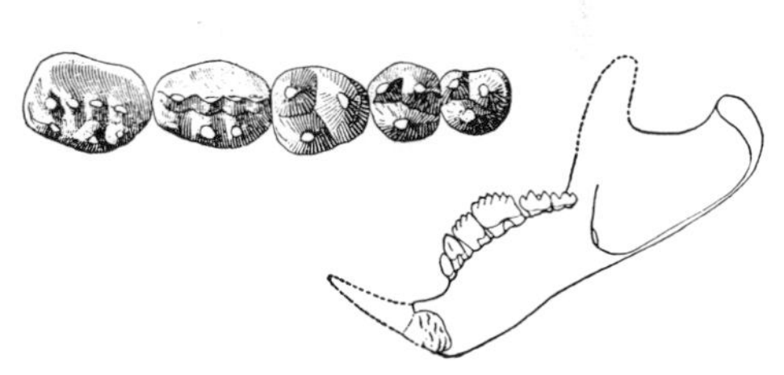

Multituberculata

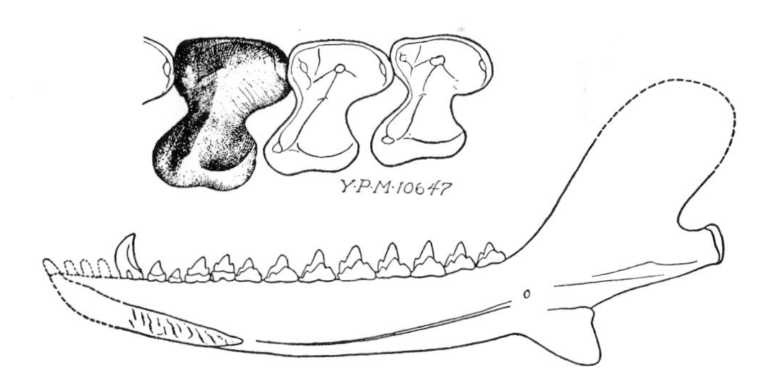

Docodonta

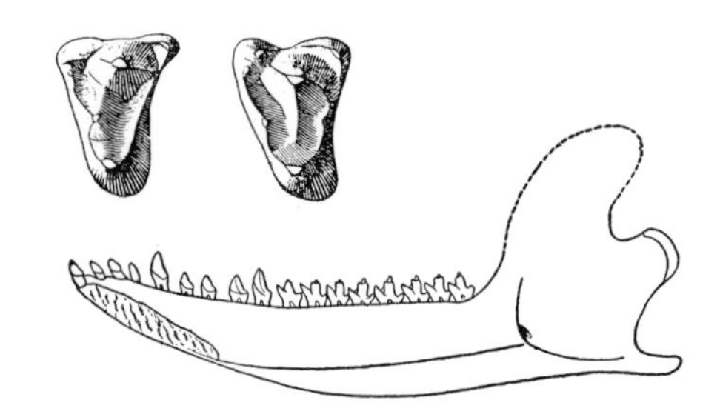

Pantotheria

Figure 268. The five orders of Mesozoic mammals, represented by right lower jaws and upper cheek teeth. (Adapted from George Gaylord Simpson.)

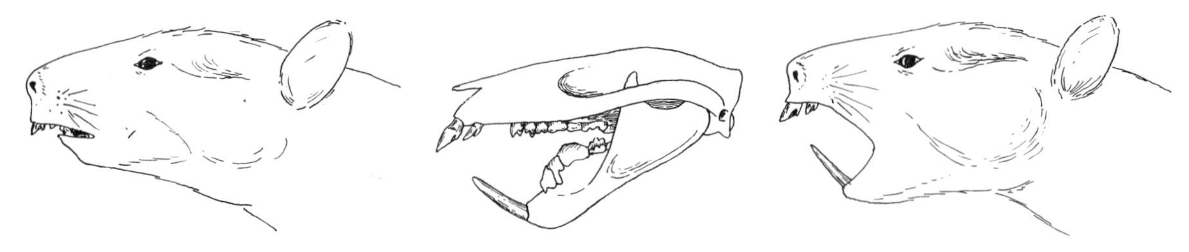

Figure 269. One of the best known Jurassic mammals, *Ctenacodon*, from the dinosaur quarries in the Morrison formation at Como Bluff, Wyoming. The skull and two views of the head. About natural size. (Restored by G. G. Simpson.)

ranged through the Jurassic and are better known from the Late Jurassic rocks (Purbeckian of Europe, Morrison of Western United States) where they are joined by two others. While three of the five apparently died out without descendants during Cretaceous time, two continued through the Cretaceous, and it was near the close of the Cretaceous before modern mammals appeared. Accordingly, these five orders are commonly known as the **Mesozoic mammals**. They deserve further discussion here.

The Mesozoic mammals are still known mostly from teeth and jaws and bits of skeleton; only a few are represented by skulls or adequate skeletal remains.[6] They were alike in being very small, and probably their superficial appearance was generally similar. The chief basis for separating them into distinct orders is the arrangement of the cusps on the jaw teeth as illustrated in Figure 268. The **Triconodonta** are characterized by three simple cones in a linear series; the **Symmetridonta** by three cones in a triangular pattern in which the middle cone is the largest; the **Multituberculata** by numerous small cones in linear rows; the **Docodonta** by blunt rectangular teeth; and the **Pantotheria** by triangular jaw teeth with broader and more complex crown; only the latter appears to have been adaptable to modification into the varied tooth pattern of the higher mammals. The Triconodonta, Docodonta, and Symmetridonta are believed to have died out without descendants in Cretaceous time; the Multituberculata survived through the Paleocene and then became extinct; and the Pantotheria alone gave rise to all later mammals.

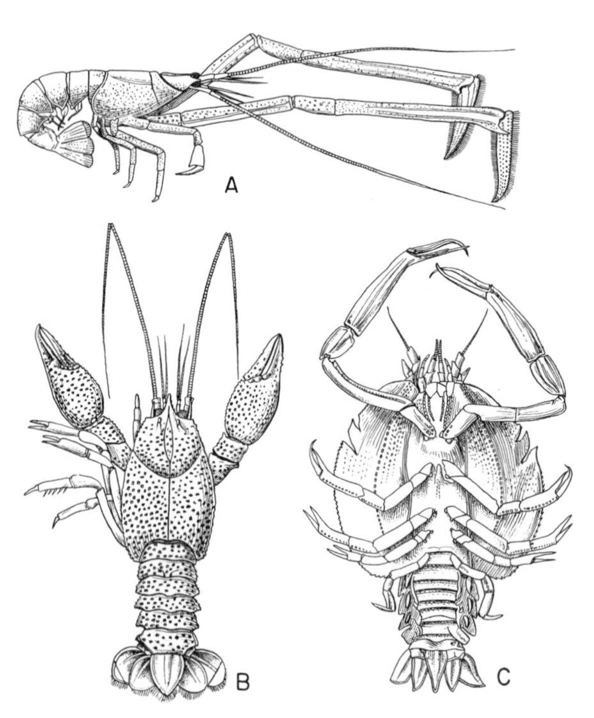

Figure 270. Crustacea from the Upper Jurassic limestones at Solenhofen, Bavaria. *A*, a shrimp; *B*, a lobster; *C*, a flattened, crablike form, *Eryon*. (After A. Oppel.)

One of the best known Jurassic Multituberculata is represented in Figure 269, and a much later and larger form from the Paleocene is shown in Figure 349, page 410.

Marine Invertebrates. The profusion of marine invertebrates and the richness of their remains in the Jurassic rocks have already claimed our attention. In many respects these faunas were essentially modern. For example, **corals** of the modern families were then extensive reef-makers, and abundant **pelecypods** (Pl. 14, figs. 6 and 7) and **gastropods** resembled modern forms in general features. True oysters had already become common, though strongly plicate species were more prominent than now. Lobsters and shrimp-like **crustaceans** were present in numbers, and one depressed form (Eryon) foreshadows the evolution of the crabs (Fig. 270). The **crinoids,** locally abun-

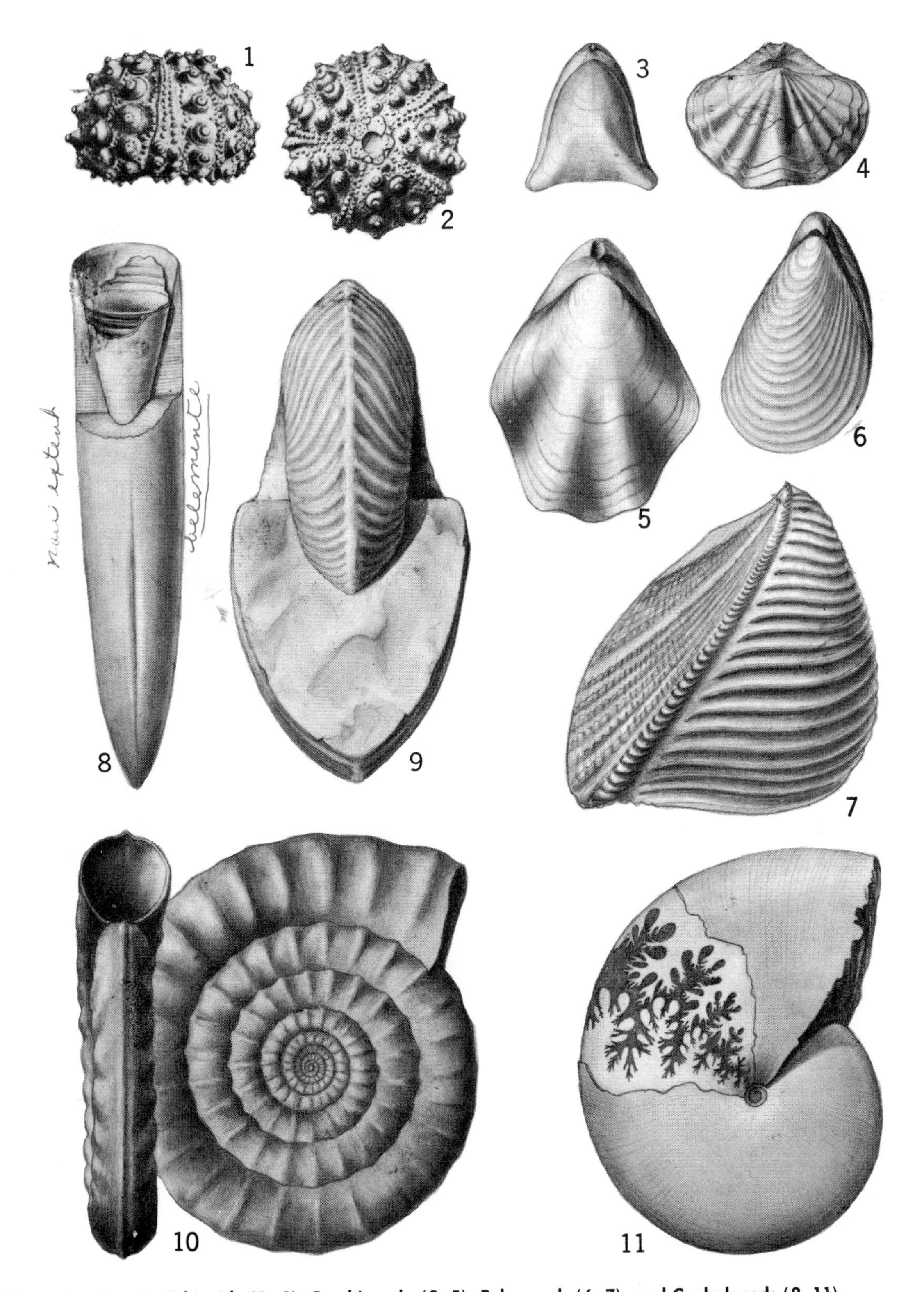

Plate 14. Jurassic Echinoids (1, 2), Brachiopods (3–5), Pelecypods (6, 7), and Cephalopods (8–11).

Figures 1, 2, *Hemicidaris intermedia* (side and upper views); 3, *Digonella digona;* 4, *Spiriferina walcotti,* last of the spiriferoids; 5, *Goniothyris phillipsi;* 6, *Aucella piochii;* 7, *Trigonia costata;* 8, *Belemnites densus* (broken to show chambered shell); 9, *Cardioceras cordiforme;* 10, *Echioceras raricostatoides;* 11, *Phylloceras heterophyllum.* All natural size. (Drawn by L. S. Douglass.)

Figure 271. Reconstruction of a belemnite darting backward and discharging a smoke screen of ink. Such animals ranged from a few inches to 5 or 6 feet in length. The internal shell is shown in figure 8 of Plate 14. (Drawn by Lathrop Douglass.)

dant, resembled either of two modern types: the large stalked forms were closely allied to the *Pentacrinus* that still lives in deep water off the Japanese coast, while small stemless species were like *Comatula*. **Sea urchins** of modern aspect were well represented (Pl. 14, figs. 1 and 2), and among these were the first of the "heart-urchins." **Sponges** were in places important reef-makers.

More prolific and more distinctive than all other kinds of shellfish, however, were the **ammonites** (Pl. 14, figs. 9–11), represented by a vast number of species, some large and some small, but all possessing delicate pearly shells. The intricacy and the variety displayed in the fluting of the ammonite septa during this period are remarkable, and the modification of bodily form of the living animals is an eloquent commentary on the plasticity of animal life. Some species, with slender shells coiled like a rope and with the living chamber occupying more than an entire volution, must have had bodies of eel-like proportions, whereas others with broadly rounded, globular shells had bodies as short as that of the octopus. The most remarkable of all modifications must have existed in those species with laterally compressed and deeply involute shells wherein the penultimate whorl of the shell was so deeply impressed in the animal's back as to divide it almost in two.

The **belemnites,** some of them 5 or 6 feet long, were also at their climax at this time, and their cigar-shaped internal shells are extremely common fossils (Fig. 271, and Pl. 14, fig. 8). Rare specimens found in the black shales of the Lower Jurassic in England and Germany show the form of the body and arms, preserved as a carbonized film about the shells. From these it is certain that the belemnites were squidlike cephalopods with six instead of ten arms and with corneous hooks instead of sucking discs on the arms. It is almost certain that true squids were also evolving from common ancestors with the belemnites, but their shells were too perishable to have left an imposing record like that of the belemnites. It is interesting to note that an ink sac exactly like that of modern squids was present in the Jurassic forms and that the pigment is sufficiently preserved in some of the Lower Jurassic specimens mentioned above so that ink can still be made of it.

Solenhofen, a Remarkable Fossil Locality. In the region about Solenhofen, Bavaria, the Upper Jurassic rocks include circular reefs of sponges and corals within which there are deposits of very pure, fine-textured limestone. For generations this stone has been quarried and shipped to all parts of the world for the engraving of etchings and lithograph prints. During this time the quarries about Solenhofen and Eichstadt have yielded more remarkable fossils than any other locality in the world except possibly that of the Burgess shale in the Cambrian (p. 122).

The flawless, fine texture of the Solenhofen stone, so essential for the reproduction of the lights and shades in lithographs, lends itself equally well to the preservation of the delicate impressions of organic tissues. It has therefore given us a knowledge of many soft-tissued Jurassic animals, such as jellyfish, and has preserved impressions of the fleshy bodies of creatures otherwise known only from their skeletons or shells. From these quarries, for example, came all the known specimens of Jurassic birds. The faithful impression of their delicate feathers is a fortunate thing, for without this evidence it would be difficult to prove that *Archaeopteryx* was not a reptile. Here also have been found specimens of pterosaurs in which the form of delicate wing and tail membrane (Fig. 263) are preserved with remarkable fidelity. Among other things rarely preserved elsewhere are 8 kinds of jellyfish and more than 100 species of insects, including moths and flies. Finally, very good specimens of the horseshoe crabs (*Limulus*) occur here. A total of 450 species of animals has been recovered from these quarries.

Evidently these are the deposits of lagoons within atolls that lay not far from the mainland. The fossils include a dinosaur, 29 species of pterosaurs, and 3 birds. On the other hand, there are no fresh-water animals, and marine fishes and marine invertebrates (mainly crustaceans and ammonites) comprise nearly all the fauna. One remarkable feature of the deposit is that most of the organisms were not dismembered before burial. There were certainly no scavengers living on the bottom, and the entombed creatures were either dead when they were washed over into the lagoon or died soon thereafter and were quickly buried by the fine limy ooze that spread in from the fronts of the reefs. It is because of this quick burial that the animals are so well preserved. The floor of the lagoon may have been in part permanently submerged and in part only a mud flat covered twice daily by the tides.

REFERENCES

1. Welles, S. P., 1954, New Jurassic dinosaur from the Kayenta Formation of Arizona. *Geol. Soc. Amer., Bull.*, vol. 65, pp. 591–598.

2. Simpson, J. B., 1937, Fossil pollen in Scottish Jurassic coal. *Nature*, vol. 139, p. 673.

3. Bird, Roland T., 1944, Did *Brontosaurus* ever walk on land? *Natural History*, vol. 53, pp. 60–67. [Fine pictures and data but exactly wrong interpretation.]

4. Stokes, W. L., 1954, Pterodactyl tracks from the Morrison Formation near Carrizo Mountains, Arizona. *Geol. Soc. Amer., Bull.*, vol. 65, p. 1309.

5. DeBeer, Gavin, 1954, *Archaeopteryx lithographica; a Study Based upon the British Museum Specimen.* British Museum of Natural History, pp. 1–68.

6. Simpson, G. G., 1929, American Mesozoic mammals. *Peabody Museum of Yale University, Mem.*, vol. 3, Part 1, pp. 1–235.

———, 1928; *A Catalogue of the Mesozoic Mammalia in the Geological Department of the British Museum.* British Museum of Natural History, pp. 1–215.

Chapter 16. *Cretaceous Time and the End of an Era*

Figure 272. Chalk cliffs at St. Margarets on the Strait of Dover, England. (Carl O. Dunbar.)

The Cretaceous Period. THE NAME CRETACEOUS (L. *creta*, chalk) was first applied to the white chalk that forms impressive cliffs along the Strait of Dover in England. It was later extended to embrace allied strata of other types, and in 1822 was formally proposed by the Belgian geologist, Omalius d'Halloy, to include all the rocks lying between the Jurassic System and what we now call the Cenozoic. It thus became one of the largest of the geologic systems, widely distributed and commonly thick. For the world as a whole the Cretaceous submergence was probably the greatest the Earth has known.

While remarkable for its vast deposits of chalky limestone in Europe and America, it embraces the full gamut of sedimentary rock of other types, and Cretaceous is really a misnomer. Furthermore, modern usage would prefer a geographic rather than a descriptive name. Nevertheless the term Cretaceous has never had a rival and no useful purpose would now be served by a change.

An attempt, early in this century, to subdivide it into two distinct systems was later abandoned. In America it is commonly divided into two series, Lower and Upper Cretaceous, but in Europe a three-fold subdivision is commonly used.

PHYSICAL HISTORY OF NORTH AMERICA

The Last Great Submergence

Early in Cretaceous time submergence was renewed on a grand scale as the continental margins were gradually flooded and a vast interior sea divided the continent into two land masses (Fig. 273). For a time almost 50 percent of the present land surface was submerged. Then the seas began a final retreat and by the end of the period North America had assumed essentially its present size and shape.

Atlantic Coastal Submergence. From New Jersey southward the Atlantic Coastal Plain is underlain by Cretaceous formations that dip seaward with increasing thickness, but thin to feathered edges where they lap out against the Piedmont Belt. The oldest of these are non-marine deposits of varicolored gravels, sands, and clays representing fluvial deposition on a low coastal plain. They are followed by marine formations that in places grade landward into brackish or fresh-water facies. All this detrital material clearly came from the present land and was spread eastward onto the continental shelf. This forms a striking contrast with the Paleozoic history of the region for, so far as they are known, the older sedimentary formations of the eastern United States were transported westward into the Appalachian Geosyncline. Such deposits as were then formed at the continental margin are either lost beneath the Atlantic or have been metamorphosed beyond recognition and form part of the crystalline complex under the continental shelf and in the Piedmont. The orogeny at the close of the Paleozoic Era had thickened the granitic crust under the Appalachian chain, transforming it into a permanantly positive axis. The old Appalachian Geosyncline had thus ceased to exist and long erosion during the Triassic and Jurassic periods had reduced the marginal land so that with the beginning of Cretaceous time the waves of the Atlantic were for the first time breaking along the eastern seaboard essentially as they do today.

Gulf Coastal Submergence. During Cretaceous time the entire Gulf border was likewise submerged and, for a time, an embayment reached as far north as Cairo, Illinois. Here, as on the Atlantic border, the Cretaceous formations dip gently seaward with increasing thickness, and toward their landward margins grade locally into non-marine sands and gravels. Deep wells reveal thick Cretaceous formations under much of Florida where the oldest ones are non-marine.

The Rocky Mountain Seaway. Early in the period the sea began to invade the Rocky Mountain Geosyncline simultaneously from the south by way of Mexico and from the north by way of the McKenzie Valley region. These embayments advanced slowly and were separated until near the close of Early Cretaceous time when they met in Wyoming (Fig. 273*A*). Thereafter they spread eastward to form a vast strait nearly 1,000 miles wide dividing the continent into two widely separated land masses, the eastern land broad, low, and stable, the western narrow and mountainous (Fig. 273*B*). Soon after this maximum inundation the northern end of the geosyncline began to emerge and the great interior seaway shrank to-

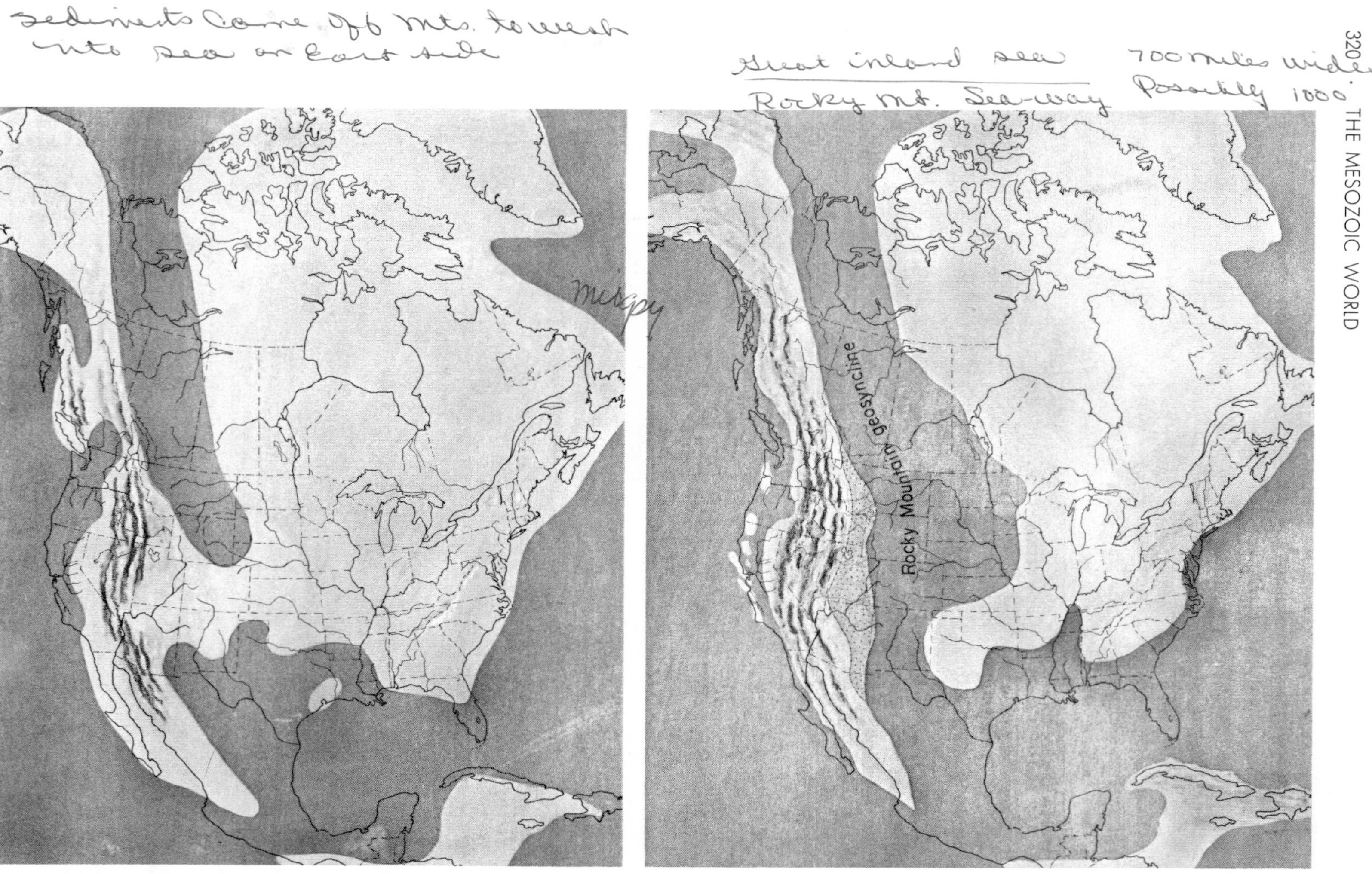

Figure 273. Cretaceous paleogeography of North America. A, left, late in the Early Cretaceous Epoch; B, right, a composite for Late Cretaceous time showing the maximum submergence.

originated from west.

age of faults decreases eastward
one layer over top of another

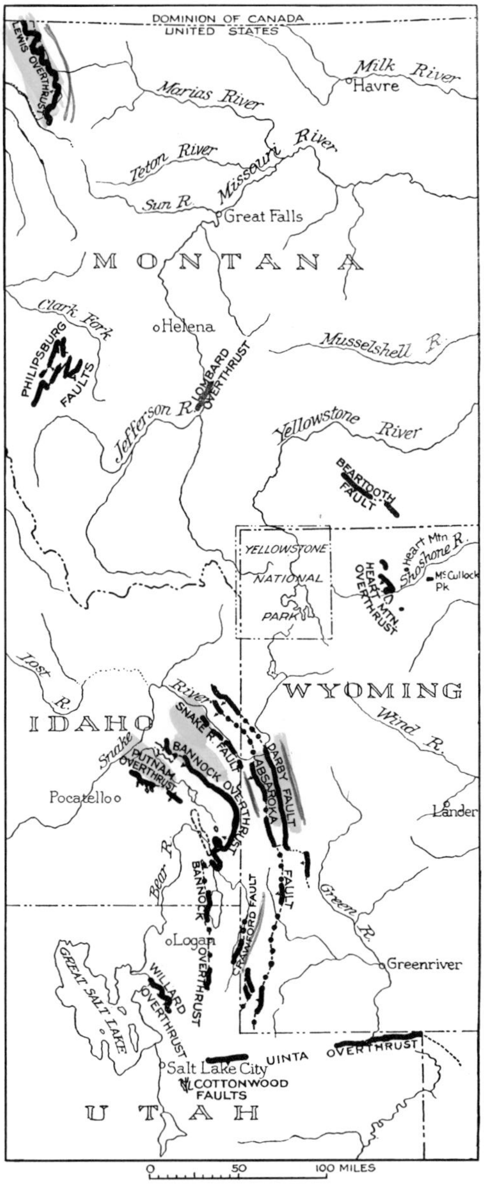

Figure 274. Traces of the major thrust faults produced by the Laramide revolution in the Cordilleran region. (After G. R. Mansfield, U.S. Geological Survey.)

ward the central part of the present Great Plains region as it was filled with sediment poured in ever-increasing volume from the rising highlands further west; its last connection with the ocean may have been via the central Gulf embayment.[1] The final retreat of the interior sea left a broad swampy lowland over which dinosaurs roamed while streams spread thick formations of sand and mud during the closing stages of the period. In the swamps of this lowland, vegetation accumulated to form coal over large areas between Mexico and Alberta.

Pacific Coast Overlap. In spite of the deformation near the end of the Jurassic Period the western parts of California, British Columbia, and southern Alaska subsided again during Cretaceous time, while thick detrital formations continued to accumulate.

Continued Growth of the Mesocordilleran Geanticline. Foreshadowed in Triassic time, the Mesocordilleran axis of the continent had become a well-established feature during the Jurassic and must have been a bold mountainous region during the Nevadian disturbance. It continued to rise and to broaden during the Cretaceous Period as, from time to time, pulses of uplift reached progressively farther to the east. The volume of mud, sand, and gravel carried eastward into the Rocky Mountain Geosyncline has been estimated at almost a billion cubic miles.[2] To supply such a colossal amount of sediment would require the erosion of an average thickness of approximately 5 miles of rock from the entire area of the Mesocordilleran land mass. Of course this does not imply that these highlands ever had an elevation of 5 miles above sealevel; the distribution of sand and gravel in the Cretaceous formations now preserved shows clearly that the source area was elevated repeatedly while it was being eroded *during* Cretaceous time. Indeed, the orogeny spread progressively eastward so that before the end of the period strong uplift occurred just west of the present Wasatch Range in north-central Utah (Fig. 277).[3]

During much of Cretaceous time the Mesocordilleran highland bore a chain of active volcanoes from which ash was blown eastward into the sea, even as far as Nebraska and Kansas. Such ash falls now form bentonite layers in the Cretaceous shales of the Great Plains.*

Laramide Revolution and the Birth of the Rockies

Crustal unrest was marked during the closing stages of the Mesozoic Era in many parts of the

*Bentonite is a claylike material formed of altered volcanic ash which has the remarkable capacity to absorb water and swell to several times its normal volume.

pressure from East toward west –
first folds – break. slide in thrust fault.

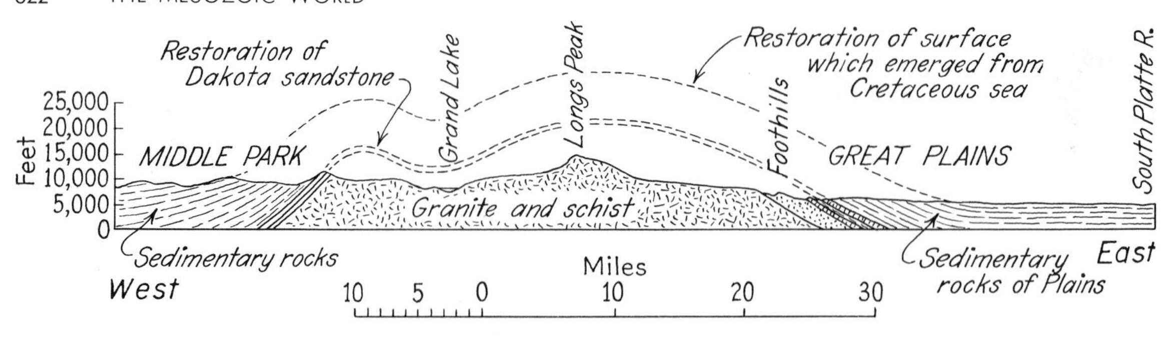

Figure 275. Section across the Front Range near Denver, Colorado, showing the arched structure and suggesting the amount of erosion that has occurred since uplift began. (After W. T. Lee, U.S. Geological Survey.)

world, but nowhere with more profound and far-reaching effect than in the western half of North America. At this time the floor of the great geosyncline, so long covered by Cretaceous seas, was subjected to folding and thrust faulting on a colossal scale; out of it rose the majestic Rocky Mountain System stretching from Alaska to Central America, with a breadth of some 500 miles in the Rocky Mountain states. This was the most profound orogeny experienced by western North America since Precambrian time and, with its counter parts in the island arcs of the Caribbean region and the Andean chain in South America, it ranks as one of the great revolutions. In North America it has long been known as the **Laramide Revolution,** so named for the Laramie Range, which forms the mountain front in Wyoming.

Nature and Extent of the Orogeny. Although the region has since suffered much erosion and was strongly uplifted in late Cenozoic time, the dominant structures in the Rocky Mountains were produced during the Laramide orogeny and are still clearly shown.

A belt of enormous thrust faults (Fig. 274) can be traced along the mountain front in Alberta and southward across Montana, eastern Idaho, and western Wyoming into north-central Utah, and then southwestward across eastern Nevada. In this belt great thrust plates were driven eastward, in places carrying Precambrian rocks up over the Cretaceous. Glacier National Park in extreme northwestern Montana, for example, is formed of a great thick plate of Beltian formations driven eastward at least 15 miles on the Lewis thrust to ride out over the Cretaceous formations of the Plains. This fault has been traced for some 50 miles along the mountain front and may be continuous with the fault west of Great Falls, a hundred miles farther south. The east front of the Absaroka Range east of Yellowstone Park in Wyoming is likewise defined by the Heart Mountain thrust which is traceable for 125 miles and on which eastward displacement has amounted to 28 miles. Along the Idaho-Wyoming border and extending southward beyond Salt Lake City, Utah, a series of roughly parallel faults have been mapped, the most important being the Bannock thrust which has been traced for 250 miles and has an eastward displacement up to 35 miles, carrying Cambrian and Ordovician formations up over Triassic. Such large-scale faulting clearly indicates strong compression from the west.

In central and eastern Wyoming and central and western Colorado the dominant structures are broad open arches. The Front Range of Colorado (Fig. 275) and its northward extension, the Laramie Range in Wyoming, is a great arch from 15 to 30 miles wide and more than 200 miles long in which the Precambrian granite floor now rises to a height of 11,000 feet and the eroded Cretaceous and older formations dip off its flanks in bold hogbacks. It is paralleled on the west by similar great arches forming the Park and the Sawatch ranges of Colorado and is separated from these by an equally large synclinal trough now occupied by North, Middle, and South Parks. The tops of these great arches were completely reduced by erosion during the next era, but the Precambrian floor, still deeply buried under the Parks and under the Plains in front of the mountains, shows a differential uplift of the great arches by at least 3 miles. Still farther east, rising like islands out of the plains are the isolated arches that form the Bighorns and the Black Hills (Fig. 305, p. 362).

Thus, in Wyoming and Colorado, the structure changes progressively from immense thrust faults in the west to open arches bounded by thrusts along their eastern flanks (Park Range), to open arches in which faulting is relatively unimportant (Front Range), and finally to isolated domes far out in the Plains. Farther south, however, the region of the present Colorado Plateau stood as a rigid block with only a few simple flexures (e.g., Waterpocket Fold) while great thrusts piled up along its western side in Nevada, and large arches formed on the east of it. In Montana, on the contrary, the thick Beltian Series seems to have formed a rigid plate that was thrust eastward with relatively slight folding, while to the west of it the intrusion of the Idaho bathylith produced a broad and lofty mountain mass.

West of the belt of thrust faulting, the Cretaceous structures are now largely obscured by the Cenozoic cover in the Great Basin and by the lavas of the Columbia Plateau. Along the Pacific Coast where Cretaceous formations are again extensively exposed they are not appreciably more deformed than the overlying Eocene formations; hence it may be inferred that movements here were no more than regional upwarping. The focus of disturbance was clearly along the Mesocordilleran geanticline.

Volcanism. Volcanoes were active intermittently on the old Mesocordilleran Geanticline throughout the Cretaceous, and toward the end of the period they spread farther east over the rising area. There is much volcanic agglomerate in some of the uppermost Cretaceous beds near Denver which must have come from volcanoes in Colorado. In fact, it is probable that during the Laramide Revolution every state west of the Great Plains had its active volcanoes.

During the crustal movements several enormous granitic bathyliths were intruded into the rising mountains (Fig. 276). Of these, the Sierra Nevada bathylith is about 400 miles long and 80 miles wide; the Coast Range bathylith is approximately 1100 miles long; and the eroded summit of the Idaho bathylith is now exposed over an area of some 16,000 square miles.

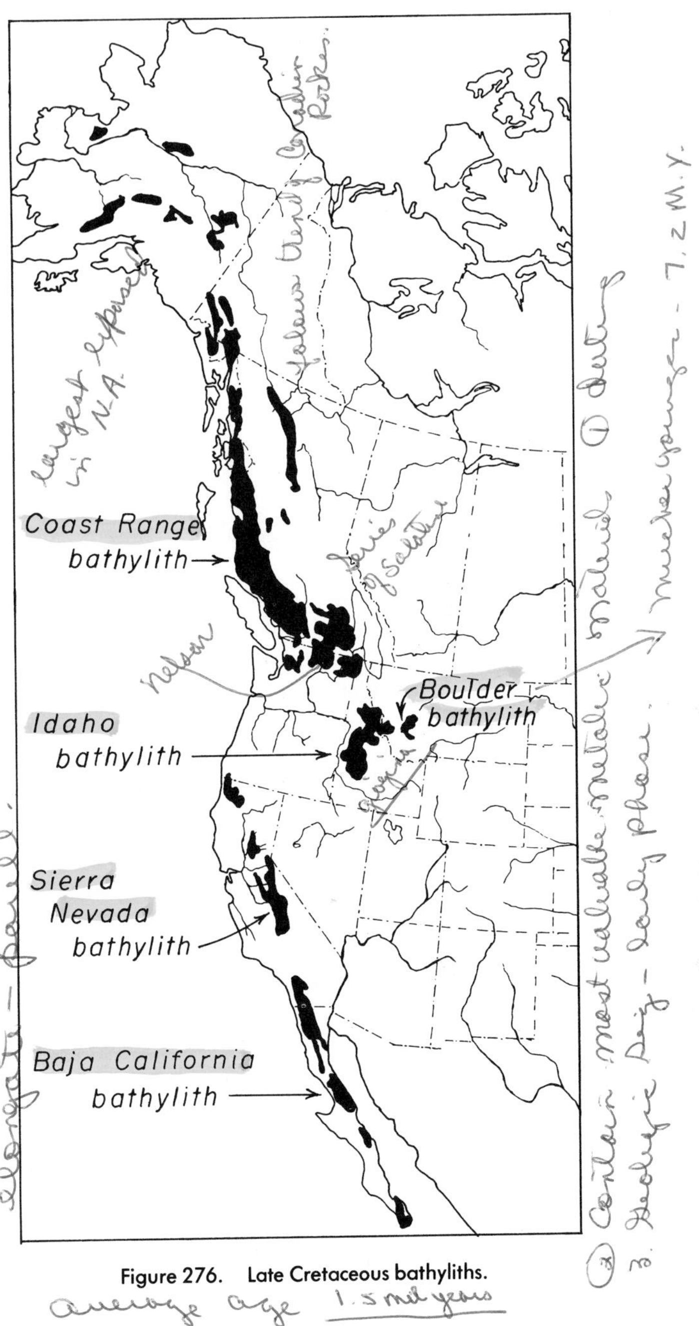

Figure 276. Late Cretaceous bathyliths.

Each of these is a complex of many intrusions of somewhat varied lithology, suggesting that in each of the areas shown in Figure 276 injections of magma followed one another during a considerable span of time. In most places the granite is intrusive into Jurassic or older rocks and is not in contact with younger Mesozoic formations. As a result, the geologic date of intrusion was not easily determined and, until recently, the Sierra Nevada and Coast Range bathyliths have been judged (on rather indirect evidence) to be probably of late Jurassic age. In 1958, however, absolute dates, based on radioactive minerals in the granites, were reported from 82 localities indicating that all the great bathyliths shown in Figure 276, except the Boulder bathylith, were emplaced shortly after the middle of the Cretaceous Period.[5] Of these dates, 10 are from Baja California, 25 are from the Coast Range in Southern California, 15 are from the Sierra Nevada, 16 from the Coast Ranges of British Columbia, and 16 from the Idaho bathylith. The dates all fall within the range of 106 ± 12 million years. At two localities in Mexico, one in Baja California and one in the province of Guerrero, the granite is known to cut fossiliferous rocks of latest Middle Cretaceous (Albian) age. In view of this new data it now seems probable that most of the Mesozoic granites of western North America were intruded within a span 10 to 20 million years during the early part of the Late Cretaceous Epoch.

On the contrary, the Boulder bathylith is younger, for it is known to cut sedimentary rocks of late Coloradoan age and some that are probably of late Montanan age, and absolute dates based on radioactive minerals in the granite range from 87 to 62 million years,[4] confirming the belief that the intrusion of the bathylith occurred very late in the Cretaceous Period or possibly early in Cenozoic time.

Finally, it must be recognized that some of the Mesozoic granites may yet prove to be Jurassic.

Date of the Laramide Orogeny. It must not be supposed that a revolution so vast and complex was accomplished in a short time, even geologically speaking, or that the movements were strictly synchronous in all parts of the Cordilleran region. Although the climax of the orogeny appears to have coincided with the end of the Cretaceous Period, this was hardly a point in time but rather a phase in a great diastrophic cycle, and it came long after the uplift had begun. Meanwhile, the latest of the Cretaceous sediments were accumulating on the flanks of the rising mountains or in the intermont basins. Moreover, the movements were not all brought to rest at once.

As the stresses accumulated, the sea floor buckled and local anticlinal folds arose as islands long before the sea had vanished. Evidence for this may be seen, for example, in southeastern Wyoming, where the Mesaverde formation of late (but not latest) Cretaceous age locally includes an erosion channel some 200 feet deep filled with sandstone and conglomerate, in which some of the boulders are of formations that lie some thousands of feet lower in the section; and the Medicine Bow formation (very late Cretaceous) includes boulders of the Precambrian granite floor. These localities are almost in the center of the geosyncline; and since such coarse material could not have traveled far, it implies local uplift and deep erosion of the rising masses in the midst of the region of deposition.

In the critically studied Wasatch region to the northeast of Salt Lake City, eight stages of deformation have been recognized.[3] The first came at the close of the Jurassic or some time early in the Cretaceous and produced local highlands in western Utah. Figure 277 illustrates the evidence that repeated uplift accurred shortly to the west of the Wasatch Range in north central Utah *during* Cretaceous time. The Indianola group is a local unit including equivalents of nearly all the Upper Cretaceous formations. Just west of the Wasatch Plateau the Indianola group, with a thickness of nearly 10,000 feet, is made of non-marine piedmont gravels. These gravels are replaced within a few miles eastward by shallow marine sandstones that in turn intertongue with the marine Mancos shale. Clearly the gravels were coming from the west and their source was not far away, since they formed a piedmont slope running down to the shore. Individual tongues, or wedges of such gravel, each hundreds of feet thick, indicate distinct pulses of uplift separated by times of lower relief when the shore migrated westward. Finally, before deposition of the Price River formation, uplift had reached into the western half of the Wasatch Plateau, and some hundreds of feet of the Indianola formation were eroded away, and large valleys were cut in these deposits to be filled later by piedmont gravels of the Price River formation. This impressive hiatus is confined to the western part of the Wasatch Plateau, however, and to the east, Mancos shale continued to form without a break. Tongues of marine sand prove that the nearshore sea was shallow and that from time to time the

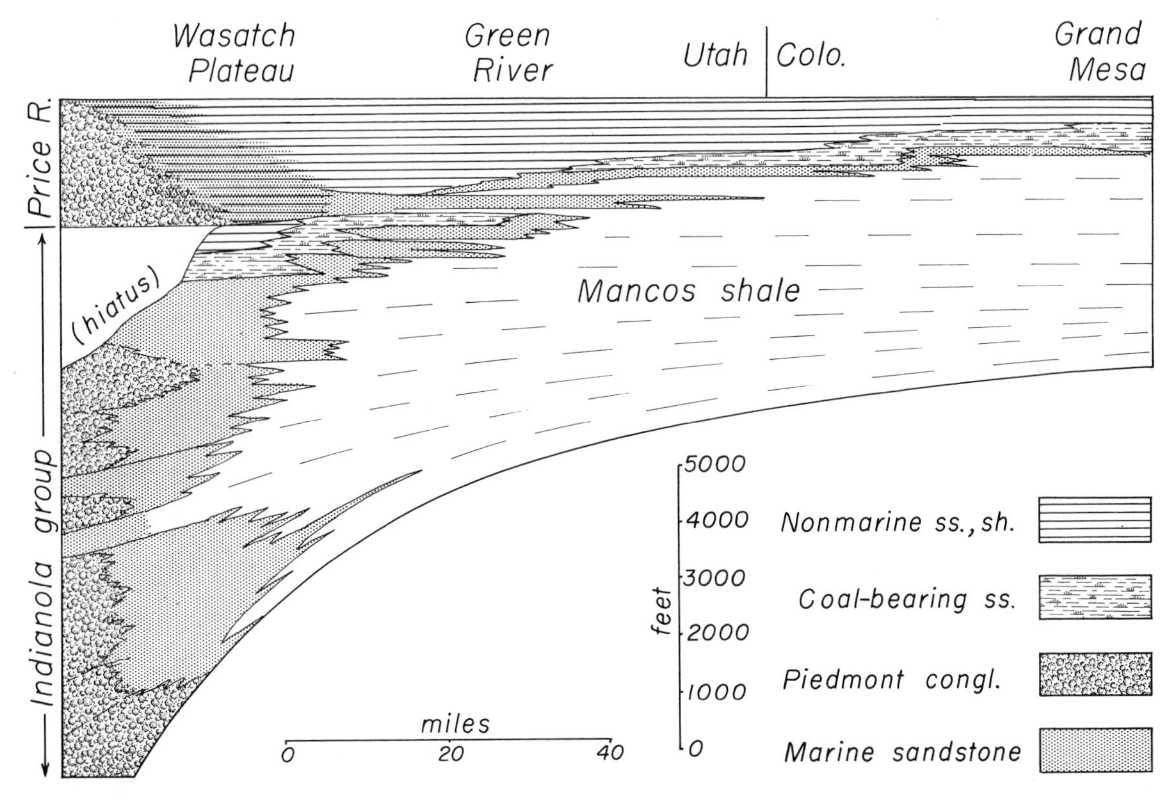

Figure 277. Restored section of the middle part of the Cretaceous System in eastern Utah and northwestern Colorado. (Adapted from Spieker, 1949.)

shoreline fluctuated back and forth. The coal-bearing sands represent swampy lowland between the piedmont and the shore. Clearly, mountains were rising near the Cretaceous shore here in north-central Utah, and the debris eroded from them eventually pushed the sea back beyond the Grand Mesa in Colorado.

The great thrusts were formed still later, and movement on them probably occurred intermittently over a considerable span of time. In some localities it is known to have continued long after the end of the Cretaceous Period, finally dying out in the Eocene Epoch or possibly in the early Oligocene. Just as the movements began earlier in some regions than in others, so also they continued longer in some of the ranges than in others. Likewise, the volcanism continued with irregularly decreasing vigor into the Cenozoic, and in many places it is not now possible, after extensive erosion, to distinguish clearly between Late Cretaceous and Early Cenozoic volcanics. The protracted nature of these orogenic movements still further complicates the difficult problem of fixing the boundary between the Mesozoic and Cenozoic rocks in the Cordilleran region.

The Boulder bathylith cuts welded volcanic tuffs that include fossil leaves identified as very young Cretaceous; and six radioactive dates based on the alpha-particle/lead ratios in the zircons of the granite range from 62,000,000 to 72,000,000 years.[4] This accords well with the date of the end of the Cretaceous. But radioactive dates for the Idaho bathylith and the bathylith of Lower California are each about 106,000,000 years,[5] indicating that injection began in these regions long before the end of the period.

Orogeny in Central and South America

During both the Paleozoic and Mesozoic there existed along the western side of South America a great Andean Geosyncline, which received thick

Chart 10. Correlation of important Cretaceous sections

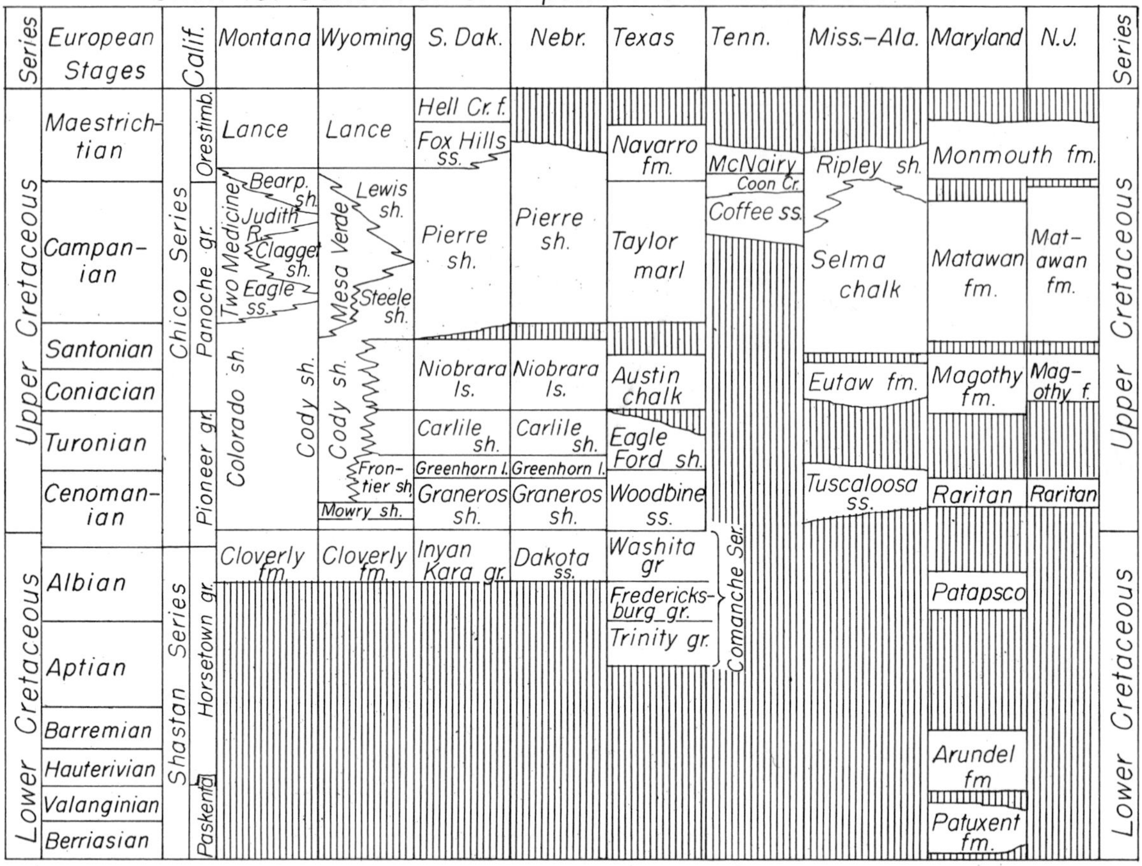

Series	European Stages	Calif.	Montana	Wyoming	S. Dak.	Nebr.	Texas	Tenn.	Miss.–Ala.	Maryland	N.J.	Series
Upper Cretaceous	Maestrichtian	Orestimb.	Lance	Lance	Hell Cr. f.; Fox Hills ss.		Navarro fm.	McNairy; Coon Cr.	Ripley sh.	Monmouth fm.	Monmouth fm.	Upper Cretaceous
	Campanian	Chico Series: Panoche gr.	Two Medicine: Bearp. sh.; Judith R.; Claggett sh.; Eagle ss.	Mesa Verde: Lewis sh.; Steele sh.	Pierre sh.	Pierre sh.	Taylor marl	Coffee ss.	Selma chalk	Matawan fm.	Matawan fm.	
	Santonian		Colorado sh.	Cody sh.								
	Coniacian			Cody sh.	Niobrara ls.	Niobrara ls.	Austin chalk		Eutaw fm.	Magothy fm.	Magothy f.	
	Turonian	Pioneer gr.			Carlile sh.	Carlile sh.	Eagle Ford sh.					
	Cenomanian			Frontier sh.; Mowry sh.	Greenhorn l.; Graneros sh.	Greenhorn l.; Graneros sh.	Woodbine ss.		Tuscaloosa ss.	Raritan	Raritan	
Lower Cretaceous	Albian	Shastan Series: Horsetown gr.	Cloverly fm.	Cloverly fm.	Inyan Kara gr.	Dakota ss.	Comanche Ser.: Washita gr; Fredericksburg gr.			Patapsco		Lower Cretaceous
	Aptian						Trinity gr.					
	Barremian											
	Hauterivian	Paskenta gr.								Arundel fm		
	Valanginian									Patuxent fm.		
	Berriasian											

sediments from a wide and repeatedly rising borderland to the west. During the last half of Cretaceous time this geosyncline was folding and rising into a great mountain chain that was completed at the end of the Mesozoic. Beginning east of Trinidad, off Venezuela, these mountains extended southwestward into Colombia and thence southward to beyond Cape Horn, a distance of nearly 5,000 miles. They were the South American counterpart of the Rocky Mountain System.

Standing athwart the course of the Rockies and the Andes is the Antillean Mountain System of Central America, also formed at this time, following the trend of the Greater Antilles.

STRATIGRAPHY OF THE CRETACEOUS ROCKS

Atlantic Coastal Plain. Cretaceous formations underlie the Atlantic Coastal Plain from New Jersey southward and form a wide belt of outcrop where not overlapped by Cenozoic beds. They are mostly sands and clays, disposed in nearly flat-lying beds that dip very gently seaward. For the most part, they are only slightly indurated, the clays being soft and the sands loose and friable, but locally the sands are solid enough to be used as building stone.

The entire system is less than 1,000 feet thick in the outcrop belt, where it thins and laps out against the land. It thickens down dip and probably reaches its full thickness some distance off shore, as shown by a well drilled in 1946 at Cape Hatteras, approximately 100 miles east of the Cretaceous outcrops, which penetrated 6,844 feet of Cretaceous deposits resting on granite at a depth of 9,878 feet. Both Lower and Upper Cretaceous formations are in the marine facies at this locality.[6]

Lower Cretaceous formations are all non-marine in outcrop, and exposures are practically limited to the Chesapeake Bay region. The shoreline was clearly farther east than the present outcrop belt. The Lower Cretaceous begins with basal sands that are coarse and gravelly, commonly arkosic, and generally cross-bedded. Sands and clays alternate and also grade laterally one into another. These features, along with the fossil land plants, crocodiles, and fragmentary dinosaur remains, indicate deposition by streams on a low coastal plain. Dark, lignite-bearing clays record local swamps, whereas brightly colored and variegated clays, such as those extensively exposed about Baltimore, were deposited on well-drained parts of the landscape.

Upper Cretaceous formations overlap and largely conceal the Lower Cretaceous south of Chesapeake Bay and form a wide belt of outcrop along the inner margin of the Coastal Plain most of the way from New Jersey to Georgia. They resemble the Lower Cretaceous formations in being detrital and relatively unconsolidated, but are for the most part marine. The higher formations include extensive deposits of "greensand marl," which is composed of sandlike granules of glauconite, a silicate mineral rich in potassium and iron. Before the discovery of rich potash salt deposits in the Permian of Germany, the New Jersey greensand was extensively quarried for the extraction of potassium used in the manufacture of fertilizer. Curiously, greensand, like chalk, is more abundant in Cretaceous rocks than in any other system, though by no means confined to them. The greatest American deposits are in New Jersey, but much glauconite occurs farther south, even in the Gulf Coastal Plain. In the Lower Cretaceous of western Europe, also, glauconite is so common that a considerable series of these strata is commonly known as "The Greensand."

Eastern Gulf Region. From Georgia to northern Mississippi and western Kentucky the Upper Cretaceous overlaps on the Paleozoic and older rocks, covering the Lower Cretaceous formations completely. Here the Upper Cretaceous attains a thickness of 2,000 feet or more (Fig. 278). Although it begins with non-marine sands (Tuscaloosa formation), it is largely a marine deposit, and in eastern Mississippi and western Alabama the upper 1,000 feet is a soft, argillaceous limestone known as the "rotten limestone" or the **Selma chalk** (Fig. 279). Eastward, in Georgia, the limestone changes into shale and sands, and to the westward the "chalk" also becomes more muddy and grades over into a thick marine shale known as the **Ripley** (Fig. 278). Still more to the west and north, tongues of sand interfinger with the shale, and the formation grades laterally into the **McNairy sandstone,** which in places bears abundant fossil land plants.

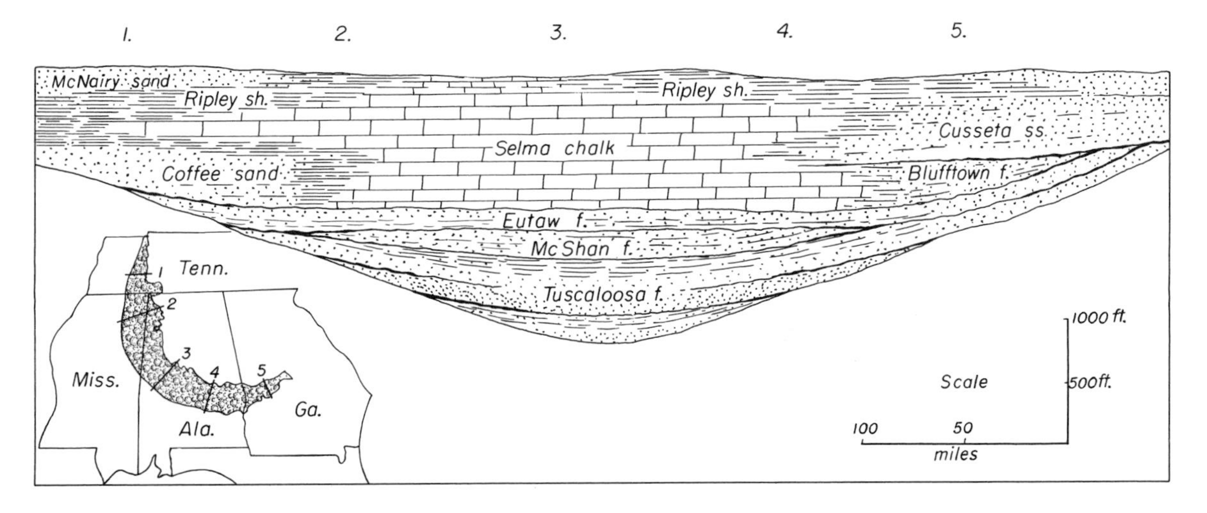

Figure 278. Section of the Upper Cretaceous formations of the eastern Gulf Coastal Plain, showing facies changes along the strike. As indicated by the inset map, the section runs nearly south from western Tennessee to east-central Mississippi, and then swings eastward into Georgia. The central part was deposited farthest from the Cretaceous shoreline and deposition began there earlier than at either end. Vertical scale greatly exaggerated. (Adapted from L. W. Stephenson.)

Figure 279. Typical exposures of the Selma Chalk, Jones Bluff, Tombigbee River, Alabama. (L. W. Stephenson, U.S. Geological Survey.)

In short, three types of sediment were forming simultaneously in the eastern Gulf region during later Cretaceous time: (1) sands and silt in western Tennessee and Kentucky (also in Arkansas), (2) silt and mud in northern Mississippi, and (3) calcareous mud farther south and east. Here is a parallel to modern conditions, wherein sand and mud are being laid down on the floor of the Gulf near the mouth of the Mississippi River, while fine mud spreads further east and limestone is forming in the clear shallow waters about Florida. The McNairy sandstone represents part of a Cretaceous delta formed by streams foreshadowing the present Mississippi River system, and, since the sands spread more and more widely as we ascend in the series, we may infer that the delta was growing southward toward the close of the period.

All of Florida now has Cenozoic strata at the surface, but deep wells indicate the presence of Upper Cretaceous formations resting on very ancient rocks. A recent deep well in western Florida (Jackson County) went through more than 4,000 feet of Upper Cretaceous strata; and another, 50 miles west of Miami, near the southern tip of Florida, penetrated 2,276 feet of Upper Cretaceous and 1,900 feet of probable Lower Cretaceous, stopping in supposed Lower Cretaceous at a depth of 10,006 feet.

Western Gulf Region. In Texas the Lower Cretaceous is largely marine and richly fossiliferous. In the Rio Grande Valley it reaches a thickness of 1,500 feet and is almost entirely calcareous, consisting in part of hard limestone and in part of weak marly limestone. Farther north it thins and passes into a complex of interbedded marls, calcareous shales, and sandstones. Here the Trinity formation, lowest of three major units, includes non-marine tongues that include important fossils plants, dinosaur skeletons, and layers bearing an amazing array of dinosaur footprints. The Upper Cretaceous begins with the Woodbine sandstone, followed by the Eagleford shale, followed by the widespread Austin chalk, and that in turn by the thick Navarro and Escondido shales.

The Cretaceous System thickens to about 4,000 feet in Mexico where it forms the high limestone plateau of the Sierra Madre Orientale, and there, as in Texas, it includes enormous reservoirs of petroleum.

The Cordilleran Region. Cretaceous formations underlie all of the Great Plains and much of the Rocky Mountain region, generally exceeding 2,000 feet in thickness in the eastern part of the area and increasing westward to the axis of the Rocky

Mountain Geosyncline where locally, in western Wyoming they reach a thickness of at least 20,000 feet. The southern embayment crossed northern Sonora and entered southeastern Arizona early in the period, and here the Lower Cretaceous is thick and almost wholly detrital. In southeastern Arizona where it constitutes the Bisbee group, the thickness is as much as 7,000 feet.

Here rapid subsidence was matched by rapid accumulation of mud and sand from the Mesocordilleran highland immediately to the west. The sea spread slowly to the north and east, reaching Colorado and Kansas late in the Early Cretaceous Epoch and then spread rapidly eastward to Iowa and northward over Wyoming. Here the **Dakota group** forms the base of the Cretaceous System. It includes the initial marine deposits of the interior seaway as well as the underlying and intertonguing non-marine deposits laid down in advance of the sea. It includes alternating sandstone and shale formations with sand predominating in the southern part (Colorado, Kansas, and Nebraska) and shale in the northern part. It contains a depauperate marine fauna now known to be largely if not entirely Lower Cretaceous. (Until recently it was considered basal Upper Cretaceous.) The Dakota sandstone, generally less than 400 feet thick, is more resistant than the underlying Jurassic formations or the overlying Cretaceous shales, and it crops out in a conspicuous hogback along the front of the Rockies in Colorado (Fig. 280) and in the rim of the Black Hills in South Dakota. Under the eastern Great Plains it is an important source of artesian water.

While the southern seaway was spreading northward, an arctic invasion spread southward to Alberta where the Kootenai group is a counterpart of the Dakota group, consisting of shallow marine units alternating with and intertonguing with non-marine formations part of which are coal-bearing. Shortly before the close of the Lower Cretaceous Epoch the northern and southern seas united in Wyoming to form a continuous strait separating the Mesocordilleran highland from the eastern part of the continent. The eastern land was a vast plain from which only fine mud was derived, whereas the western land continued to rise, supplying a vast amount of both sand and mud which from time to time formed a wide low coastal plain along the west side of the geosyncline over which non-marine formations were laid down. These thin eastward and tongue out in the marine shales that accumulated over the deeper part of the geosyncline.

The general stratigraphic relations may be illustrated by two idealized cross sections, Figures 281 and 282. Under the northern Great Plains (from

Figure 280. East flank of the Front Range near Denver, showing hogbacks of Cretaceous and older strata arched up during the Laramide Revolution. An aerial view looking north, from an altitude of 7,100 feet. The great hogback in the foreground is formed by the Dakota sandstone, and smaller ones to the left are formed by the Fountain sandstone of Pennsylvanian age. The mountains at the left are of Precambrian granite. Longs Peak is at the horizon just left of the center of the view. (T. S. Lovering and F. M. Van Tuyl, U.S. Geological Survey.)

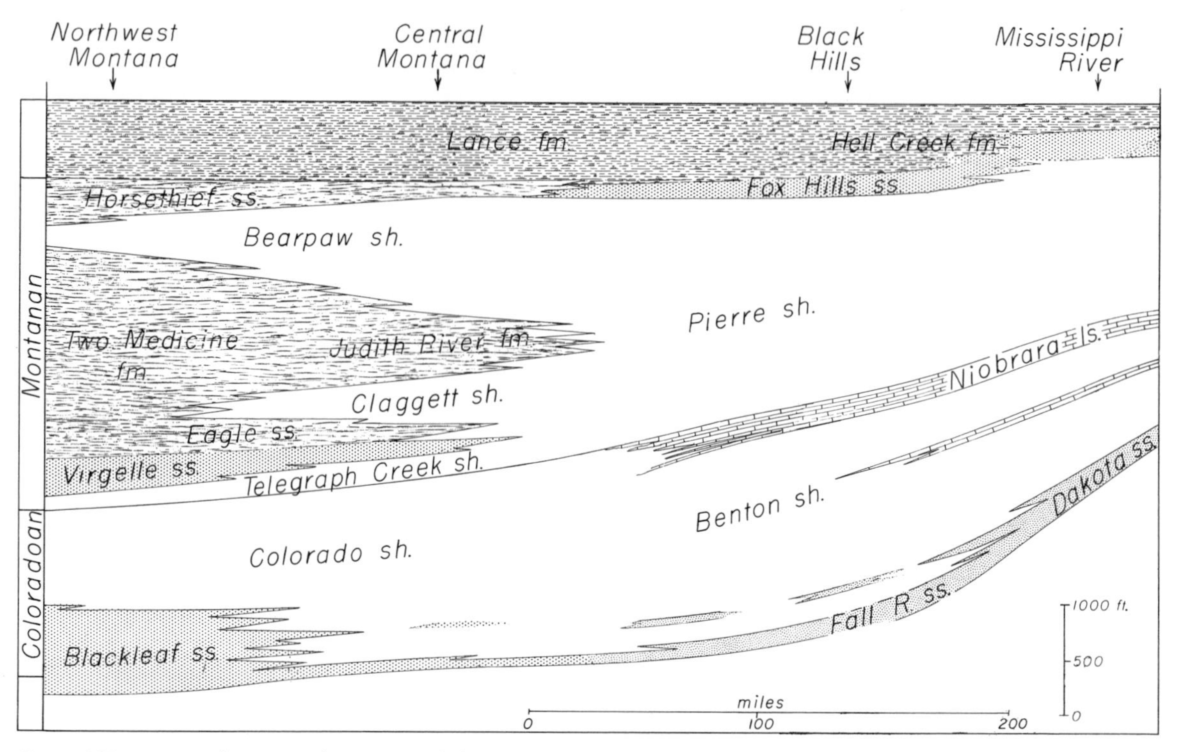

Figure 281. Restored stratigraphic section of the Cretaceous formations from Northwestern Montana to the Mississippi River in South Dakota.

Kansas to the Dakotas) the section is all marine except part of the Dakota group at the base and the Lance formation at the top. An important key horizon separating the Benton from the Pierre shale is the widespread Niobrara "chalk" or limestone, which has yielded such important fossils as the great marine lizards (Mosasaurs), the greatest of all pterosaurs, and the toothed birds (*Hesperornis*) described on later pages. Toward the west it becomes shaly and finally is entirely replaced by shale in Wyoming.

Along the west side of the geosyncline non-marine formations predominate, tonguing out eastward into the marine section. The Two Medicine formation of extreme northwestern Montana, for example, consists of interbedded sandstone and shale with beds of coal at many levels, and it includes fossil land plants and dinosaurs. The bedding is irregular, and the sands are rather poorly sorted and commonly cross-bedded, indicating deposition by sluggish streams flowing eastward across a broad low coastal plain. The coal beds, of course, record swamps. Having a thickness of more than 2,000 feet this formation records a long period of slow subsidence when rapid deposition held back the sea.

Eastward the Two Medicine formation divides into two great tongues of similar lithology separated by the Claggett tongue of the Pierre shale and overlain by the Bearpaw tongue. The Eagle and Judith River formations represent times when the sea was pushed far to the east as a wide coastal plain or a great delta was built out in front of the Mesocordilleran highlands. The Claggett and Bearpaw formations, on the contrary, record times when building did not keep pace with subsidence and the sea spread far to the west.

The Horsethief formation records another period of expanding coastal plain and its non-marine deposits intertongue with and grade eastward into the Fox Hills sandstone, which is a shallow marine deposit.

The Laramie group includes the non-marine deposit spread widely across the geosyncline by aggrading streams during the closing scene of the Cretaceous Period. It is locally coal-bearing, includes abundant plant fossils, and bears the last of the dinosaurs, among them the ceratopsians and the great *Tyrannosaurus* (Fig. 285). In local basins in Wyoming the Laramie group attains a thickness of several thousands of feet, but it thins to a few hundreds of feet in the northern Great Plains where it is known as the Lance formation.

The Cretaceous record in the southern part of the Rocky Mountain Geosyncline (Fig. 282) is essentially similar to that sketched above, though different formational names are in use. The Mesaverde formation of New Mexico and Colorado is a counterpart of the Two Medicine formation farther north, though not strictly synchronous with the latter. Indeed, in the Black Mesa Plateau of northeastern Arizona, non-marine deposition was taking place while the Benton shale and the Niobrara chalk were forming farther east, and in the Black Mesa coal fields beds of Mesaverde facies are older than the typical Mesaverde formation of Colorado. Here the Fruitland and the Kirtland formations are local members of the Laramie group and bear fossil plants and dinosaurs.

California and British Columbia. As parts of California and western British Columbia subsided after the Nevadian disturbance, detrital sediments from the mountains poured westward into the basins and accumulated rapidly to form deposits of sandstone, siltstone, and shale whose aggregate thickness may exceed 50,000 feet. Such deposits in the Great Valley of California alone have been estimated at more than 13,000 cubic miles. Fossils are generally rather sparse in the Lower Cretaceous of California, and the deposits are partly of brackish or fresh water and locally bear coal; but marine fossils are scattered through the section and five distinct faunal zones prove that all the major divisions of the Lower Cretaceous are represented. The Lower Cretaceous forma-

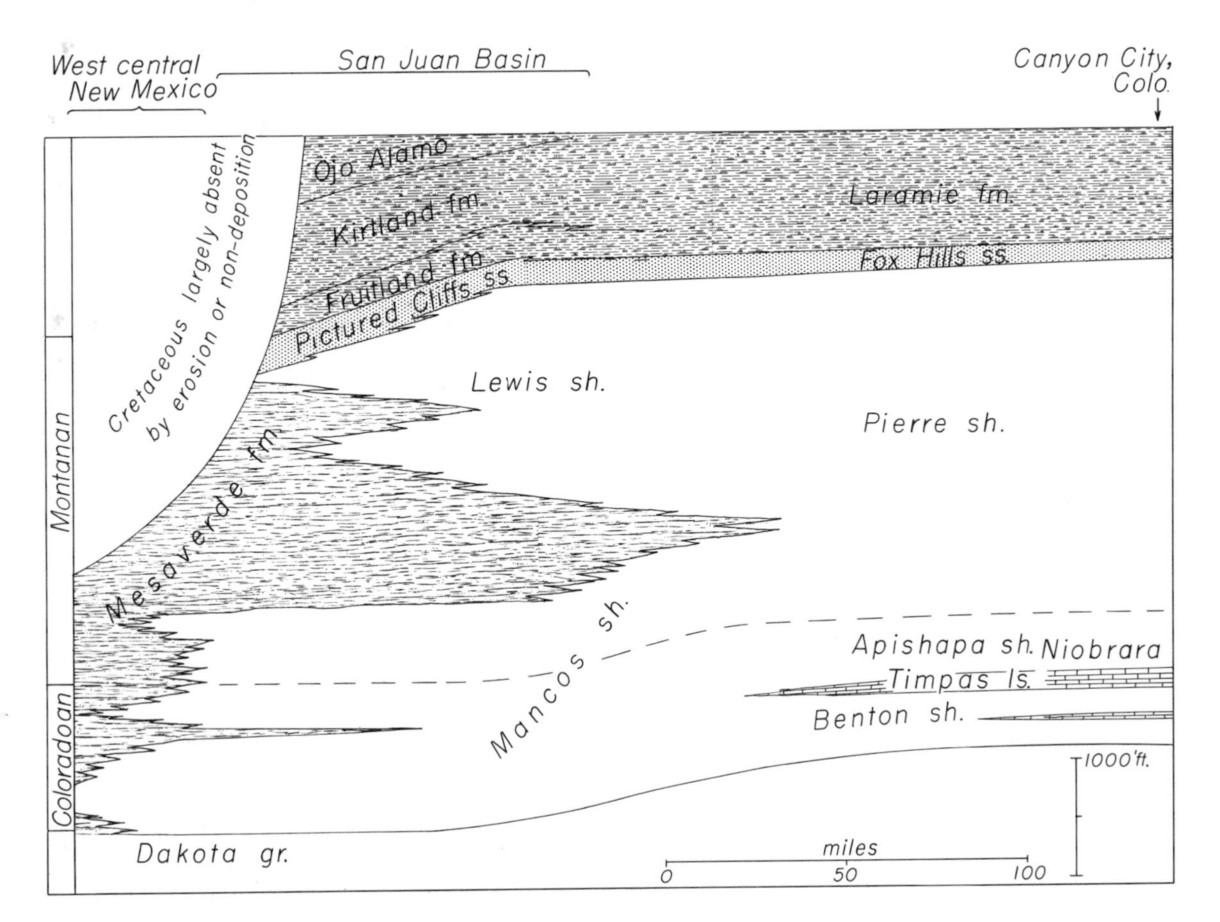

Figure 282. Restored stratigraphic section of the Cretaceous formations from west-central New Mexico to central Colorado.

tions, comprising the **Horsetown Series,** are best developed along the west side of the Sacramento Valley in northern California. The Upper Cretaceous formation, embraced in the **Chico Series,** are more widespread, resting on the Horsetown Series west of the Sacramento Valley but overlapping them and extending far to the south along the west side of the San Joaquin Valley and into the Peninsula of Lower California.

The Cretaceous rocks of California have been variably deformed by the late Cenozoic orogeny in the Coast Ranges, but it is noteworthy that they were not greatly disturbed at the end of the Mesozoic Era while great deformation was taking place in the Rocky Mountain region farther east.

Equivalents of the Chico Series are thick and coarse along the coastal belt of British Columbia from Vancouver Island to Alaska, measuring some 5,000 feet thick in Vancouver Island and 11,000 feet in Queen Charlotte Islands where they include much volcanic material.

CLIMATE

The temperature seems to have fallen somewhat after the Nevadian disturbance, for reef corals were more restricted in the Early Cretaceous than they had been in the Jurassic. Moreover, in the middle part of the Early Cretaceous (Aptian time) the highland plateau of eastern Australia appears to have been ice-capped, with glaciers flowing westward into the sea. In any event, icebergs dropped into the interior sea well-striated stones in sizes ranging up to 6 feet across, and these erratics are known through some 600 miles of outcrops.[8]

With the greater spread of the seas early in Late Cretaceous time, the climate gradually became mild and equable over most of the land surface of the Earth, especially during the latter part of the period. Upper Cretaceous rocks preserve, even in high latitudes, abundant remains of land plants belonging to genera now restricted to warm-temperate or subtropical regions. In central-western Greenland, for example, the Cretaceous beds contain figs, breadfruits, cinnamons, laurels, and tree ferns, and in Alaska they have yielded cycads, palms, and figs. Although most of these are commonly thought of as strictly tropical trees, each of the genera has representatives in the temperate zone, and it is not necessary to conclude, as some have done, that tropical climate extended into polar latitudes. Nevertheless, there is sufficient evidence for maintaining that Greenland was without an ice cap and that the climate there was then temperate rather than frigid.

The abundance of the great dinosaurs in Alberta and Mongolia during part of the Cretaceous seems to imply a very mild temperate climate at least that far north.

Conglomerates at the top of the Cretaceous and the base of the Cenozoic deposits in the San Juan Mountains of southwestern Colorado, believed for a time to be tillite, are now considered to be due to mudflows formed under normal climatic conditions.[9]

LIFE OF CRETACEOUS TIME

Spread of Modern Plants

Deciduous trees suddenly became conspicuous in the Early Cretaceous, and long before the close of the period dominated the landscape in all the continents, just as they do today. Among the oldest of these were the magnolia, fig, sassafras, and poplar, all of which appear in the middle Lower Cretaceous deposits. By the middle of the period the forests were essentially modern, including such trees as beeches, birches, maples, oaks, walnuts, planes, tulip trees, sweet gums, breadfruit, and ebony, along with shrubs like the laurel, ivy, hazelnut, and holly (Fig. 283).

With these, of course, there were evergreens, just as now, but they no longer dominated the landscapes as they had done during the earlier Mesozoic. Among the conifers a conspicuous type was the sequoia; although none is known so large as the modern giants of California, it is interesting to note that the race was widely distributed over the northern hemisphere at this time.

As in the Jurassic Period the cycadeoids were the most distinctive plants of the upland slopes and their short stocky trunks are preserved in abundance and extraordinary perfection in the lower part of the Dakota sandstone group (Lakota sandstone) in the Black Hills region, and in the Upper Cretaceous (Mesa Verde sandstone) in the San Juan Basin of Colorado. In both regions the woody tissue has been replaced by quartz, yet all the details of woody structure are faithfully preserved (Fig. 284).

Most deciduous trees belong to the **angiosperms**, the highest order of the plant kingdom and the one that includes all the true flowering plants. Besides the hardwood trees mentioned above, this order includes the grasses and cereals as well as the seed- and fruit-bearing shrubs, annuals, and our common vegetables. The strong deployment of this group of plants in the Cretaceous was one of the

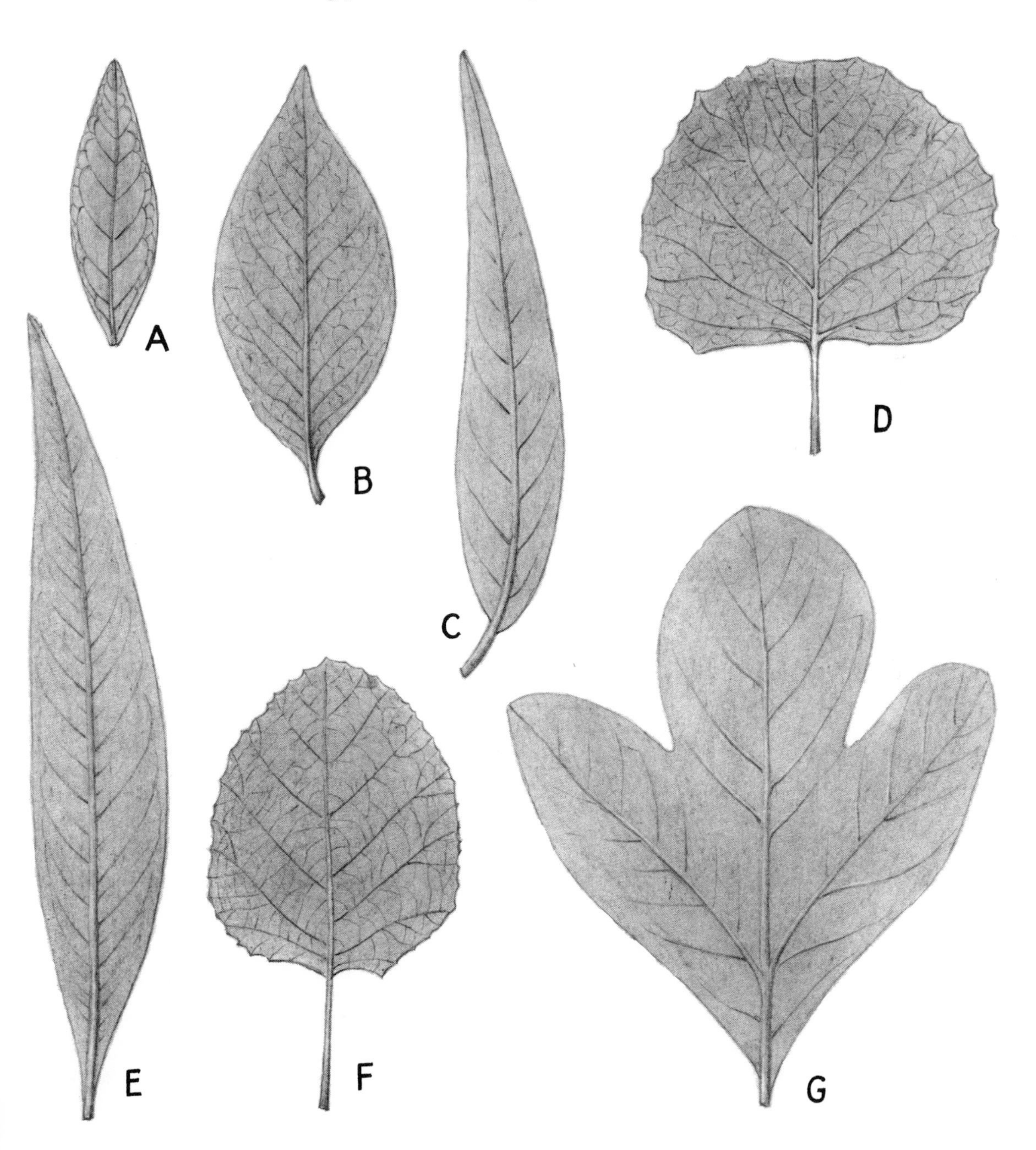

Figure 283. Cretaceous plants. Leaves of deciduous trees. *A, Andromeda*, a relative of the rhododendron; *B, Magnolia*; *C, Salix*, a willow; *D, Populites*, a poplar; *E, Ficus*, a fig; *F, Betula*, a birch; *G, Sassafras*. (After E. W. Berry and L. F. Ward.)

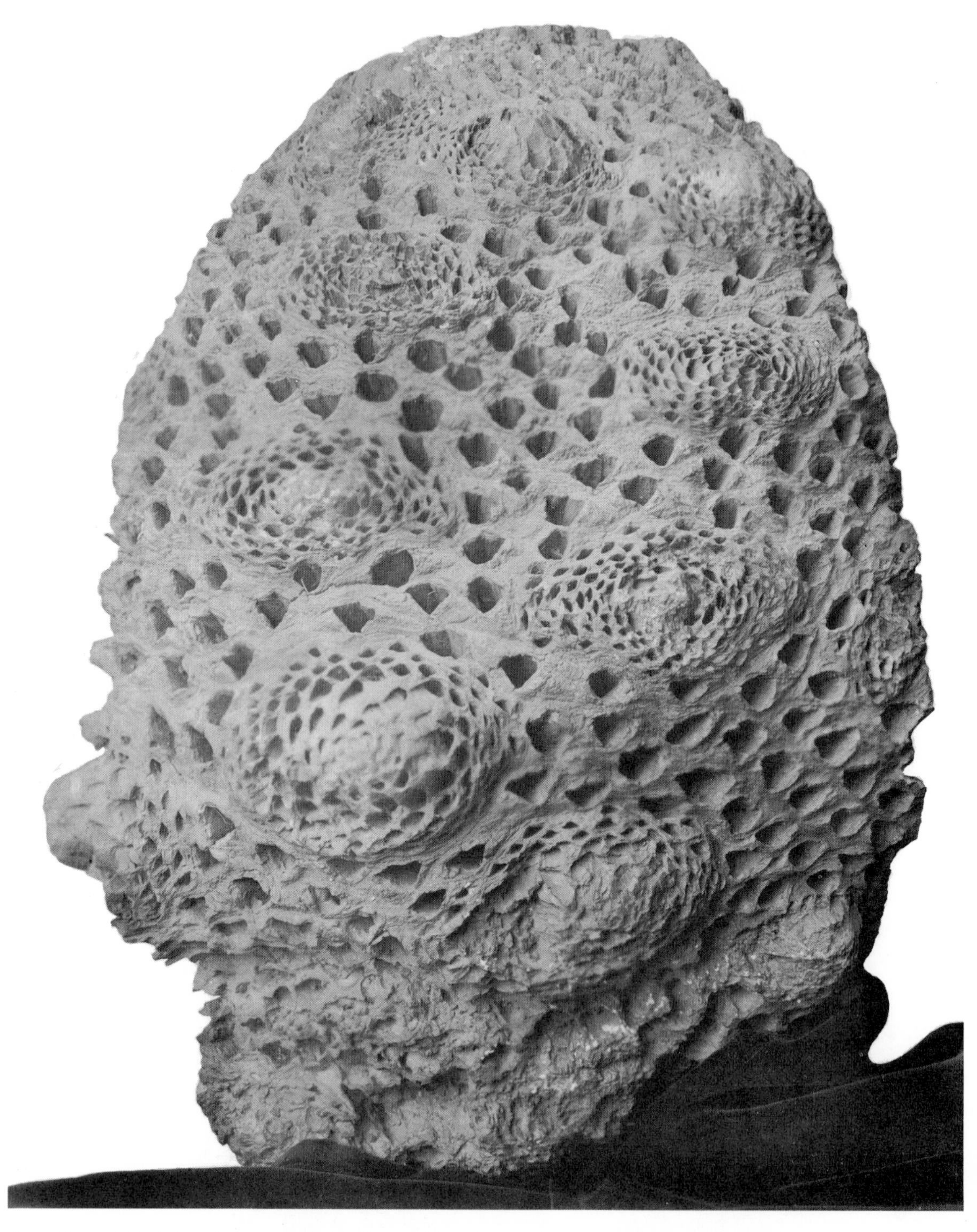

Figure 284. Silicified trunk of a cycadeoid, *Cycadeoidea*, from the Dakota sandstone in the rim of the Black Hills, South Dakota. The nodes are areas where flower buds were about to appear and the deep pits were formed by the shedding of old leaves. See Figure 262 for a restoration of the living plant, and Figure 243 for a modern cycad. (G. R. Wieland, Yale Peabody Museum.)

Figure 285. Late Cretaceous landscape in Wyoming, with dinosaurs amid flowering plants. Part of a great mural by Rudolph F. Zallinger. Animals: 1, *Tyrannosaurus rex*; 2, *Trachydon*; 3, *Triceratops*; 4, *Struthiomimus*; 5, *Ankylosaurus*; 6, *Pteranodon*. Plants: 7, sedges; 8, a conifer; 9, *Ginkgo*; 10, a palm; 11, willow; 12, live-oak; 13, dogwood; 14, sassafras; 15, laurel; 16, *Magnolia*. (Yale Peabody Museum.)

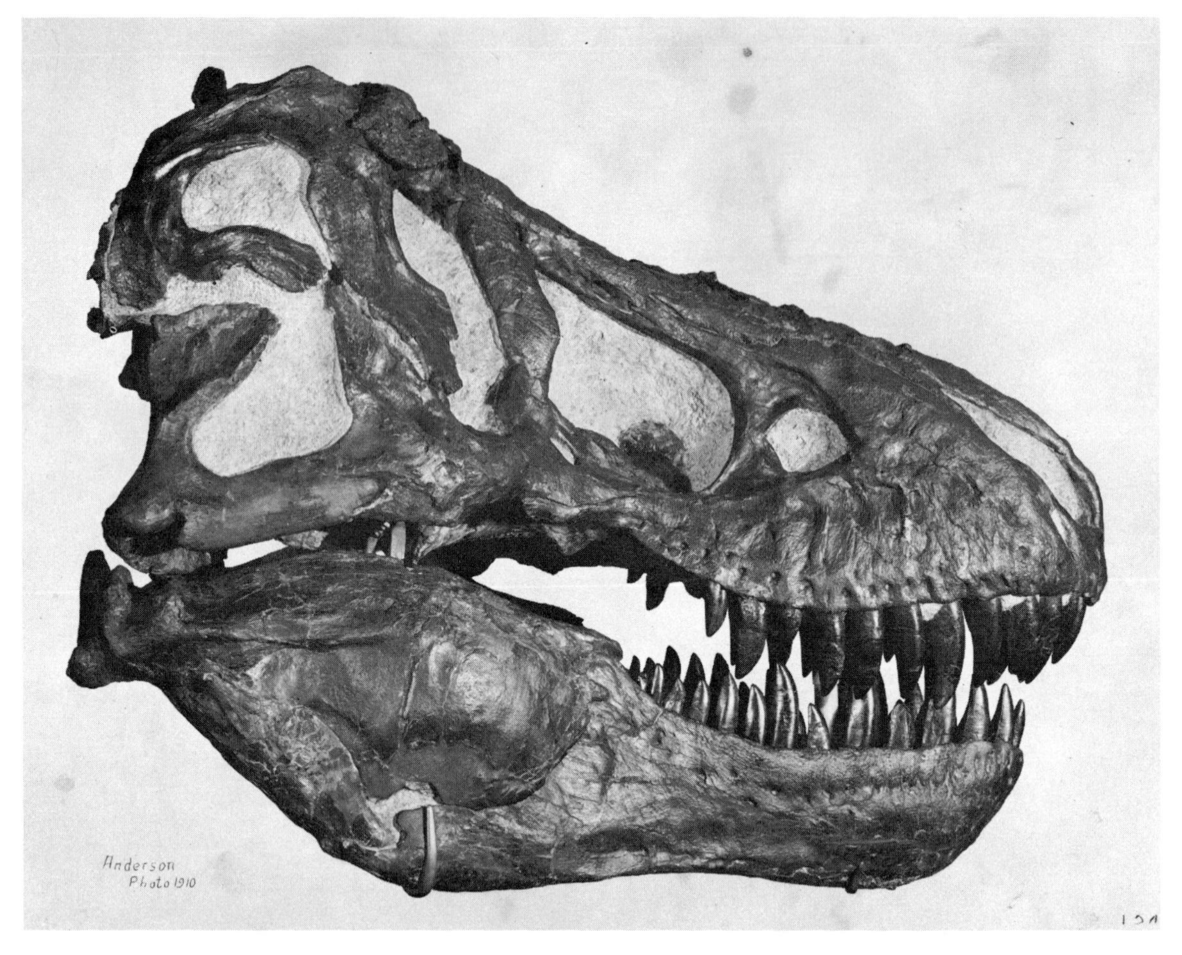

Figure 286. Skull of *Tyrannosaurus rex*, greatest of all known carnivorous dinosaurs. Length of skull, 4 feet 3 inches. (American Museum of Natural History.)

most significant advances in the whole evolution of plant life, second only to the spread of plants over the lands. On their own account, this was an important milestone in the history of life, for the angiosperms are the most highly specialized of all plants and the ones destined to dominate the Earth during later geologic time. In addition, their indirect effect upon the advances of the higher animals can hardly be exaggerated, for they supply nearly all the plant food for the mammals that now dominate all other life upon the Earth. Angiosperms provide the nuts and fruits of the forest, the grasses of the prairies, the cereals which furnish fodder and grain for man and his domestic animals, and all the vegetables and fruits that man has cultivated, to say nothing of the flowers that add so much pleasure and inspiration to human surroundings. It would hardly be too much to say that the great expansion of the mammals and the birds had to wait upon the evolution of the flowering plants; it was certainly no accident that in the next period the reptilian hordes gave way to a spectacular rise of warmblooded vertebrates.

The angiosperms appear in some abundance almost simultaneously in New Zealand, in Texas, and in the coastal plain of Maryland. Of these the best-known occurrence was described from the Paluxy sand of the basal Cretaceous Trinity group in Erath County, central Texas.[10] Three types of deciduous tree leaves were found, one of which is a species of cinnamon. From middle Lower Cretaceous rocks angiosperms are known in Portugal and Maryland. The oldest Cretaceous formation of the Atlantic Coastal Plain (Patuxent) has yielded none of these modern plants, though it has plenty of evergreens like the Jurassic floras. In the middle member (Arundel) of the Lower Cretaceous of Maryland, however, several species of deciduous trees are represented. Before the middle of the period they had spread over the Rocky Mountain region, and they comprise more than 90 percent of the known plants of the Upper Cretaceous.

The resting stage represented by the ripening of the seeds and the shedding of the foliage of angiosperms is clearly an adaptation to seasonal and rigorous climates, either of winter cold or of drought. Probably the evolution of these plants out of the older types took place on the highlands where the climate was cool and the growth was seasonal, but, if so, it was not until they had migrated into the lowlands where sedimentary deposits were forming that they left a record of their existence. It is quite possible, therefore, that they were actually present on the uplands in some abundance during Jurassic and even Triassic time. The recent discovery of a Triassic palm was noted on an earlier page.

Culimination of the Reptilian Dynasty

Dinosaurs held the center of the stage until the curtain dropped on the last scene of the Mesozoic drama (Fig. 285). The great sauropods persisted locally and are known from the Lower Cretaceous in Wyoming and from the Upper Cretaceous in New Mexico, Utah, and Texas. Fragmentary remains have been found also in the Cretaceous rocks of Maryland and of South America.

The plated dinosaur, *Stegosaurus*, was almost extinct but a specimen has been found in the Dakota group (Lakota s.s.) in the Black Hills region. Descendants of the stegosaurs appeared in the Late Cretaceous in heavily plated, short-legged forms such as *Ankylosaurus* (Fig. 285).

The carnivores (Theropoda) now reached their greatest size in *Tyrannosaurus rex*, the largest terrestrial carnivore of all time. This beast attained a length of some 45 feet and could carry its massive head 20 feet from the ground (Figs. 285 and 286).

Figure 287. Restoration of the duck-bill dinosaur *Trachydon mirabilis*, from the late Cretaceous (Lance) deposits of Converse County, Wyoming. (From a painting by Charles R. Knight, American Museum of Natural History.)

Figure 288. Portion of the tail of a herbivorous dinosaur, *Corythosaurus*, with part of the skin preserved. Late Cretaceous in Red Deer River Valley, Alberta. (C. W. Gilmore, U.S. National Museum.)

Many of the carnivores were much smaller, however, and a few such as *Ornithomimus* (Fig. 285 no. 4) had lost their teeth and had jaws rather like those of an ostrich.

The bipedal herbivores (Ornithopods) were among the commonest of late Cretaceous dinosaurs. Among the largest of these were the "duck-billed" dinosaurs (Figs. 285 and 287) some of which reached a length of 25 feet. Many of these herbivores had laterally compressed tails like that of the crocodile, and it is inferred that they may have been powerful swimmers, taking to the water when necessary to escape the large carnivores of the time. Some, at least, of the ornithopods had skins armored with small tubercles (Fig. 288).

A fifth great tribe embraced the *Ceratopsia* or horned dinosaurs. These were ponderous quadrupedal herbivores of rhinoceroslike form. Their massive skulls typically bore three stout bony horns, one on the nose and one over each eye (Fig. 285), but the earliest forms were hornless and in some of the later ones the nasal horn was much the largest.

The earliest known ceratopsians are from the Lower Cretaceous of Mongolia (Fig. 289) where many skeletons were found along with nests of unhatched eggs that had evidently been covered and preserved by drifting sand during Cretaceous time (Fig. 290). With the exception of this small primitive genus all the other known ceratopsians are from North America. Some of these from the latest Cretaceous in Wyoming were as much as 20 feet long and more than twice as bulky as a large modern rhinoceros. Pieces of some unidentified dinosaur egg shell were found in the Lance formation near Red Lodge in Montana.

Ceratopsians and duck-billed dinosaurs lived until the very end of the Cretaceous Period and are common in the Laramie group, especially in the Lance formation. Curiously, no dinosaurs were known from the Pacific Coast region until bones of a single trachydont were found near Patterson, California.

Reptiles of the Sea. Ichthyosaurs passed their heyday before the close of the Jurassic and were unimportant in the Cretaceous seas. On the other hand, the clumsy **plesiosaurs,** though less numerous than before, attained their greatest size. One species of these (*Elasmosaurus*), found well preserved in the Niobrara chalk of Kansas, reached a length of 40 to 50 feet, of which about half consisted of a very slender, agile neck. The dominant group of marine reptiles was a newly evolved tribe of marine lizards, the **mosasaurs** (Fig. 291), which made its appearance at this time. At first sight mosasaurs might be mistaken for ichthyosaurs, from which they differ, however, in four obvious characteristics. First, they had scaly skins like a snake's. Second, the lower jaw had extra joints, one at the chin and one near the middle of each side, which permitted the mouth to widen as it gaped (exactly as in a snake) so that very large animals could be swallowed. Third, the limbs were less specialized than those of ichthyosaurs, being simple five-fingered flippers. Finally, the tail lacked flukes. The mosasaurs were obviously rapacious carnivores and were probably the most ruthless pirates of the Mesozoic seas. The largest reached a length of about 35 feet. Marine **turtles** were present, and one specimen of phenomenal size (*Archelon*) has been found in the Pierre shale of South Dakota, measuring 11 feet in length and 12 feet across the flippers (Fig. 292). In the rivers both broad-nosed and narrow-snouted **crocodiles** were common.

Figure 289. The primitive ceratopsian dinosaur, *Protoceratops*, with nest of eggs. This species attained a length of only 8 to 10 feet. (Painting by Charles R. Knight, based on skeletons and nests from the Gobi Desert in Mongolia, Chicago Museum of Natural History.)

Figure 290. Dinosaur nest with broken eggs weathering from the rock. The eggs are about $4\frac{1}{2}$ inches long, and are believed to be those of *Protoceratops.* Lower Cretaceous, Gobi Desert, Mongolia. (American Museum of Natural History.)

Figure 291. A mososaur, *Clidastes*, from the Niobrara chalk in Kansas. The species was 12 to 15 feet long. (After S. W. Williston.)

Last of the Winged Dragons. Pterosaurs, though less varied and numerous than before, were large and remarkably specialized. The largest known form, *Pteranodon*, had the amazing wingspread of 23 to 25 feet, thus greatly exceeding any other winged creature of all time. Even so, the body was not larger than that of a wild goose, and with its delicate hollow bones the creature must have been almost as light and fragile as a kite. The remains of *Pteranodon* are found in the Niobrara chalk in Kansas far from the Cretaceous shoreline (Fig. 293), and it was clearly adapted to soaring over the waves like the modern albatross. In fact, this great reptile would have been quite helpless on the ground, for the hind limbs were so small and degenerate that they probably could not have borne even its light weight; everything had been sacrificed to achieve sustained flight.

Unlike the Jurassic pterosaurs, the known Cretaceous species were toothless, their horny

Figure 292. *Archelon*, the largest turtle of all time. From the Pierre shale on the South Fork of Cheyenne River about 35 miles southeast of the Black Hills in South Dakota. (Yale Peabody Museum.)

Figure 293. *Pteranodon*, the greatest of the flying reptiles. Wingspread between 23 and 25 feet. (U.S. National Museum.)

beaks displaying a remarkable parallelism with those of the post-Mesozoic birds.

Birds with Teeth

Fossil birds are still extremely rare in Cretaceous rocks. Best known is the large flightless bird, *Hesperornis regalis* (Fig. 294) of which numerous specimens have been found in the Niobrara chalk of Kansas. It was adapted, like the modern penguin, to life in the sea where it could swim and dive. Only vestiges of wings were present and its legs were articulated so as to move laterally as efficient swimming organs, but could hardly have been used for walking. Furthermore, all known specimens have been found in marine deposits far from shore. The most remarkable feature of *Hesperornis* was its long bill armed with slender conical teeth, not unlike those of the Jurassic bird, *Archeopteryx*.

Several of the modern orders of birds are now known to have existed in Cretaceous time—ancestral ducks, grebes, and pelicans—all of which were probably toothless, but their remains are still rare and fragmentary.

Mammals Bide Their Time

So long as the dinosaurs held sway and the cereals and fruits had not become common, the mammals could only bide their time, taking refuge among the rocks and crannies. Probably they were more numerous in suitable places than their fossil remains would imply, but in any event, all those known were tiny creatures scarcely larger than mice or rats.

Fragmentary remains, mostly teeth and fragments of jaws, are now known from two horizons in America, one near the top of the Lower Cretaceous in Texas, the other in the Laramie group at the top of the Upper Cretaceous in the Western Interior. The Lower Cretaceous occurrence was discovered accidentally in 1949 but the locality has since yielded about 300 specimens. Most of these are single teeth or fragments of teeth, but they are sufficient to show that the 5 orders of Mesozoic mammals known from the Jurassic rocks persisted into the Lower Cretaceous.[11]

Of these only the Multituberculates (Fig. 268, p. 313) are known from the Laramie group, and the other four apparently failed to survive to the end of the Mesozoic Era. However, two new orders made their appearance in the Laramie—the **marsupials** (pouch-bearers like the opossum) and the **insectivores** (primitive mammals of the group to which modern shrews and moles belong) (Fig. 295). Some of the late Cretaceous marsupials were remarkably similar to the modern opossum.

Modernization of the Invertebrates

By Cretaceous time the evolution of most of the invertebrate tribes had been practically accomplished, and nothing but details (genera and species)

Figure 294. *Hesperornis*, the great diving bird of the Cretaceous seas. Over-all length about 4½ feet. (Yale Peabody Museum.)

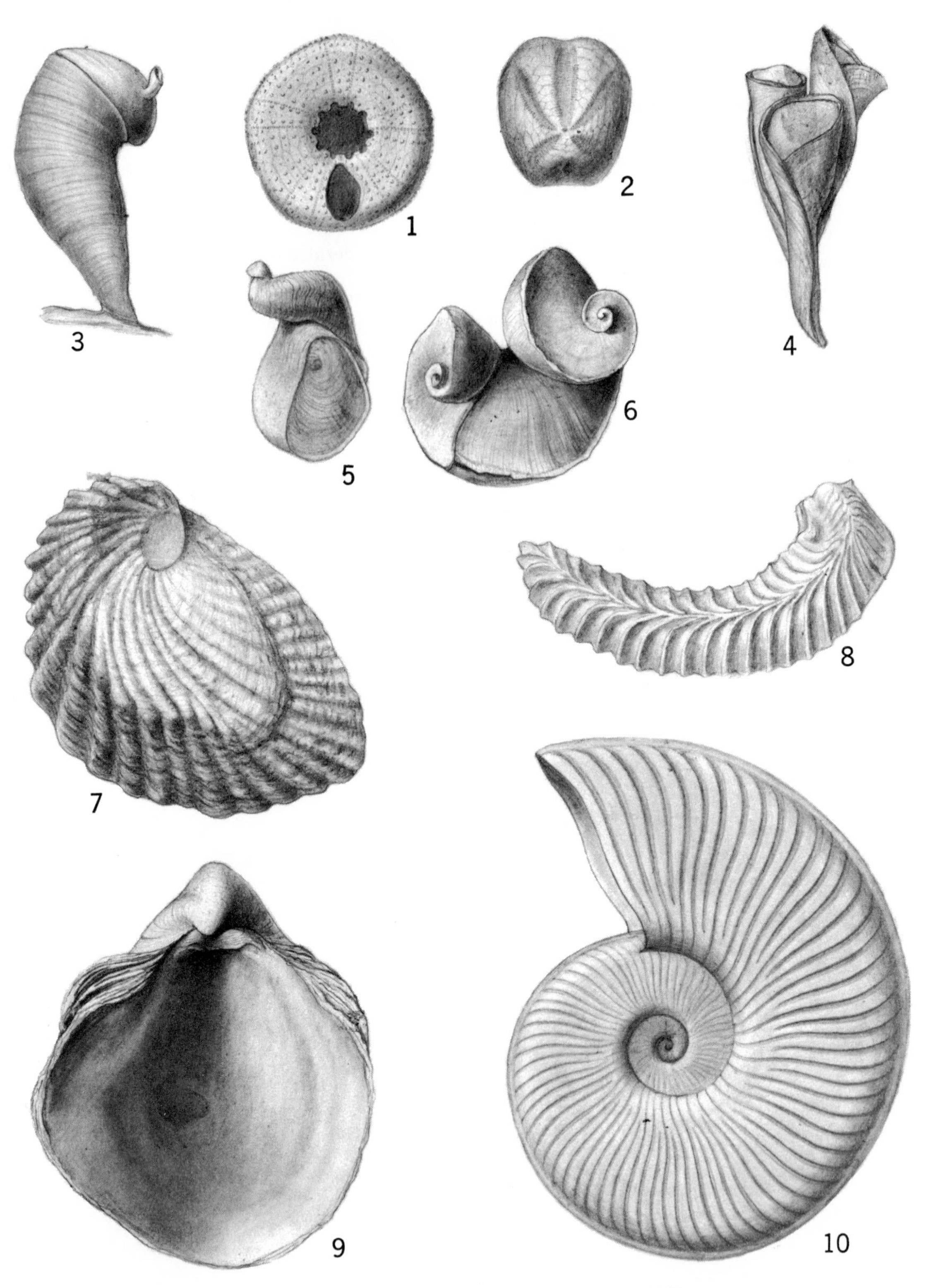

Plate 15. Lower Cretaceous Echinoids (1, 2), Clams (3–9), and Ammonite (10).

Figure 1, *Holectypus planatus;* 2, *Enallaster texanus;* 3, *Monopleura pinguiscula;* 4, *M. marcida* (a cluster of three); 5, *Exogyra arietina;* 6, *Toucasia patagiata;* 7, *Exogyra texana;* 8, *Alectryonia* cf. *A. carinata;* 9, *Gryphaea tucumcari* (inner view of larger valve); 10, *Oxytropidoceras acutocarinatum.* All natural size. (Drawn by L. S. Douglass.)

were left for the Cenozoic Era (Pl. 15–17). Only the **ammonites** and **belemnites** gave the marine faunas a medieval aspect. Both were on the decline numerically, though the ammonites still played a conspicuous role until the final ebb of the Cretaceous sea. Many species forsook their symmetrical plan of coiling, and developed bizarre shapes; some became spiral, like a snail's shell, a few straightened, many became loosely coiled, and a few lost all semblance of regularity or symmetry (Pl. 16). The significance of this extraordinary development in a decadent race is not fully understood. In any event, not a single species lived past the end of the Cretaceous.

Clams (Pl. 15, figs. 3–9; Pl. 17, figs. 4–8) and **gastropods** (Pl. 17, figs. 9–11) of many kinds and of essentially modern appearance were abundant, but there was also a remarkable development of sessile, reef-making clams (**chamids**, Pl. 15, figs. 3, 4, 6, and **rudistids**) that gave a distinctive element to many of the Cretaceous faunas. Several of these were attached by the beak of one valve. This valve then grew up into a deep conical shell while the opposite valve served as an operculum. Many of these shells resemble corals and, like the latter, they contributed actively to the reefs in the Cretaceous seas. One form in Jamaica grew 5 feet tall. **Oysters** (Pl. 15, figs. 8–9; Pl. 17, fig. 3) were very common, and two related stocks, the Exogyras and Gryphaeas, are among the most distinctive invertebrates of this time.

Brachiopods were no more common than they are today, and are abundant only locally in Cretaceous rocks. Corals were plentiful in Europe but not in America. Siliceous sponges also were important reef-makers in Europe but are seldom seen here. The **heart-urchins** are particularly common in the Comanche Series of Texas and in the Upper Cretaceous of Europe. **Crabs** were common in the sandy sublittoral zone, then as now.

Insects are not common fossils simply because suitable deposits have not been found, but it is fairly certain that all the chief modern types were already represented. Probably early in the Cretaceous the insects adapted themselves to feeding upon the nectar of the newly arisen flowering plants and thus gradually assumed their important role in pollenization. One of the most remarkable recent discoveries is a fossil wasp nest from the Upper Cretaceous of Utah.

CLOSE OF THE PERIOD: "THE TIME OF THE GREAT DYING"

The end of the Cretaceous, like the close of the Paleozoic, proved to be a great crisis in the history of life. Several stocks of animals declined markedly *during* the period; others flourished till near its end only to become extinct. For example, the dinosaurs were highly varied and apparently adaptive right up to the end of Laramie time, yet not one is known to have lived to see the dawn of the Cenozoic Era. The pterosaurs specialized perhaps too far, attaining their greatest size only to die out considerably before the close of the period. Among the great marine reptiles, the ichthyosaurs and plesiosaurs were already on a marked decline, while the mosasaurs underwent

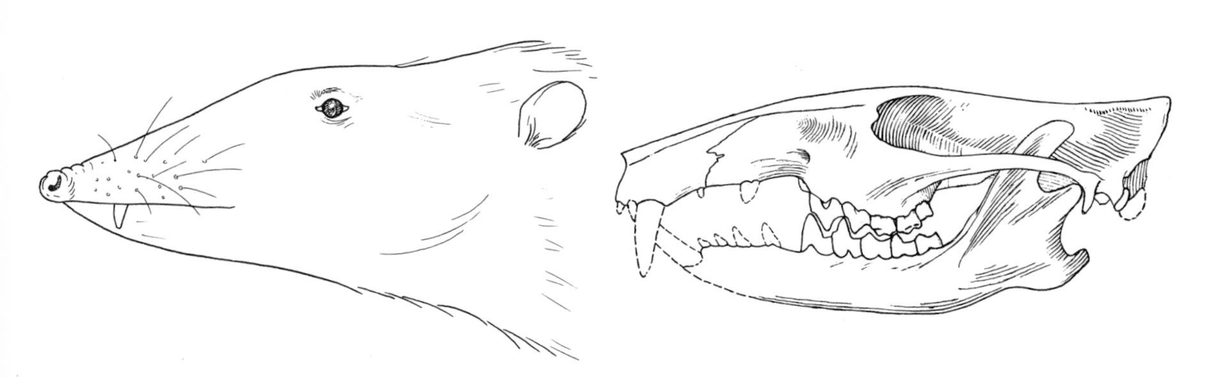

Figure 295. A Cretaceous insectivore, *Zalambdalestes*, from Mongolia. Flesh restoration (left) and composite reconstruction of the skull (right). Slightly enlarged. (After G. G. Simpson.)

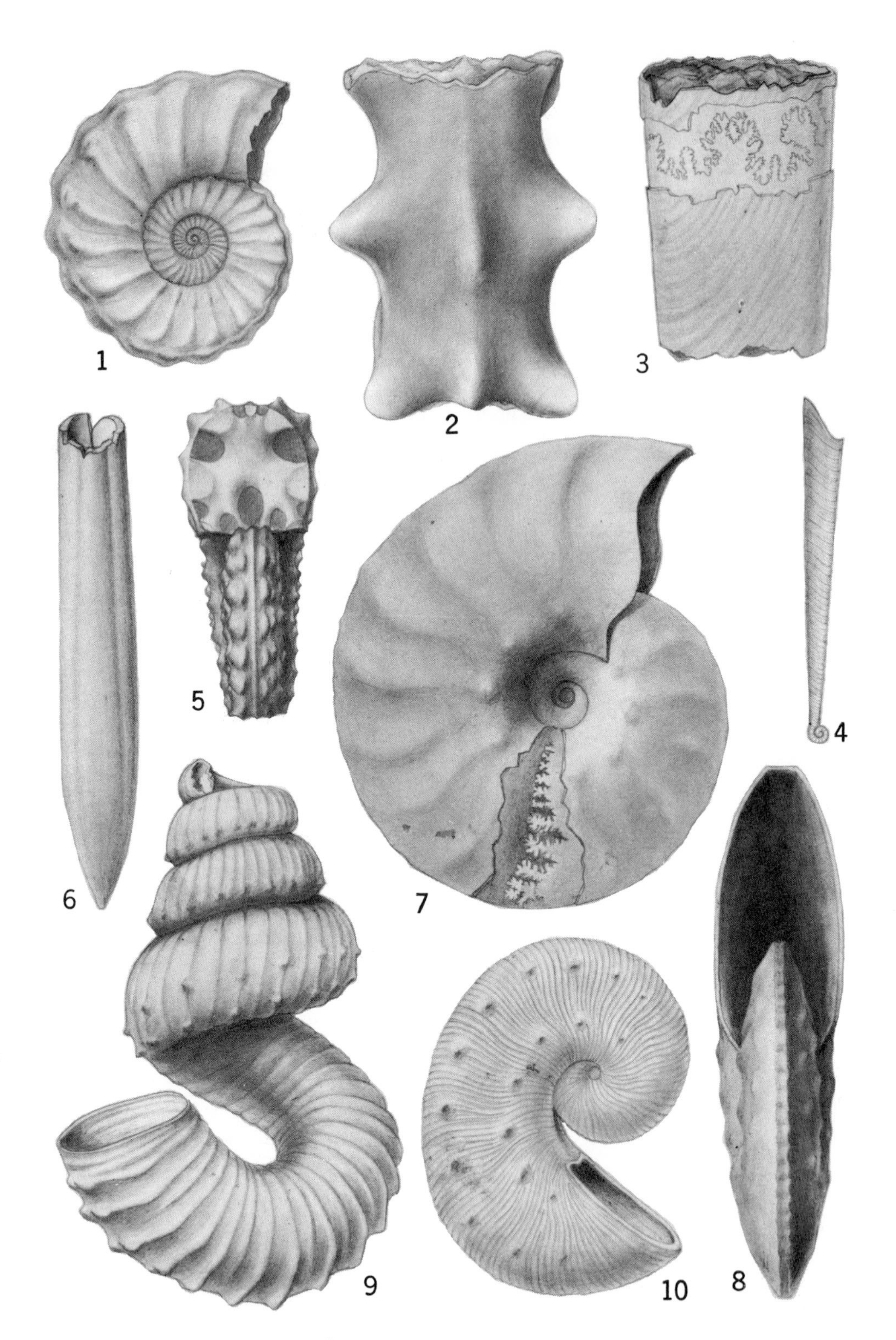

Plate 16. Upper Cretaceous Cephalopods.

Figures 1, 2, *Prionotropis woolgari* (young shell and ventral view of fragment of large shell); 3, 4, *Baculites compressus*, a straightened ammonite (a juvenile shell, × 3, showing initial coiled stage; and a section from an adult shell showing sutures); 5, *Mortoniceras texanum* (edge view of a shell with living chamber broken away revealing last septum); 6, *Belemnitella americana*, one of the last of the belemnites; 7, 8, *Placenticeras lenticulare*, lateral and edge views; 9, *Heteroceras* sp., an ammonite irregularly coiling at maturity; 10, *Scaphites nodosus*. All natural size, except Figure 3. (Drawn by L. S. Douglass.)

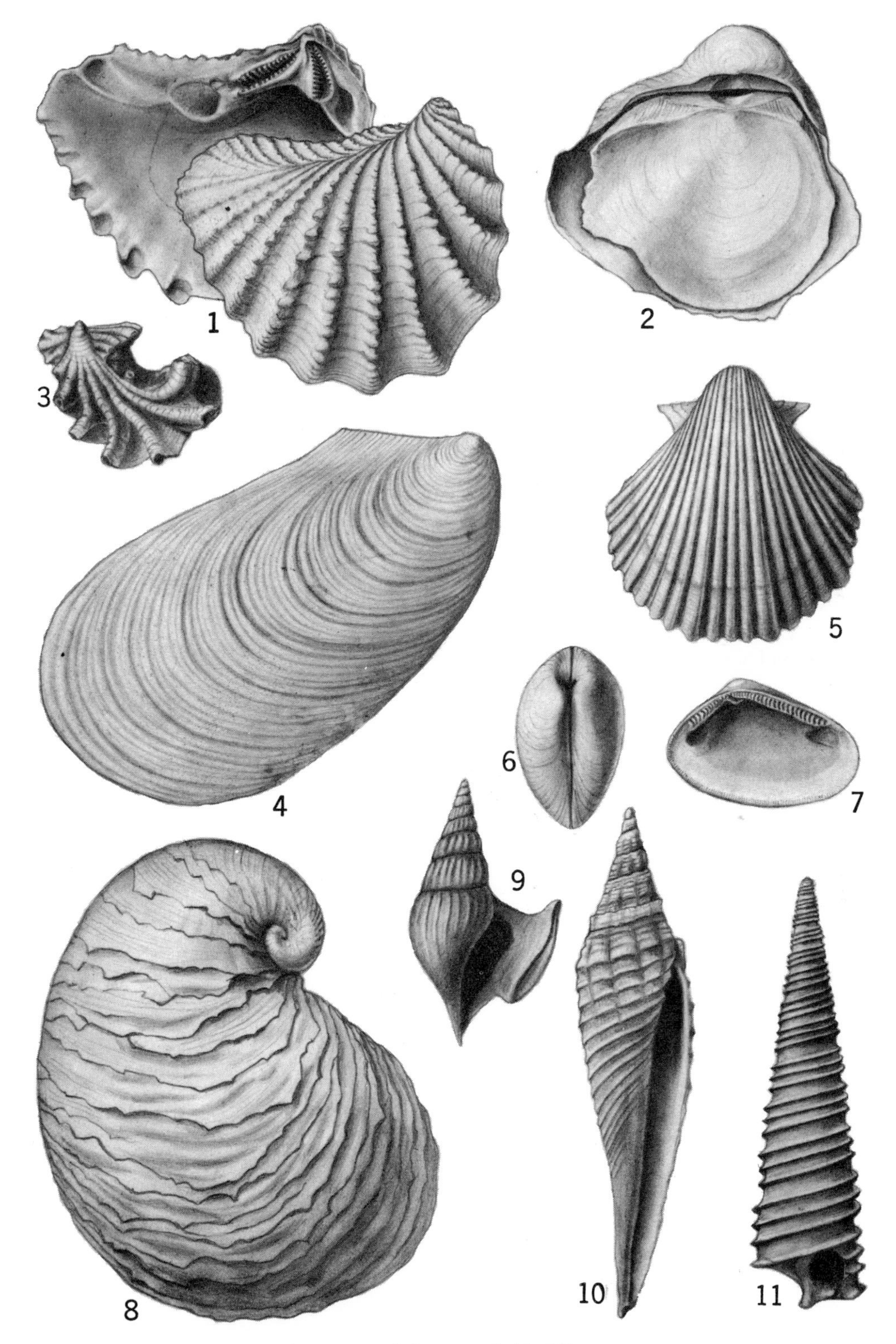

Plate 17. Upper Cretaceous Pelecypods (1–8) and Gastropods (9–11).

Figure 1, *Trigonia thoracica* (valves parted to show interior); 2, *Gryphaea convexa* (showing unequal valves); 3, *Alectryonia placenta* (a ribbed oyster); 4, *Inoceramus labiatus;* 5, *Pecten* (*Neithea*) *quinquecostata;* 6, 7, *Nucula percrassa* (dorsal view and interior of right valve); 8, *Exogyra ponderosa* ($\times \frac{1}{3}$), an oyster-like clam with spirally twisted beak; 9, *Anchura lobata;* 10, *Volutoderma appressa;* 11, *Turritella trilira.* All natural size, except Figure 8. (Drawn by L. S. Douglass.)

a meteoric evolution, yet all these died out and only the marine turtles survived. The decline and extinction of the ammonites and belemnites at the very close of the period, and the passing of the several stocks of reef-forming clams (rudistids) show that the marine invertebrates did not escape the crisis.

It is difficult to account for the simultaneous extinction of great tribes of animals so diverse in relationships and in habits of life. Perhaps no single cause was responsible. The great restriction and final disappearance of the epeiric seas at the end of the era, the rise of highlands from Alaska to Patagonia, a sharp drop in the temperature accompanying the Laramide uplift, the vanishing of the swampy lowlands, and the vastly changed plant world have all been invoked to account for the extinction, and the consequent rising of the weak and lowly into new kingdoms. Whatever the cause, the latest Mesozoic was a time of trial when many of the hosts were "tried in the balance and found wanting"—wanting in adaptiveness to the new environment. Walther has picturesquely called it "The time of the great dying."

REFERENCES

1. Karl M. Waagé, personal communications.

2. Gilluly, James, 1949, Distribution of mountain building in geologic time. *Geol. Soc. Amer., Bull.*, vol. 60, pp. 561–590.

3. Spieker, E. M., 1946, Late Mesozoic and early Cenozoic history of central Utah. *U.S. Geol. Surv., Prof. Paper 205-D*, pp. 117–161.

4. Knopf, Adolph, 1957, The boulder bathylith of Montana. *Amer. Jour. Sci.*, vol. 255, pp. 81–103.

5. Larsen, E. S. Jr., David Gottfried, Howard W. Jaffe, and C. L. Waring, 1958, Lead-alpha ages of the Mesozoic batholiths of western North America. *U.S. Geol. Surv., Bull. 1070-B*, pp. 35–62.

6. Richards, Horace G., 1947, Developments in Atlantic Coast states between New Jersey and North Carolina in 1946. *Amer. Assoc. Petroleum Geol., Bull.*, vol. 31, p. 1106–1108.

7. Waagé, Karl M., 1953, Refractory Clay Deposits of South-Central Colorada. *U.S. Geol. Surv., Bull.* 993, pp. 1–104.

8. David, Sir T. W. E., 1932, *Explanatory Notes to Accompany a New Geologic Map of Australia.* Sidney, Australia, pp. 84–85.

9. Van Houten, F. B., 1957, Appraisal of Ridgeway and Gunnison "Tillites," southwestern Colorado. *Geol. Soc. Amer., Bull.*, vol. 68, pp. 383–388.

10. Ball, O. M., 1937, A dicotyledonous florule from the Trinity group of Texas. *Jour. Geol.*, vol. 45, pp. 528–537.

11. Patterson, Bryan, 1956, Early Cretaceous mammals and the evolution of mammalian molar teeth. *Fieldiana: Geology*, vol. 13, no. 1, pp. 3–105.

PART IV

PART IV

THE MODERN WORLD UNFOLDS

Figure 296. View across Yellowstone Park. Grand Canyon of the Yellowstone River in the middle distance, and beyond it Mt. Washburn; Upper Geyser Basin and Firehole River in the nearest foreground; Rocky Mountains in the distance. (Spence Air Photos.)

Chapter 17. Physical History of the Cenozoic Era

General Features. EVERY FEATURE OF THE MODern landscape was shaped during the last short era of geologic time. The Alps and the Himalayas have come up from the sea floor; the Rocky Mountains have been worn down and then uplifted to their present height; the Appalachian ridges have been etched into relief; and the other mountain ranges of the world have been elevated and sculptured to their present form since the beginning of the Cenozoic Era. The streams also have attained the courses they now follow, and climatic zones have assumed their modern character. During this time also, the mammals evolved from unimpressive Mesozoic forebears to culminate in man. This era saw the modern world unfold!

It was a time of crustal unrest, lying between the Laramide and the Cascadian-Alpine revolutions from which we are just emerging. Movements still continue in many parts of the world where active volcanoes and violent earthquakes mark mobile zones still "alive." The climax of the disturbance is but recently past, if, indeed, we have seen its culmination, and the Earth is now in a rather exceptional stage of its history, the continents being abnormally large and emergent, the highlands probably more extensive and the mountains more lofty than normal, and the climatic zones more strongly diversified. The landscape is therefore more varied, the scenic features grander, and the Earth as a whole more interesting than it has been during much of the geologic past. For this reason the Cenozoic history will be treated at greater length than that of previous periods.

Time Units and Terminology. The first attempts to subdivide the geologic record and establish a chronology in Earth's history goes back to the year 1759 and to Giovanni Arduino, who had studied the southern Alps and the plains of Italy where he recognized four divisions of the Earth's crust, formed one after another. These were: (1) the core of the mountains formed of crystalline rocks, plutonic and metamorphic; (2) the flanks of the mountains formed of limestone and marble, commonly fossiliferous and steeply dipping or strongly folded; (3) foothills composed of gravels, sands, and marls, and including the volcanics such as those about Vesuvius; and (4) alluvial material over the surface.

Arduino called the crystalline rocks **Primary**, because they were obviously the first formed of this series; the deformed and well-indurated strata of the mountain flanks he called **Secondary**; and the unconsolidated sediments of the Italian plain he named **Tertiary**. A fourth division, **Quaternary**, was added about the year 1830 to include the glacial, fluvial, and lake deposits that cover much of western Europe and that were originally thought to be the deposits left by the Biblical flood.

Arduino's scheme of subdivision, based on the degree of metamorphism, the structure, and the degree of induration of the rocks, was natural for the region he knew. Unfortunately, it soon was applied to other parts of Europe and was used as a general scheme of classification both there and in America until after 1800. Yet obviously it could not serve as a universal scheme unless all mountain ranges were of the same date and had a similar history. We now know, as Arduino did not guess, that some mountain ranges are ancient and others relatively young, and that the granite or metamorphic core of one range cannot be assumed to be of the same date as that of another remote mountain system. As this fact was realized, about the beginning of the Nineteenth Century, Arduino's scheme of classification was abandoned and the terms Primary and Secondary were dropped, but, curiously, the term Tertiary was perpetuated and used for the preglacial formations that we now call Cenozoic, while the term Quaternary persisted for the deposits of the Pleistocene ice ages. It is still common practice to subdivide the Cenozoic rocks into Tertiary and Quaternary systems, but this is certainly no longer justifiable; the Quaternary (=Pleistocene) is merely a short epoch of the Cenozoic Era; of which there is yet but a single period. This period should have a geographic name, but unfortunately no such name has been used in this sense, and it would be premature to suggest one in this book. The words Tertiary and Quaternary are vestiges of a misconception long since outgrown, and they should be abandoned.

The Cenozoic rocks were first critically studied in the Paris basin, where richly fossiliferous marine strata alternate with non-marine formations. As the beautifully preserved faunas of these rocks were described and analyzed by the French paleontologists, notably by Deshayes, it became evident that the uppermost marine beds contained many species of shell-bearing molluscs that still live in modern seas, and that successively older groups of strata contain fewer and fewer living species. Grasping this idea, the great English geologist, Lyell, (Fig. 297) proposed a classification based on the percentage of still-living shelled invertebrates, and coined names for three **series** of the Cenozoic rocks accordingly. This scheme as eventually perfected is still in use, and may be expressed in tabular form as follows:

Name of Series	Percentage of Modern Species
Pleistocene (Gr. *pleistos*, most + *kainos*, recent)	90–100
Pliocene (Gr. *pleios*, more + *kainos*)	50–90
Miocene (Gr. *meios*, less + *kainos*)	20–40
Oligocene (Gr. *oligos*, little + *kainos*)	10–15
Eocene (Gr. *eos*, dawn + *kainos*)	1–5
Paleocene (Gr. *palaios*, ancient + *kainos*)	0

Figure 297. Sir Charles Lyell.

Lyell originally proposed only the three terms, Eocene, Miocene, and Pliocene; the others have been added later. It is now known that the exact percentage of living species in rocks of a given date varies from region to region and is not a satisfactory basis of correlation, but the six series of strata (and six epochs of Cenozoic time) are nevertheless recognized throughout the world.

CENOZOIC HISTORY OF NORTH AMERICA

At the close of Cretaceous time North America had assumed approximately its present size and configuration. The Atlantic and Gulf coastal plains were partly submerged from Paleocene to Oligocene epochs but emerged more and more completely thereafter (Fig. 298). Small embayments covered parts of California, Oregon, and Washington, and, for a very brief time at the beginning of the era, a seaway covered a small part of the northern Great Plains. The maximum submergence, however, scarcely flooded 10 percent of the present lands, and the average for the era was only about 3 percent.

The stratigraphic record therefore lies chiefly in non-marine formations which, fortunately are both widespread and richly fossiliferous. A study of land forms also adds much to our knowledge of Cenozoic history. Remnants of uplifted peneplanes, for example, tell of erosion cycles and give a measure of uplifts in both the Appalachian and Rocky Mountain regions.

The history can best be told by natural regions, taking each in its turn.

Eastern North America

Coastal Plain Overlap. From New Jersey to Mexico the outer part of the Coastal Plain is formed of Cenozoic formations. Like the Cretaceous beds, they are but slightly consolidated sands, clays, and marls, dipping gently seaward. Eocene and Miocene beds are most widespread along the Atlantic coast, especially in the Chesapeake Bay region, where both are marine and richly fossiliferous (Fig. 299). From the Carolina coast to Alabama the Eocene to Miocene deposits are mostly calcareous and very fossiliferous (Fig. 300). Paleocene and Eocene clays and sands are most widespread along the Gulf border, commonly reaching 100 to 200 miles inland, and in the Mississippi Valley extending up to Cairo, a distance of 600 miles from the coast. In the central and western Gulf Coastal Plain the Paleocene (Midway) and early Eocene (Wilcox) formations are largely non-marine and contain much lignite, showing the influence of the Mississippi River and

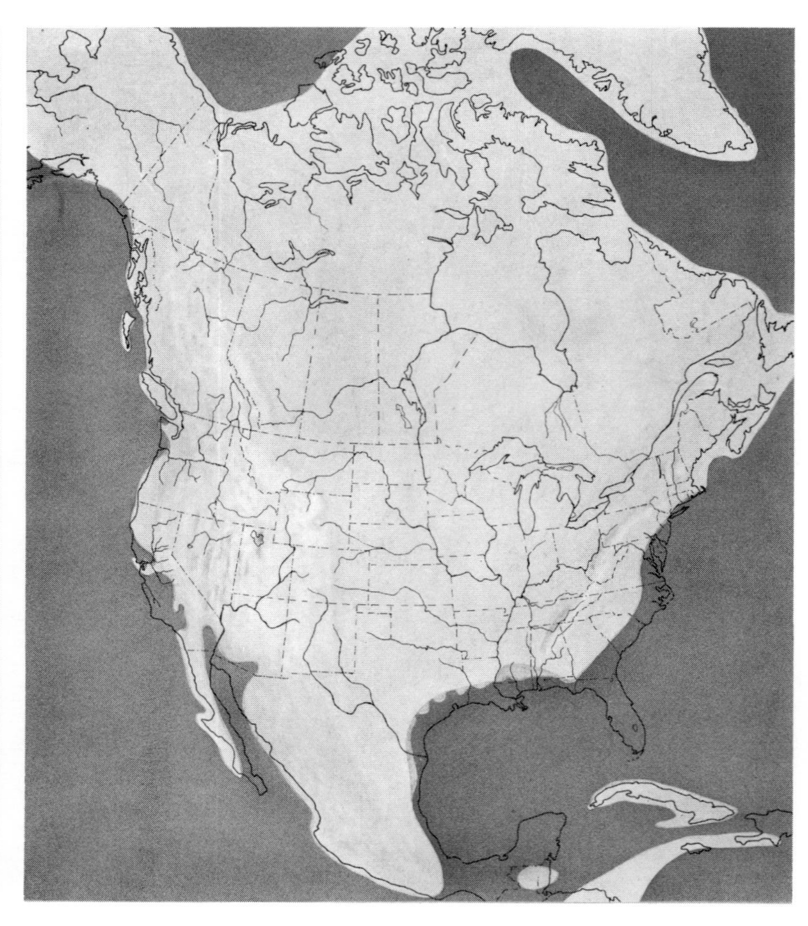

Figure 298. Cenozoic paleogeography of North America. Left, Eocene Epoch; right, Miocene Epoch.

its tributaries, which maintained a broad swampy coastal lowland here during early Cenozoic time.

Oligocene formations are in general less extensive, but in Florida and Central America they are widespread. In both these regions they are largely calcareous, but in the central and western Gulf area, where the influence of the Mississippi River was strong, the Oligocene is represented by thick clays and sands. Miocene and Pliocene formations are generally still more restricted, showing that the eastern and southern margins of the continent were progressively emerging.

Along the Atlantic border the Cenozoic formations form a great wedge, thickening seaward to beyond the present coast. From a feathered edge at their landward margin, they thicken to 700 to 1,000 feet at the coast. A deep well on the barrier beach at Cape Hatteras, however, has revealed a thickness of 3,034 feet of Cenozoic strata.[1] Not only do these formations dip seaward, but the older ones dip more steeply than the younger, proving that the continental shelf has been tilted seaward during deposition.

Along the central Gulf border rapid subsidence has been counterbalanced by the growth of the Mississippi Delta, and there Cenozoic formations reach an impressive thickness. Oil wells along the Louisiana coast are still in Miocene beds at a depth of 12,000 feet, and a study of regional dips and data from deep wells indicate a thickness of probably 30,000 feet of Cenozoic deposits under the coastal margin of Louisiana.[2] Oil wells recently driven to a depth of approximately 25,000 feet have not reached the base of the system. This is more than twice the maximum depth of the Gulf of Mexico and indicates excessive downwarping and suggests a geosyncline in the making (Fig. 301). The axis of this trough approximately parallels the present coastline of Louisiana and Mississippi.

Florida is made largely of Cenozoic limestones resting on a Cretaceous floor. These reach a maximum thickness of more than 5,000 feet and repre-

Figure 299. Calvert formation (Miocene) in the sea cliff at Kenwood Beach, Maryland. Shell beds are conspicuous in the lower part. (Carl O. Dunbar.)

Figure 300. Choptank formation (Miocene) showing abundance of fossils. Sea cliff at Calvert Beach, Maryland. (Carl O. Dunbar.)

sent all the epochs of the Cenozoic. For the most part they are clearly the deposits of a shallow sea and indicate that Florida was not a peninsula but a shallow submarine bank during most of the era. The finding of vertebrate fossils near Gainesville, however, proves that during a part of the Miocene Epoch a large, low island existed over the central part of the state.[3] A fauna of 22 species, including three-toed horses, deer, rhinoceroses, and carnivores, was found in the fill of a stream channel cut during the period of emergence. There is also reason to believe that central Florida was emergent at the close of the Eocene Epoch, and perhaps for short periods at other times in the era. Until the Miocene, Florida was too far from shore to be reached by detrital sediment, but during late Pleistocene and Recent times, long-shore currents have spread fine quartz sand southward from the coast of South Carolina and Georgia to beyond Cape Canaveral. This veneer of clean sand, overlying the limestone platform is responsible for such fine shore resorts as Myrtle Beach in South Carolina, and the Jacksonville and Daytona beaches in Florida. A similar veneer of clean quartz sand forms a belt several miles wide along the west coast as far south as Tampa Bay.

Origin of the Gulf of Mexico. A belt of Cretaceous and Cenozoic formations encircles the Gulf of Mexico, forming a low coastal plain from Florida to Yucatan. These formations obviously accumulated under conditions approximating those of the present, and make it certain that the Gulf of Mexico was then in existence even though it was probably not as deep as now. Deep wells have revealed that Jurassic formations also underlie the western Gulf Coastal Plain, dipping seaward with the Cretaceous beds (Fig. 252).

On the contrary, the pre-Jurassic rocks of the Gulf region have a very different arrangement. In the Antillean Islands they are metamorphic and volcanic and appear to be remnants of a deformed land mass. In Florida a deep well has revealed Cretaceous beds resting on deformed Cambrian or early Ordovician strata.[4] Furthermore, the late Paleozoic formations of the Ouachita Trough indicate that Llanoria was a rugged upland in the western Gulf region as late as Permian time. It may be inferred, therefore, that this great depression began to form in Jurassic time and that it was well outlined in the Cretaceous Period; but its present depth may be the result of Cenozoic movements.

The present great delta of the Mississippi was formed in Pleistocene time and its late history has been worked out in magnificent detail by Dr. Fisk and his colleagues. Older deltas of similar type undoubtedly lie deeply buried in the Gulf border, since streams were converging toward the axis of the present Mississippi lowland as early as Paleocene time, when deposits were forming as far north as Cairo, Illinois, and the Mississippi River system must date from early in the Cenozoic Era. Sands and muds delivered to the Gulf border from this source produced the detrital facies that characterizes nearly all the Cenozoic formations in western Alabama, Mississippi, and Louisiana.

During Pleistocene time sealevel was lowered by some hundreds of feet during each glacial stage, and at such times the delta region was subjected to erosion, and valleys were cut across it. But during each ensuing interglacial age a new

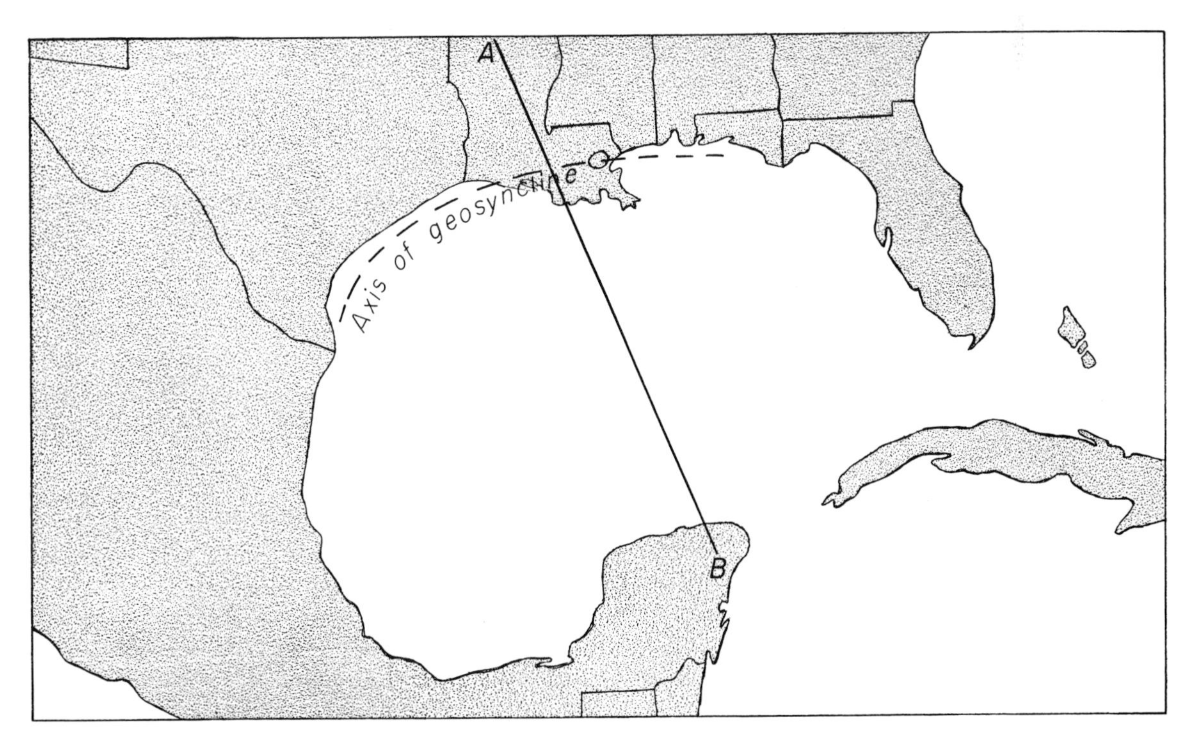

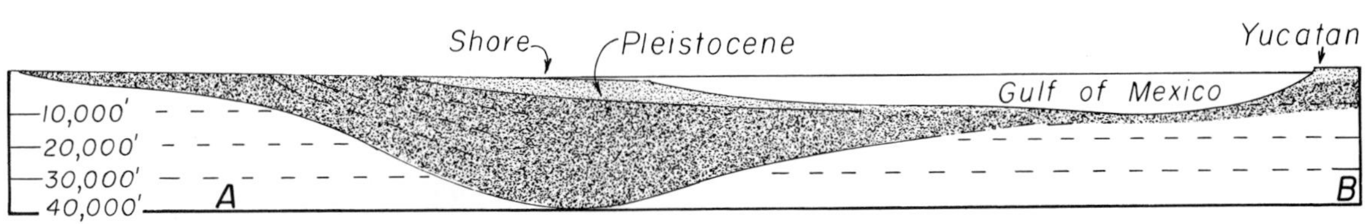

Figure 301. Section across the Gulf Coast Geosyncline and the Gulf of Mexico. The axis of the geosyncline lies along the dashed line of the inset map, and the section follows the line *AB* from Shreveport, Louisiana, to Yucatan. Depths are indicated in feet. (Adopted from Fisk, 1956.)

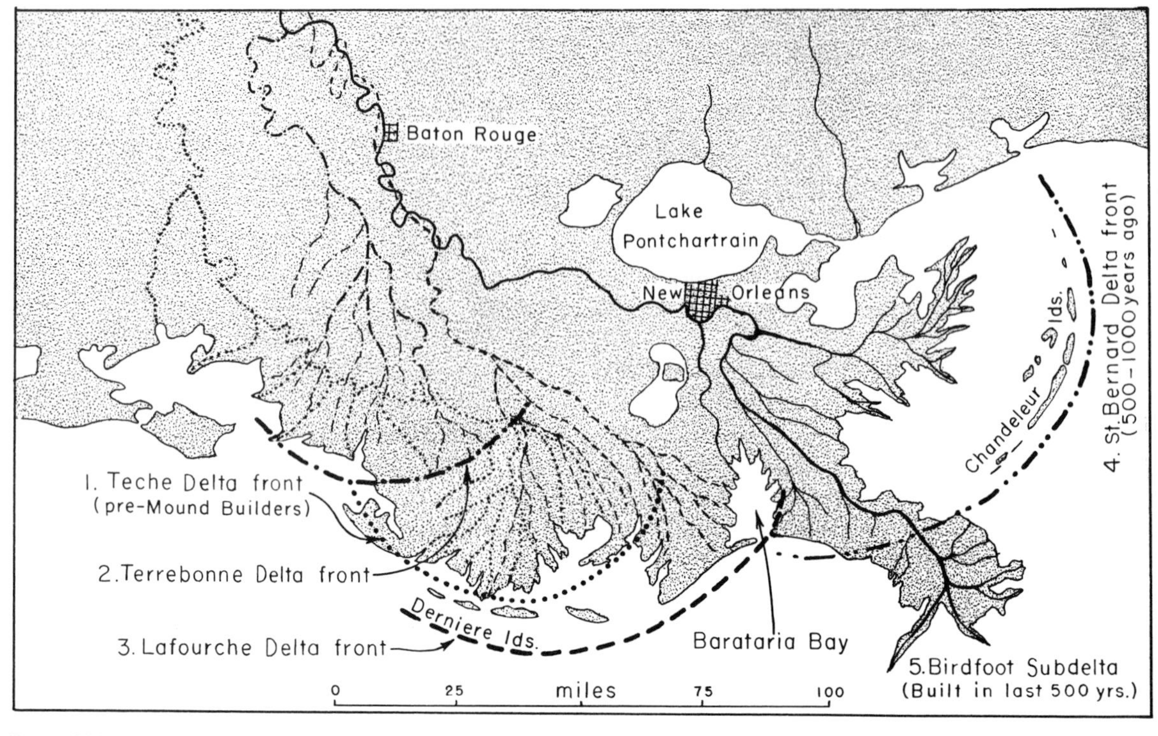

Figure 302. Map of the exposed surface of the Mississippi Delta showing the position of 5 subdeltas that have formed in succession as the river shifted its course in postglacial time. (Adapted from Fisk, 1944.)

delta grew out over this old surface. The present delta was formed in latest glacial and postglacial time. Some features of its complex history are indicated in Figure 302.

The Mississippi River discharges an annual load of fine sand, silt, and clay estimated at 500,000,000 tons. In the absence of strong waves and competent marine currents, the river is able to build the land surface seaward at a rapid rate, until it has extended a large lobe of the delta so far as to reduce its gradient below a critical limit. This has happened several times in the past. Then it overflowed a lower part of the delta and established a new channel to the sea. Thus, a series of subdeltas were built out one after another in different sectors of the great delta. The youngest of these, the Birdfoot Subdelta, is known from archeological data and radiocarbon dating, to have formed during the last 500 years. Older subdeltas, now partly buried and partly cut back by the sea, are indicated in Figure 302. The modern delta deposits are thin beneath the present land, reaching a thickness of about 850 feet at 20 miles off shore, but probably exceeding 2,000 feet farther out, as indicated by recent off-shore drilling.

Sculpturing of the Appalachians. At the beginning of the Cenozoic Era nearly all the Appalachian region was peneplaned, the exceptions being a chain of monadnocks rising to 2,000 or 3,000 feet along the border between eastern Tennessee and North Carolina and scattered hills in northern New England. These unreduced areas form the crest of the modern Great Smokies, the summit of the White Mountains, and such scattered peaks as Mount Katahdin and Cadillac Mountain in Maine; they show no evidence of ever having been reduced to a level summit. Elsewhere in the Appalachian region, however, remnants of a widespread and remarkably flat erosion surface may be seen in the even crests of the highest ridges (Fig. 303) and in the summits of the Allegheny Plateau. This old surface has been named the **Schooley peneplane.** When it was formed, the surface must have been near sealevel, and the region was obviously a low plain.

The present mountains are therefore due almost wholly to Cenezoic changes. They are not, however, the result of either folding or faulting but of (1) **gentle regional upwarp,** which produced the present elevation, and (2) **sculpturing by erosive agents** that have carved out the weaker rocks and created the local **relief;** the mountain **structures** were already present, inherited from the Appalachian revolution and the Palisade disturbance.

The erosional history of the region is suggested in Figure 304. After the completion of the Schooley peneplane (block 2), at a time not yet accurately dated, the region was gently arched and uplifted a few hundred feet (block 3). The streams then incised themselves to the new baselevel and opened out extensive lowlands on the weak formations, while the resistant rocks stood up as ridges (block 4). Remnants of these flat lowlands are still conspicuous about Harrisburg, and this flat erosion surface, present on the weak formations only, has been named the **Harrisburg surface.**

A second gentle upwarp along the axis of the Appalachians caused the streams to incise their valleys into the Harrisburg surface and to excavate new lowlands of more local extent at a lower elevation (block 5). Still younger and more frequent uplifts of this sort have produced strath terraces along the major streams as they carved their present deep valleys. Thus, by a series of gentle uplifts the Schooley peneplane has been warped up to its present maximum height of about 4,000 feet along the crest of a broad simple arch, and the ridges and valleys have been etched into relief. From an axis running near the eastern edge of the Allegheny Plateau, the surface of the old Schooley peneplane slopes gently away to the east, and likewise to the west, declining but a few feet to the mile. It is preserved only on the most resistant rocks and has been completely destroyed throughout most of the piedmont belt. If it could be restored, it would have the form of a vast low arch several hundred miles wide and less than one mile high along the crest of the Appalachians. Near the present coast it would descend to sealevel and pass under one of the coastal-plain for-

Figure 303. Remnants of the Schooley peneplane preserved in the accordant summits of the Appalachian ridges near Harrisburg, Pennsylvania. The view is westward into the Susquehanna Gap, showing Kittatinny Mountain (K), with Second Mountain (S) and Peters Mountain (P) in succession beyond it. (George H. Ashley.)

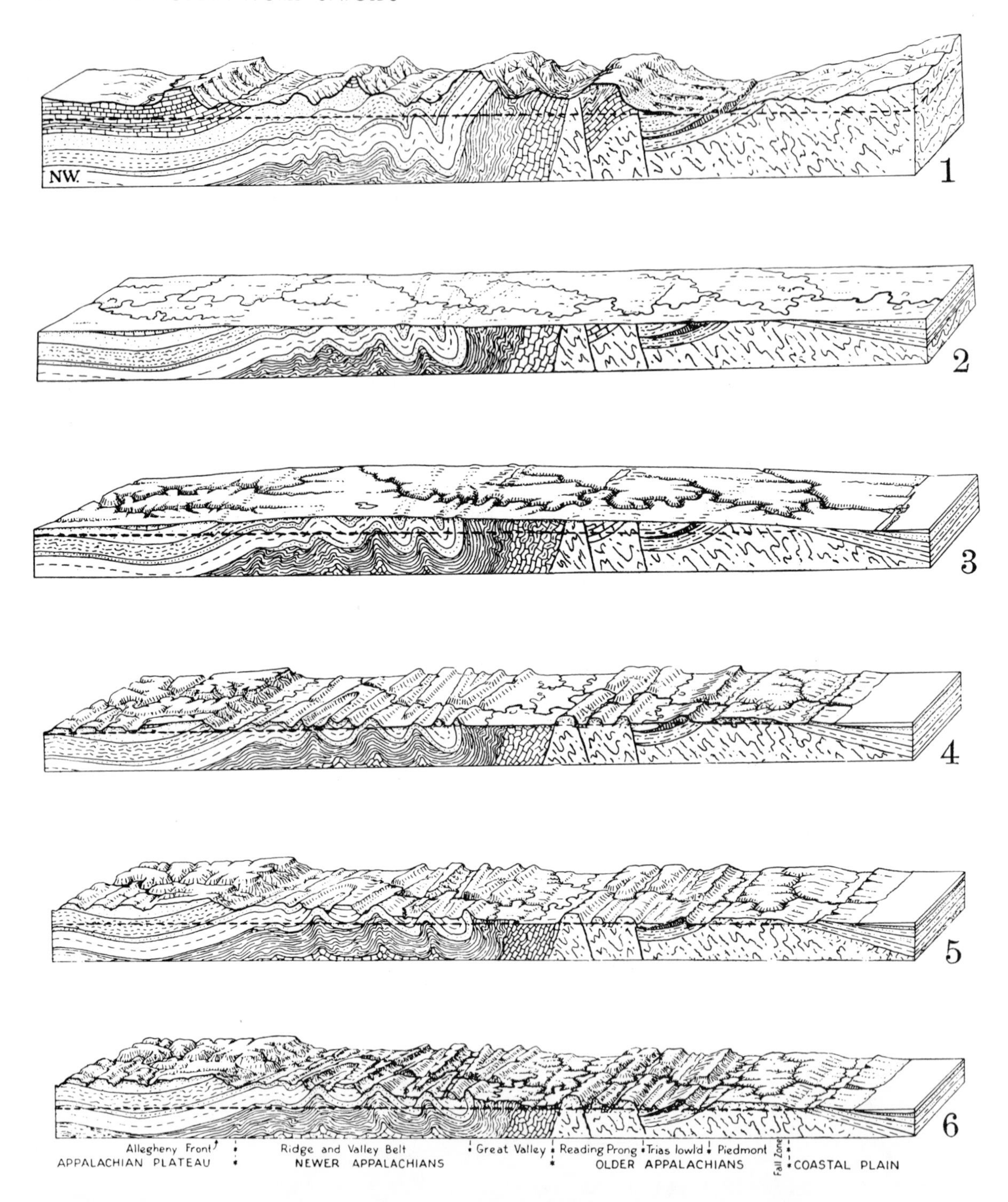

Figure 304. Evolution of the modern topography of the middle Appalachian region: 1, Rough topography of early Jurassic time, resulting from dissection of the structure produced by the Appalachian revolution and the Palisade disturbance; 2, development of Schooley peneplane; 3, arching of Schooley peneplane and incision of drainage; 4, dissection of Schooley peneplane and local development of Harrisburg erosion surface beveling belts of weak rock; 5, further uplift and dissection, with development of a lower erosion surface (Somerville) beveling only the weakest rocks; 6, latest uplift and dissection. (Modified slightly from D. Johnson.)

mations, for it is clear that, as the Appalachian Arch came up, the continental shelf was depressed and tilted eastward. If stages of uplift in the mountains could be correlated with deposits in the coastal-plain region, the erosional history could be dated in detail, but unfortunately such correlations are not yet secure.

The Central Interior

Throughout Cenozoic time the great interior of the continent stretching westward from the Appalachian Plateau to the Great Plains was a lowland undergoing but slight degradation. The stages in its development are far more obscure than are those of the Appalachian region. River gravels widely distributed over the interstream areas bear evidence that the surface has been reduced to its present form by long-continued stream erosion and mass wasting.

In the Great Lakes region, where the Paleozoic formations overlap upon the Canadian Shield, the beveled edges of the more resistant limestones were brought into relief as cuestas, while the weaker formations were reduced to broad lowlands which, in the Pleistocene Epoch, were modified by glaciers to form the basins of the Great Lakes.

Decay and Rebirth of the Rockies

Basin Filling and Peneplanation. Nearly all the major *structures* of the Rocky Mountains date from the Laramide revolution at the end of the Cretaceous. As noted before, the folding and faulting continued locally into the Eocene, and died out gradually. This left the region bold and mountainous in early Cenozoic time.

Among the ranges were several great structural basins which have persisted, with little deformation, up to the present (Fig. 305). Such are the Powder River, the Bighorn, and the Green River basins of Wyoming, and the Uinta Basin and North and South parks in Colorado. As the mountains were eroded, the sediment converged into these basins, where much of it was trapped. Fans formed about the margins, but most of the debris was spread as broad alluvial deposits across the basin floors. Thus, they were gradually filled as the mountains were worn down. Meanwhile, through-flowing streams were aggrading the plains region east of the Rockies. By the middle of the era the intermont basins were full and the mountains were largely peneplaned to the level of this surface of aggradation, as represented in Figure 306. Along the axes of some of the ranges, rounded monadnocks stood a few hundred or even 2,000 to 3,000 feet above the peneplane, but for the most part the mountains were then buried in their own debris, and the streams wandered widely over this thick alluvial cover.

This flat surface of combined erosion and deposition was probably 2,000 or 3,000 feet above sealevel along the present continental divide, because the streams had hundreds of miles to flow before reaching the sea, and even a very low gradient would leave considerable altitude at their source. Peneplanation had been accomplished by late Oligocene time.

Cascadian Uplift and Erosional Sculpturing. In Miocene and Pliocene time uplift was resumed, not in the form of local deformation but rather as a broad upwarp of the whole region into a low arch hundreds of miles across.[5] It correlates in time with the Cascadian deformation farther west, and may therefore be spoken of as a Cascadian uplift. This movement continued intermittently, but with acceleration, to a culmination in the late Pleistocene, and brought the peneplaned surface to a maximum elevation of 10,000 to 11,000 feet along the continental divide. With this uplift the streams were rejuvenated and began to deepen their valleys, to reexcavate the basins, and to sculpture the exhumed mountain masses (Fig. 307). Thus, the *height* of the Rockies is due to broad regional upwarp, but their present *form* and *relief* were determined by late Cenozoic erosion.

Thus far it has been assumed that all parts of the Rocky Mountain region were peneplaned at the same time, and only once. This picture is undoubtedly too simple. Within a region so vast, the ranges possess individuality in structure and in lithology, and probably moved with some independence. The final uplift was long and intermittent, and a series of partial peneplanes was probably formed locally as the baselevel changed—indeed, there is clear evidence of more than one in many of the ranges. Nevertheless, in most parts of the region, remnants of one peneplane are so much more striking than any others that they ap-

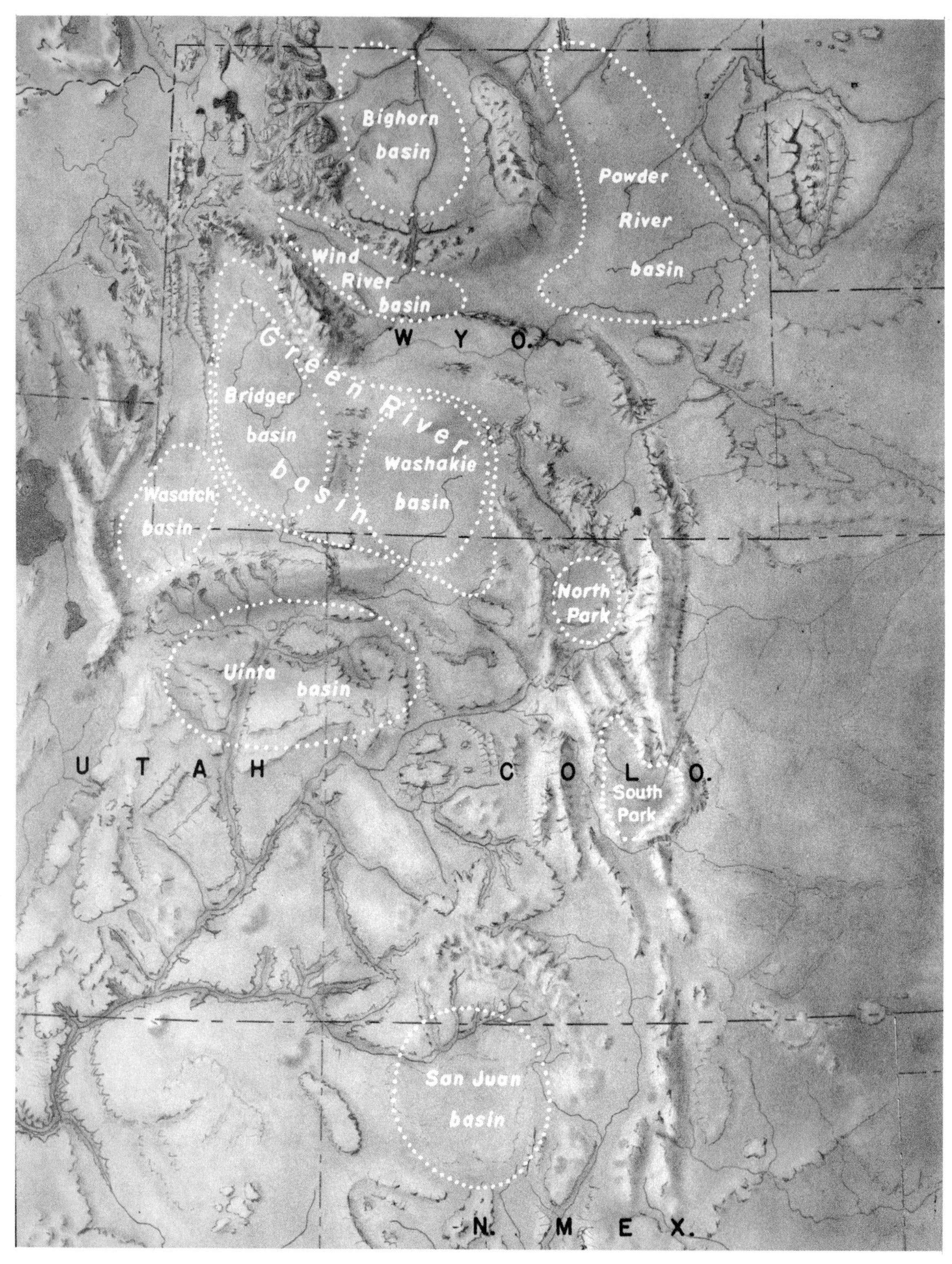

Figure 305. Structural basins within the middle and southern Rocky Mountains. The topography is that of the present; the structures date from the Laramide Revolution. (Drawn by Milton Wallman.)

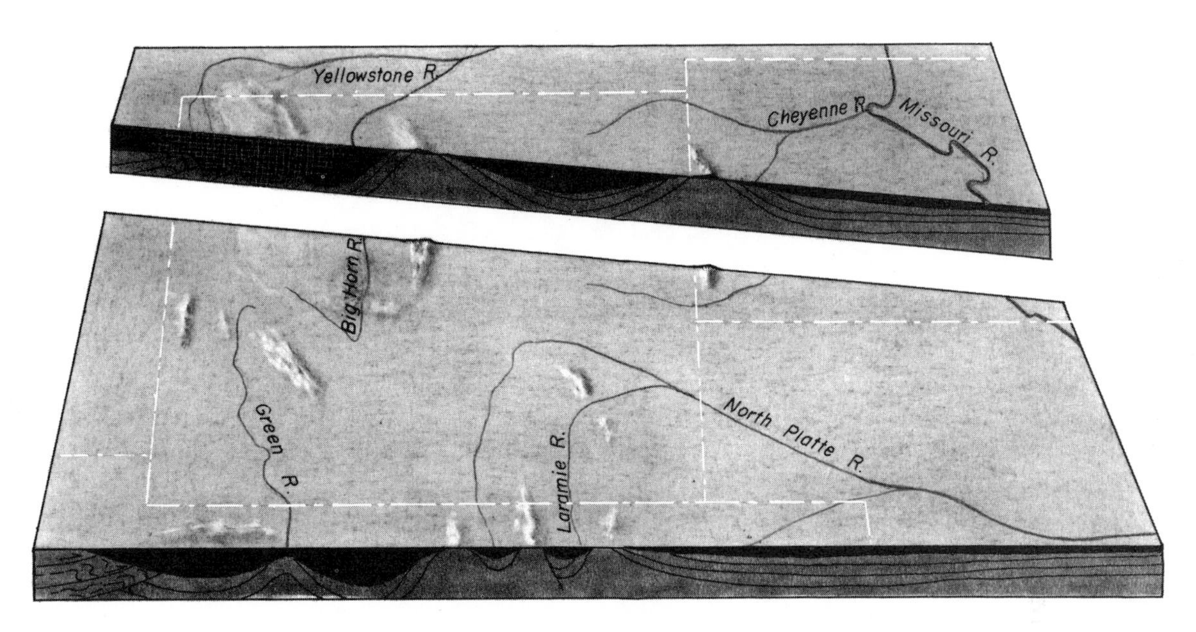

Figure 306. Block diagram showing topography of early Miocene date when the basins in the Rocky Mountain region were filled with Cenozoic sediments (black) and the ranges were peneplaned to the level of this graded plane except for a few low monadnocks. The block has been cut in two and the pieces parted to show the structure along a line passing through the Yellowstone Park and the Black Hills. In the area of Yellowstone Park and the Absaroka Plateau the basin filling was largely by volcanics (white-lined). Streams then flowed for the most part upon alluvial deposits that hid the buried ranges. (Suggested by a figure by Atwood and Atwood.)

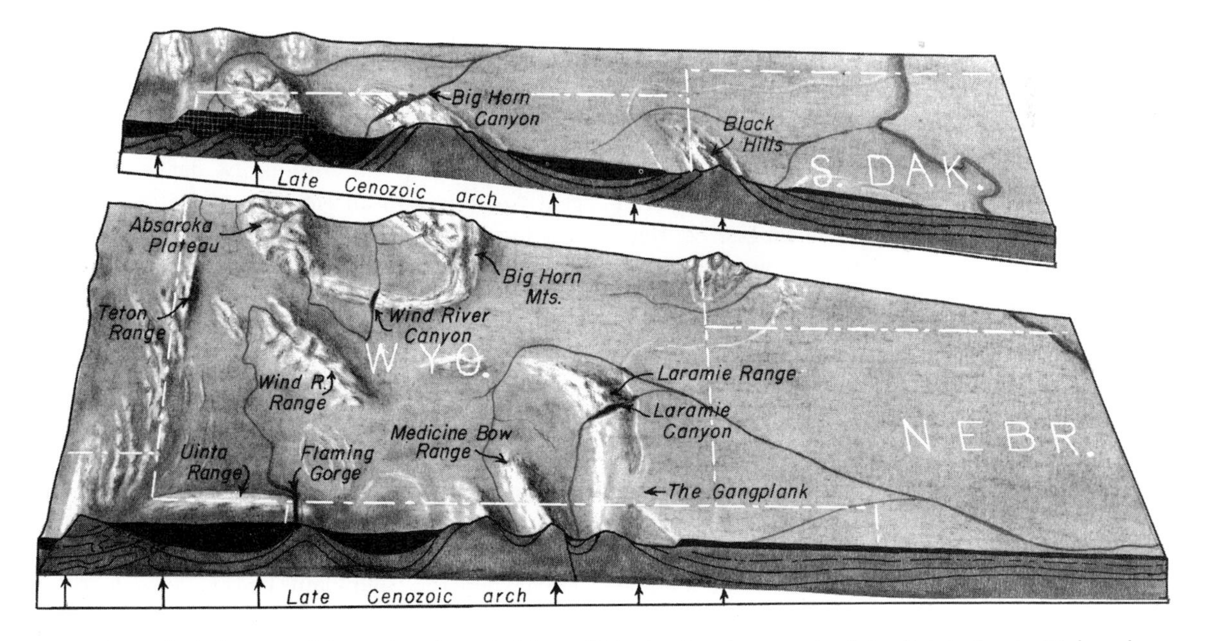

Figure 307. Block diagram of the region shown in Figure 306, showing the present relief, which is due to (1) broad regional uplift and arching during Pliocene and Pleistocene time and (2) excavation by erosion of most of the weak Cenozoic sediments from the basins. In the removal of the basin fill the streams were in many places superposed on the ranges they now cross in imposing canyons. (Adapted from Atwood and Atwood.)

Figure 308. Peneplane on the granite summit of the Laramie Range near Buford, Wyoming. The view is north. Monadnocks rise above the peneplane in the distance at the left. (Carl O. Dunbar.)

pear to belong to one general **Rocky Mountain peneplane** (Fig. 308). If, instead of one, there are several peneplanes in the Rocky Mountains, then the history is more complicated in its detail, but in fundamentals it is essentially as outlined above.

Evidence of the history just sketched may be seen in (1) peneplane remnants still preserved along the summits of most of the ranges, (2) remnants of the Cenozoic formations around the margins of the basins, (3) superposition of many of the streams across the present ranges, and (4) the stratigraphy of the Cenozoic formations in the High Plains east of the Rockies.

These features are illustrated in Figure 307. A particularly fine peneplane remnant may be seen along the summit of the Laramie Range in southeastern Wyoming. Here, at an elevation of 8,000 feet, is a nearly flat surface 10 or 12 miles wide, cutting across granite and other types of igneous rock of the mountain core (Fig. 308).

Roads run in almost every direction; and the Union Pacific Railroad crosses the divide, not through a deep pass but across an open plateau. At the station of Sherman one may look for miles in almost any direction, and it is with difficulty that he realizes that his viewpoint is 8,000 feet above sealevel, or as high as the summit of many of the rugged mountains of the Northwest.[6]

East of the Laramie Range lie the High Plains, capped by Miocene (and locally Pliocene) beds. Their surface is extraordinarily flat and slopes gently eastward to an elevation of not over 2,000 feet in central Nebraska and Kansas. This great flat area is a remnant of the aggraded plain that existed when the mountains were peneplaned. Generally its most elevated western margin has been dissected and eroded back several miles from the mountain front, especially where large streams cross it, but locally in southeastern Wyoming it extends up to the mountains, rising to the level of the summit peneplane. Here it forms the "Gangplank" (Fig. 307) by which the Union Pacific Railroad crosses the mountains from the plains. Even where the High Plains beds have been eroded back several miles it can be seen that, if they were projected toward the mountains, their surface would meet the peneplaned summit.

Several miles north of the Gangplank, the Laramie River crosses the range in a granite gorge more than 1,000 feet deep. It rises west of the range and flows northward for some 50 miles along the floor of the Laramie Basin at an elevation of less than 7,000 feet, and then turns east and cuts through the range instead of following the lowland northward to the Platte. Such an anomalous course is easily understood if the Laramie Basin was once filled with sediment that slightly covered the range, as represented in Figure 306, for then the stream flowed on a graded plain from which it was superposed on the range after uplift. The Cenozoic fill has been almost completely removed from Laramie Basin, but a telltale remnant still exists along its western margin, flatlying along the front of the Medicine Bow Range at an elevation of 8,500 feet. The greatest remnants of Cenozoic deposits at high altitudes, however, are along the southern end of the Absaroka Range, where Eocene and Oligocene strata are interbedded with, and protected by, volcanics. Here flat-lying Oligocene strata at an elevation exceeding 10,500 feet rim the northern side of the Wind River Basin.

The course of Laramie River in crossing the range is not exceptional; the major streams flow radially out of the Rocky Mountains, crossing basins and ranges alike. As shown in Figure 307, Bighorn River, originating in the Wind River Basin, cuts through the Owl Creek Mountains and flows for 100 miles across Bighorn Basin, only to turn east and cut through the north end of the Big Horn Range in an imposing chasm. Likewise, Green River flows south across Green River Basin, swings east along the north side of the Uinta Mountains, and then cuts through them in the magnificent Flaming Gorge. Farther south, South Platte River, heading in South Park at an elevation of about 9,000 feet, flows northeast through the Front Range in another great gorge; and the Arkansas, after flowing across South Park Basin, cuts through the Front Range in picturesque Royal Gorge, whose sheer walls tower 1,400 feet above the stream.

All these and other anomalous features of the drainage are simply explained by the fact that the

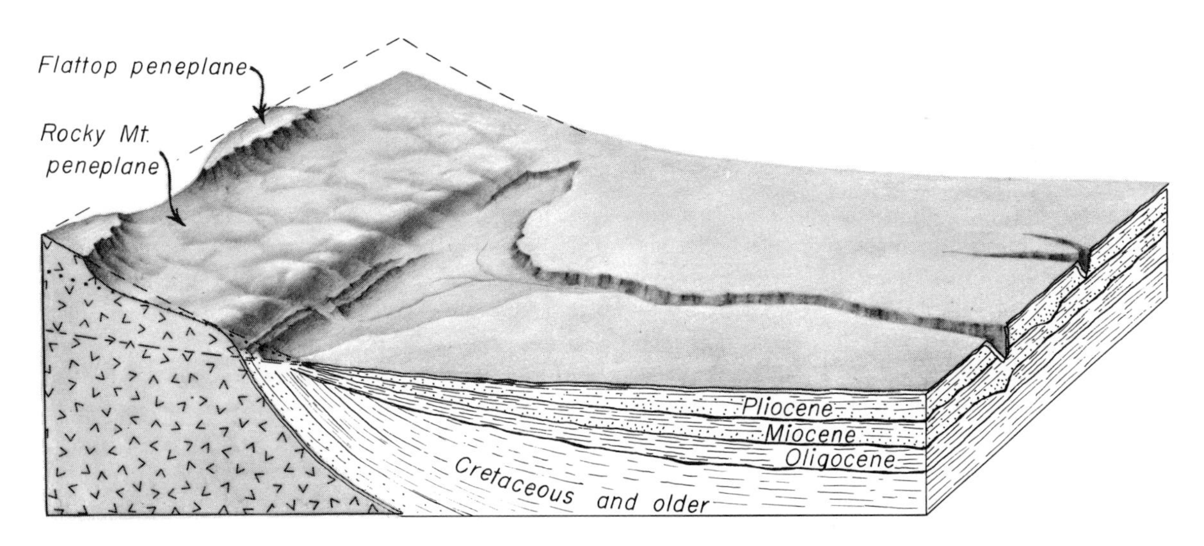

Figure 309. Idealized diagram to show the relation of sedimentary deposits in the High Plains to erosion surfaces in the Rocky Mountains. It is drawn on the assumption that the Flattop peneplane was completed during late Oligocene time and the Rocky Mountain peneplane late in the Miocene Epoch before renewed uplift started canyon-cutting in the mountains. If this be true, the upwarped Flattop surface was once continuous with the upper surface of the Oligocene beds, and the Rocky Mountain erosion surface originally joined the erosion surface separating the Miocene from the Pliocene formations. Although these correlations appear probable, they are not certainly proved, because after the latest upwarp the streams have not only cut valleys in the deposits of the High Plains, but also have stripped back their western margins most of the way along the front of the mountains; this has left a gap several miles wide between the remnants of the erosion surfaces in the mountains and their counterparts in the High Plains. (Adapted from an unpublished figure by R. F. Flint.)

Chart II. Correlation of important Cenozoic sections

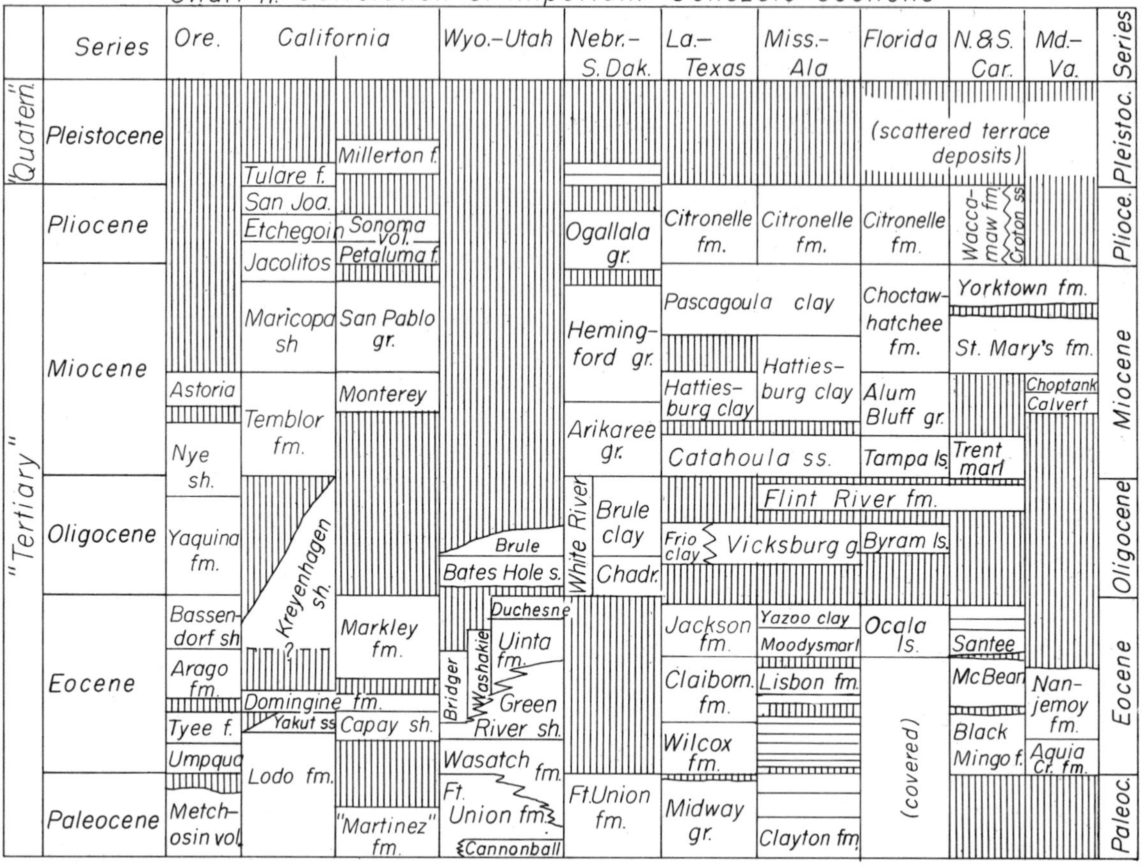

	Series	Ore.	California		Wyo.–Utah	Nebr.–S. Dak.	La.–Texas	Miss.–Ala	Florida	N. & S. Car.	Md.–Va.	Series
"Quatern."	Pleistocene		Tulare f.	Millerton f.					(scattered terrace deposits)			Pleistoc.
"Tertiary"	Pliocene		San Joa. Etchegoin Jacolitos	Sonoma vol. Petaluma f.		Ogallala gr.	Citronelle fm.	Citronelle fm.	Citronelle fm.	Waccamaw fm. Croton ss		Plioce.
	Miocene	Astoria Nye sh.	Maricopa sh Temblor fm.	San Pablo gr. Monterey		Hemingford gr. Arikaree gr.	Pascagoula clay Hattiesburg clay Catahoula ss.	Pascagoula clay Hattiesburg clay Catahoula ss.	Choctawhatchee fm. Alum Bluff gr. Tampa ls.	Yorktown fm. St. Mary's fm. Trent marl	Yorktown fm. St. Mary's fm. Choptank Calvert	Miocene
	Oligocene	Yaquina fm.	Kreyenhagen sh.		Brule Bates Hole s.	White River: Brule clay, Chadr.	Frio clay Vicksburg g	Flint River fm. Vicksburg g	Flint River fm. Byram ls.			Oligocene
	Eocene	Bassendorf sh Arago fm. Tyee f. Umpqua	Kreyenhagen sh. Domingine fm. Yakut ss Lodo fm.	Markley fm. Domingine fm. Capay sh.	Duchesne Uinta fm. Bridger Washakie Green River sh. Wasatch fm.		Jackson fm. Claiborn. fm. Wilcox fm.	Yazoo clay Moodys marl Lisbon fm.	Ocala ls. (covered)	Santee McBean Black Mingo f.	Nanjemoy fm. Aquia Cr. fm.	Eocene
	Paleocene	Metchosin vol.	Lodo fm.	"Martinez" fm.	Ft. Union fm. Cannonball	Ft.Union fm.	Midway gr.	Clayton fm	(covered)			Paleoc.

basins were formerly filled completely with Cenozoic sediments until the ranges were covered where the streams now cross them.

Stratigraphy of the Cenozoic Deposits. The fluvial deposits that were spread as an immense debris apron east of the Rockies during Cenozoic time have been partly destroyed by later erosion along both their eastern and western margins, but the great central portion is still intact in the High Plains (Fig. 309). Here they include clay, silt, and sand, with linear bodies of coarse sand and gravel marking old stream channels. In general the beds are weak, and in areas of rapid erosion appear as "badlands" (Figs. 310, 311, 312). Much volcanic ash, derived from sources farther west, is included in the stream-laid deposits.

The thickness of the entire deposit ranges up to 2,000 feet over extensive areas, but is nowhere much greater. It includes formations of Paleocene, Oligocene, Miocene, and Pliocene dates, but none of these was continuous over the whole region. They were deposited by streams flowing nearly at grade and ever seeking the lowest places to drop their loads. The result is an intricate patchwork of formations, mostly local in character. A few are more widespread and represent times of more general deposition.

The oldest beds present here constitute the **Fort Union formation** of Paleocene date, which occupies a vast area in the northern Great Plains, chiefly in the Dakotas, Wyoming, Montana, and Alberta. It includes friable yellow sandstones, somber gray shales, and enormous deposits of coal (Figs. 313 and 314). Over a considerable area in the center of the Dakotas there is present at its base the **Cannonball marine member,** with oyster banks and other evidence of shallow brackish and marine water (Fig. 315). A fauna of about 150 species of marine animals has been identified from these beds

Figure 310. Lower Eocene (upper Wasatch) exposures along Cottonwood Draw near Lost Cabin, Wyoming. Mesozoic hills in the background. (American Museum of Natural History.)

Figure 311. Lower Eocene (Wasatch) Badlands along Gray Bull River in Bighorn Basin. (American Museum of Natural History.)

Figure 312. Big Badlands of South Dakota cut in Lower Oligocene (Brule) clay. These beds have yielded a rich fauna of fossil mammals, notably oreodonts and titanotheres. (N. H. Darton, U.S. Geological Survey.)

(about 80 molluscs and 64 foraminifers). Until recently this marine zone was referred to the underlying Lance formation of latest Cretaceous date, but study of the associated land plants and of the Foraminifera indicates that the Cannonball horizon is Paleocene.[7] Thirty-eight species of the Foraminifera occur also in the Paleocene (Midway group) of the Gulf Coast, and of these 13 are limited to Paleocene beds in other regions.

In the plains, the Fort Union formation is the chief coal-bearing horizon. Here it has yielded abundant plants, but almost no vertebrate remains. Farther west, however, it holds an amazing array of strange, small, primitive mammals.

With the exception of small areas of Early Eocene (Wasatch) beds in eastern Montana and the Dakotas,[8] no true Eocene formations occur east of the Rockies, although they are thick and widespread in the intermont basins (Figs. 310, 311). Evidently by this time relief in the mountains was reduced somewhat, and the streams were at grade. In the plains the Paleocene beds are succeeded by the Oligocene **White River group** which is widespread in Montana and Wyoming, reaching eastward into the Dakotas and southward into Nebraska. It forms the Big Badlands southeast of the Black Hills (Fig. 312) and is one of the most prolific sources of fossil vertebrates in the whole Rocky Mountain region. It ranges from 200 to 500 feet in thickness and consists generally of clay and fine silt along with much volcanic ash. The general lack of sands and gravel indicates that the region farther west had but slight relief at this time.

The overlying **Arikaree group**, of Miocene date, is relatively coarser, including great quantities of sand. It extends farther than the Oligocene beds and locally reaches a thickness of about 2,500 feet, though in most places it is far thinner. Recently the **Hemingford group** was defined to include Upper Miocene formations, which in the past have been included in part in the Arikaree. Evidently uplift was under way in the mountain region, and the streams emerging onto the plains were once again heavily laden with sand as well as mud.

The Pliocene is represented by the **Ogallala group,** which ranges from 300 to 500 feet in thickness and, like the Miocene beds, consists of clay, fine silt, sand, and gravel, mostly unconsolidated.

Pleistocene deposits include glacial drift and loess north and east of the Missouri River, and very limited and patchy areas of bedded sand and gravel farther south.

The character of these formations in the High Plains obviously reflects the erosional history of the mountains (Figs. 306 and 307). The coarse, sandy Paleocene deposits indicate high relief in the mountain area as the streams emerged heavily loaded with sand and gravel as well as mud. The lack of Eocene deposits east of the mountains shows that the streams then flowed at grade across the plains; evidently the relief in the mountains was considerably reduced by this time. The very fine grain of the widespread Oligocene deposits, both here and in the intermont basins, indicates very low relief, and the upper surface of these beds is to be correlated with peneplane remnants on the summits of the Front Range. The coarser nature and the considerable thickness of the Miocene beds show that uplift in the mountain region had been resumed and the streams were once again emerging heavily laden with sand. By Pliocene time, arching along the axis of the Rockies had tilted the surface of the High Plains eastward so that the streams were again at grade, in most places carrying their load of debris through to the Mississippi River.

The intermont basins are occupied chiefly by Paleocene and Eocene deposits which reach an aggregate thickness of several thousand feet. Like the Cenozoic formations of the plains, they are mostly fluvial deposits of clay, silt, and sand. Thick basal and marginal conglomerates occur in places where alluvial fans were built at the mouths of torrential streams. Deposition was independent in the several basins, the accumulation depending on the amount of subsidence; and, since the warping was irregular and intermittent, there is no complete record in any single basin. Nevertheless, the abundant fossil mammals permit a correlation of zones from basin to basin and the building up of a composite sedimentary section of these oldest Cenozoic formations amounting to between 10,000 and 20,000 feet. (For basins, see Fig. 305.)

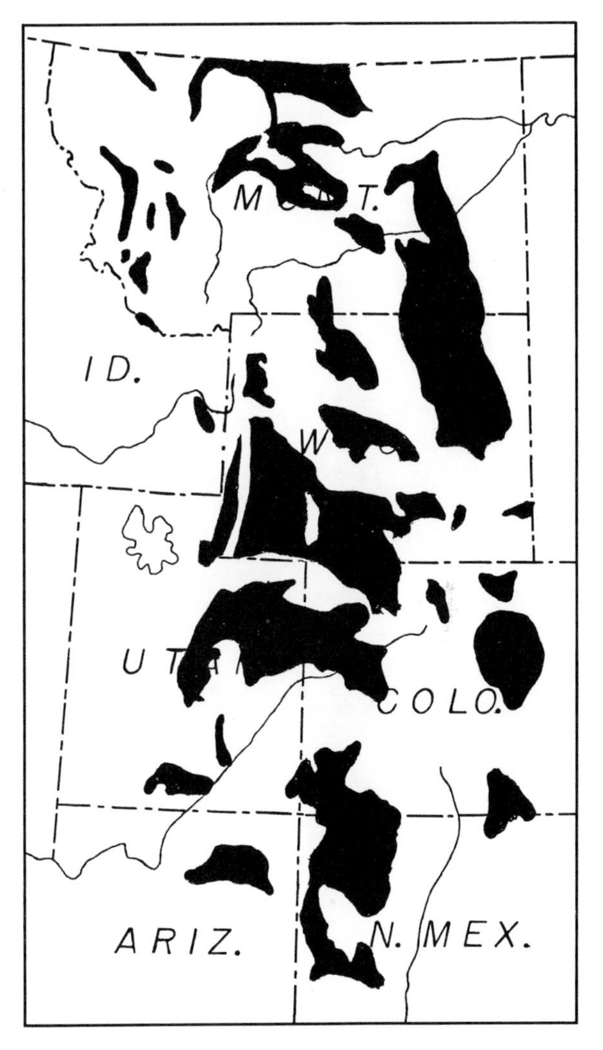

Figure 313. Cretaceous and Cenozoic coal fields of the Rocky Mountain region. (After M. R. Campbell, U.S. Geological Survey.)

These deposits, like those of the plains, commonly form badlands, a typical view of which is shown in Figure 311. Four major groups are widely recognized, three of them named from the basin where best exposed. The oldest of these is the **Paleocene horizon,** which embraces the Fort Union and equivalent beds. Next comes the **Wasatch formation** (Fig. 311), marked by the first

Figure 314. Coal bed 90 to 100 feet thick in the Fort Union formation 6 miles east of Gillettte, Wyoming. A similar bed north of Buffalo, Wyoming reaches the remarkable thickness of 215 feet. (Karl M. Waagé.)

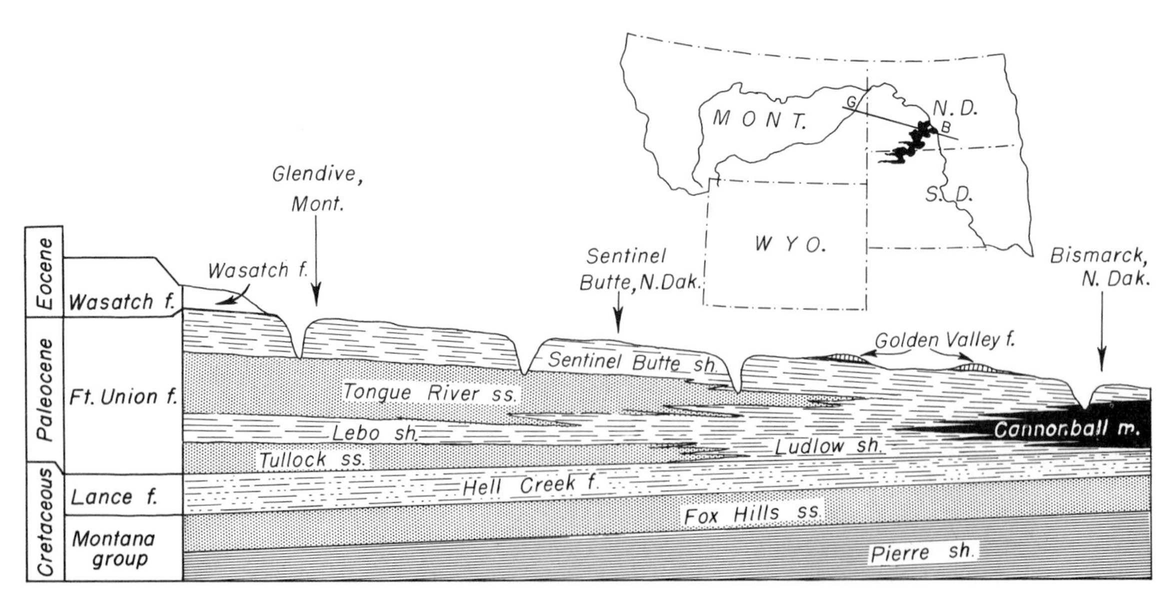

Figure 315. Stratigraphic section showing the relation of the Cannonball marine member of the Fort Union formation. The inset map shows the outcrop of the Cannonball member (black) and the line of section (G–B). The Golden Valley formation of Eocene age appears as outliers near Bismark, North Dakota. Length of section about 250 miles; vertical scale greatly exaggerated.

great invasion of modernized mammals, including the "dawn horse," *Eohippus*. Above this comes the **Bridger formation**, with younger mammalian faunas, and finally the **Uinta formation**, with the last and largest of the archaic mammals represented by the grotesque uintatheres.

The **Green River Basin** of Colorado and Wyoming was occupied by a vast shallow lake during much of middle Eocene time, and here accumulated the fine, evenly bedded oil shales (so called because they yield oil by destructive distillation), of an average thickness of 2,000 feet. Around the margins of the basin, however, the lake beds grade laterally into fluvial sediments of the Wasatch and Bridger formations. Most of the Green River strata are laminated (Fig. 316), and, on the assumption that the layers are seasonal, it has been estimated that their deposition required 6,500,000 years.[9] On this basis the Wasatch required 11,000,000 years, the Bridger 4,000,000, and the Uinta nearly 2,000,000.

In Montana occur rather extensive lake deposits of Oligocene date, formed in broad valleys that were obstructed by warping and local faulting. These are the Bozeman Lake beds. Near Florissant, Colorado, a similar but smaller intermont lake existed in early Oligocene time, and its deposits form one of the richest of all localities for fossil insects and plants. The sediments are largely of volcanic ash, which appears to have overwhelmed and buried the life in its fall. The John Day Basin of central Oregon was another intermont lowland encircled by active volcanoes during late Oligocene time, and here was formed one of the richest known deposits of Cenozoic fossil mammals.

Central Cordilleran Region

Figure 317 displays the relations of the major structural units of the Cordilleran region. On the east lie the Rockies and on the west the Sierra Nevada and the Coast ranges, while the central Cordilleran region is formed by the Colorado Plateau and the Basin and Range Province (which farther north gives way to the Columbia

Figure 316. Elko lake beds, similar to the Green River beds, near Elko, Nevada. (Carl O. Dunbar.)

Figure 317. Relief model of the Cordilleran region showing relations of its major structural elements.

Plateau). The Basin and Range Province, with an average height of 6,000 feet, lies more than a mile below the crest of the Sierra Nevada, and a few thousands of feet below the Colorado Plateau. Its ranges are tilted fault blocks of Mesozoic and Paleozoic rocks flanked round and partly buried by the Late Cenozoic sediments. The Colorado Plateau, on the contrary, consists of relatively flat-lying Mesozoic and Paleozoic formations at an elevation ranging from 7,000 to 11,000 feet. The rocks of the plateau were thrown into broad swells, with local monoclinal flexures, during the Laramide disturbance, and have been broken by a number of normal faults during Cenozoic time; yet, by and large, it is a unit contrasting in simple structure with the Basin and Range Province on the one side and the Rockies on the other.

Origin of the Basin and Range Province. The Basin and Range Province (Fig. 317) lies in the zone of the enormous Laramide thrusts. Those movements probably continued into the Eocene, and during Early Cenozoic time the region had a high mountainous surface and exterior drainage. For this reason Eocene and Oligocene strata are practically absent here. Miocene formations, on the contrary, are present and locally are of great thickness. Their character speaks eloquently of the events that were occurring. For example, in southern Nevada the Miocene deposits begin with coarse conglomerate that ranges up to 3,000 feet in thickness and lies across the beveled edges of Early Mesozoic and Paleozoic strata. The conglomerate varies greatly in thickness within short distances and includes angular and subangular fragments of all the older rocks. Overlying the conglomerate are clays and silts, including thick beds of gypsum, magnesite, and borax. The conglomerate is clearly the coarse debris of fans formed in a region of bold relief, and the clays and silts, with their saline deposits, could have formed only in arid basins of interior drainage much like the present basins.

In short, normal faulting had begun on a grand scale, and the Basin and Range Province had its inception in the Miocene.[10] As the new ranges were greatly elevated during the Pliocene Epoch, the intervening basins, all in the rain shadow of the Sierra Nevada, assumed a desert character like that of today. The faulting had only begun

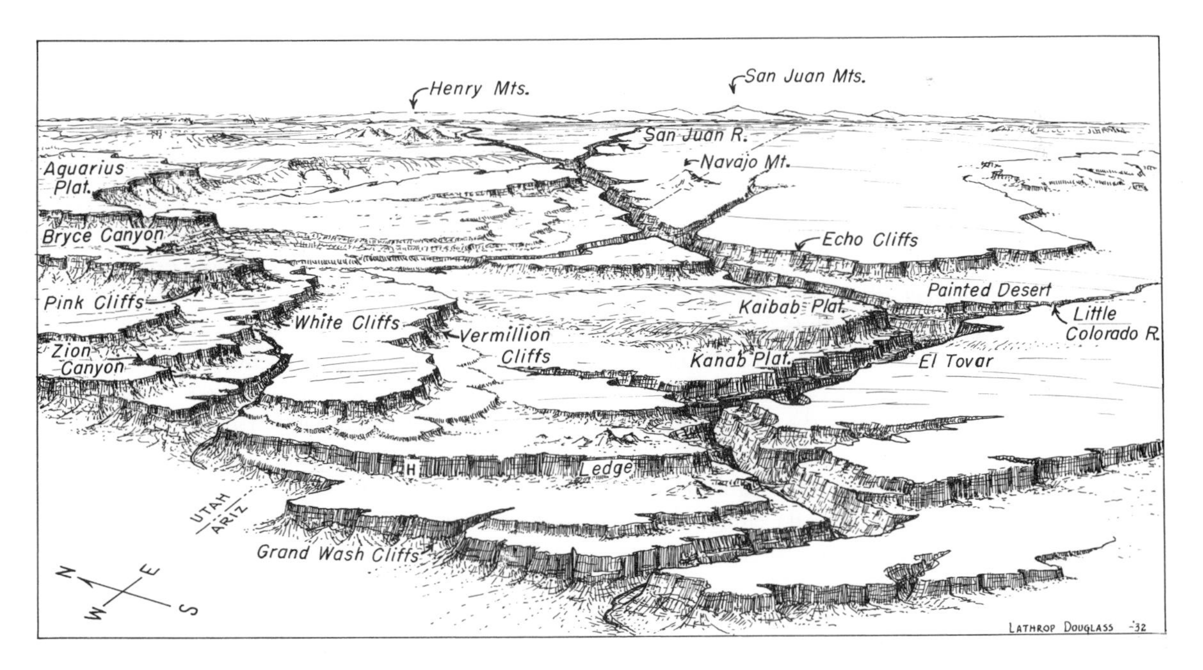

Figure 318. Aerial view of the Grand Canyon district, looking east-northeast across the mouth of the canyon where it cuts through Grand Wash Cliffs and enters the lower country to the west of the Colorado Plateau. The Grand Canyon proper extends up to the mouth of the Little Colorado River, above which the gorge is called Marble Canyon as far as Echo Cliffs, and above that, Glen Canyon.

Figure 319. Eocene (Wasatch) strata in the north rim of Bryce Canyon, Bryce Canyon National Park, Utah. View along the rim from Sunrise Point, Boat Mountain in the middle background. These Eocene beds form the Pink Cliffs of the Colorado Plateau (Figure 318). (National Park Service.)

in late Miocene time, for the deposits of that age were themselves later steeply tilted and truncated, so that they now lie with strong angular unconformity below the Pliocene beds. The latter, ranging up to 1,800 feet thick and including gypsum and salt beds as much as 100 feet thick locally, bear witness to continued deepening of the basins. The well-defined fault scarps, as well as historically dated faulting, prove that the movements are still going on. In résumé, this province came into existence through profound normal faulting that began in Miocene time, reached its climax during the Pliocene, and has continued to the present.

Stripping and Canyon Cutting in the Colorado Plateau. The Colorado Plateau is remarkable for tabular plateaus, cliff-bound mesas, and deep canyons, all of the most impressive magnitude. Gently dipping formations of Triassic, Jurassic, and Cretaceous age rise one above another in terraced plateaus bounded by unscalable cliffs many hundreds of feet in height (Fig. 318). These cliffs are the receding edges of resistant formations, truncated during an Early Cenozoic erosion cycle; and their grandeur bears witness to the vast amount of stripping that the region has suffered since the end of the Cretaceous.

The region was more or less extensively covered by Eocene sediments (Fig. 319) like those of the Green River and San Juan basins, and since no Oligocene formations are present, it appears that by Oligocene time the area had a low relief and well-established exterior drainage.

At some later date there was regional uplift with more or less profound normal faulting. This started a new cycle of erosion that resulted in extensive degradation but left no later Cenozoic sediments within the region. It is therefore difficult to date precisely the stages of uplift or to determine how many cycles of erosion are represented.

The presence of Eocene beds unconformably overlying truncated folds in the Mesozoic formations (Fig. 320) indicates that a large amount of the degradation and stripping had been accomplished during the interval between the Laramide uplift and the local beginning of Eocene deposition. On the other hand, the Eocene beds mantled an old surface of low relief; hence the present ruggedness of the region has come into being during later Cenozoic time.

The Grand Canyon proper is incised in a part of the area that was most uplifted, though it has since been reduced by erosion to a level 2,000 or 3,000 feet below the plateaus farther north. The Grand Canyon district is, in fact, a broad, nearly flat-topped dome about 100 miles across, from which more than 6,000 feet of Mesozoic strata has been stripped (Fig. 321). The strata dip gently over this dome, but are more abruptly bent down at its eastern margin in a pair of great monoclinal flexures. The west side of the dome has broken down along a great normal fault, leaving the Grand Wash Cliffs facing westward toward the lower country of the Basin and Range Province.

Before the cutting of the canyon began, the stripping of this huge dome had reached almost its present stage and left the high cliffs of the region about as they are now. Although these towered above the intervening benches with a relief of a few thousands of feet, the region as a whole was much nearer sealevel than at present. The final uplift of the region led to a reorganization of the drainage, initiated the present Colorado River system, and started the canyon cycle.

The date of this uplift can be determined west of the Grand Wash Cliffs where the river emerges from its canyon and crosses the Great Basin, flowing over Miocene beds that are known from their salt and gypsum deposits to have formed in arid basins without exterior drainage. Obviously, the Colorado River did not exist, or at least did not have its present course, in Miocene time. Hence the great uplift of the plateau and the carving of the canyon are the work of Pliocene, Pleistocene, and Recent time.[10]

Building of the Columbia Plateau. North of the Basin and Range Province, and occupying the area between the Northern Rockies and the Cascade Range (Fig. 317) lies the Columbia Plateau, a vast upland built of Cenozoic basalt flows that cover an area of more than 200,000 square miles and reach a maximum thickness of over 5,000 feet. The total volume of the lava is estimated at 24,000 cubic miles. For the most part it emerged through fissures in a very fluid condition and spread widely in sheets a few feet to a few tens of feet thick. These flows sought the lowest places, filling the old valleys and encroaching on the flanks of hills and mountains. In time the prebasalt topography was buried, and a relatively flat basalt plain was constructed.

The larger streams, such as Snake and Spokane rivers, have since cut through the lava flows in some places, especially near the eastern margin of

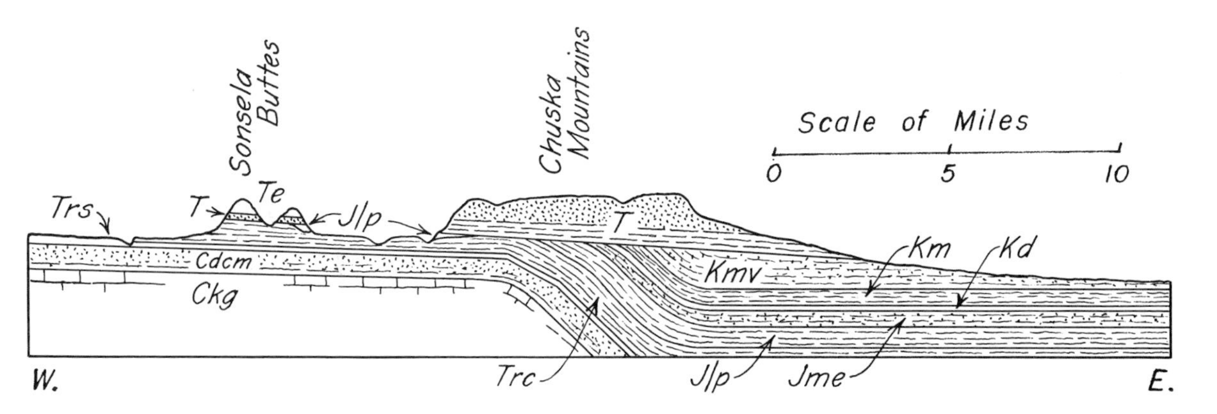

Figure 320. Section through the Chuska Mountains, northeastern Arizona, showing early Cenozoic (Eocene ?) sediments (*T*) resting unconformably on truncated Cretaceous (*Kd*, *Km*, *Kmv*) and older formations in the Defiance monocline. (After H. E. Gregory, U.S. Geological Survey.)

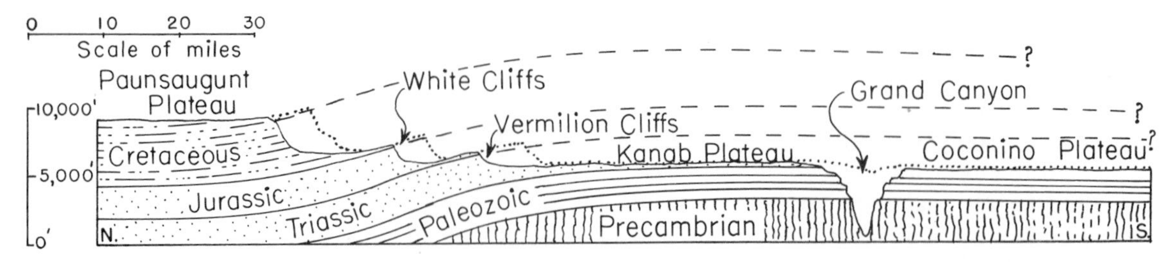

Figure 321. North-south section across the Grand Canyon region south of Kanab, Utah, showing relation of the present surface to the structure. The base line is drawn at sealevel. Dashed lines indicate the position Mesozoic formations would assume if the eroded portions were restored; dotted line indicates the profile before the last uplift, which initiated the cutting of the Grand Canyon.

the plateau, revealing a prebasalt surface of considerable relief (at least 2,500 feet), formed on schists, granites, and other pre-Cenozoic rocks.

As the flows spread over this region, they interrupted the drainage, damming streams and giving rise to local lakes and swamps in which sediments accumulated, entombing plant and vertebrate remains. Such fossiliferous deposits, now locally interbedded with the lavas, serve to date the eruptions. A noteworthy example is the **Latah formation** exposed in the valley of Spokane River near Spokane, Washington. Consisting of sands and clays and including much reworked volcanic ash, it has an exposed thickness of about 500 feet, but deep wells reveal 1,500 feet of such beds with interbedded lava flows. The deposit lies at the eastern margin of the Columbia Plateau and was formed in swamps and lakes created when the lava, flowing eastward, dammed the streams that flowed westward from the Rocky Mountain region in Idaho. The Latah formation has yielded a large number of well-preserved Miocene plants.

A similar deposit is the **Payette formation** exposed in the Snake River Valley on the Idaho-Oregon boundary about 250 miles south of Spokane. It has yielded both plant and vertebrate fossils of Miocene date. These and similar fossiliferous deposits interbedded with the flows indicate that the major part of the basalt eruption took place during Miocene time, though in some areas it continued into the Pliocene. In fact, Snake River Valley (which forms a southeastern lobe of the Columbia Plateau) is covered by black lavas of Pliocene and Pleistocene date in which the fresh appearance of spatter cones, like those of Craters of the Moon National Park, suggest activity within Recent time.

During eruption, and also in later epochs, the Columbia Plateau was broken locally by normal faults, and was subjected to extensive, though gentle, warping; hence the plateau surface now varies from 3,000 feet to more than 8,000 feet in elevation. In part, the warping may have compensated for the extrusion of the great volume of molten rock from beneath the crust.

The Pacific Border

The Cenozoic history of the region west of the Basin and Range Province is extremely complex, and not yet fully understood. As shown in Figures 317 and 322, it embraces two great mountain chains, separated by a series of large troughs. The eastern chain consists of two independent units, the Sierra Nevada of California and the Cascade Mountains of Oregon and Washington; the western chain embraces the Coast Ranges. The latter continue far to the north along the coast of British Columbia and have a counterpart to the south in the peninsula of Lower California. Between the Sierra Nevada and the Coast Ranges lies the California Trough, a structural basin which has its counterparts farther north in the Puget Sound Basin and to the south in the Gulf of California. The history of these units is complexly interrelated.

During Cenozoic time these structural troughs were depressed as the bordering mountains rose, and the sedimentary formations of this region are enormously thick, aggregating more than 50,000 feet. The sea repeatedly invaded the California Trough but seldom covered more than a small part of it, while non-marine sediments were accumulating in other parts. The Coast Range belt was in part submerged while undergoing complex deformation (both folding and faulting), with the result that relatively small embayments subsided to receive great depths of sediment from adjacent island masses that were rising.

Uplift of the Sierra Nevada. Figure 322 shows the structure and mutual relations of the Sierra Nevada, the California Trough, and the Coast Ranges of California. Although genetically related to the others, each has its distinctive form and structure.

The Sierra Nevada represents part of a colossal fault block more than 100 miles wide and 300 or 400 miles long. The eastern margin of this block has been uplifted to an elevation of about 13,000 feet (Fig. 323), and its western edge depressed perhaps 25,000 feet below sealevel. The uplifted part forms the Sierra Nevada, and the depressed half the California Trough.

The Sierra Nevada are sculptured from this single fault block of Jurassic and older rocks, and a great Cretaceous granite bathylith. Its early Cenozoic history is obscure, but by Miocene time the region had been peneplaned.

Axelrod[11] has studied fossil plants from near the Miocene-Pliocene boundary in 20 localities widely distributed from the lowlands of west-central California across the Sierra Nevada and the basins of western Nevada. The species are still living elsewhere or are closely allied to living types, and the floral assemblages are all closely related to living communities whose topographic and climatic requirements are well known. On the basis of this evidence Axelrod concludes that in late Miocene and early Pliocene time the site of the present Sierra Nevada was a broad plateau about 3,000 feet above sealevel and the lower land in western Nevada was at an altitude of about 2,000 feet. The temperature was then much milder and the rainfall over western Nevada was more plentiful than now. Uplift of the Sierra Nevada by more than 6,000 feet since early Miocene time has lowered the rainfall in the basins to the east and reduced the temperature over the mountain region.

Uplift began later in Miocene time accompanied

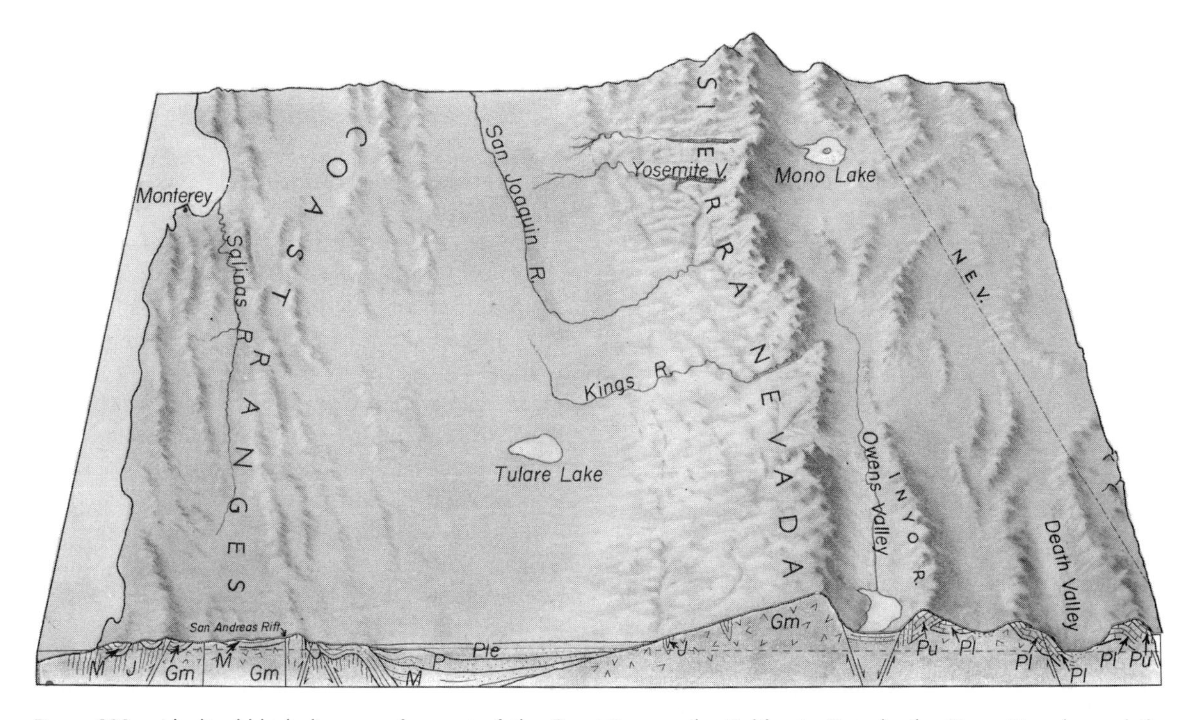

Figure 322. Idealized block diagram of a part of the Coast Ranges, the California Trough, the Sierra Nevada, and the Basin and Range Province. The view is northward. Length of section along front face, about 250 miles. Vertical scale exaggerated about 50 times. *Gm*, Mesozoic granite; *J*, Jurassic; *K*, Cretaceous; *M*, Miocene; *P*, Pliocene; *Ple*, Pleistocene; *Pl*, Lower-Paleozoic; *Pu*, Upper Paleozoic.

Figure 323. East face of the Sierra Nevada, a great fault scarp 2 miles high. Telephoto view westward from Owens Valley, California. Compare Figure 322. (F. E. Matthes, U.S. Geological Survey.)

by normal faulting along the eastern front of the Sierra Nevada. This produced only moderate relief and during Pliocene time westward-flowing streams then opened out broad valleys. About the beginning of the Pleistocene, new uplift and westward tilting began, but the great uplift occurred near the middle of this epoch, after the second glacial age. This elevation of several thousands of feet brought the mountains to their present altitude and started the westward-flowing streams cutting canyons within their broad valleys.

Evidence of these distinct stages of uplift is found in (1) the cross-profiles of the valleys (Fig. 324), and (2) the character of the deposits formed by these streams in the California Trough.

RÉSUMÉ OF CENOZOIC OROGENY AND VOLCANISM: THE CASCADIAN REVOLUTION

From the foregoing account, it must be clear that the Cenozoic was an age of great crustal disturbance and extraordinary volcanic activity in the western half of North America. The Laramide thrusting died out irregularly during the long Eocene Epoch, and the Oligocene was a time of comparative quiet during which most of the Cordilleran region was again reduced to lowlands.

Renewed disturbance began in the Miocene and continued intermittently to its culmination in the far-flung regional uplift of the Pleistocene. This last great orogeny has been called the **Cascadian Revolution.** The Cascade Mountains were in the midst of the vast area of disturbance but actually comprised only a small part of it. The movements were complex and diversified, but on the whole they were predominantly vertical movements (epeirogenic, not orogenic) accompanied by normal faulting. In this we see a marked contrast with the Laramide Revolution, which involved great horizontal forces and eventually produced enormous thrust faults and great folds. During the Cascadian movements, folding was largely confined to the Coast Ranges and the Puget Sound Basin. In the former it probably resulted largely from the squeezing or wedging produced by differential subsidence of fault blocks. In the Puget Sound area, where the thick Eocene beds are steeply upturned, the horizontal compression may have come from the intrusion of a large granitic bathylith into the northern part of the Cascade Mountains during Miocene time.

Throughout the Cordilleran region the last movements were chiefly those of regional uplift in late Pliocene and Pleistocene time. The greatest crustal movement in California evidently took place in middle Pleistocene time, because the later deposits lie unconformably on the deformed early Pleistocene strata.

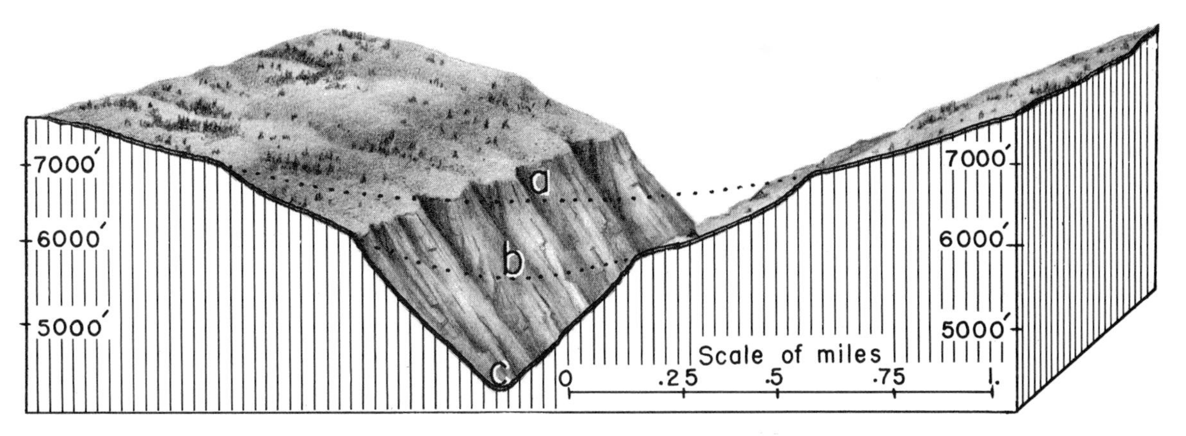

Figure 324. Cross-profile of Merced River Valley below Yosemite Valley, showing evidence of two stages of uplift. *a*, profile of the old, broad valley, probably of late Miocene date when the region was still low; *b*, profile of the mountain valley stage (probably late Pliocene), cut after the first strong uplift and westward tilting of the Sierra block; *c*, canyon stage, cut during the Pleistocene in consequence of the last great uplift of the Sierra. (After F. E. Matthes, U.S. Geological Survey.)

In every respect the Pleistocene Epoch is allied with the Pliocene, and if it were not for its extensive glaciation, the Pleistocene would probably never have been differentiated. The Pleistocene is clearly a part of the Cenozoic Era. Whether the climax of orogeny and uplift is now past, only the future can tell; we are too close to it to judge.

Volcanic activity occurred in the Cordilleran

Figure 325. Lava flows of the Absaroka Range present the appearance of horizontal strata from a distance. Looking north across Shoshone Canyon about 25 miles west of Cody, Wyoming. (Carl O. Dunbar.)

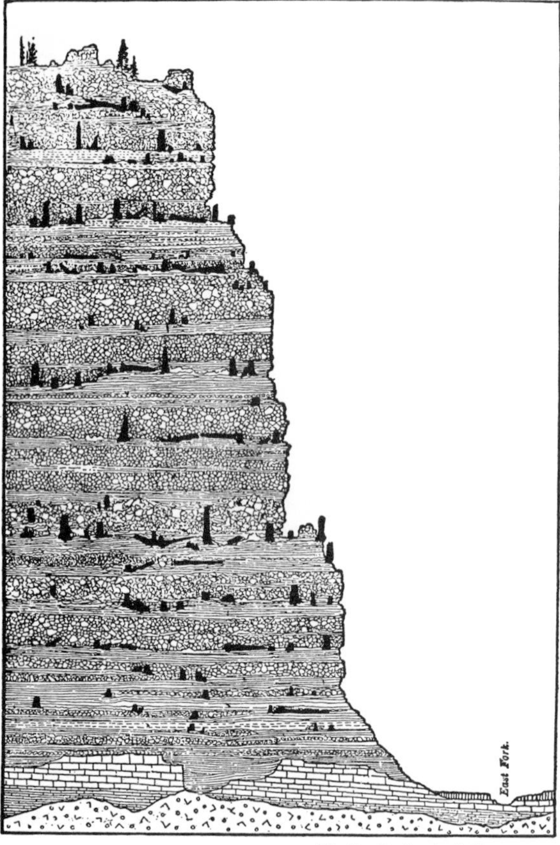

U. S. Geological Survey.

Figure 326. Profile section of Amethyst Cliff in Yellowstone Park, showing remains of 18 successive forests, each killed and buried in turn by volcanic materials. Section about 2,000 feet thick. (U.S. Geological Survey.)

region during this era on a scale not approached at any other time since the remote Precambrian. Volcanoes were active at the beginning of the era in most if not all of the western states. Great basalt flows during the Eocene covered an area in western Washington and Oregon more extensive than all New England. At the same time andesitic flows built up the Absaroka Range (Fig. 325) and the plateau upon which Yellowstone Park is located, covering fault-block ranges of Mesozoic and older rocks to a depth of many hundreds of feet. Here the lavas overwhelmed forests at successive intervals of hundreds of years, as seen in Amethyst Cliff, where the stumps of 18 successive forests stand petrified (Figs. 326, 327).

Sedimentary beds interstratified with the lava and pyroclastics along the southern border of the Absaroka Plateau prove that volcanoes were active there during middle and late Eocene as well as Oligocene time. The older volcanics of the Yellowstone Park are also of Eocene age, and the younger ones chiefly Miocene, though present geysers and hot prings indicate that volcanic heat still smoulders.

Many explosive volcanoes were active in Oligocene time, for the White River sediments are in considerable part reworked volcanic ash. During this epoch, John Day Basin in central Oregon was filled to a depth of 2,000 to 3,000 feet with reworked volcanic ash that has preserved an amazing array of fossil mammals.

The Miocene was, however, the time of truly colossal volcanism. During this epoch occurred most of the basic eruptions of the Columbia Plateau, Snake River Valley, and the Cascade Mountains, a vast field of basalt covering an area of more than 200,000 square miles. At the same time a great field of volcanoes in southwestern Colorado built up the San Juan Mountain mass. Volcanoes were scattered over the Basin and Range region and the Colorado Plateau, and spread over much of western Mexico to form the Sierra Madre Occidental. Igneous activity in the Black Hills of South Dakota gave rise to a remarkable series of laccoliths whose partly denuded forms are now striking features of the region.

In many of these regions volcanism continued with decreased vigor through the Pliocene and into the Pleistocene, no fewer than 120 fields of volcanoes being known with cones that were still active in the Pleistocene. Near Trinidad in the foothills of eastern Colorado occur other impressive features of Cenozoic igneous activity. Spanish Peaks are a pair of denuded majestic Eocene intrusives with a unique display of great radial dikes. A short distance southeast of these lie Raton Mesas and Mesa de Maya (Fig. 328), which are remnants of Pleistocene basalt flows that spread eastward over the plains almost to the Kansas line.

CENOZOIC OROGENY AND VOLCANISM IN OTHER CONTINENTS

The history of the Andean chain of South Amer ica paralleled that of the Rockies in many respects. Folded at the close of the Mesozoic, the Andes were extensively peneplaned during the earlier half

Figure 327. Fossil tree trunks exposed in the face of Amethyst Cliff, Yellowstone Park. Compare with Figures 326, and 19, p. 33. (J. P. Iddings, U.S. Geological Survey.)

of the Cenozoic and then, chiefly during Pliocene and Pleistocene time, were vertically elevated by several thousands of feet to their present height.

The Alpine-Himalayan systems, stretching from western Europe to the East Indies, had a complex and spectacular Cenozoic history (Fig. 329). The beginning of the Alps goes back to the Mesozoic, when a very broad geosyncline occupied by the greater ancestral Mediterranean (Tethys) spread over all southern Europe and eastward across the Himalayan region. In Jurassic time horizontal compression from the south caused two or three great folds to rise out of this sea. Although this marks the beginning of the Alpine structures, the region as a whole remained submerged during much of Cretaceous time. At the close of the

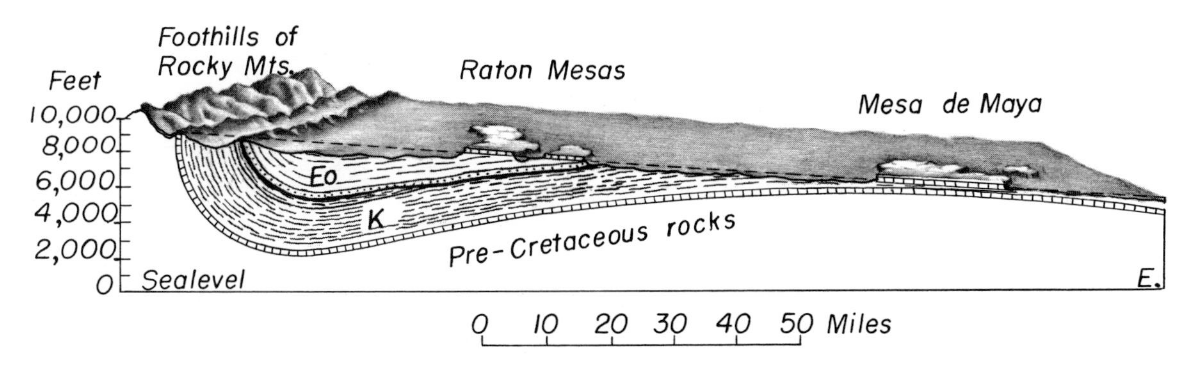

Figure 328. East-west section through Raton Mesas and Mesa de Maya, near Trinidad, Colorado. The mesas are remnants of a Pleistocene lava flow that spread from the foothills of the Rockies almost to the Kansas line. The lava rests on beveled Eocene strata, which in turn rest on Cretaceous. *Eo*, Eocene; *K*, Cretaceous. (After Willis T. Lee, U.S. Geological Survey.)

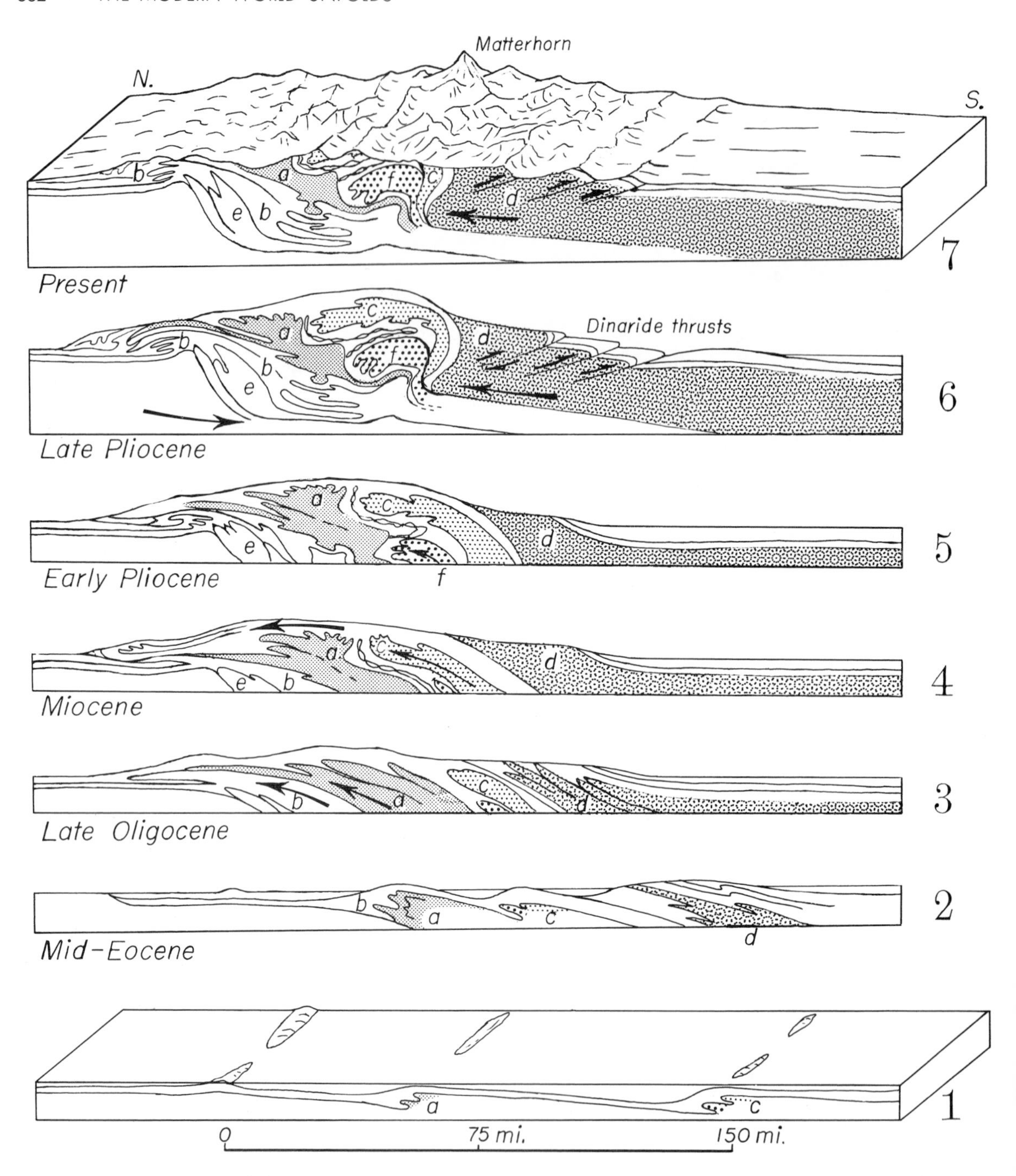

Figure 329. Development of the western Alps. Block 1 represents a belt across the Alpine region in late Mesozoic time when it was still largely covered by the Tethyan Sea; block 7 shows a corresponding area in the modern Alps; and blocks 2 to 6 show how the modern structure developed during Cenozoic time as a series of nappes were thrust one over another toward the north. Finally, in late Pliocene time, underthrusting steepened the roots of the southern nappes and caused a series of thrusts toward the south, now seen in the Dinaric Alps. *a*, Great St. Bernard nappe; *b*, nappes of the Pre-Alps; c, Dent Blanche nappe; *d*, nappe of the southern Alps; e, Mont Blanc massive; *f*, Monta Rosa nappe. (Adapted from a figure by Collet, after Argand.)

Cretaceous there was further compression and some uplift, and in the Eocene the first decided thrust, but marine waters returned between the rising geanticlinal folds and persisted widely until middle Oligocene time. Then occurred the first great paroxysm of Alpine orogeny as the compression from the south caused great recumbent folds to rise as mountain arcs out of the sea, and to ride forward over the old foreland north of the geosyncline, where they piled up as a series of nappes (Fig. 329).

Before these great thrusts lay a lowland, now the Swiss Plateau. Over this was spread, during late Oligocene and Miocene, a vast piedmont deposit (the **Molasse**) of sand and coarse gravel derived from the rising mountains. Most of it is of fresh-water deposition, like the Cenozoic deposits east of the Rockies, but marine horizons show that the sea still had access to the northern border of the Alps as late as Miocene time. In the Pliocene came further great thrusts from the south that caused the older nappes to ride out over the Molasse and buckled up the Jura folds that now form the northern front of the Alps. This also gave a great regional uplift that reached its culmination in the Pleistocene.

The history thus sketched for the Alps is, in general, that of the Carpathians, the Dinaric Alps of Dalmatia, and the Himalayas. In the southern one of the three ranges that make up the Himalayan System, marine Eocene formations now occur at an elevation of 20,000 feet, bearing witness to the tremendous uplift experienced by that region since Early Cenozoic time. The foothills of the southern Himalayas are believed to have suffered an uplift of 6,000 feet since the beginning of the middle Pleistocene.

Many countries also had volcanic activity during Cenozoic time. In Central America especially, and in Mexico, the Antillean Islands, and the Andean Plateau, there were great outpourings of lava. The North Atlantic was also the scene of large basalt flows, now displayed in northern Ireland (Giant's Causeway), northwest Scotland, the Orkney Islands, the plateau of Iceland, and eastern Greenland. The great rift valleys of East Africa constituted another arena of great eruptions. Finally, during Pliocene and Pleistocene time, volcanic chains became active in the Mediterranean region and in Alaska, Japan, and the East Indies, completing the "Ring of Fire" around the Pacific.

CENOZOIC CLIMATES

Fossil plants throw much light on Cenozoic climate. The forest trees have come down to us with only trivial change since early Cenozoic time and probably have not changed appreciably their preferred habitat. Moreover, it is well known that most of them are restricted in their distribution by rainfall and temperature, each preferring a definite environment. Accordingly, the vegetation of a subtropical lowland like Florida has little in common with that of a desert basin, or with the forests of a temperate mountain slope, or with the subarctic barrens. Thus it is possible to infer the climatic conditions under which a Cenozoic flora lived.

A comprehensive study of such material throughout western North America has shown a striking change of climate since early Cenozoic time. During the Eocene and Oligocene epochs subtropical types of trees, now restricted to moist lowlands, ranged widely over the United States and Europe. Palms and alligators were then common as far north as the Dakotas, suggesting a climate like that of modern Florida and Louisiana. At the same time a moist temperate forest existed in high northern latitudes, notably in Alaska, Greenland, Spitzbergen, and northern Siberia. It was dominated by the giant redwood and included such deciduous trees as the basswood, beech, chestnut, and elm. Even cycads, magnolias, and figs then lived in Alaska.

The O^{18}/O^{16} ratio in fossil shells from cores in the deep ocean floor strikingly confirms the evidence from land plants. The reasoning is as follows: water from the polar regions settles to the bottom and spreads over the deep ocean basins. As a result, under present conditions, the temperature below a depth of 15,000 feet is nearly constant and is barely above the freezing point even in low latitudes. But bottom-dwelling foraminiferal shells in cores from the Pacific Ocean floor west of South America indicate that the bottom temperature was about 51°F. at a date of 32,000,000 B.P. The polar regions must then have had a warm temperate climate.[12]

The climate was not only milder and more humid, but also more uniform than now over the far western United States, evidently because the region was generally low and the mountains were not lofty enough to interfere seriously with the moisture-bearing westerly winds.

After Eocene time there was a slow but general southward migration of the various plant assemblages, indicating a gradual cooling of the climate that became more marked in Pliocene time and culminated in the Pleistocene glaciation. Meanwhile, in Miocene and Pliocene time, the climate became more diversified in the western United States as the rising mountains intercepted the winds, producing moist western slopes with arid regions in their lee. The diversity was not nearly so extreme or so widespread in Miocene time as it is today, though the salt and other precipitates entombed in the Miocene deposits of southern Nevada indicate rather intense local aridity in the basins then forming. Even as late as early Pliocene time, however, a flora like that of southern California was still living in western Nevada (the Esmeralda flora), indicating a rainfall of 12 to 15 inches a year in a region where the present rainfall is only 4 inches. The final uplift of the Cordilleran ranges in late Pliocene and Pleistocene time gave the intermont basins and the Great Plains their present degree of aridity.

Supposed glacial tillite (Ridgeway formation) of southwestern Colorado is now believed to be made of mudflows formed under normal, humid climate.[13] The widespread plant evidence indicated above shows that by Eocene time warm temperate climate had spread as far north as the Arctic Circle.

ECONOMIC RESOURCES

Petroleum. Two of the major American oil fields draw their production from Cenozoic rocks. The Gulf Coast pools of Louisiana and southeast Texas are in small domes associated generally with stocklike plugs of rock salt that have pressed up from below into Miocene sands and clays. The California oil fields likewise draw nearly all their oil from Miocene (over 30 percent) and lower Pliocene (65 percent) strata.

Although the greatest American oil fields are in Paleozoic or Mesozoic rocks, it is a very striking fact that nearly all the foreign fields are in Cenozoic formations. For example, the rich Baku fields of Russia produce from the Miocene, the Galician fields from the Eocene, Oligocene, and Miocene, the Rumanian fields from Oligocene to Pliocene, and those of Burma, Sumatra, Java, and Japan from the Miocene, and those of the Persian Gulf chiefly from the Miocene.

Coal. Lignite occurs in the Eocene of the Gulf Coast but is not commercially exploited. In the Puget Sound region, however, the strong folding of the coal-bearing series has advanced the Eocene coals to a sub-bituminous rank. These coals are now being extensively used west of the Sierra Nevada and Cascade ranges. Production of 1,202,000 tons in 1957 was, however, scarcely one-fifth of one percent of the coal mined in the United States. About 2,500,000 tons of lignite was produced in North Dakota in 1957, chiefly from the Fort Union formation. In most parts of the world, Cenozoic coals are of lignite or low-grade sub-bituminous rank, and therefore of little present value.

Placer Gold. As noted before, the placers, which yield about two-thirds of the annual gold of California, were formed during Cenozoic time by streams degrading the Mother Lode belt in the Sierra Nevada. During the early decades nearly all the gold was secured from placers, and they still yield about two-thirds of California's gold. In 1957 the placer gold was valued at more than $4,000,000.

Metalliferous Veins. The fabulous wealth of gold, silver, and copper so widely distributed throughout the Rocky Mountain region is for the most part a by-product of the intrusions of Cenozoic time. The mineral-bearing solutions of various sorts formed the vast copper deposits of Bingham, Utah, of Morenci, Arizona, and of Santa Rita, New Mexico. The silver of Park City, Utah, as well as of the great Comstock Lode, Tonopah, and other localities in Nevada, was similarly formed in middle and later Cenozoic time. The gold of many of the spectacular mining camps of the West, such as Goldfield, Nevada, and Cripple Creek in the Rockies, had a similar date of origin.

Mexico, Central America, Peru, and Bolivia also provide notable examples of the great mineral wealth we owe to the crustal disturbances and intrusive activity of the Cenozoic.

Diatomaceous Earth. Diatomite, a white porous rock formed of diatom shells, now finds many uses in industry. It is used for insulation, as a filter for purifying water, alcoholic beverages, antibiotics, sugar, oil and solvents, and as a filler in paper, paints, plastics, and soap. In 1957 the production in the United States was over 638,000 tons valued at $2,230,000. All of it comes from Cenozoic rocks and the chief source is in the Miocene formations of California.

REFERENCES

1. Swain, F. M., 1947, Two recent wells in Coastal Plain of North Carolina. *Amer. Assoc. Petroleum Geol., Bull.*, vol. 31, pp. 2054–2060.

2. Howe, Henry, et al., 1935, Geology of Cameron and Vermillion Parishes. *Louisiana Geol. Surv., Bull. 6*, pp. 1–242.

3. White, T. C., 1942, The Lower Miocene Mammalian Fauna of Florida. *Bull. Mus. Comp. Zool.*, vol. 92, pp. 1–49.

4. Applin, Paul L., 1951, Preliminary report on buried pre-Mesozoic rocks in Florida and adjacent states. *U.S. Geol. Surv., Circular 91*, pp. 1–27.

5. Atwood, Wallace A., and Wallace A. Atwood, Jr., 1938, Working hypothesis for the physiographic history of the Rocky Mountain region. *Geol. Soc. Amer., Bull.*, vol. 49, pp. 957–980.

6. Blackwelder, Eliot, 1909, Cenozoic history of the Laramie region, Wyoming. *Jour. Geol.*, vol. 17, pp. 429–444.

7. Dorf, Erling, 1940, Relationship between floras of type Lance and Fort Union formations. *Geol. Soc. Amer., Bull.*, vol. 51, pp. 213–235.

Fox, S. K., and R. J. Ross, Jr., 1942, Foraminiferal evidence for the Midway (Paleocene) age of the Cannonball formation in North Dakota. *Jour. Paleontology*, vol. 16, pp. 660–673.

8. Benson, W. E. and W. M. Laird, 1947, Eocene in North Dakota. *Geol. Soc. Amer., Bull.*, vol. 58, p. 1166.

9. Bradley, Wilmot H., 1929, The varves and climate of the Green River epoch. *U.S. Geol. Surv., Prof. Paper 158*, pp. 87–110.

10. Longwell, Chester R., 1946, How old is the Colorado River? *Amer. Jour. Sci.*, vol. 244, pp. 817–835. The principle advanced by Longwell is valid but the later discovery of Miocene vertebrate fossils in the Muddy Creek formation proves that the river may be as old as Miocene instead of Pliocene age.

11. Axelrod, Daniel I., 1956, Mio-Pliocene floras from west-central Nevada. *Univ. of California Publ. in Geol. Sci.*, vol. 33, pp. 1–322.

12. Emiliani, Cesare, 1947, Ancient temperatures. *Scientific American*, vol. 198, no. 2, pp. 54–66.

13. Van Houten, F. B., 1957, Appraisal of Ridgeway and Gunnison "Tillites," southwestern Colorado. *Geol. Soc. Amer., Bull.*, vol. 68, pp. 383–388.

Figure 330. Margin of a continent still in the Ice Age. Shore zone north of Gneiss Point, Antarctica. At the right glacier ice is flowing into the sea; in the left foreground a tabular iceberg is surrounded by floe ice. (Official United States Navy photograph.)

Chapter 18. Ice Sculptures the Final Scene

The Pleistocene Ice Ages. GLACIER ICE HAS RECENTLY covered approximately one-third of the land surface of the Earth. Its effects may be seen on every hand—in the serrate crests of mountains carved by valley glaciers, in the lake lands of Canada and Scandinavia, and in the drift plains of the north-central states and of north-central Europe. Over large parts of the Northern Hemisphere, human culture and industry have been profoundly influenced by this event, for the glaciers stripped away the soil from some regions, made swamplands of others, deposited coarse boulder till in places, and over large areas spread the materials of an uncommonly deep, rich soil. In such parts of the world, ice has given the final touches in the shaping of the modern landscape.

In view of the far-reaching influence of glaciation during this last geologic epoch, the Pleistocene has picturesquely been called **The Ice Age.** Such a term, however, is a misnomer. It disregards the fact that there was not one ice age but four, and that together they comprised but a small part of Pleistocene time. In other respects this last epoch is closely allied to the Pliocene and earlier epochs of the era, and for that reason it was treated with the rest in the preceding chapter. The long interglacial ages differed in no important respects from the preceding ages of the Pliocene. Nevertheless, the glacial ages have such interest and importance that this special chapter is devoted to that one aspect of Pleistocene history.

Extent of the Glaciation

Distribution of Glacier Ice. Three major ice sheets were present in the Northern Hemisphere

Figure 331. Pleistocene ice sheets of the Northern Hemisphere.

(Fig. 331). One of these, centered over Hudson Bay, occupied nearly all of Canada and spread southward into the United States; another centered over Scandinavia and reached the plains of north Germany and spread eastward across north-central Siberia; and the third occupied the highlands of eastern Siberia. Greenland was ice-capped then as now, and the Scandinavian Ice Sheet extended southward across the floor of the North Sea and covered all of the British Isles except the southern edge of England. In the Southern Hemisphere Antarctica undoubedly was ice-covered, and the highlands of Patagonia in South America and of South Island in New Zealand were heavily glaciated. In addition, nearly all the lofty mountains of the world were capped by snow, and valley glaciers reached far below the present snowline.

It is remarkable that the glacier ice covered great areas of lowland, and in central United States reached south of latitude 40° where, at present, summer temperatures of 100°F. are not rare and where the regional snowline is at least 6,000 feet above sealevel.

In the United States the higher parts of the Rocky Mountains were glaciated as far south as New Mexico (Fig. 332), and the Sierra Nevada and Cascade ranges were also ice-covered. Glacier National Park in the Rockies and Yosemite Valley in the Sierra Nevada afford well-known illustrations of the work of these Pleistocene glaciers. The Alps, the Himalayas, the Caucasus, the Pamir, and other lofty ranges of Eurasia carried great snowfields from which valley glaciers pushed out beyond the foothills onto the plains. The higher parts of the Andes in South America also had extensive glaciers.

The directions of ice movement in North America are indicated in Figure 332. These have been determined by mapping the end moraines, by plotting the direction of glacial striae, and by noting the distribution in the drift of boulders of distinctive types of rock that could be traced back to their sources. The striking fact is that the ice did not spread southward from the polar region but radiated from centers in the latitude of Hudson Bay.

Two quite distinct sheets can be distinguished, even though they formed parts of a single great field of ice. The larger of these is the **Laurentide Ice Sheet,**[1] which centered over Hudson Bay and thence spread southward for a distance of some 1,600 miles across the Great Lakes region into the Mississippi Valley. It also spread westward up the long slope of the High Plains to the foothills of the Rockies and northward to the Arctic islands. On the east and northeast the ice pushed out to sea and, at its maximum, may have been continuous with the Greenland Ice Sheet.

It is probable that the Laurentide glacier ice first began to form over the mountains of eastern Labrador and Baffin Island[1] and from there grew westward until the center of accumulation was in the Hudson Bay area.*

The second major ice sheet was the **Cordilleran Glacier Complex,** which occupied the mountainous region of western Canada. Ice probably began to form here as valley glaciers that radiated from the highest parts of the Coast Ranges and the Rockies. As these rivers of ice were extended to the lowlands, they developed into a complex of piedmont glaciers that not only spread over the foothills east of the Rockies and into the sea west of the Coast Ranges, but also converged to fill the broad basin between the two mountain systems. Up to this time the high ranges, intercepting the moisture-bearing winds, had been the chief centers of accumulation, and the spread of ice had been in part centripetal. As the intermont basin was filled, however, it became the chief center of accumulation from which movement radiated over both the Coast Ranges and the Rockies.

Thickness of the Ice. There is no direct evidence of the thickness attained at the center of the Laurentide Ice Sheet. The area of this Pleistocene sheet (4,800,000 square miles) was somewhat greater than the existing ice cap of Antarctica (4,000,000 square miles). The surface of the ice in Greenland and on Antarctica is about 10,000 feet above sealevel and appears almost flat except near the periphery, where it slopes off with increasing steepness to the wasting margins. During maximum glaciation the ice of the Laurentide sheet flowed westward up the long slope to the foothills of the Rockies, where it reached an elevation of about 4,000 feet, and in its southward flow it covered the White Mountains (exceeding 5,000

*The current belief that there were two independent centers of accumulation in this region, one west of Hudson Bay and another over Labrador, is not borne out by recent studies.[1]

feet) and probably all of the Adirondacks (exceeding 4,000 feet). Since ice moves in the direction toward which its surface slopes, the altitude at the center of accumulation must have exceeded by a considerable amount the height of these features which the ice overrode near its periphery. Since the surface of the land about Hudson Bay is near sealevel (and was then probably depressed by a thousand feet or more under the weight of the ice), it is not unlikely that the glacier was at least 8,000 to 10,000 feet thick over a large area.

GLACIAL AND INTERGLACIAL AGES

When erratic boulders strewn over the plains of northern Europe and over New England were recognized as the work of a former ice sheet, they

Figure 332. Pleistocene glacier ice in North America. Somewhat generalized to show the maximum extent of glaciation. Arrows show general direction of ice movement. (Adapted from R. F. Flint.)

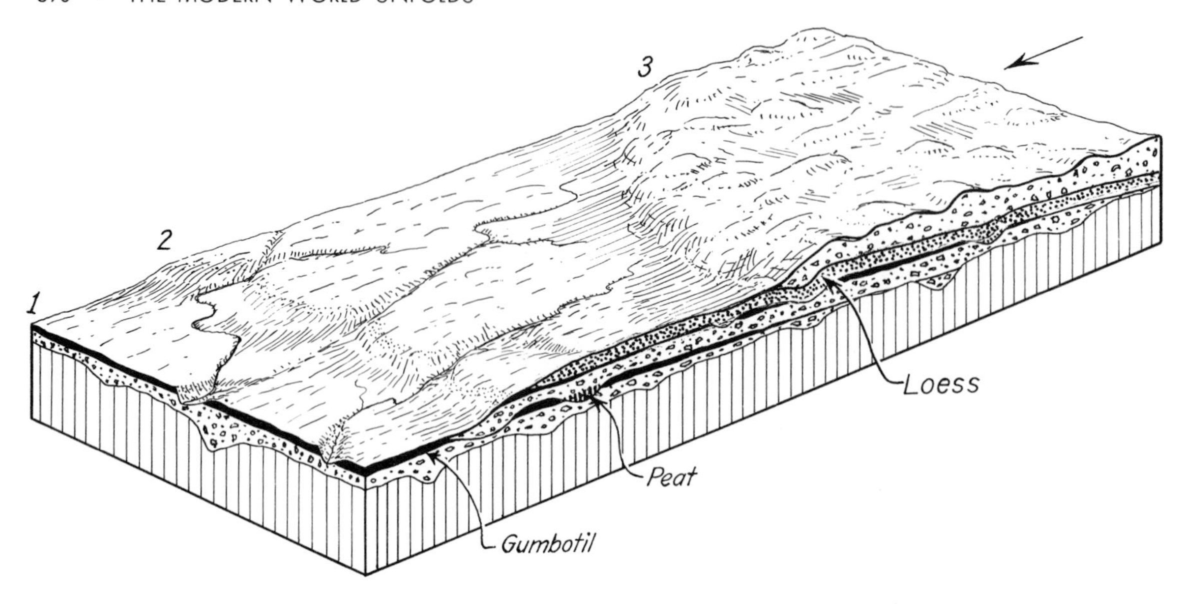

Figure 333. Idealized block diagram showing the relations of three imbricated drift sheets. The block represents an area many miles across, and the vertical scale is exaggerated. The first glaciation spread till across the entire region. In the long interglacial age that followed, the surface of this first drift sheet was weathered to gumbotil (*black*). The second advance of the ice fell short of the first, and in a broad marginal belt the glacier ice overrode the older till, gumbotil, and peat deposits. During a second interglacial age this till in turn suffered long weathering and developed a gumbotil. In connection with the third glaciation, loess was spread widely over the older drift, and this in turn was overridden by the glacier ice, which fell short of the middle of this area. No gumbotil has yet formed on the youngest till.

were at first quite naturally attributed to a single glaciation. But as the study of the glacial deposits was carried westward into Illinois, Wisconsin, and Iowa, two distinct sheets of drift were found at many places to be separated by old soil, beds of peat, or layers of till that had been leached and decayed (Fig. 333). Here the uppermost drift, like that in New England, appeared fresh, but the buried drift sheet showed the effect of chemical decay and was obviously much the older. Moreover, in places, the soil and peat or gravels between two such sheets of till included fossil wood, leaves, or bones, recording the existence of animals and plants of temperate climate. Thus it came to be realized, about 1870, that a continental ice sheet had developed more than once, and that warm interglacial ages had intervened during which the ice melted away, forests grew over the glaciated regions, and plants and animals from warm temperate climates migrated northward even beyond their present limits. Eventually four glacial and three interglacial ages were recognized in the upper Mississippi Valley. Each glacial age was named after a state in which its deposits are well displayed. These are, in chronologic order, the **Nebraskan, Kansan, Illinoian,** and **Wisconsin** Ice Ages (Table II). The interglacial ages are named for localities where their records are well displayed.

While this chronology was being worked out in America, four glacial and three interglacial ages were recognized also in Europe and were given local European names. It is now certain, however, that the glacial ages were essentially synchronous on both sides of the Atlantic.

Records of the Wisconsin Ice Age are so fresh and so widespread that its history has been worked out in even greater detail, revealing that the ice sheet receded a considerable distance to the north and then readvanced on three successive occasions. As a result, the Wisconsin glacial age is now divided into four glacial and three interglacial subages, as indicated in Table II.

Evidence of Multiple Glaciation

Stratigraphy of the Drift Sheets. In the region of growth, moving glacier ice scours away the loose mantle and leaves a surface of bare rock, but toward its thinning margin it tends to drop its load and may even override loose mantle and soil. Wherever melting balances forward movement for a time and the ice front remains stationary, a marginal moraine builds up to form a record of the ice margin at that particular time; and when the ice sheet becomes stagnant and finally melts away, it leaves a widespread ground moraine. If a succeeding ice advance were more extensive than the first it would destroy the earlier record, but if less extensive it may leave a second drift sheet superposed on the older one, as indicated in Figure 333. Fortunately, across the Mississippi Valley the Nebraskan Ice Sheet advanced farthest south, the Kansan not quite as far, and the Illinoian and Wisconsin in turn stopped still farther north (Fig. 334). Here, then, four distinct sheets of till are superposed in imbricated fashion as ideally represented in Figure 333, and even the interglacial deposits are locally preserved between successive till sheets (Fig. 335).

The **Wisconsin** drift sheet, being the youngest, is the most easily mapped and the best understood. Its end moraines loop across the Central Lowlands in festoons that outline the great southern lobes of the ice. Its surface retains the characteristic features of a glacial deposit—the swells and swales of the end moraine, and the broad undulations and lakes and swamps of the ground moraine, locally diversified by drumlins. A thin soil has formed over it and peat has accumulated extensively in the lakes and swales, but chemical decay is limited to slight leaching to a depth of 2 or 3 feet and most of its boulders are as fresh and solid as quarried stone. Except along the main streams

TABLE II

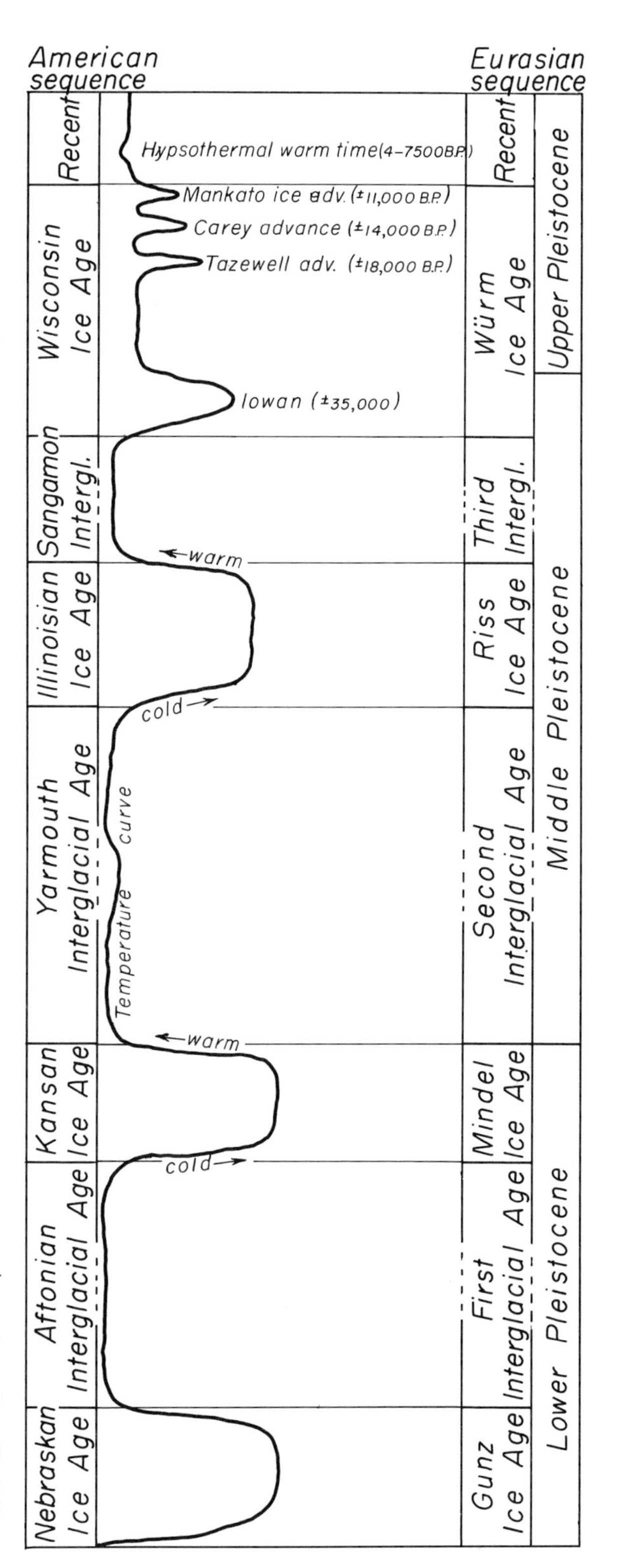

Subdivisions of the Pleistocene Epoch based upon the glacial record. Space allotted to subdivisions of the Wisconsin Age are to scale and are based on C^{14} dates. Space allotted to the older subdivisions are not based on radioactive dates and are probably too small as indicated by the broken lines. The Aftonian and Yarmouth interglacial ages are inferred from the degree and depth of weathering of the preceding till sheets to have been several times as long as postglacial time. The temperature curve is idealized and without scale.

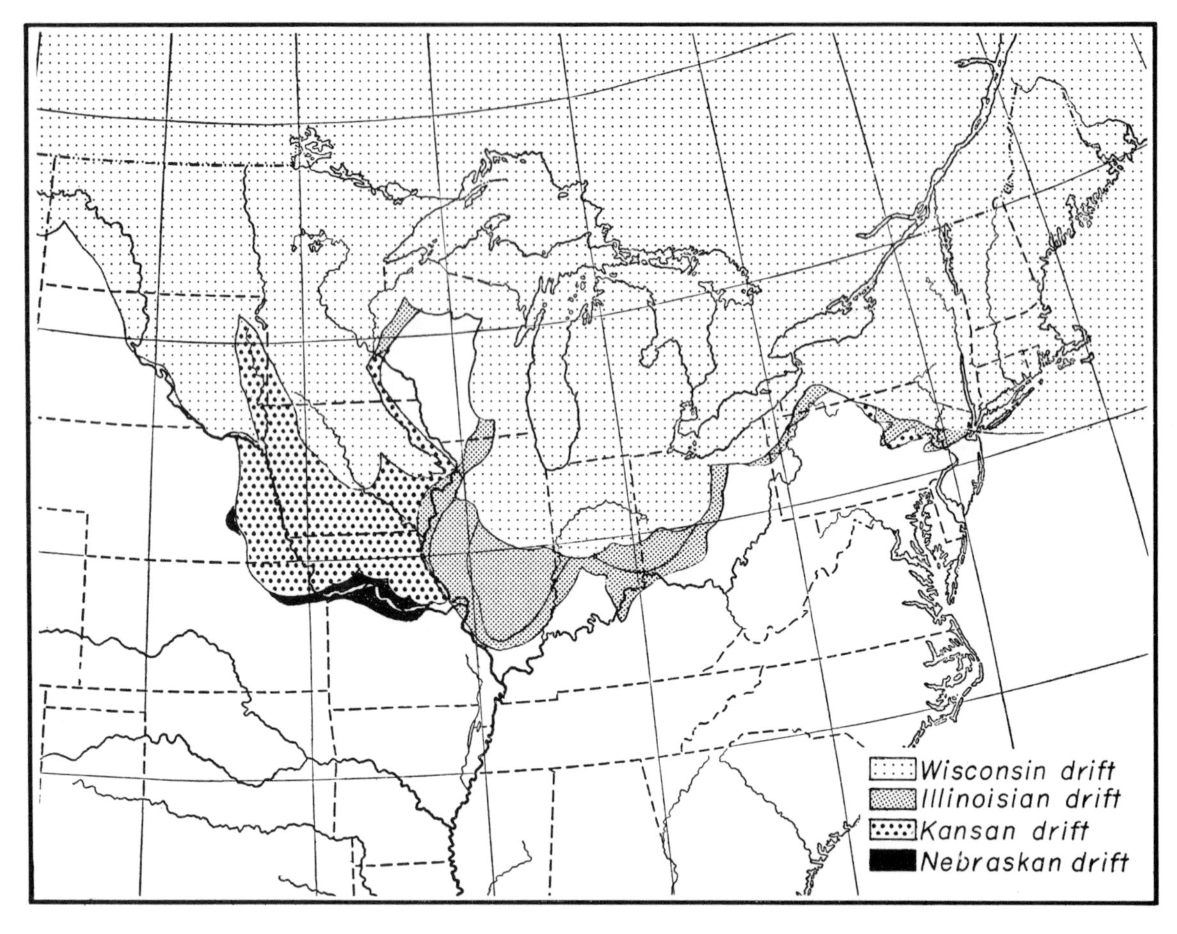

Figure 334. Map showing the southern limit of glacial drift in the United States. Note that in the Mississippi Valley the older drift sheets extend farther south than the youngest, and here four sheests are differentiated. (After R. F. Flint.)

its surface has scarcely been altered by erosion and the outwash plains and valley trains beyond the marginal moraines are still easily recognized. Obviously the Wisconsin till was formed in the recent past.

The **Illinoian** drift extends well south of the Wisconsin drift in Illinois, southern Indiana, and central Ohio, and here it is obviously the older. Its surface retains traces of moranic topography but long weathering and mass wastage on the swells, and deposition in the swales, have softened the relief. In contrast to the freshness of the younger till, the Illinoian drift has been extensively oxidized to a depth of 10 to 25 feet and chemical alteration of the fine particles near the surface has produced a distinctive layer of sticky clay, known as **gumbotil**, about 4 feet thick. Obviously the Illinoian drift has been exposed to weathering much longer than the Wisconsin till; and since the gumbotil is present even where overlapped by the Wisconsin drift, it is evident that the long weathering took place before Wisconsin glaciation.

Furthermore, the Illinoian drift is widely covered by a deposit of wind-blown dust (the Loveland loess) that passes under the Wisconsin drift and must also have formed before the last glaciation.

The **Kansan** drift sheet is widely exposed in Iowa, Missouri, and northeastern Kansas where it averages about 50 feet in thickness. It is even more deeply weathered and decayed than the Illinoian, and its capping of gumbotil is much thicker, averaging about 11 feet (Fig. 335). In places the Kansan till is covered with outwash gravels and in these the granite pebbles and boulders are so weathered that they crumble and fall to pieces at a blow from a hammer. A thick layer of loess covers the Kansan drift (Fig. 335) and in several places beds of peat have been preserved between the Kansan and Illinoian till.

The **Nebraskan** drift had about the same distribution as the Kansan, and its exposures are therefore limited, but it lies buried beneath most of the outcropping Kansan till, where it averages 100 feet or more in thickness and rests on an irregularly eroded preglacial surface. The gumbotil on the Nebraskan drift averages about 8 feet thick, and scattered lenses of peat are preserved between it and the Kansan till.

Pollen Analysis. Modern plants are grouped in characteristic assemblages each adapted to a distinct climatic environment. Such, for example, are the tundra plants of the north barrens, the fir-spruce forests of the north, the tamarack assemblage, and the pine-mixed hardwood forests of the temperate zone. Fortunately each species produces pollen grains of distinctive size and shape by which it can be readily identified. Study of the pollen abundantly preserved in a peat bog thus enables us to determine the type of vegetation surrounding it while the peat was accumulating.

In this way pollen analysis of the peat associated with interglacial and postglacial deposits has in recent years thrown much light on climatic variation during Pleistocene time. For example, peat of the Sangamon interglacial stage at Wapello, Iowa, records vegetation identical with that now inhabiting the area, suggesting that while this peat was forming the climate in Iowa was like that of the present. On the other hand, beds of peat found at several places in the Yarmouth interglacial deposits have yielded pollen predominately

Figure 335. Superposed sheets of till with gumbotil and loess exposed in a railroad cut southwest of Rhodes, Iowa. The scale is indicated by the man at the left above. (George F. Kay.)

of balsam fir, pine, and tamarack, suggesting a climate somewhat cooler than the present one in that area.

Analysis of the pollen from different levels in a peat bog may also indicate marked fluctuations of climate. For example, such study of peat deposits at five localities in the Aftonian interglacial deposits in Iowa indicate at first a long time when the region was occupied by pine forests suggesting a climate cooler than that of the present, then a landscape covered with grasses indicating long endurance of a climate like that of the present, and finally a return of conifer forests and cooler climate, as the Kansan glacial age approached.

Pollen analysis of a peat deposit near Quincy, Illinois, indicates a forest of fir, tamarack, pine, and birch—an assemblage that now lives at least 200 or 300 miles farther north. But interglacial deposits at Toronto, Ontario, (the Don beds) include the pawpaw and other plants indicating a mean temperature at least 2° or 3° higher than at present.

Fossil Mammals. As the climate grew colder, and the ice sheets spread over Canada and northern Europe during the last ice age, the mammals of the far north were driven southward and animals of the temperate zone likewise migrated to lower latitudes. At the height of glaciation the reindeer, the woolly mammoth, and the arctic fox ranged widely across Europe, while in North America the reindeer and the woolly mammoth were at home in New England and the musk-ox ranged as far south as Arkansas. With the waning of the ice and amelioration of the climate in postglacial time, these arctic mammals have all retreated to their homeland in the High Arctic barrens as warm temperate species returned northward across Europe and southern Canada.

Fossil mammals found at many places in the interglacial deposits indicate similar mass migrations as the climate changed, and some of these confirm the plant evidence that, at times, the interglacial ages were warmer than the present. In the last interglacial age, for example, such African forms as the lion and the hippopotamus were common in southern Europe.

It is clear, therefore, that the climate was colder than at present during the four glacial ages when ice covered far more than half of North America and approximately half of Europe, and that it was somewhat warmer than at present during at least some parts of the interglacial ages, and that the ice sheets then had retreated far to the north and probably had disappeared both from the mainland of North America and from Europe.

RADIOCARBON DATING AND THE PLEISTOCENE TIME SCALE

In the study of Pleistocene history the dating of organic remains by means of radiocarbon (carbon-14) has provided a major breakthrough. Although this method has been extensively used only since about 1950, we now have several hundred absolute dates for interglacial and postglacial deposits. Because the half-life period of radiocarbon is short, the method is applicable only to organic remains less than forty or fifty thousand years old and is therefore useful only for the Wisconsin glacial age and postglacial time, but for this span an absolute time scale is now possible.

A recent discovery near Meriden, Connecticut, will illustrate the application of the method. Here a fossil log was discovered at the base of the till, representing a tree that was obviously pushed over and overridden by the ice. The ratio of carbon 14 to carbon 12 in this fossil wood proves that the tree was alive approximately 32,000 years ago.[2] This gives the date at which the ice was advancing across southern New England.

Another significant date for this region was secured from the radium content of varved clay at Hartford, Connecticut. This gives a date of approximately 18,000 years ago,[3] and since varved clay formed in proglacial or periglacial lakes, it is evident that the ice was then receding from southern New England.

Further evidence was secured from the peat in post-glacial Linsley Pond in Connecticut which gives a date of 8,323 ± 400 years. Pollen analysis proves that the pond was then surrounded by pine forest, and it is evident that if an ice sheet still existed its front was then considerably farther north.

From these three dates it is concluded that the last ice sheet to cover southern New England crossed the latitude of Meriden, Connecticut, about 32,000 years ago and reached its southern limit (at Long Island) somewhat later and that it was receding again by 18,000 years ago and was far to the north by 8,000 years ago. A bog deposit at Plissey Pond in Aroostook County, Maine, adds further information. Pollen analysis here indicates a pine forest similar to that about Linsley Pond in Connecticut, and the date is approximately 6,000 years before the present. The ice front by that time must have been somewhere in Canada if, indeed, the ice had not completely disappeared.

Similar methods applied to fossil wood preserved in the interglacial deposits in the upper Mississippi Valley show that the Wisconsin Ice Sheet advanced and receded and then readvanced in that region so that four glacial and three interglacial subages can be recognized and dated as indicated in Table II; and by comparing dates from different localities in a single interglacial stage it has been possible in some instances to estimate with some assurance the actual rate of advance of the ice.

A particularly significant locality is at Two Creeks in Wisconsin, where a fossiliferous deposit occurs immediately below the Mankato till and is dated as 11,000 years old.[4] This dates the last significant advance of the ice in this region and proves that the ice age was not over. Clearly this advance did not reach into southern New England and there is abundant evidence that the ice disappeared rapidly between 10,000 and 11,000 years ago. By radiocarbon dating it is known, for example, that pine forests spread over England, and prehistoric people with a mesolithic culture were living there about 9,000 years ago.

Study of the foraminifera in widely spaced deep-sea cores in the Atlantic Ocean indicates that a marked amelioration of the climate began about 11,000 years ago; and with this the Wisconsin Ice Age came to a close and the Recent Epoch began.

For the older glacial and interglacial ages radiocarbon dating is not applicable, and age determinations are indirect and thus far must be considered very tentative. Two methods of attack have been used.

The first method involves comparison of the amount of weathering and chemical decay of the several till sheets with that of the Wisconsin drift for which we have absolute dates. Since the Wisconsin drift, even the Iowan stage, is still fresh and is covered by a thin soil but no gumbotil, it is obvious that the interglacial ages were much longer than the 25,000 years or so that have elapsed since the Iowan till was laid down. On this basis Kay estimated that the Sangamon interglacial age lasted for approximately 135,000 years, the Yarmouth 310,000 years, and the Aftonian some 200,000 years, and that Pleistocene glaciation began approximately one million years ago. Unfortunately no basis is known for a quantitative measure of the rate at which chemical leaching and gumbotil formation take place, and the figures suggested by Kay are little more than "guesstimates" even though they appear to be of the right order of magnitude.

Another method, currently under investigation, for dating the pre-Wisconsin ages of the Pleistocene, involves the study of cores from the deep ocean floor where accumulation of sediment has been so slow that the record of the entire Pleistocene Epoch is only a few feet thick. Where these are rich in globigerina ooze, the pelagic foraminifera from different depths in a core may be segregated and tested for the oxygen-18/oxygen-16 ratio, which gives a measure of the temperature of of the surface water in the ocean at the time these individuals lived. Thus, general fluctuations of the temperature in the oceans may be recognized that can be correlated with glacial and interglacial epochs. Then the age of the clay sediments at successive levels may be determined by the potassium/argon ratio or by the radium content. Only a beginning has been made in such studies and the preliminary results may be wide of the mark. The technical difficulties and uncertainties are too complex to discuss here, but we may hope that by such methods a valid timescale for the whole of the Pleistocene Epoch will eventually be achieved.

EFFECTS OF GLACIATION

Fluctuations of Sealevel. If the modern ice sheets of Greenland and the Antarctic Continent were melted, sealevel would rise, it is estimated, by as much as 100 feet, drowning the low coastal plains and transforming the lower courses of many streams into estuaries. But if, on the contrary, the former great Pleistocene ice sheets were restored, the water thus withdrawn from the oceans and piled up on the lands would lower sealevel by 300 feet or more, shifting the shoreline seaward almost to the present 50-fathom line.

There is clear evidence that such striking fluctuations of sealevel have taken place repeatedly since the beginning of the Pleistocene. During times of maximum glaciation, streams were extended across the exposed parts of the continental shelves, cutting valleys that are now submerged. In subtropical regions the reduced temperatures at the same time inhibited the growth of corals and permitted the waves to cut wide benches about oceanic islands and along exposed coasts. These benches have since been transformed into lagoons by the growth of barrier reefs along their margins as the sealevel rose. Some of the low wave-cut benches extensively preserved along the modern coasts may have been cut during interglacial ages when the ice sheets of Greenland and the Antarctic Continent were reduced and the sealevel stood higher than now.

The lowering of sealevel by 300 feet or more made dry land out of extensive areas of shallow sea and permitted migrations of land animals and plants that would now be impossible. England, for example, was united to the continent of Europe, so that the hippopotamus crossed the channel from France; and Borneo and Sumatra in the East Indies were a part of Asia, so that elephants, rhinoceroses, and other large mammals crossed the lowlands now submerged to form the floor of the Java and Sunda seas. Alaska and Siberia were also united by land, and the woolly mammoth crossed freely.

Depression of the Ice-Covered Regions. The ice caps that formed over Canada and Scandinavia were loads too great for the Earth's crust to support, and both regions sagged to the extent of many hundreds of feet at the very least. The depression was greatest where the ice was thickest, and in Canada it amounted to about a thousand feet in the area midway between the Great Lakes and James Bay. Since the ice wasted away, there has been substantial recovery, but before the upwarping took place, unmistakable records of the depression had been made in the form of beach ridges and wave-cut cliffs along the shores of vast proglacial lakes. These features, still recognizable, have been studied and mapped. One of them, marking the shore of glacial Lake Algonquin, is at an elevation of nearly 600 feet in west-central Michigan, but rises to 935 feet at Sault Ste. Marie, 1,150 feet at North Bay on Lake Huron, and apparently 1,450 or 1,500 feet at Goudreau Lake, 150 miles north of Sault Ste. Marie. This indicates a relative upwarp in postglacial time of 335, 550, and 850–900 feet, respectively, at the places named. The beaches of glacial Lake Agassiz (Fig. 340) in Manitoba show a similar upwarp toward the north amounting to at least 400 feet.

When the ice had wasted back far enough to free the St. Lawrence Valley, the region was still so much depressed that marine water spread up the St. Lawrence and into the Champlain Valley and probably into Lake Ontario, depositing a layer of blue clay with abundant shells of an arctic molluscan fauna. This is the **Leda clay,** so called for a small but characteristic clam. In this deposit the skeleton of a baleen whale was recently found at Daveluyville about 60 miles southwest of Quebec, at an elevation of 275 feet above present sealevel.[5] It was associated with 8 species of the Leda fauna and was evidently buried when this locality was below sealevel. Two whale skeletons were found also in bog deposits above the glacial till in Michigan, indicating that at one time the surface of the Great Lakes was at sealevel. Marine shells and the bones of whales have been found in the Leda clays at least 500 feet above sealevel at the Vermont-Quebec boundary, nearly but not quite up to the Lake Ontario level at Kingston, and at about 600 feet in the Montreal-Quebec area. The postglacial upwarp thus indicated is probably a minimum measure of the depression caused by the ice.

Glacial Erosion beneath the Ice Sheets. Radial movement of the Laurentide Ice Sheet stripped the mantle from a vast area of the Canadian Shield, leaving a floor of fresh bedrock scoured unevenly into thousands of shallow basins now occupied by lakes (Fig. 336). The areas of bare rock showing through the scant cover of vegetation advertise the fact that the glaciation cost eastern Canada one of her greatest resources, the soil that had formed during the ages before the coming of the ice.

Over a broad peripheral belt the ice spread its load of drift, filling pre-existing valleys with till and smoothing the inequalities of the surface. Thus, the material stripped wholesale from the southern part of Canada was spread widely over the north-central United States to form the source of a very deep rich soil (Fig. 337).

Drainage Changes. As the ice sheets advanced southward into the United States, all north-flowing streams were blocked, and the meltwater was turned along the margin of the ice until it spilled over divides into south-flowing streams. The channels thus formed at the maximum advance were in many places held after the disappearance of the ice, because former channels were obliterated by the drift. The present course of the Ohio River is due, thus, to the welding together of many short tributaries to different streams, several of which had flowed northward in preglacial times (Fig. 338). The course of the Missouri was also locally shifted to the southwest. For this reason the Ohio and Missouri rivers record rather closely the limits attained by the ice sheets at their greatest extent.

Development of the Great Lakes. Before the glaciations the basins now occupied by the Great Lakes were probably broad lowlands eroded by preglacial streams. The Lake Superior Basin marks an ancient synclinal structure occupied by relatively weak rocks in which a broad valley had been eroded; the other lake basins were carved on the outcrops of relatively weak rocks in front of or between the cuestas that had been sculptured by Cenozoic erosion of the Paleozoic formations overlapping on the Canadian Shield. These lowlands were drained by streams, some of which probably flowed southward through gaps in the cuestas, while others may have flowed northeastward into the St. Lawrence. As the successive ice sheets flowed outward, they filled these lowlands with thick ice lobes that gouged and deepened them, especially where, as in the case of Lakes Superior and Michigan, the axis of the depression nearly coincided with the directions of ice flow.

South of the Great Lakes basins, on the other hand, the ice sheets spread a thick mantle of drift that filled and deeply buried the old valleys for scores of miles. As a result, when the ice later retreated northward over the Great Lakes region,

Figure 336. Barren lakelands of the Canadian Shield stripped of soil by glacier ice that gouged out basins now occupied by a maze of lakes. Looking south from Tookcaret Lake. (Royal Canadian Air Force.)

Figure 337. Fertile wheatland of the Red River Valley about 20 miles south of Fargo, North Dakota. This is a part of the floor of glacial Lake Agassiz (see Figure 340). (North Dakota Agricultural Experiment Station.)

its front became deeply lobate, with a great tongue of ice occupying each of the deepened basins. As these shrank back, lakes formed about the end of each of the lobes, the water standing at the level of the lowest spillway that would lead southward across the drift into the Mississippi drainage system. At first the overflow was southward via both the Wabash and Illinois rivers, but somewhat later it was westward along the front of the ice to the vicinity of Chicago (Fig. 339*A*), where an outlet was found via the Illinois River. Eventually the Mohawk Valley in New York was freed of ice, and this opened a much lower spillway whereby the drainage was for a time diverted east into the Hudson River (Fig. 339*B*). At a still later stage the St. Lawrence Valley was opened, and the drainage of the upper Great Lakes escaped northeast from the Lake Huron basin across southern Ontario by way of the Ottawa Valley (Fig. 339*C*). As the ice wasted away, there was gradual recovery from the depression it had caused, resulting in progressive upwarp of the region northeast of a hinge line that ran through central Michigan and southern Ontario. This ultimately raised the Ottawa outlet until the lowest spillway was across the edge of Niagara cuesta at Lewiston. At this stage, the Niagara River increased greatly in size.

Various other important lakes were formed by the glaciation. The Finger Lakes of central New York, for example, mark open valleys carved in the margin of the Allegheny Plateau by northward-flowing streams in preglacial times. As the ice rode southward, it gouged deeply where it was crowded into these narrow valleys. Upon its retreat, these overdeepened places became lakes. The greatest of all the glacial lakes was Lake Agassiz, previously mentioned (Fig. 340), which formed in the plains of eastern North Dakota, northwestern Minnesota, and Manitoba, while the ice still occupied the basin of Hudson Bay, impounding the water until it overflowed the divide to the south by way of the Minnesota River. Although the lake attained an area nearly five times as great as that of Lake Superior, it was relatively shallow, the old strandlines indicating a probable maximum deepth of about 400 feet at the international boundary. The disappearance of the ice allowed the lake to drain away into Hudson Bay. The floor of the former Lake Agassiz is now the remarkably flat and fertile wheat land of North Dakota and the Red River Valley of Manitoba (Fig. 337).

An interesting drainage change associated with history of Lake Agassiz is indicated in Figure 340. In the center of Minneapolis the Mississippi leaves a very shallow open valley and plunges over St. Anthony Falls, below which it flows for about 7 miles in a deep gorge before emerging again into a broad open valley at Fort Snelling. The preglacial drainage is shown in white on the inset map. The Mississippi River then flowed in a wide valley, its main trunk following approximately the present course of the Minnesota River. When the last ice sheet overrode this area, it filled the old valleys with till, and when the ice finally melted back, the streams at first wandered over the surface of the drift and eventually incised new valleys.

As Minnesota was exposed, three main streams, the St. Croix, the upper Mississippi, and the Minnesota united near St. Paul. Cutting down through the drift, the trunk stream discovered the old preglacial valley just below St. Paul (see inset of Fig. 340, p. 401) and proceeded to remove the loose fill below this point with relative ease. But from St. Paul to a point just south of Fort Snelling the new stream was superposed upon the old upland of horizontal limestone beds. Here its downcutting was greatly retarded, and, as it plunged from the surface of the limestone into the old valley, a fall was initiated that gradually migrated upstream until it again cut through into the buried preglacial valley a short distance southwest of Fort

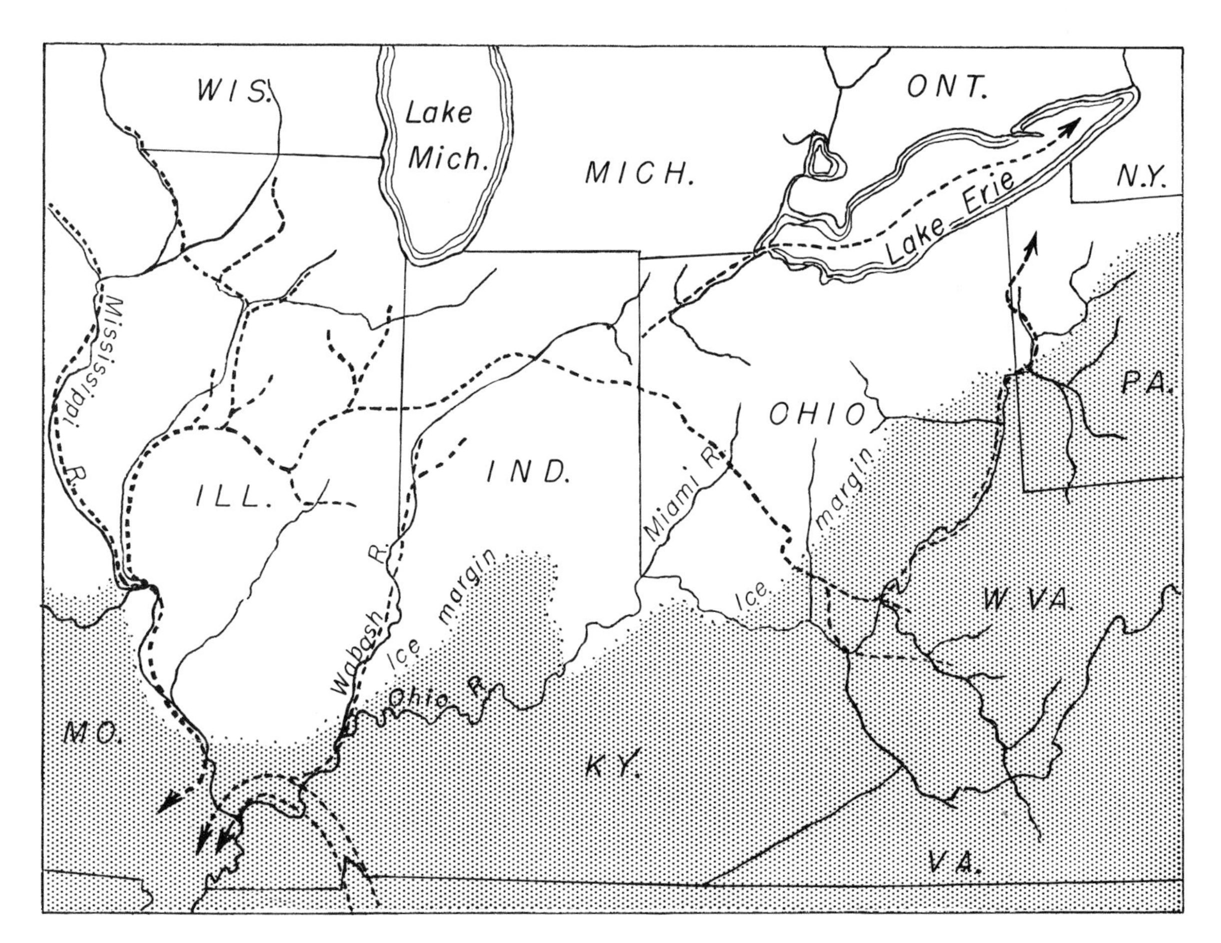

Figure 338. Drainage changes in the Ohio and Mississippi river basins produced by glaciation. Preglacial drainage courses are shown in broken lines. (Adapted from R. F. Flint, 1947.)

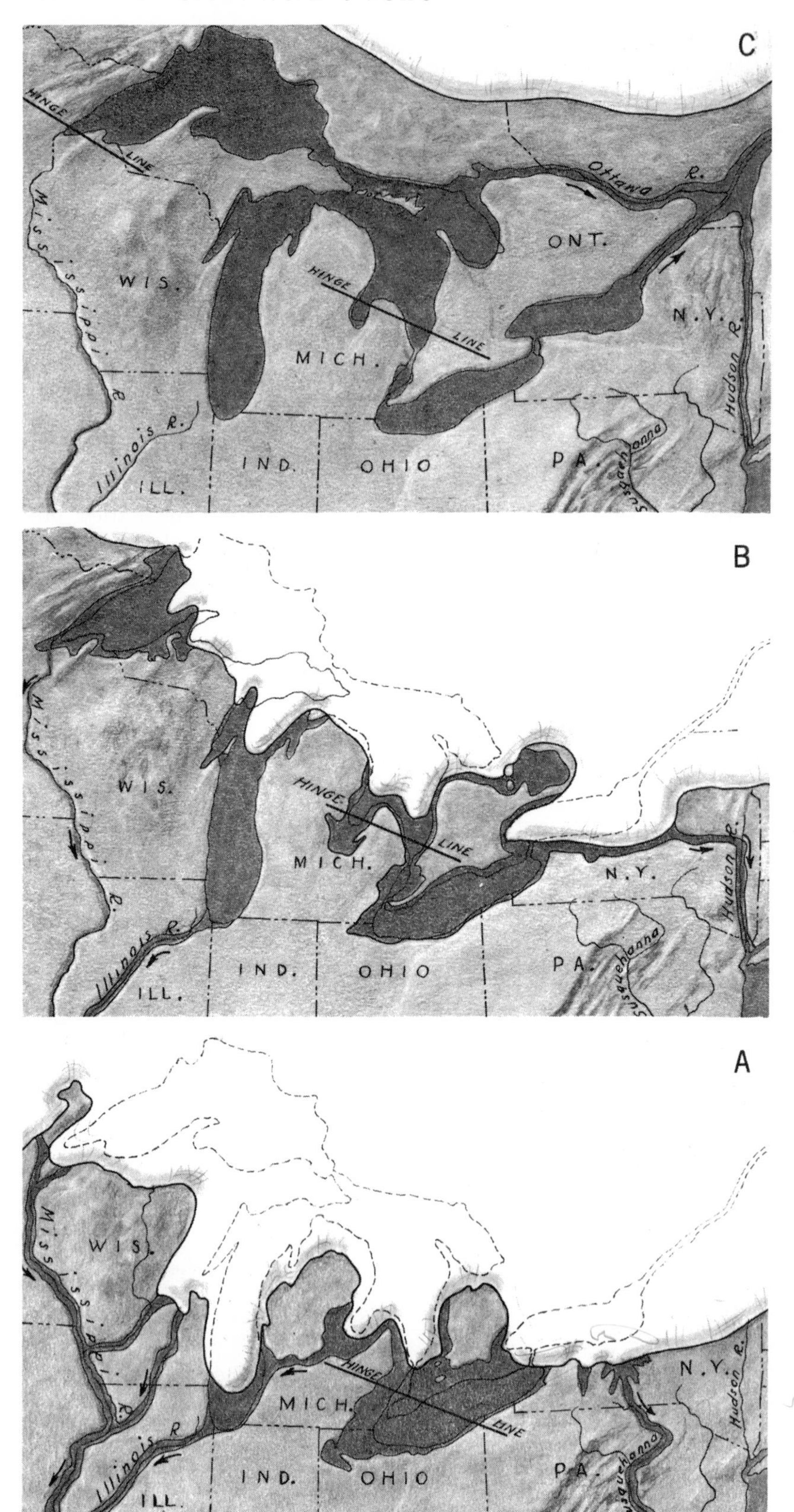

Figure 339. Three stages in the development of the Great Lakes during the waning stages of the Pleistocene ice sheet. (Adapted from Leverett and Taylor, U.S. Geological Survey.)

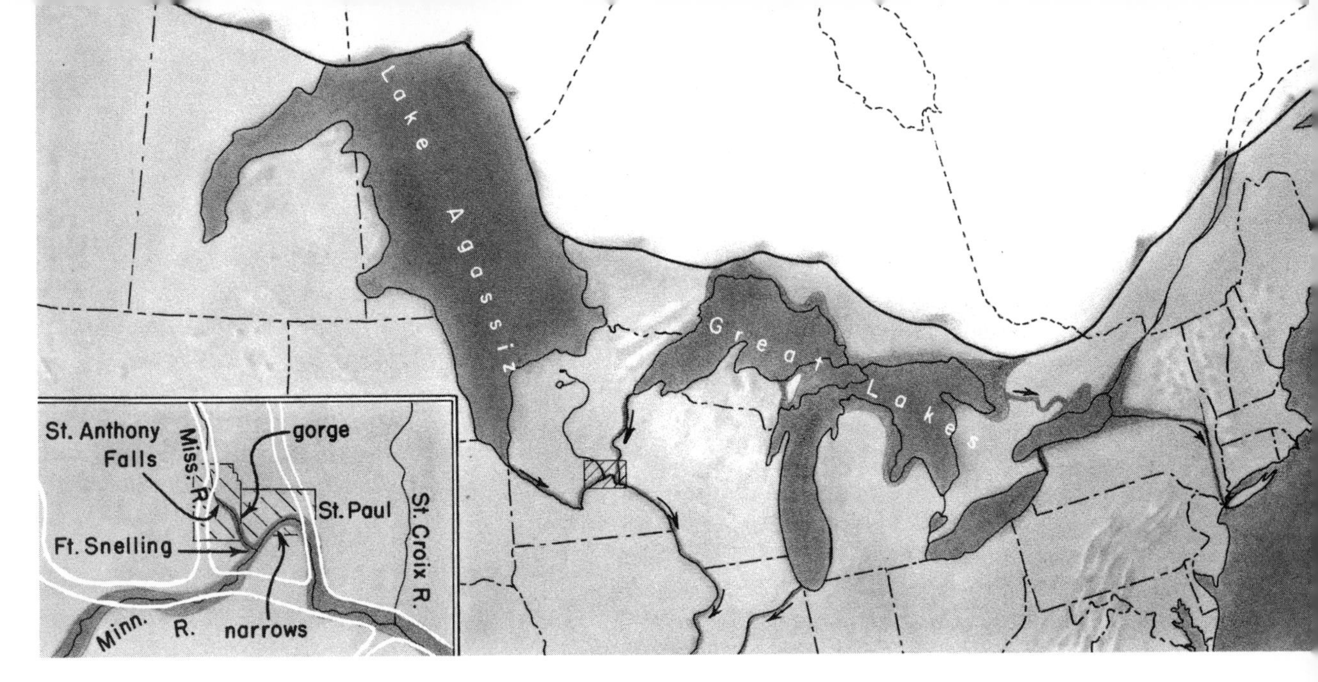

Figure 340. Glacial Lake Agassiz and St. Anthony Falls of the Mississippi River at Minneapolis. (Based on data from Leverett and Taylor and from G. M. Schwartz.)

Snelling. The recession of this great falls produced the narrows in the valley at St. Paul.

For a time after deglaciation of the region around Minneapolis, all three stream branches carried great volumes of meltwater, but after the ice margin had reached the Canadian border, the drainage through the upper Mississippi diminished to something like its present volume. That of the Minnesota River, on the contrary, increased greatly as it became the outlet of the vast glacial Lake Agassiz, which formed over the Red River Valley while the ice still prevented drainage to the north. Thus, until the disappearance of Lake Agassiz, the stream we now know as the upper Mississippi was but a second-rate tributary to a great glacial stream that followed the present valley of the Minnesota River above St. Paul. The cutting of the narrows at St. Paul was chiefly the work of this great glacial stream and was accomplished while Lake Agassiz was discharging the meltwater from a great area of the ice. This gives us the clue to the position of the ice margin when the postglacial gorge at St. Paul was cut.

END OF THE ICE AGES

If our time scale for the Pleistocene Epoch in any sense approaches reality, it is clear that we probably are now in a minor interglacial subage in which the icefields have shrunk from a maximum of 32 percent of the area of the land surface of the Earth to about 10 percent. There are still more than 5,000,000 square miles of ice sheets in Antarctica and Greenland, and the polar seas are choked with floe ice, while lofty mountains the world around bear active glaciers. Furthermore, it is estimated that a decline in the mean annual temperature of not more than 5°C. would bring a return of the ice sheets as they were during the last advance.[6]

Judged by every criterion we know, the interglacial ages vastly exceeded the time that has elapsed since the last ice sheets began to wane; and fossils preserved between the drift sheets prove beyond doubt that the climate at times during those interglacial ages was appreciably warmer than it is now. Furthermore, there is clear evidence that postglacial world climates reached a maximum of warmth between 6,000 and 4,000 years ago and since then, with minor oscillations, have become cooler and more moist down to the present time. Whether the ice sheets will spread again or will disappear completely during the next few thousands of years, it is quite impossible to judge; but clearly the **Present** is only an age in the Pleistocene Epoch.

Meanwhile the sword of Damocles hangs over us. If the ice sheets should again spread to the limits they occupied a few thousands of years ago, mass migrations would occur on a scale without precedent in the history of mankind, for the densely populated centers of Europe and the United States, to say nothing of all Canada, would slowly become uninhabitable. And, if, on the contrary, the climate should return to its geologic norm and the last of the ice sheets should disappear, the meltwater would raise sealevel by 70 to 100 feet, slowly submerging all the great seaport cities of the world. In any event, the changes will come too slowly to concern anyone now living, but they may profoundly shape the destiny of civilization within the next few thousands of years.

We can only guess when the end of the Ice Ages will come, as we contemplate some of the problems it will entail for mankind!

REFERENCES

1. Flint, R. F., 1957, *Glacial and Pleistocene Geology.* John Wiley, New York, pp. 1–553.

2. Barensen, G. W., E. S. Deevey and L. J. Gralenski, 1957, Yale natural radiocarbon measurements, III. *Science,* vol. 126, pp. 908–919.

3. Urry, W. D., 1948, The radium content of varved clay and a possible age of the Hartford, Connecticut, deposits. *Amer. Jour. Sci.,* vol. 246, pp. 689–700.

4. Flint, R. F., and E. S. Deevey, Jr., 1951, Radiocarbon dating of late-Pleistocene events. *Amer. Jour. Sci.,* vol. 249, pp. 257–300.

5. Laverdière, J. W., 1950, Baleine fossile de Daveluyville, Quebec. *Canadian Naturalist,* vol. 77, pp. 271–282.

6. Flint, R. F., 1947, *Glacial geology and the Pleistocene Epoch,* John Wiley, New York, pp. 1–589.

Figure 341. An Eocene landscape in the Rocky Mountain states. Here among palms and modern types of deciduous trees lived a strange assemblage of primitive mammals. 1, a lemur, *Notharctus;* 2, a catlike creodont, *Oxyaena;* 3, a condylarth, *Phenacodus;* 4, an amblypod, *Coryphodon;* 5, the "dawn-horse", *Eohippus;* 6, a primitive titanothere, *Palaeosyops;* 7, a creodont, *Mesonyx;* 8, a creodont, *Tritemnodon;* 9, an amblypod, *Eobasileus;* 10, an amblypod, *Uintatherium;* 11, a flightless bird, *Diatryma.* (Painting by Rudolph F. Zallinger, from *The World We Live In,* courtesy of Time, Inc.)

Chapter 19. Mammals Inherit the Earth

THROUGHOUT THE LONG MESOZOIC ERA—FOR more than a hundred million years—reptiles completely dominated life on the Earth; but at its close their dynasty suddenly collapsed. Turtles, lizards, snakes, and crocodiles survived, but they are mostly small and restricted in their range, and few are aggressive. At the dawn of the Cenozoic Era the dinosaurs were extinct, the pterosaurs had disappeared, and the great marine reptiles were gone. Now the way was open for the mammals to begin their conquest of the world. At first they were small and unimpressive, but with a meteoric expansion they soon dominated the Earth as completely as the reptiles had done in their day. Thus the Cenozoic has well been called **The Age of Mammals.**

TRENDS OF MAMMALIAN EVOLUTION

Comparative study of early Cenozoic fossils clearly indicates that the first mammals resembled the modern hedgehog (Fig. 342) in the following respects: (1) they were small; (2) they were short-legged and walked on the soles of the feet; (3) they had 5 toes on each foot; (4) they had 44 teeth of which all but the canines were short-crowned; (5) their brains were small and their intelligence was of a low order; (6) they were long-faced, the jaws exceeding the brain case in size. Unlike the hedgehog, however, they had a long tail. From ancestors of this sort all the modern orders of mammals evolved. In this development four major trends can be detected in most of the groups.

Increase in Size. This was a common trend. The Eocene ancestor of the horse was scarcely larger than a fox, that of the camels no bigger than a jack rabbit, and even the elephants can be traced back to ancestors no larger than a hog. The Eocene forebears of man were tiny half-apes of the size of squirrels. In short, the Paleocene mammals, like those of the Mesozoic, were all small. As the modern orders evolved, each in time attained larger average size, and several of them produced relative giants. Progress in this regard was not synchronous among the different groups of mammals, however, some having reached their maximum size before the middle of the Cenozoic Era and others much later.

Specialization of the Brain. Unquestionably the most significant trend was specialization of the brain. The earliest mammals, like their reptilian

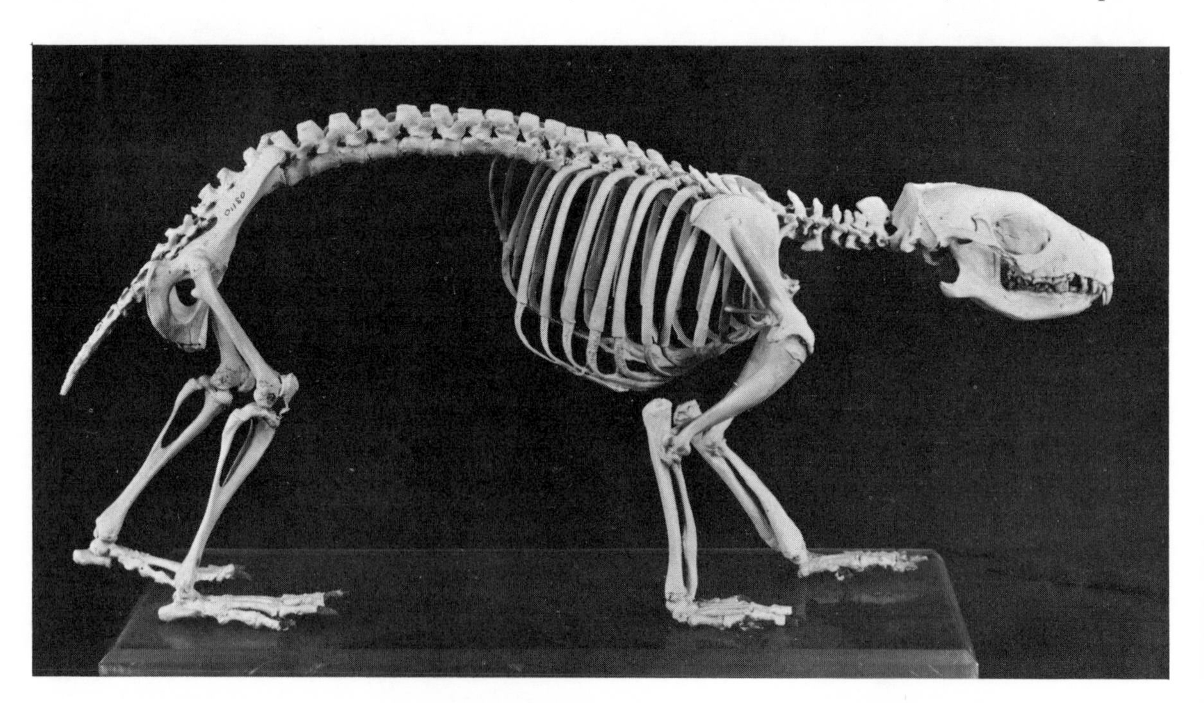

Figure 342. Skeleton of a modern hedgehog, a persistently primitive and generalized mammal. About ⅖ natural size. (Yale Peabody Museum.)

ancestors, had relatively small brains concerned chiefly with the physical senses. Their mentality was probably comparable to that of a modern shrew or an opossum. Progress involved increase in actual size as well as in the ratio of brain to body weight (Fig. 343). More significantly, it involved a disproportionate increase in the cerebrum, which is the seat of memory and reason. In this respect, however, progress has been very unequal among the several orders of mammals. At one extreme stand the insectivores (shrews, hedgehogs, and moles) that have improved but little and have survived as stupid, retiring creatures, and at the other extreme stand the highest primates (man) with skulls grotesquely distended to house a brain capable of pondering the mysteries of time and space and of harnessing atomic energy!

Specialization of the Teeth. This was a third important development. In the primitive placental mammal the cheek teeth had sharp piercing or shearing cusps but were low-crowned and attained full growth early in life. The insectivores and opossums, having stuck to a diet of insects and other delicate food, show little change (Fig. 344); but most other groups of mammals have teeth highly specialized according to their feeding habits. Omnivorous feeders such as the swine, the bears, and man, show only moderate specialization and have short-crowned jaw teeth with low, blunt cusps. Carnivores, on the contrary, show greatly enlarged canines for holding and tearing flesh, and narrow, shearing jaw teeth. The most remarkable specialization is seen in the grazing animals of the prairies whose teeth must resist the wear of the harsh and commonly dusty grasses while maintaining a rough grinding surface. In these the cheek teeth are large and high-crowned and continue to grow throughout life (Fig. 345). Furthermore, the enamel is deeply enfolded into the crown, so that even after wear it forms sharp ridges, thus maintaining a good grinding surface. Each order has a distinctive pattern of enfolded enamel, making it almost as easy to identify the order of a fossil mammal by its teeth as by a whole skeleton (Fig. 346).

Specialization of the Feet and the Limbs. This was a fourth major change. Primitively the feet were short, and the animal walked flat on the soles with the heels touching the ground (Fig. 342); but, during the ages, marked specialization occurred according to environment and habits. Tree-dwelling types, like the monkeys and squirrels, developed prehensile hands with opposable thumb and great toe; carnivores evolved claws to seize and hold struggling prey; and the herbivorous animals of the plains, dependent on fleetness of foot for safety, underwent a remarkable specialization involving a rise onto the very ends of their

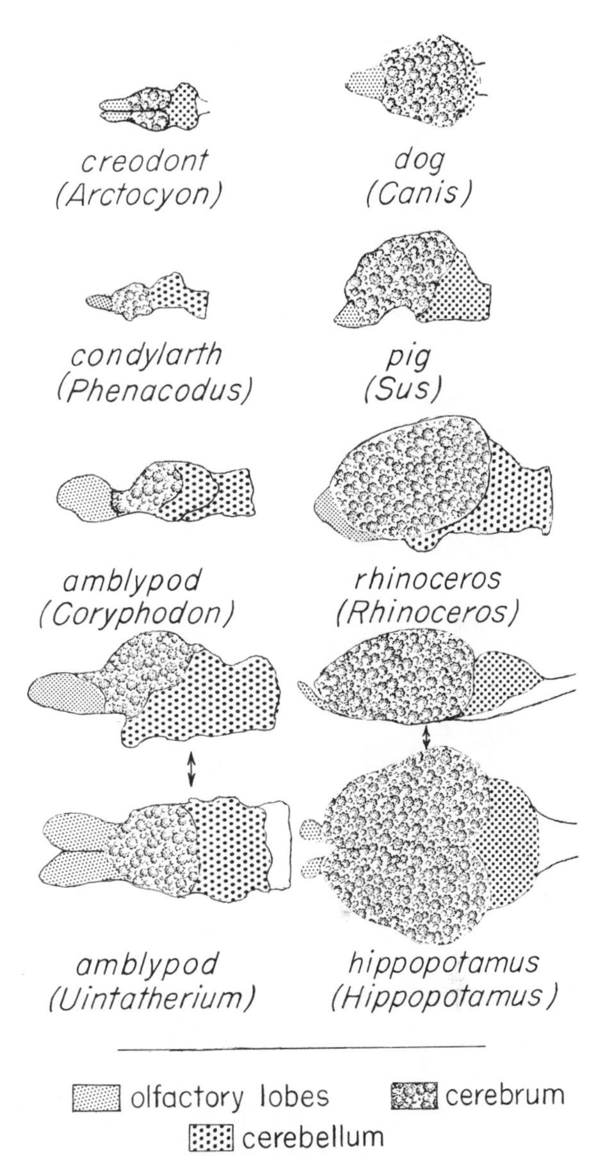

Figure 343. Brains of archaic mammals (left) paired with brains of modern mammals (right) of equal body size. (Adapted from H. F. Osborn.)

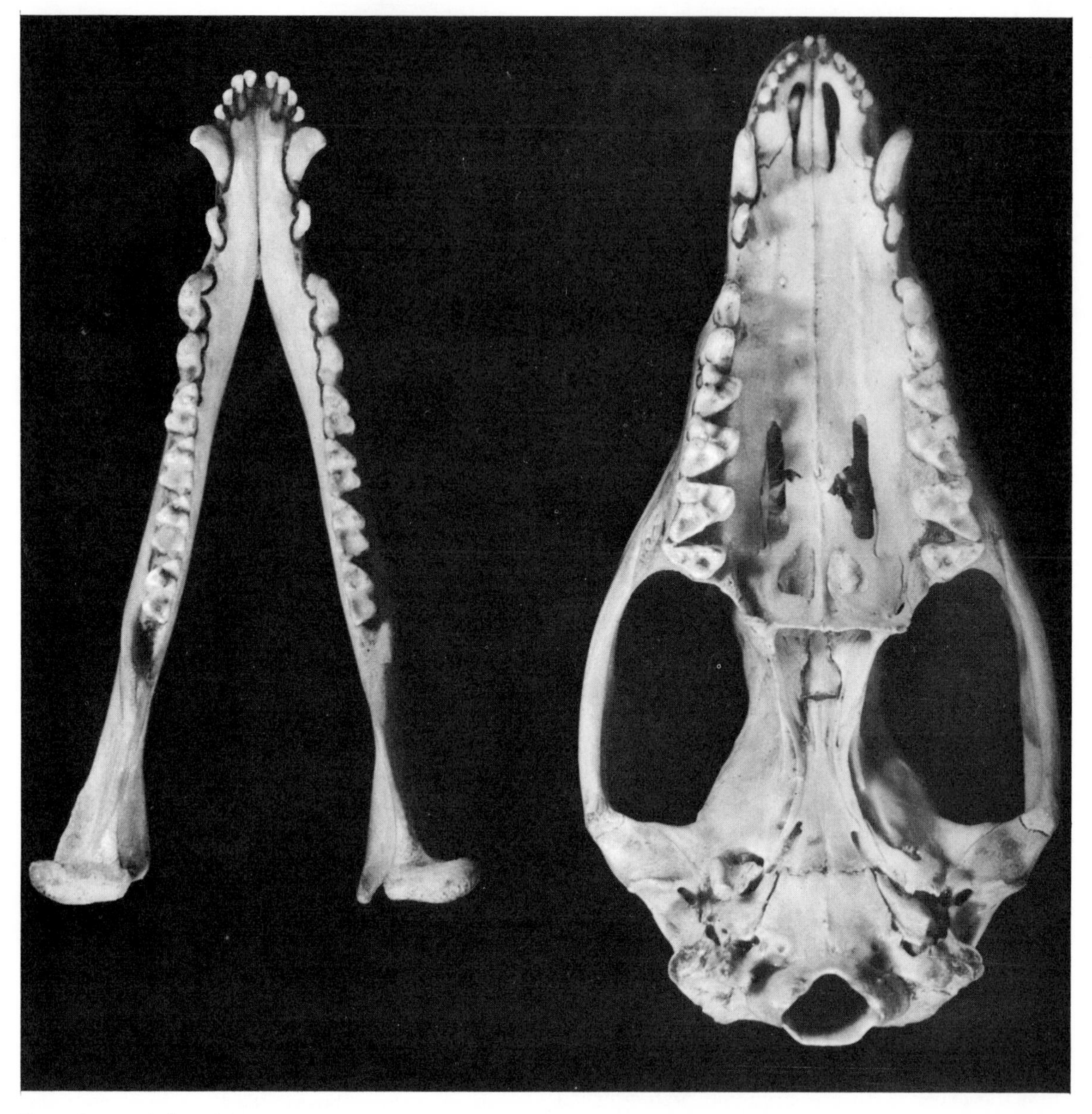

Figure 344. Skull and lower jaw of an opossum to show the character of primitive mammalian teeth. (Yale Peabody Museum.)

toes, the development of hoofs, and a reduction and loss of some or all of the side toes.

In swift running, an animal tends to rise up on its toes to attain a longer stride, and those endowed with long, slender limbs have a natural advantage. In the struggle for existence, therefore, many of the plains animals were subjected to an age-long selection in which a great premium was placed on longer limbs and the ability to remain on the toes. The ultimate result is illustrated by the limb of a modern horse, contrasted with the unspecialized limb of a bear (Fig. 347). Above the heel there is little difference in size and proportions, the greater height of the horse being due to the elongation of the foot and to the fact that he stands on tip-toes with the heel far above the ground. This affords a great stride and leaves the powerful leg muscles bunched near the body where they can swing the slender extremity of the limb without sharing in its motion. The hoof developed, of course, as a protective armor for the tip of the toe.

Since the middle toes of a mammal are primitively and normally longer than the side toes, a rise to the ends of the digits lifts the side toes off the ground and leaves them dangling. In this condition they tend to degenerate and disappear (Fig. 348). In the odd-toed, hoofed mammals (Order Perissodactyla), the axis of the foot lies in the middle digit and, in the reduction, digits 1 and 5, as a rule, disappeared, leaving a three-toed foot. Heavy-bodied types such as the rhinoceros did not proceed further in this direction, but in the horse digits 2 and 4 were reduced to mere vestiges (Fig. 52, p. 74, and Fig. 352), leaving a one-toed foot. In the cloven-hoofed mammals (Order Artiodactyla), the axis of the foot lies between digits 3 and 4. In this group, digit 1 was lost at a very early stage, producing a four-toed foot, as in the hog. Further specialization caused a simultaneous reduction and loss of digits 2 and 5, leaving a two-toed foot, such as that of the cattle, the deer, and the camel.

THE PALEOCENE VANGUARD

At the beginning of Cenozoic time, the mammals expanded like a race delivered from bondage. Although only three orders are recorded from Late Cretaceous rocks, fourteen are now known from the Paleocene Series. Notable among these are the *multituberculates, marsupials,* and *insectivores* that survived from the Cretaceous, and the *pri-*

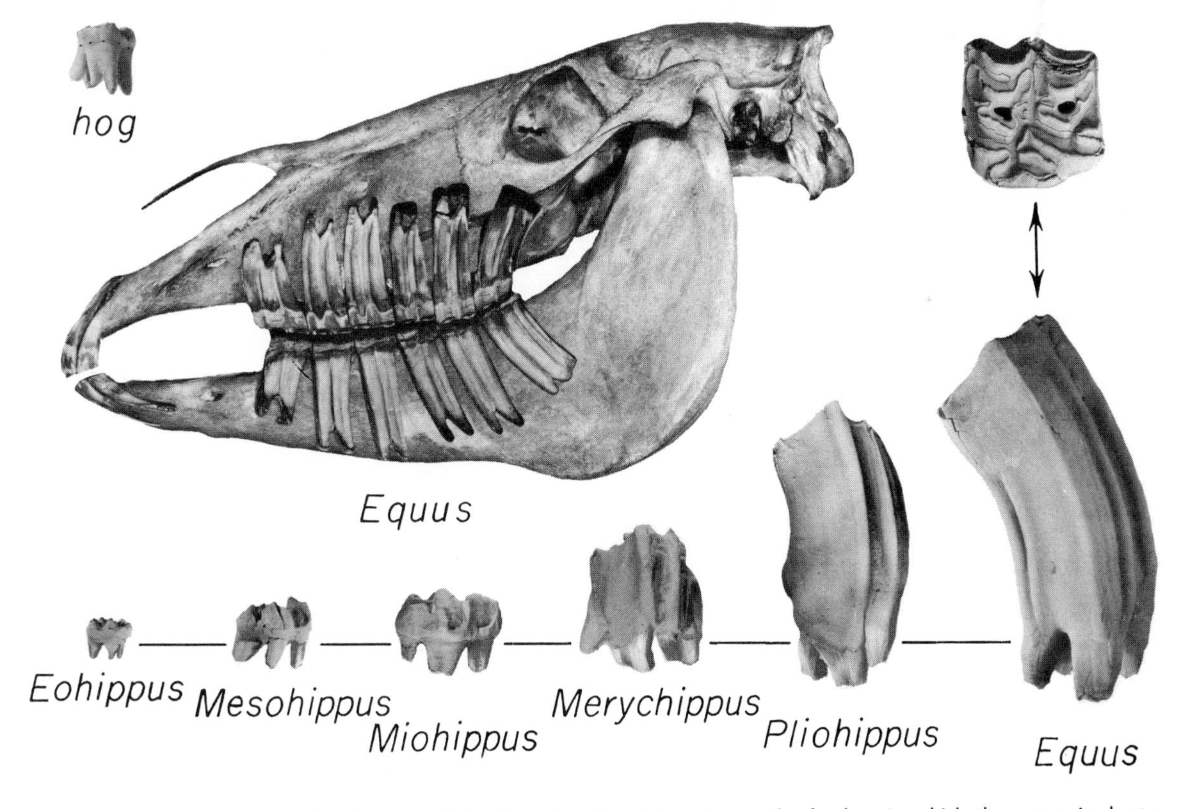

Figure 345. Low-crowned and high-crowned cheek teeth. Top left, molar tooth of a hog in which the crown is shorter than the roots; right, corresponding tooth of a modern horse, *Equus*, in which the crown is about 5 times as long as the roots. Center, skull of the horse ($\times \frac{1}{6}$) dissected to show the high-crowned cheek teeth in place. Lower row, corresponding upper left molars of fossil horses from *Eohippus* to *Equus*, all at a uniform scale (about $\frac{1}{2}$ natural size). The crown is low in *Eohippus, Mesohippus,* and *Miohippus,* then increases rapidly in height from *Merychippus* to *Equus*. The crown view of the worn tooth shows the ridges formed of the enfolded enamel. The skull was dissected by S. H. Chubb. (Yale Peabody Museum.)

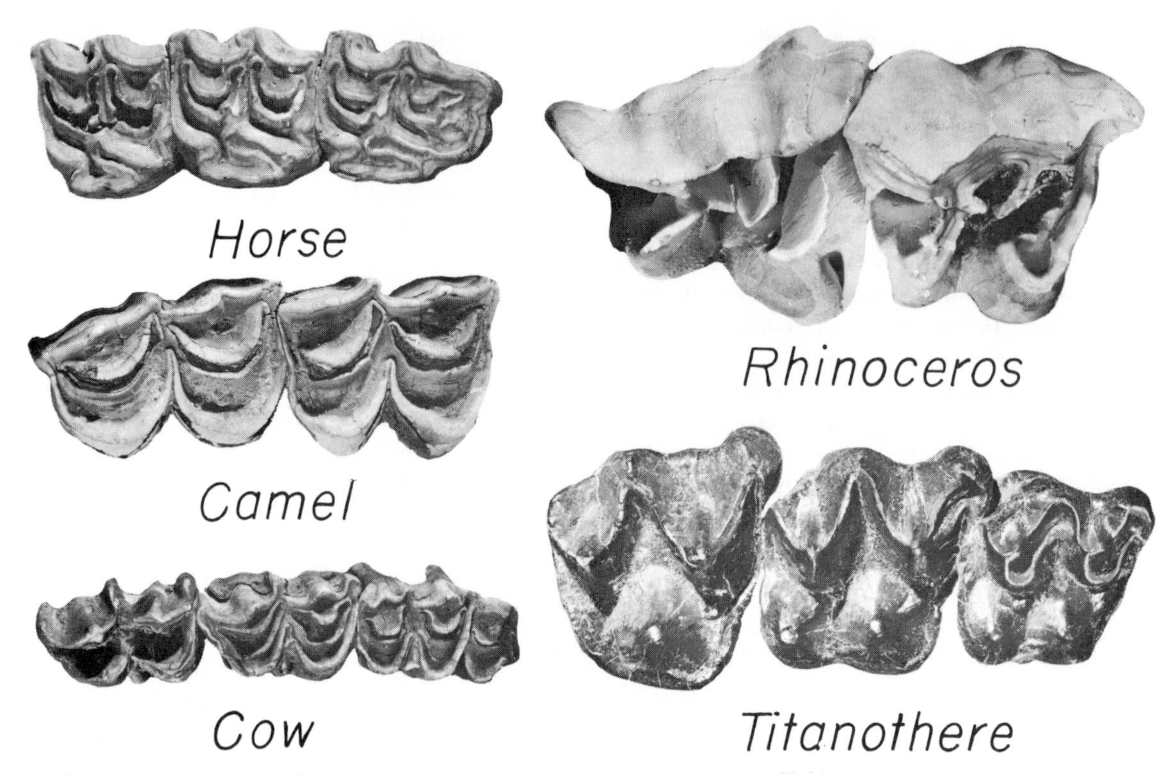

Figure 346. Crown view of left upper molar teeth of horse, camel, cow, rhinoceros, and titanothere, to show the distinctive patterns of the enamel folds. (All on the same scale, about × ½.) (Yale Peabody Museum.)

mates, rodents, carnivores, condylarths, and *amblypods* that first appeared with the Paleocene.

The **multituberculates** (Fig. 349) were small plant feeders with chisel-like incisors and large jaw teeth crowned with long rows of blunt tubercles. In size and appearance they probably resembled a modern woodchuck; but the resemblance is superficial. Although common in the Paleocene Epoch they died out early in the Eocene Epoch.

The **marsupials** were essentially like the modern opossum and at this time were possibly world wide in distribution. Outside of Australia and South America, however, they have never competed successfully with more progressive types, and have never risen above the modest and retiring role played by the living opossum.

Insectivores were likewise small and much like the modern shrew and hedgehog. They appear to be the ancestral stock from which the other groups of placentals evolved, but did not themselves share in that evolutionary advance.

Rodents include the modern gnawers, such as mice and rats and squirrels. The oldest representative of this order was found in the Paleocene beds of Montana in 1937.

Primates are represented in the Paleocene by small half-apes (tarsioids and lemurs) scarcely larger than squirrels.

Creodonts were precursors of the modern carnivores. Even in Paleocene time they showed considerable specialization, some being doglike and others catlike. Some had shearing teeth and sharp claws; others strangely blunt teeth and flattened toenails. Their brains, however, were less than half as big as those of modern carnivores of equal stature, and they must have been stupid brutes (Fig. 343).

The **condylarths** and **amblypods** (primitive ungulates) were the dominant orders of herbivorous animals during Paleocene time and both ranged up into the Eocene. The condylarths were light-bodied and relatively agile, the amblypods stocky and ponderous. *Phenacodus* of the lower Eocene (Fig. 350) was a typical condylarth. The slender body, arched back, long tail, and short, five-toed feet give it a superficial resemblance to the carnivores; but each toe bore a small hoof, and its teeth were clearly those of a plant feeder. The brain was relatively small, and the teeth primitive and low-crowned. The condylarths appeared early in the Paleocene and ranged upward to the middle of the Eocene Epoch, when they were replaced by the more advanced ungulates.

Coryphodon (Fig. 351) of the lower Eocene, a typical amblypod, was about waist-high to a man. It was thickset and had stout legs and blunt, five-toed feet, each toe bearing a hooflike nail. The canine teeth were tusklike, but the cheek teeth were relatively small and low-crowned. The amblypods appeared early in the Paleocene and ranged through to the close of the Eocene Epoch. The earliest forms were scarcely larger than a sheep, but they increased rapidly in size and culminated in *Uintatherium,* which had the bulk of a circus elephant and was the largest of the American land animals during late Eocene time.

In short, the Paleocene faunas would have presented a strange, unfamiliar appearance to a modern, for the dominant forms belonged to groups that are long since extinct, and many of the groups that are now dominant were completely lacking.

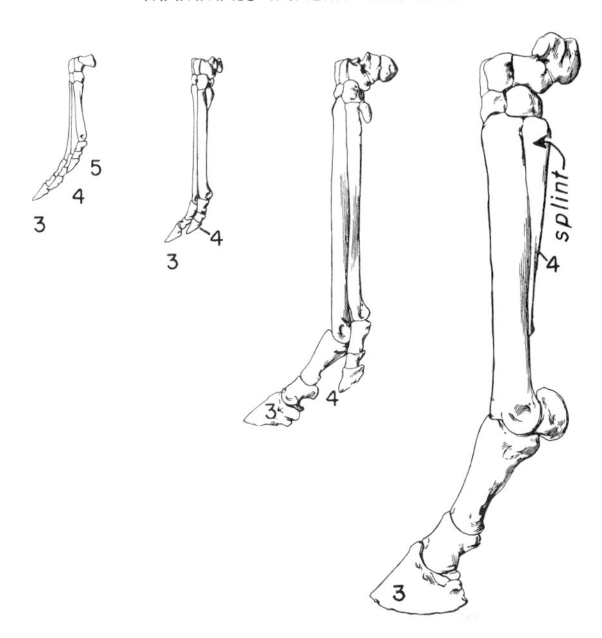

Figure 348. Loss of lateral digits in the horse. From left to right, the forelimbs of *Eohippus* of the lower Eocene Epoch; *Mesohippus* of the Oligocene; *Merychippus* of the Miocene; and *Equus*, the modern horse. Corresponding digits bear the same number.

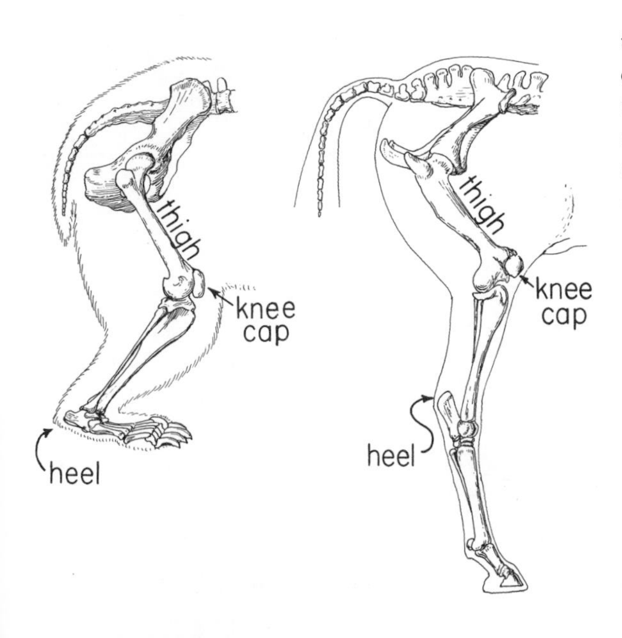

Figure 347. Hind limb of bear (left) and horse, showing correspondence of parts.

EOCENE IMMIGRANTS

At the beginning of Eocene time the ancestors of the modern horse, the rhinoceros, the camel, and other modern groups of mammals appeared simultaneously in Europe and the United States. This sudden advent implies that these modernized stocks had been evolving somewhere in the northern land mass and at this time migrated southward along two different routes. From this stage on, the history of several of these stocks can be followed in detail and constitutes one of the most fascinating chapters in the history of life.

CENOZOIC PARADE

***Eohippus* and His Progeny.** The horse was a native of North America from early Eocene to late Pleistocene time and underwent most of its development here. Skeletons assembled from successive horizons reveal a gradual evolution in teeth, limbs, feet, and size hardly equaled for any other stock of animals. The record is graphically shown in Figure 352.

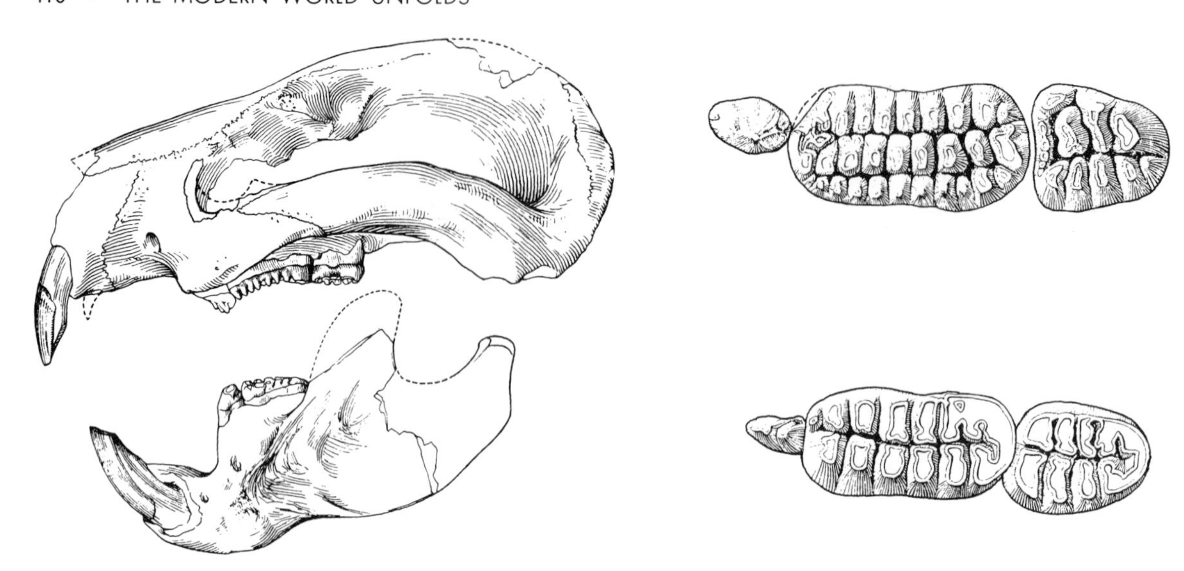

Figure 349. A Paleocene multituberculate, *Taeniolabis*, from New Mexico. Side view of skull ($\times \frac{1}{2}$) and crown view of upper and lower left cheek teeth (enlarged). (Granger and Simpson.)

Figure 350. Restoration of *Phenacodus,* a condylarth from the Paleocene of Wyoming. The grasslike vegetation consists of sedges, not true grasses. (From a painting by Charles R. Knight, American Museum of Natural History.)

Figure 351. Restoration of *Coryphodon*, an amblypod from the lower Eocene of Wyoming. (From a painting by Charles R. Knight, American Museum of Natural History.)

Eohippus,* the "dawn horse," oldest known member of the race, was a graceful little animal, scarcely a foot high, with a slender face, arched back, and long tail (Fig. 353). Its hind feet bore three toes, and the front feet four toes. Its Paleocene ancestor, we may infer, possessed five toes all around, but no such stage has yet been discovered.

The evolution that followed was long and complex but may be epitomized by noting three of the stages intermediate between *Eohippus* and the modern horse, *Equus*. Of these, *Mesohippus* of the Oligocene, about the size of a sheep (Fig. 352), had three toes on each foot, subequal in size and all touching the ground, so as to share equally in the animal's weight. Its cheek teeth were still low-crowned, as were those of *Eohippus*. *Merychippus* of the Miocene grew to the size of a small pony. It possessed three toes on each foot, but the middle toe was much the largest, the others failing to touch the ground and dangling like the dew-claws of cattle. The jaws of this little horse had deepened appreciably, for its molar teeth were becoming high-crowned and prismatic (Fig. 345). *Pliohippus*, the first one-toed horse (Fig. 352), was somewhat larger than *Merychippus*, and had high-crown teeth and long jaws approximating the condition seen in a modern horse. The side toes were represented only by a pair of splint bones lying alongside of the cannon bone (Fig. 52, p. 74) and invisible externally. The modern horse, *Equus*, appeared about the close of the Pliocene Epoch and survived in America until the last ice sheet of the Pleistocene had disappeared. Wild

*According to Simpson (1945, p. 136), the name *Hyracotherium* has legal priority over *Eohippus*, having been applied to the same genus in Europe 36 years before the name *Eohippus* was coined. For the present we continue to use the latter name because it is so much more widely known and applied.

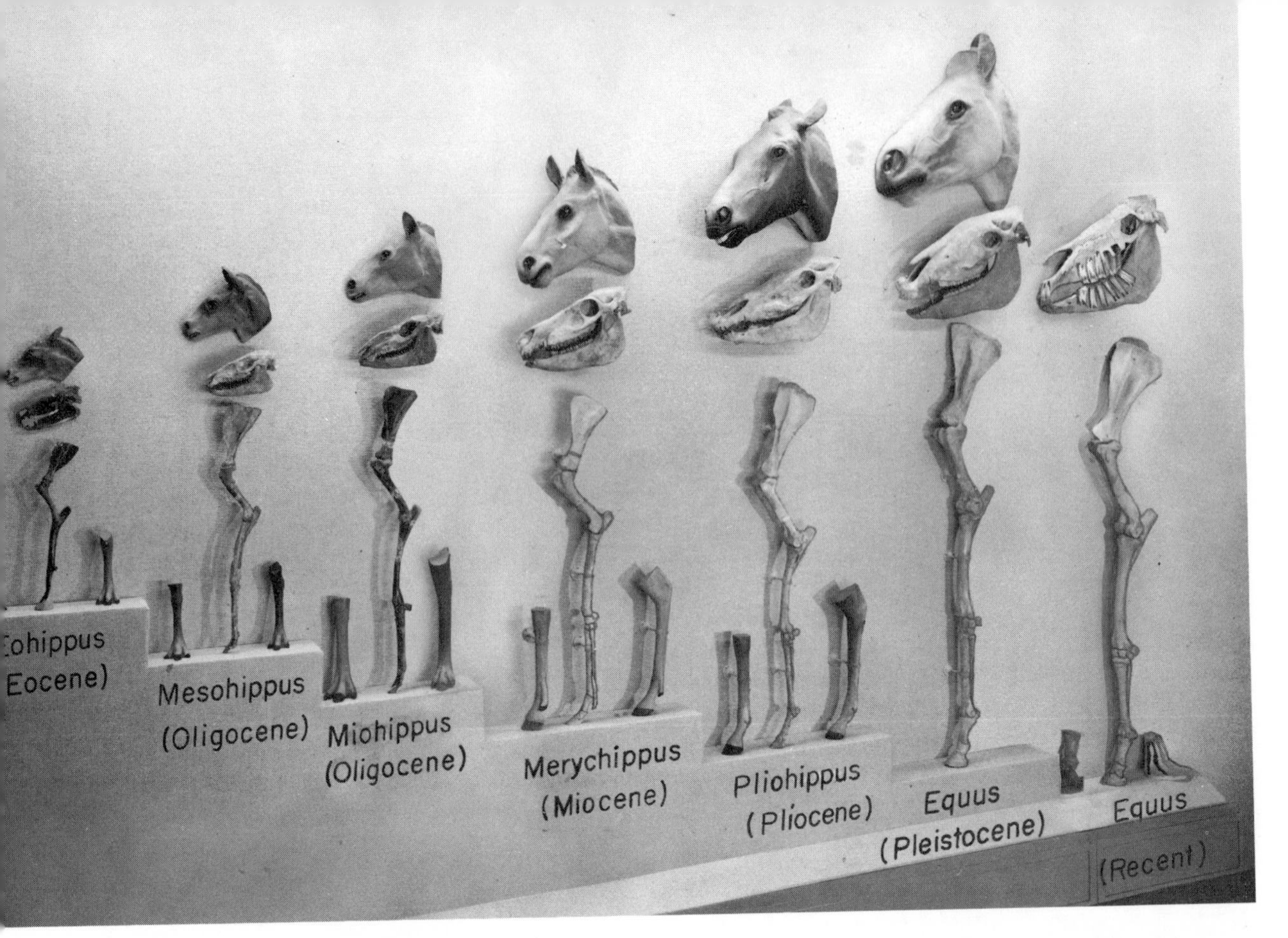

Figure 352. Evolution of the horse, as shown by limbs and skulls from successive zones in the Cenozoic rocks of western United States. The forelimb in each case indicates the approximate height at the shoulder, and the position of the skull shows the height at which the head of each genus of horse was carried. (Yale Peabody Museum.)

horses roamed the American plains in great herds until late in the epoch and then, for some unknown reason (possibly an epidemic like the modern hoof-and-mouth disease or sleeping sickness), became extinct. Meanwhile, fortunately, they had spread to the Old World (probably via Alaska and Siberia), where they survived to become a servant and a friend of man. The present wild horses are descendants of those brought over by the Spaniards during their early conquests.

Rhinoceroses. The rhinoceros (Figs. 354 and 359) also is primarily of North American stock. The group first appeared near the beginning of the Eocene and by early Oligocene time was abundant and had specialized into three distinct tribes: (1) the **true rhinoceroses**, which gradually developed into modern types; (2) the **running rhinoceroses**, which were small, light-bodied, and fleet-footed; and (3) the **amphibious rhinoceroses**, which were semiaquatic and, like the hippopotamus, became thick-bodied and very short-legged. The last two stocks died out during Oligocene time, but true rhinoceroses were very common in the Great Plains region during Miocene time and were then more varied than they are today in East Africa. One of the stiking Miocene forms was *Teleoceras*, a barrel-chested rhinoceros with extremely short legs (Fig. 359). In America the rhinoceroses declined to extinction in the Pliocene Epoch, but those that had migrated into the Old World survived.

The early rhinoceroses were small and hornless. The true rhinos were still scarcely 3 feet high in Oligocene time, although one of the amphibious tribe then reached a height of 6 feet and a length of 14 feet. In America few of the Cenozoic forms were as large as modern species, but in Asia an aberant stock of hornless giants developed during Oligocene and early Miocene time and in *Baluchitherium* (Fig. 354) attained the largest size of any known land mammal of any age, standing about 18 feet high at the shoulders, and at least 25 feet long.

Titanotheres. Titanotheres constitute another magnificent tribe of mammals, remotely related to the rhinoceroses and the horses (Figs. 355 and 372). They were ponderous beasts of rhinoceros-like appearance, many of them with great nasal horns made of bony outgrowths from the skull. Early Eocene titanotheres were scarcely larger than a big hog and were hornless, but the tribe developed rapidly to great size before its extinction about the middle of the Oligocene Epoch. One of the latest was *Brontotherium*, which stood about 8 feet high at the shoulder and far outbulked the largest living rhinoceros. During Oligocene time this was the largest land animal in America.

Titanotheres are known only from the United States, Mongolia, and Europe. They left no descendants, either collateral or direct. Like the rhinoceros, they possessed three toes on each hind foot and four toes on each front foot. The great weight probably prevented further reduction of the digits in either of these stocks of plains-dwelling mammals.

Chalicotheres. Perhaps the strangest of all the odd-toed mammals were the chalicotheres, a group now extinct, but represented by *Moropus* (Fig. 373) in the Great Plains region during Miocene

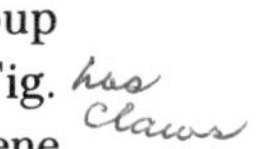

Figure 353. *Eohippus*, the "dawn horse," from the Eocene (Wind River) beds. Height at the shoulder about one foot. (Restoration by Charles R. Knight, American Museum of Natural History.)

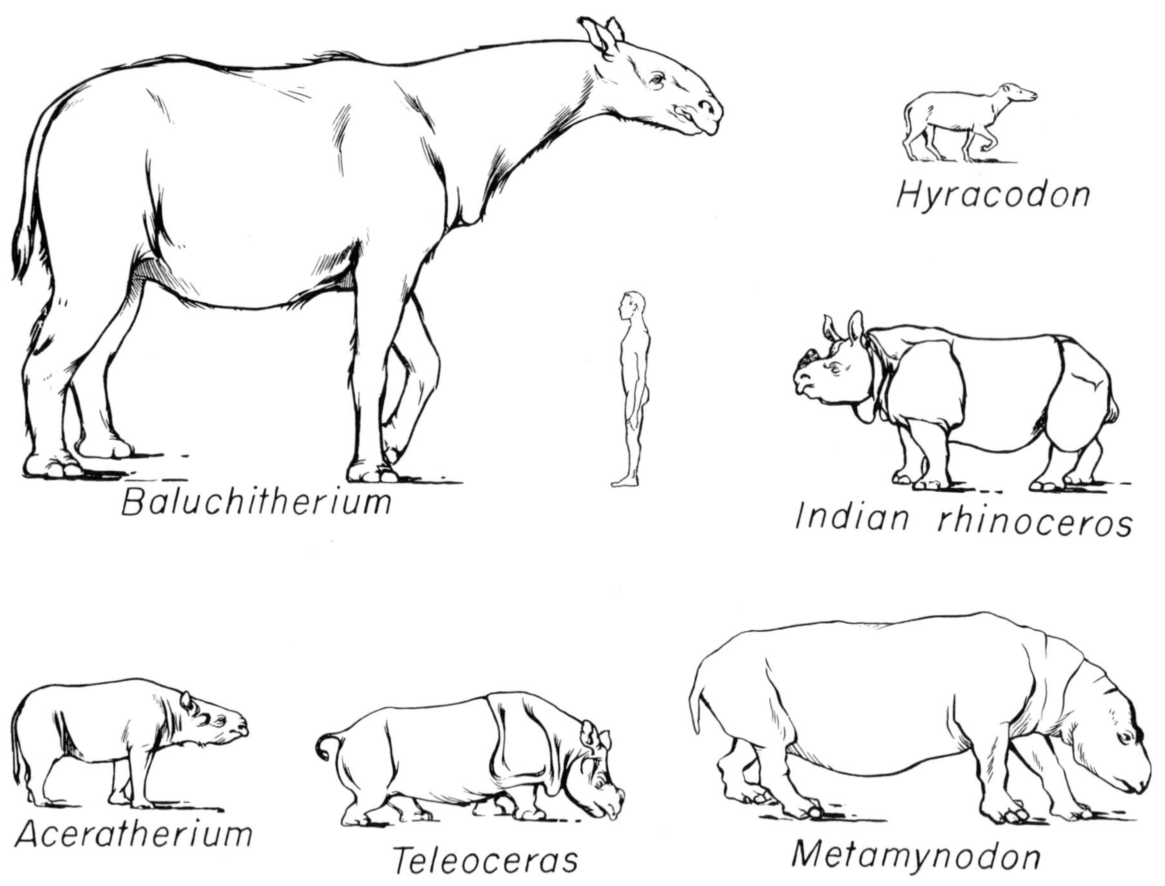

Figure 354. Fossil rhinoceroses (facing right) and the modern rhinoceros (facing left). The human figure gives the scale. *Hyracodon* is one of the running rhinos of Oligocene date; *Metamynodon* is one of the amphibious rhinos, also of Oligocene date; *Baluchitherium,* the greatest land mammal of all time, represents the giant tribe of baluchithere rhinos; the others represent the main line of rhinoceroses.

time. The skull of this grotesque creature was shaped like that of a horse, but its body was deep and short-coupled like that of a camel, and its feet bore narrowly compressed claws. There were three toes on the hind feet and three, plus a vestige of the fourth on the front feet. This is the best-known American form, and its remains are not rare in the Miocene beds of Nebraska; but the chalicotheres were present also in Europe and Asia and are known to have lived from late Eocene to late Pliocene time.

Camels. Camels underwent a long evolution remarkably paralleling that of the horse. One of the earliest genera, *Protylopus* of the upper Eocene, was a slender, four-toed creature scarcely larger than a jack rabbit. By Oligocene time camels had attained the size of sheep and were associated with *Mesohippus* of the same size. These little camels displayed their true affinities in the enamel pattern of their teeth and in the peculiar carriage of their heads. The toes had by this time been reduced to two on each foot, but were still free.

In Miocene time the camels diverged into several tribes (Fig. 373). The main line continued through *Procamelus* of the Miocene into *Camelops* of the Pliocene and Pleistocene. The latter survived until comparatively recent time in southwestern United States. A larger genus (*Gigantocamelus*) inhabited the Great Plains during Pleistocene time and reached a height of 7½ feet at the shoulders, carrying its head about 9 feet above the ground.

Among the divergent stocks that appeared in the Miocene were the small and very slender "gazelle camels" and the long-necked "giraffe camels."

Like the horses, the camels lived through the several ice ages in America and then for some unknown reason died out before the arrival of the white man. Meanwhile, however, they had migrated to both South America and Eurasia where they still survive (the alpaca and the vicuna of South America and the dromedary and two-humped camel of the Old World).

Oreodons. Among the commonest Mid-Cenozoic animals of western United States were the **oreodons** (Figs. 356 and 372). These small creatures are not closely allied to any living animals and are therefore difficult to characterize in non-technical terms. Most of them were of the size of sheep or goats. Although they appeared long-bodied and short-legged like a hog, this resemblance was quite superficial. In a sense they were remote cousins of the camels, for they had similar teeth, they were even-toed, and they were cud-chewers. They were both browsers and grazers, and, if we may judge by the extraordinary abundance of their remains in the Big Badlands of Dakota, they roamed the plains in vast herds. They appeared in late Eocene time, reached a climax in the Oligocene, and persisted into the early Pliocene before dying out, but during all this time they were strangely conservative, retaining four toes (some a small fifth) and short legs, keeping their low-crowned teeth, and failing to increase notably in size. Their short-leggedness was a mark of conservatism; their toes had failed to lengthen as rapidly as those of most other plains animals. So far as is known, oreodons were confined to North America.

Entelodonts. The **entelodonts**, or "giant pigs," were another group of even-toed mammals that assumed a spectacular role for a short time during the Mid-Cenozoic (Fig. 373). They were remote cousins of the swine and, like the latter, were adapted for rooting and grubbing in the forest. They are characterized by a large bony extension from the zygomatic arch of the cheek, a structure whose function is entirely problematic. They appeared during Oligocene time, reached their greatest size (6 feet high at the shoulder) in the early Miocene, and then died out.

Bovids. Cattle, sheep, and goats belong to the family Bovidae, which also includes the bison, the musk-ox, and the antelopes. In spite of superficial

Figure 355. First and last of the titanotheres. Right, *Eotitanops* of the Eocene Epoch; left, *Brontotherium* of the Oligocene Epoch. The latter stood about 8 feet high at the shoulders. (Adapted from a figure by H. F. Osborn.)

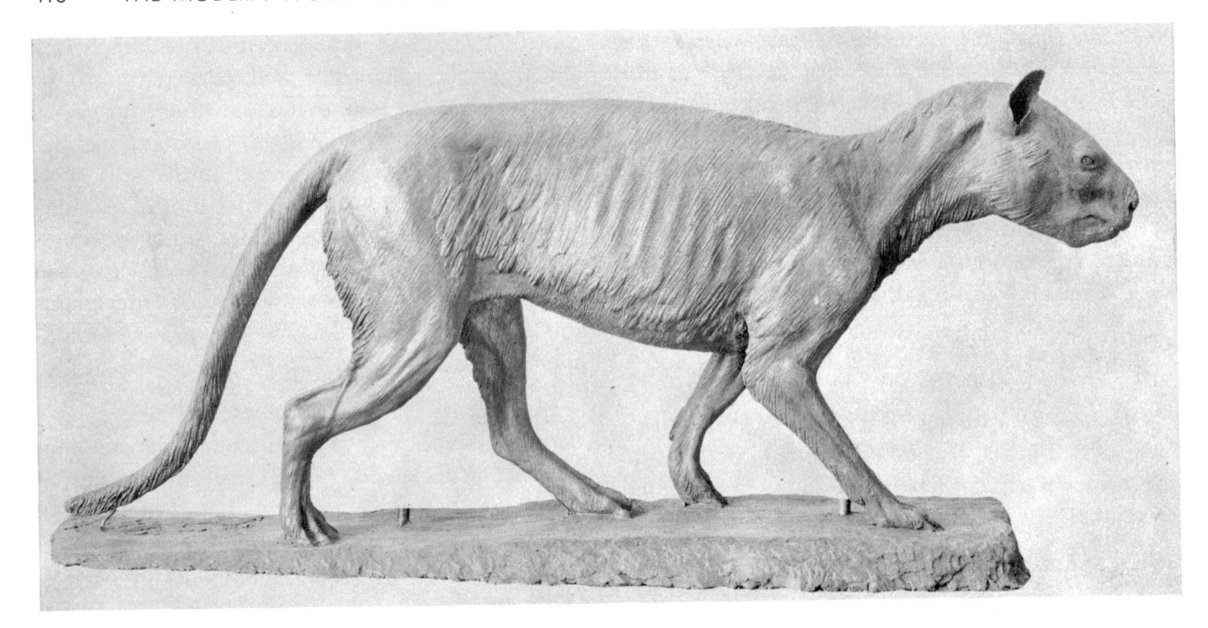

Figure 356. Model of oreodon, *Merycoidodon gracilis,* based on a skeleton from the Oligocene (White River) beds of Sioux County, Nebraska. The animal was about as tall as a sheep. (Model by Richard S. Lull, Yale Peabody Museum.)

differences, these animals are closely related and have many peculiarities in common. Among other things, they all lack front teeth in the upper jaw, and they possess true horns with an unbranched bony core covered by a horny sheath. Since the beginning of civilization this great family has contributed more than any other to human welfare. To hunting peoples it has been a source of food and of clothing and tents and thongs. Indeed, the very beginning of civilization is closely linked with the domestication of cattle, goats, and sheep, and the tending of flocks.

Unlike the horses and camels and rhinos, this family is essentially an Old World stock. The oldest known forms appeared in Eurasia late in Miocene time, having evolved from stocks now extinct. They became highly diversified there in the Pliocene and reached their modern estate during the Pleistocene Epoch, the cattle apparently having developed out of antelopes similar to the Gnŭ. During the Ice Age most of them migrated out of Europe, finding a more suitable environment in the plains of Asia and Africa, but only a few managed to reach America. The buffalo is one of the exceptions. It probably arrived via the Bering land bridge about the beginning of Pleistocene time, soon became enormously abundant, and developed into numerous species, some much larger than living forms. The musk-ox also reached North America in Pleistocene time, having no difficulty in crossing the snowfields of the North.

Elephants and Their Kin. Elephants of many sorts ranged over Europe, Asia, Africa, and North America in Pleistocene time; and, while the last glacial ice was waning, they were still more common in eastern United States than they are now in East Africa.

Compared with the ancestral placental mammal, the elephants show amazing specialization in several respects. Not the least of these is the fusion of nose and upper lip to form the trunk or **proboscis**, from which this order takes the name **Proboscidia**.

The earliest known proboscidians are found in North Africa, which appears to have been their ancestral home. Several species of the genus *Moeritherium* (Fig. 357) have been discovered in the late Eocene and early Oligocene beds of the Fayûm Desert not far west of Cairo. When these beds were forming, the climate was humid in North Africa, and the Fayûm area was occupied by the delta of an ancient Nile. The moeritheres were thickset animals scarcely waist-high to a man, and apparently they were semiaquatic, living in and along the river. They had neither tusks nor trunk and showed little resemblance to an elephant; yet they displayed the beginnings of specializations that betray their relationship. As shown in Figure 357, the head was long and low, and the upper lip was prehensile, as in a modern tapir. Among the front teeth the second incisors were enlarged and bore a band of enamel on the outer side. These are the teeth that developed into tusks in the later proboscidians. The limbs were thick and stout but not otherwise specialized. In this same region a more advanced type, *Phiomia*, appeared early in the Oligocene epoch, and for a time it lived along with the last of the moeritheres. This animal (Fig. 357) had the proportions of a small elephant and was about shoulder-high to a man. Its jaws were long and its head was low as compared with an elephant. The second pair of incisors was much enlarged and was directed strongly forward as small tusks, in both the upper and lower jaws. A real trunk was present, though still relatively short. The cheek teeth of *Phiomia* were rather large but low-crowned and bore three pairs of low, blunt cones.

Out of this early stock evolved an amazing

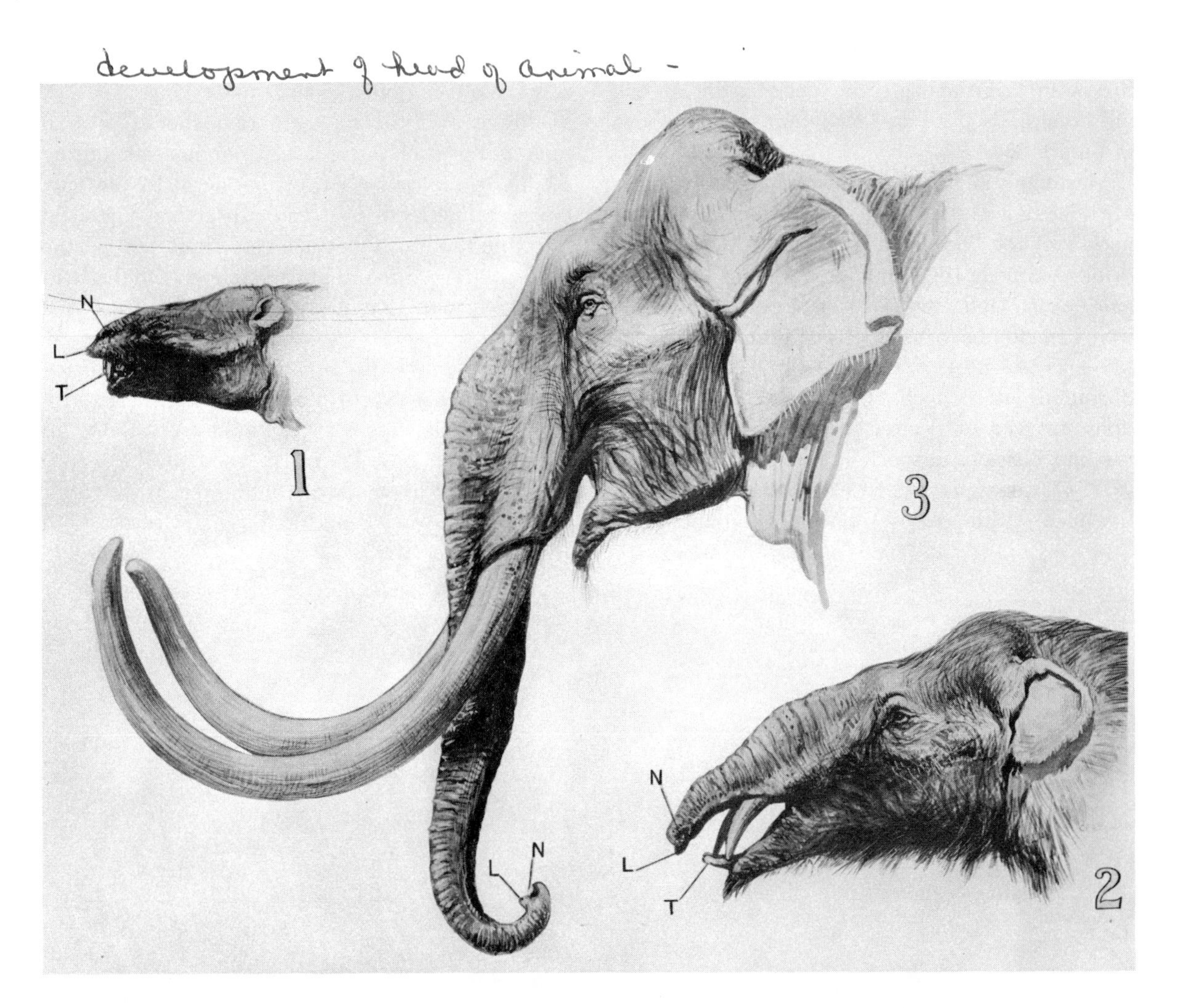

Figure 357. Restoration of proboscidian heads, showing stages in the development of tusks and trunks. 1, *Moeritherium* (early Oligocene); 2, *Phiomia* (later Oligocene); 3, *Elephas* (Recent). *T*, incisor tooth; *L*, upper lip; *N*, nostril. (After a drawing by Charles R. Knight, American Museum of Natural History.)

variety of animals known as **mastodons.** In most regards they resembled the elephants, but their teeth were quite different (Fig. 358). The name mastodon (Gr. *mastos,* breast + *odons,* tooth) refers to the characteristic shape of the large blunt cusps on their cheek teeth.

Phiomia possessed only three pairs of cusps on each molar tooth. Many of its descendants retained this number, but others added one or more pairs of cusps, and in all the later mastodons there was a tendency to unite individuals of each pair by a cross ridge (Fig. 358). The mastodons possessed their normal complement of permanent cheek teeth (six in each side of each jaw) throughout adult life.

Most of the mastodons had tusks in the lower as well as the upper jaw. In many, the lower tusks remained smaller than the upper, but in some stocks they were large and greatly specialized. A striking example is the long-faced four-tuskers shown in Figure 359.

Mastodons migrated widely over Eurasia during Miocene time and reached North America near the middle of the epoch via a Siberian-Alaskan land bridge. Among these immigrants were long-faced **four-tuskers** and **shovel-tuskers,** both of which were common in western United States during late Miocene and part of Pliocene time but died out during the latter epoch. More conservative mastodons survived until after the last glaciation, and the fine Pleistocene species, *Mammut americanus* (Fig. 374), may have been exterminated by primitive man within the last several thousand years.

The mastodons were predominantly browsers, living in the timber, and their cheek teeth were relatively unspecialized.

The **elephants,** on the contrary, were grazers and were for the most part at home on the plains. They are readily distinguished from the mastodons by a remarkable specialization of the cheek teeth, in which the cross ridges have become numerous and high and thin. As a result, the tooth is enormous in size, is high-crowned, and is made up of many transverse plates of enfolded enamel embedded in cement (Fig. 358). So large have these teeth become that there is room for only one in each side of each jaw—even in an elephant's mouth! Hence, the full set of teeth does not appear simultaneously. Instead, one tooth appears in each side of each jaw, and as it is worn out, a second tooth grows down, crowding out the first and taking its place. In this manner the six teeth that should exist in each half of each jaw succeed one another during the life of the individual, which normally has only four grinding teeth in the mouth at one time. In turn, the jaws have become very short, so that the head of the elephant appears short and high as compared with that of a mastodon (*cf.* Figs. 374 and 375).

Of this family (Elephantidae) the genus *Mammuthus* reached North America during the Pleistocene and was then represented by a number of species. The best known of these is the **woolly mammoth** that lived on the tundra and in the forest bordering the ice fields, and ranged across both

Figure 358. Cheek tooth of a mastodon (left) and of an elephant (right).

Figure 359. Late Miocene landscape in Nebraska showing at the left a group of the short-legged rhinoceros, *Teleoceras*, and at the right a pair of four-tusked, long-jawed mastodons. (From a painting by Charles R. Knight, Chicago Natural History Museum.)

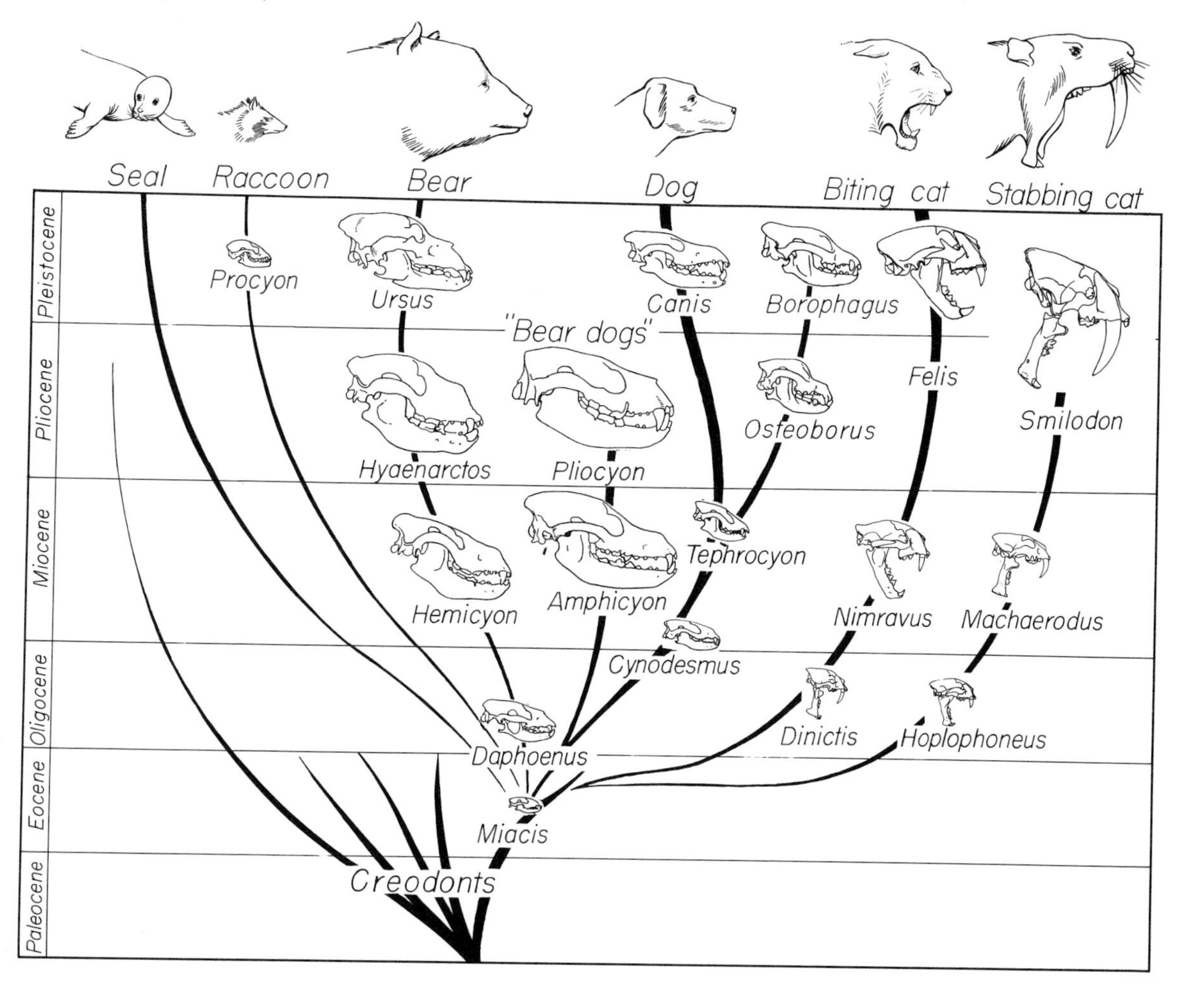

Figure 360. Family tree of the carnivores, all on the same scale. Note that the "bear dogs," a branch of the canine tribe, attained large size during the Miocene and Pliocene Epochs and then became extinct. (Diagram based on data from Matthew and Romer.)

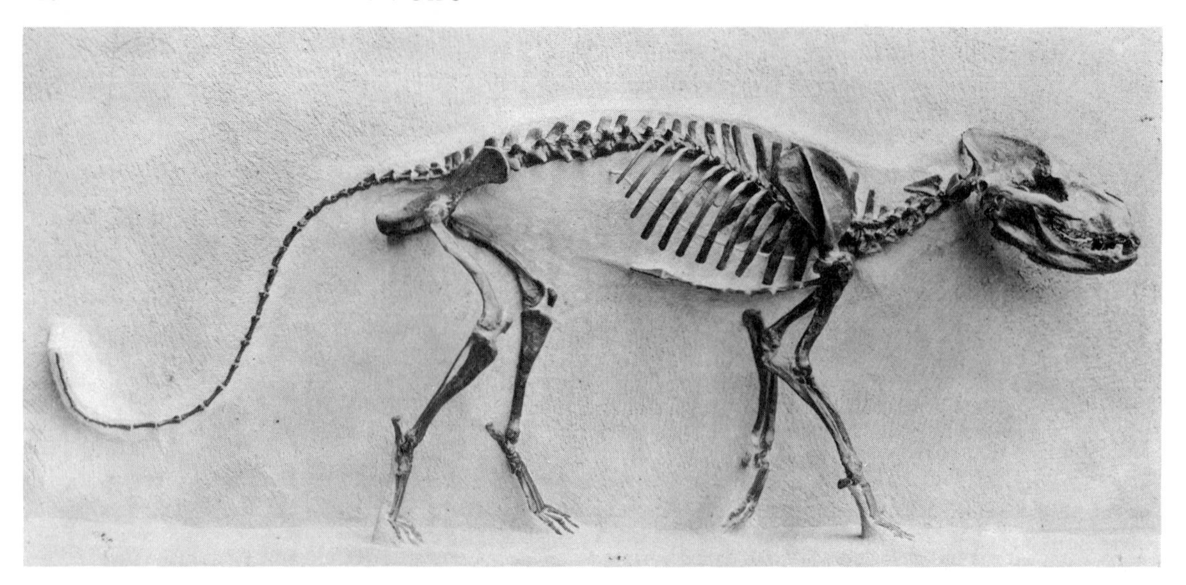

Figure 361. Skeleton of a creodont, *Dromocyon vorax,* from the Eocene (Bridger) of Henry's Fork, Wyoming. Animal about the size of a large dog. (Yale Peabody Museum.)

Eurasia and northern North America. In Siberia frozen carcasses have been found, showing that it bore a heavy coat of woolly hair (Fig. 375, and Fig. 15, p. 29). Other species inhabited the warmer regions, particularly the plains of the central and southwestern states. One of these, the **Imperial mammoth** of the Southwest, attained a height of 13 or 14 feet at the shoulders and bore tusks as much as 13 feet long. In their present fossil state, a pair of such tusks weighs almost half a ton!

Carnivores. Flesh-feeders have a long and complex geologic history (Fig. 360). They are intelligent, travel easily, and are highly adaptive. The dog and cat show their typical specializations—clawed feet, enlarged canines, and narrow shearing cheek teeth. These are devices for holding and devouring active prey. Among the modern forms, the dogs, cats, bears, hyenas, raccoons, and seals represent as many well-defined families, but when they are traced back toward the early Cenozoic, these distinctions decrease, and they seem to converge toward a common Eocene ancestor.

Small primitive carnivores appeared in some abundance in the Paleocene, and during the Eocene epoch they diverged into at least five distinct families, adapted themselves to a wide variety of habits, and attained a considerable range of size, a few reaching the stature of a large bear. Some superficially resembled wolves (Fig. 341) or cats or other living types, but in all these early forms the brains were very small, as compared with those of modern carnivores, and they must have been a stupid lot. Moreover, certain specializations of teeth or other parts show that four of these families were incapable of developing into any of the modern carnivores. For this reason, they are commonly set off as a distinct order, the **Creodonta** (Fig. 361).

Nearly all the creodonts were defective or inadaptive in some respects, and three of the families died out by the end of the Eocene, the other barely surviving through the Oligocene, with one genus ranging up into the Pliocene in India. Thus the first great experiment in carnivore evolution came to an inglorious end!

The fifth family of Paleocene and Eocene flesh-feeders had a higher destiny, even though, at the time, it would have seemed unpromising. It included small slender animals of the size of weasels; but they had better brains than the rest, and adaptive feet; and their teeth were already specializing in the direction followed by the higher carnivores. Among these small Eocene types, the genus *Miacis* appears as a probable ancestor of all modern carnivores.

This second upsurgence of carnivores was under

way in the Eocene, and before the close of that epoch the modern families began to emerge. The dogs were represented by *Pseudocynodictis*, of the size of a fox, and the cats by *Dinictis*, as large as a small leopard.

The Miocene was a time of rapid expansion, and before its close all the modern families were well defined. In the Pliocene formations of western United States several species of wolves are represented, some large and others small, and by Pleistocene time the species were similar to modern ones. In the asphalt deposits at Rancho La Brea in California a common fossil is the dire wolf (Fig. 362), which had the stature of a large gray timber wolf.

By Miocene time the cats were diverging into two quite distinct families, the **biting cats** and the **stabbing cats.** In the former, to which all modern cats belong, the lower and upper canines are subequal, and the lower jaw is strong. Such cats kill their prey by biting. In the stabbing cats the lower canines were small, and the upper ones were extended into saberlike blades; the lower jaw was weak and could be opened to a very wide angle so as to clear the upper teeth, which were then used to stab and tear, bleeding the prey to death.

Figure 362. The dire wolf, *Canis dirus*, a common species in the asphalt pits at Rancho La Brea, near Los Angeles, California. Size about that of a modern timber wolf. Pleistocene. (Model by R. S. Lull, Yale Peabody Museum.)

Figure 363. The great saber-toothed tiger, *Smilodon*, common in the asphalt pits at Rancho La Brea, in Los Angeles, California. Height about 3 feet. Pleistocene. (Model by R. S. Lull, Yale Peabody Museum.)

The biting cats are well represented in both the Pliocene and Pleistocene deposits of America, culminating in the panther and lynx. *Felis atrox* of the Pleistocene faunas of southern California was the size of a lion. The true lion, *Felis leo*, ranged widely over Europe during the interglacial ages of the Pleistocene.

The stabbing cats were even more common from Oligocene to late Pleistocene time, culminating in the **saber-toothed tiger** of the Rancho La Brea tar pits (Fig. 363). It was the last of its race, becoming extinct during the Pleistocene Epoch.

Man's Family Tree. Among all the animals, man's closest relatives are obviously the great apes and monkeys; but his family tree also includes two lower branches, the tarsioids and lemurs. All these together constitute the order **Primates** (Fig. 364).

Lemurs (Fig. 365) superficially resemble foxes rather than monkeys. They are distinctly quadrupedal, have long bushy tails, and run on all fours. Furthermore, their brains are relatively small, their muzzles slender and pointed, and their eyes far apart. Their teeth, however, so closely resemble those of insectivores as to make it quite clear that the primates evolved out of primitive insectivore stock.

The **tarsier** of the East Indies (Fig. 366) is the sole survivor of a group of small primates that was far more common and more widely distributed during the early part of the Cenozoic Era. In nocturnal habits and some other respects the living form is highly specialized, but its ancestors among the fossil tarsioids bridge the gap between lemurs and monkeys. When compared with the lemurs, for example, tarsioids have a relatively larger brain and a shorter muzzle, but the most significant advance is in the eyes, which have migrated to the front and are so close together that both can focus on the same point. This permits stereoscopic vision, an achievement which no other animals have attained save the monkeys and apes and man.

From the start, the primates specialized for an arboreal life, finding in the trees a refuge from their more powerful enemies on the ground. Prehensile hands and feet, with opposable thumb and great toe, were developed early; and the depth of focus inherent in stereoscopic vision opened new possibilities for locomotion in the trees. Instead of running along the limbs like a squirrel, such animals could safely hang by their arms and swing from limb to limb or even from tree to tree.

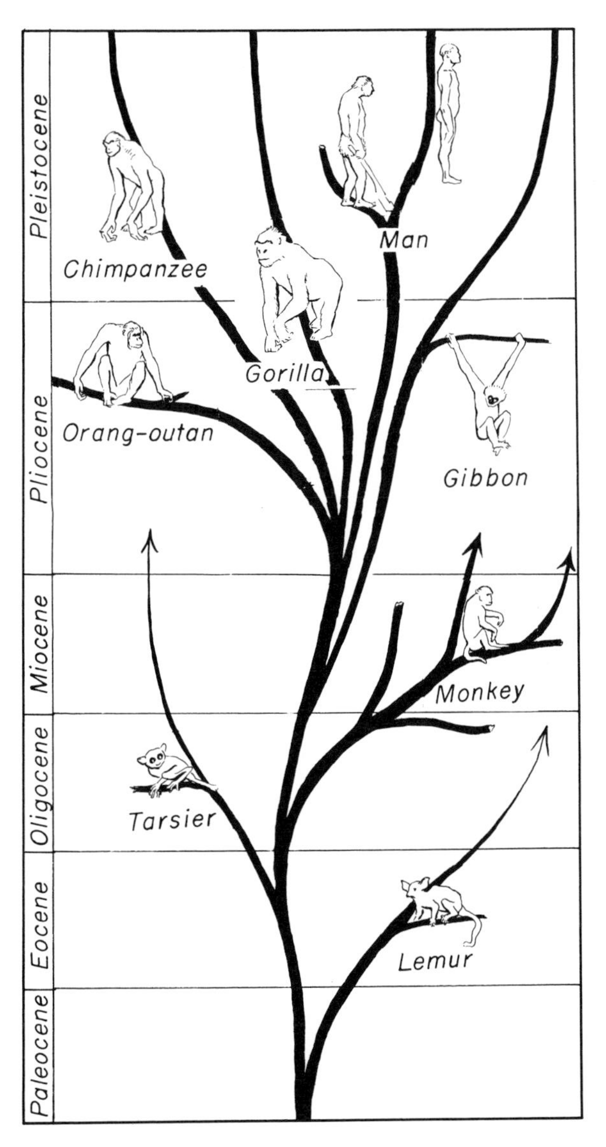

Figure 364. Man's family tree.

Such free and rapid locomotion through the forest had great selective value. It led first to the evolution of the monkeys and shortly thereafter to gibbonlike apes, in which the arms are longer and more powerful than the legs. This in turn opened

Figure 365. *Galago*, the "bush baby," a small lemur of rather advanced type from northern Rhodesia, Africa. The body of the animal is about 6 inches long. (Yale Peabody Museum.)

Figure 366. The *Tarsier*, a native of the Philippine Islands. About natural size. (Lilo Hess photograph.)

Gibbon

Orang-outan

Chimpanzee

Gorilla

Figure 367. The four living great apes drawn to the same scale. They do not live together, but are here posed symbolically to indicate their normal habit. The gibbon and orang-utan inhabit southeastern Asia and the East Indies, whereas the chimpanzee and the gorilla inhabit the tropical forests of Africa. The gibbon travels rapidly by swinging under the limbs, and thus leaping from tree to tree; the orang-utan makes nests in the trees and is a slow, lazy climber; both the chimpanzee and the gorilla spend much time on the ground and are able to walk upright.

up new possibilities when the forests shrank, during late Cenozoic time, and some adventurous apes returned to life on the ground, for now their long arms gave them almost an upright position even when walking on all fours. Bipedal gait was thus easy to achieve and the hands were freed for better uses. Special interest therefore attaches to the tarsioids, whose vision in Paleocene time started us on the highway toward the human estate!

The lemurs and tarsioids were well adapted to the mild, moist climate that prevailed over Europe and the United States during the early part of the Cenozoic Era, and their fossil remains are relatively abundant, though fragmentary, in both these regions in Paleocene and Eocene strata. But during Oligocene time subtropical forests gave way to open plains in the present temperate lowlands, and the primates retreated to lower latitudes. During the Miocene and Pliocene epochs the climate generally became both cooler and drier, and the tropical and subtropical forests gradually shrank to their present distribution. As a result, most of the higher primate evolution took place in parts of Africa and Eurasia that are not yet well known paleontologically.

Lemurs and tarsioids died out in the United States during Oligocene time, and no record whatever is known of monkeys or apes in all of North America. Small monkeys had reached South America (or had evolved there out of tarsioids) and survive to the present, undergoing an evolution entirely independent of the rest of the world, and reaching no greater attainment than that of the cebid monkeys used by itinerant organ-grinders.

The earliest evidence of Old World **monkeys** is a lower jaw with most of its teeth, found in Lower Oligocene beds of Egypt. The Miocene record is still very meager, and that of the Pliocene only somewhat better. Tropical forests provide a very poor environment for the preservation of fossils, because the organic acids in the soil cause rapid decay of bones. For this reason we may never have as much evidence for the geologic history of the primates as for most of the other groups of animals. Pliocene monkeys are referred to families still living.

The manlike **apes** (Fig. 367) include four living types—the gibbon, the orang-outan, the chimpanzee, and the gorilla—and a number of fossil genera. In these the arms are longer than the hind legs, so that when walking on all fours the body is in an almost upright position, and bipedal gait is not difficult.

Figure 368. Left upper dentition of *Oreopithecus bambolii* from the Grosseto Lignite in the Province of Grosseto, midway between Rome and Pisa, Italy. (After Hürtzeler.)

Although the living great apes are more manlike than any other animals, each type is highly specialized for a lazy life in the tropical forest, and none could possibly be considered the direct ancestor of man. Instead we must go back to fossil forms of the late Miocene for the stock that left the forests and started the human lineage. The oldest known form that can, with assurance, be placed in the line leading directly to man is *Oreopithecus* whose fragmentary remains occur in abundance in the late Miocene lignite beds of central western Italy.[1] Critical study of the teeth (Fig. 368) indicate that this small primate is closer to the human line than to any of the great apes.

A closely similar genus, *Dryopithecus*, is known from Miocene beds in both Europe and Africa.

The most important fossil evidence for early human evolution has been found in limestone caverns in the vicinity of Johannesburg, South Africa.[2] Remains of more than 30 individuals are now known (including various growth stages). Although described under four generic names, all are now believed to represent a single genus, *Australopithecus*.* The material is beautifully preserved and includes almost complete skulls and dentition as well as much skeletal material.

The brain of *Australopithecus* was scarcely half as large as that of modern man and the cranium was scarcely as large as the jaw frame (Fig. 369) so that the living animal was probably apelike in appearance; but many technical details of skull and teeth prove it to be in the human line, and the pelvic bones indicate clearly that the animal was

*This name, meaning southern ape, is unfortunate, because it might be mistaken to indicate that the source was in Australia, and because the animal was not an ape.

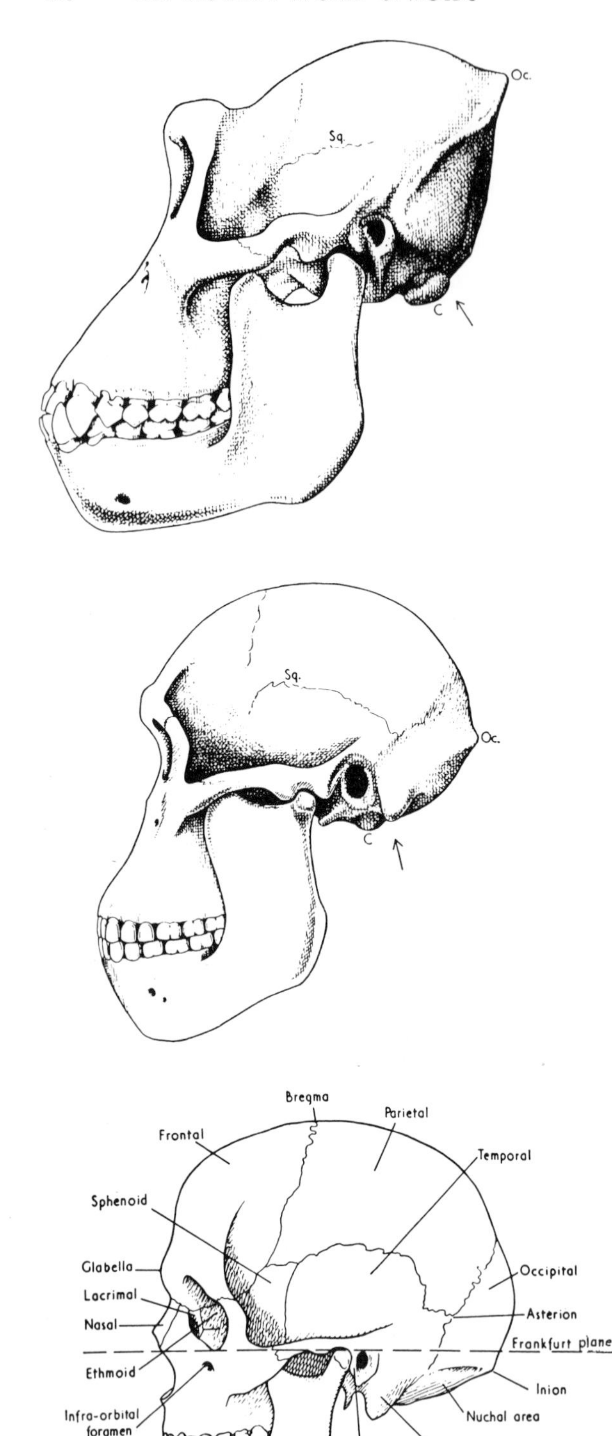

Figure 369. Skull of *Australopithecus* (center) compared with that of the gorilla (above) and of modern man (below). (Figures from Le Gros Clark.)

adapted to upright posture in the open veldt of South Africa. Among other things, for example, the canine teeth were reduced to the level of the other teeth (as in man) and the jaw was evenly arched, contrasting strongly in both regards with the great apes (Fig. 370). *Australopithecus* is of Early Pleistocene age and is discussed further in Chapter 20.

RECAPITULATION

Paleocene Faunas. G. G. Simpson has said, the most dramatic and in many respects

> the most puzzling event in the history of life on the earth, . . . is the change from the Mesozoic, Age of Reptiles, to the . . . Age of Mammals. It is as if the curtain were rung down suddenly on a stage where all the leading roles were taken by reptiles, especially dinosaurs, in great numbers and bewildering variety, and rose again immediately to reveal the same setting but an entirely new cast, a cast in which the dinosaurs do not appear at all, other reptiles are mere supernumeraries, and the leading parts are all played by mammals of sorts barely hinted at in the preceding acts.[3]

Clearly these Paleocene mammals (Fig. 371) came for the most part as migrants from some region (probably northern Asia) where they had been developing even before the close of the Mesozoic. Among them were holdovers of three groups already known in the Cretaceous world—multituberculates, marsupials, and insectivores. But the dominant groups—condylarths, amblypods, and creodonts—belonged to three "archaic" orders that appeared suddenly, thrived for a while, and then died out. Although these orders lived on into Eocene time and some then attained considerable size, the Paleocene species were small, the largest scarcely exceeding the size of a hog or a small bear.

With these "archaic" stocks were associated the forerunners of several orders that are still extant, notably the rodents and primates, but these were all small.

Nearly all the Paleocene mammals had long narrow heads with small brain cases, and long slender muzzles. They were quadrupedal, with fore and hind legs nearly equal in length. All had five toes, and the earliest known examples of each stock walked on the sole of the foot. The distinction between the marsupials and all the rest was already so complete as to suggest that the placental mam-

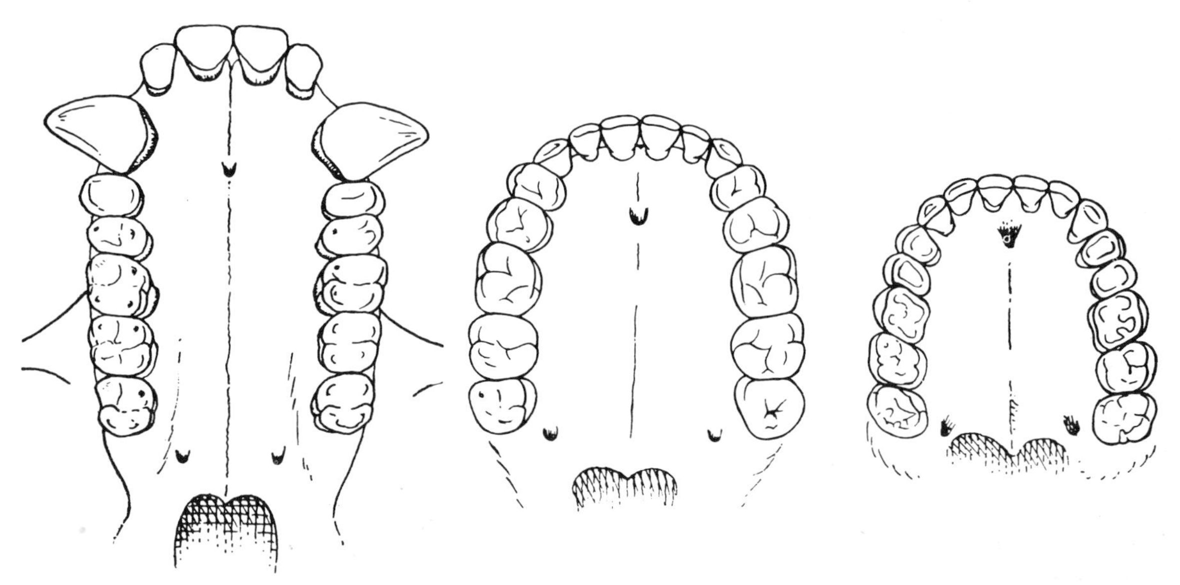

Figure 370. Lower jaw and dentition of *Australopithecus* (center) compared with that of the gorilla (left) and of modern man (right). (Figures from Le Gros Clark.)

Figure 371. A Paleocene landscape in the Rocky Mountain states. 1, a boa constrictor hanging from a breadfruit tree; 2, a soft-shelled turtle; 3, a crocodile; 4, a flying lemur, *Planetetherium*; 5, a primitive condylarth, *Tetraclaenodon*; 6, a primitive amblypod, *Pantolambda*; 7, another amblypod, *Barylambda*. Painting by Rudolph Zallinger, from Life's *The World We Live In* (Courtesy of Time, Inc.)

Figure 372. An Oligocene landscape in Dakota. 1, a herd of oreodons; 2, an entelodont, *Archeotherium;* 3, a titanothere, *Brontops;* 4, a primitive horse, *Mesohippus;* 5, a deer, *Protoceras;* 6, a creodont, *Hyaenodon;* 7, a rhinoceros, *Subhyracodon;* 8, a tapir, *Protapiris;* 9, a primitive cat, *Hoplophoneus;* 10, a primitive camel, *Poëbrotherium.* (Drawn by Rudolph F. Zallinger for Life's *The World We Live In.* (Courtesy of Time, Inc.)

mals were not direct descendants of the marsupials, but cousins descended from a common Mesozoic ancestor.

Eocene Faunas. The most striking feature of the early Eocene life (Fig. 341) was the appearance in considerable numbers of progessive forms ancestral to the modern orders of mammals. Among these were diminutive **horses**, small hornless **rhinoceroses**, equally small **titanotheres**, tiny **cameloids**, the first **oreodons**, squirrel-like **rodents**, **bats**, and small **primates**. None of these attained a considerable size, and the largest would hardly have stood waist-high to a man.

With them were associated the "archaic" mammals, some of which were far larger. **Creodonts** were the carnivores of that time, and of these some were doglike, some hyenalike, and others more catlike. Common American types reached a maximum size similar to that of a modern timber wolf, though one of the latest Eocene types was as large as a great bear. The greatest of all Eocene carnivores, however, was the Mongolian *Andrewsarchus*, with a skull about 2½ feet long. The **condylarths** were common during the early half of the epoch but died out before its close. The great animals of this time were the ponderous **amblypods**, which increased gradually to their maximum bulk in *Uintatherium* of the late Eocene.

In the later Eocene occurred the first mammal adaptation to a marine life, in the form of whale-like animals (**zeuglodons**), whose fossil bones occur abundantly in parts of our southern states, in Egypt, and in Europe. One of these, *Basilosaurus*, must have been the "sea serpent" of its time, with 4 feet of head, 10 feet of body, and 40 feet of tail! But even a mammal of this size met its match in the great **sharks** of those seas, one of which (*Carcharodon*) had jaws about 6 feet across.

Oligocene Faunas. By Oligocene time (Fig. 372), the modernized types comprised nearly the entire mammalian fauna. A single genus of creodonts remained, but ambylypods and condylarths were wholly extinct, and marsupials and insectivores were as inconspicuous as they are today. In western America the **oreodons** roamed in vast herds over the plains. Three-toed **horses** (*Mesohippus*) scarcely larger than sheep were common. **Rhinoceroses** of several kinds were present, the largest of them being amphibious, though not related to the hippopotamus; probably all the Oligocene species were hornless. The **titanotheres** displayed a meteoric evolution, and with the exception of the giant Asiatic rhinoceros, *Baluchitherium*, they became the largest land animals of this time before dying out abruptly about the middle of the epoch. Small camels were present, and so were peccaries and tapirs. The rodents were represented by beavers, squirrels, rabbits, and mice. Among the carnivores there were many small **dogs**, as well as both **biting cats** and **stabbing cats**. In the Old World the Proboscidea were beginning their career, being represented by the first mastodons, which were only about 5½ feet high. Early primates had become extinct in North America, and the only known great ape was represented in Europe by a single species.

Miocene Faunas. The Miocene was the "Golden Age" of mammals (Fig. 373). The spread of the prairies and the change to a more arid climate led to rapid evolution of the grazing stocks, and the formation of a Bering land bridge permitted intermigration between North America and Eurasia.

Within the groups of animals already present there was a rapid expansion into new genera and species and an increase in size in many stocks. The

Figure 373. A Miocene landscape in Dakota. 1, a chalicothere, *Moropus;* 2, an entelodont, *Dinohyus;* 3, herd of primitive horses, *Merychippus;* 4, a four-horned antelope, *Syndyoceras;* 5, small camels, *Procamilus;* 6, herd of oreodons; 7, a giraffe-camel, *Alticamilus;* 8, four-tusked mastodon, *Gomphotherium.* Drawn by Rudolph F. Zallinger for Life's *The World We Live In.* (Courtesy of Time, Inc.)

Figure 374. Scene in the Mississippi Valley during Pleistocene time. At the left, the American mastodon; center, the Royal bison; right, the wild horse, *Equus scotti*. (From a mural by Charles R. Knight, American Museum of Natural History.)

habit of feeding on the harsh prairie grasses resulted in a remarkable change in the teeth of many groups, whereby the jaw teeth became long and prismatic and continued to grow throughout life, thus counteracting the rapid wear at the crowns. **Horses** now attained the size of small ponies, but the many species all had dangling side toes. **Camels** were especially abundant and varied, some being little larger than sheep, while others rivaled the modern giraffe in height. **Oreodons** were still very common. **Rhinoceroses** of several kinds were abundant. At this time the "**giant pigs**" reached their climax in a species (*Dinohyus hollandi*) known from Nebraska that was as tall as an ox and had a skull 4 feet long. *Moropus*, the clawed **ungulate**, was also most common at this time. **Rodents** like those of the Oligocene continued through the Miocene. Of **carnivores** there were numerous wolf-like dogs, as well as biting and stabbing cats. There were no North American primates, but in the Old World a great ape (*Dryopithecus*), somewhat related to the gorilla, but much smaller, ranged over Europe and northern Africa. The four-tusked proboscidians arrived in America.

Pliocene Faunas. The Pliocene faunas of North America are still imperfectly known because the terrestrial formations of this age are so sparsely preserved. At this time there was further immigration from the Old World, bringing us the **true mastodons. Horses** continued their rapid evolution and were represented in America by several genera, among which appeared the first single-toed horse, *Pliohippus*. **Rhinoceroses** were still very abundant. **Camels** continued to be among the most common animals of the plains. The last straggling survivors of the oreodons were extinct before the close of the epoch.

Pleistocene Faunas. Throughout the Pleistocene Epoch North America and Europe were both inhabited by great game animals fully as varied and impressive as those of modern East Africa. In the United States the **elephants** were perhaps the most impressive, for there were at least four species, two of which exceeded modern elephants in size. The tall, rangy Imperial mammoth of the southern Great Plains stood nearly 14 feet high at the shoulders. Another species (*Mammuthus arizonae*) was at home in the basins of Arizona and Nevada. Numerous remains of *Mammuthus columbia* and *M. imperator* have been found in the uppermost beds of glacial Lake Bonneville, and these elephants must have been common in the Great Basin region until after the last of the glacial ages. Throughout the forests mastodons (*Mammut americanus*) browsed in great herds (Fig. 374); their remains are common in the peat bogs of the eastern states, no fewer than 217 individuals having been discovered in the bogs of New York State alone. In Florida, New York, and elsewhere the remains of this species are associated with human artifacts in such a way as to indicate that mastodons survived the last ice age and may have lived until within the last several thousand years. The woolly mammoths (Fig. 375) ranged widely over the glaci-

ated areas, extending northward into Alaska and eastward across Siberia, where their skeletons and tusks are still incredibly numerous in the frozen soil, about half the present ivory of commerce being derived from this source. Siberian ivory was imported into China as early as the fourth century B.C., and began to be extensively transported into Europe early in the nineteenth century. Between 1800 and 1850 the annual sale of tusks at the trading center of Yakutsk averaged about 18 tons, and to date not less than 46,750 pairs of tusks have been recovered in Siberia.[4]

Horses were still common, and at least ten species are known from North America. Most of these were of the size of small ponies, but one fully equaled the greatest modern draught horse. **Buffaloes** roamed the plains in great herds as they did when the white man first reached America. There were at least seven Pleistocene species, and one of these (*Bison latifrons*) was a colossal beast with a horn-spread of fully 6 feet (Fig. 374). **Camels** also were common. **Wild pigs** (peccaries), now confined to Texas, Mexico, and Central America, then ranged over the United States.

Carnivores were abundant and varied, including species of such modern types as the wolves, foxes, pumas, lynxes, raccoons, badgers, otters, skunks, and weasels. In addition, there were extinct types of which the great saber-tooth (*Smilodon*) was perhaps the most striking. Another great cat (*Felis atrox*), also known from the tar pits of Rancho La Brea, was very much like the modern lion in form and size. The great wolf (*Canis dirus*) which was so common in southern California exceeded in size any modern American canines. True bears apparently made their appearance in America at this time as immigrants from the Old World.

One of the striking elements of the Pleistocene fauna was due to the immigration from South America of the **glyptodonts** and the great **ground-sloths.** These both reached Texas in the Pliocene, and the latter spread over the United States in the Pleistocene. The ground-sloths (Fig. 30, p. 42) were clumsy beasts with the bulk of an elephant, but they were short-legged and curiously club-footed—their ancestors had lived so long in the trees and had developed such long curved claws that it was impossible for them to walk on the bottoms of the feet when they became too heavy to live longer off the ground. These creatures are common fossils in the tar pits of southern California, and at least one genus (*Megalonyx*) ranged eastward to the Atlantic states. A claw of this form was discovered in a cave in Virginia by President Jefferson, who was the first to describe and name the genus but thought it to be a mighty lion.

North and South America were separated throughout Cenozoic time until they became united by the present Isthmus of Panama in the late Pliocene. Just before this connection, South America had 29 families of mammals and North America 27, but with 2 doubtful exceptions they had no families in common.[3] Shortly afterward, in the Pleistocene, they had 22 families in common, 7 of South American origin and 14 of North American origin and 1 doubtful. Those emigrating to South

Figure 375. Pleistocene landscape in Europe during the last Ice Age, with woolly mammoth in the foreground and woolly rhinoceros in the right middle distance. (Chicago Natural History Museum.)

America included the mastodons, horses, tapirs, camels, and peccaries; those coming in the opposite direction included the ground-sloths, armadillos, and glyptodonts.

Another striking element of the Pleistocene faunas was supplied by the arctic animals that migrated southward during the glacial ages. For example, the musk-ox is recorded as far south as Arkansas and Utah, while in Europe the reindeer, the woolly rhinoceros, the woolly mammoth, and the arctic fox ranged southward into France and Poland.

There were no primates in North America until primitive man reached here from the Old World. Although evidence of the presence of early man in America has been claimed repeatedly, it is still scanty. On the other hand, savage races were present in Europe and in eastern Asia and northern Africa throughout much if not all of the Pleistocene Epoch. The geologic history of man is reserved, however, for Chapter 20.

In Europe, the Pleistocene fauna of the warm interglacial ages included most of the types of great game animals now found in Africa. Such, for example, were the lion, the rhinoceros, the hippopotamus, the elephants, antelopes, and lesser animals.

CONTEMPORARY LIFE

Spread of the Prairies. Forests were essentially modern at the beginning of the Age of Mammals. Most of the genera of hardwood trees had appeared during the Cretaceous Period, and their subsequent evolution has been in the main a matter of specific details. However, the development of the grasses during this era was one of the great milestones in the history of life,[5] and for the evolving mammals its importance can hardly be overemphasized. It is this stock, for example, that includes not only the forage plants but also the cereals—notably wheat and rice and oats and corn—that provide the basic food supply for the modern world.

Grass is poorly adapted for preservation, and almost no direct evidence of its early history is known. However, it contains an appreciable amount of silica and tends to wear out the grinding teeth of the grazers, that is, grass-feeders. To compensate for such wear, the modern plains mammals have high-crowned cheek teeth that grow at the roots throughout life (Fig. 345). Pre-Miocene representatives of each of these groups, like the modern forest-dwellers that browse on more succulent leaves, had low-crowned cheek teeth. It appears evident that the high-crowned grinding teeth are a direct adaptation to a grazing habit; and since this specialization began early in the Miocene, it is inferred that prairie grass had then, for the first time, become widespread. About 1940, fossil grass seeds were discovered in some of the sandy beds of western Nebraska, and it was soon found that they are abundant over the High

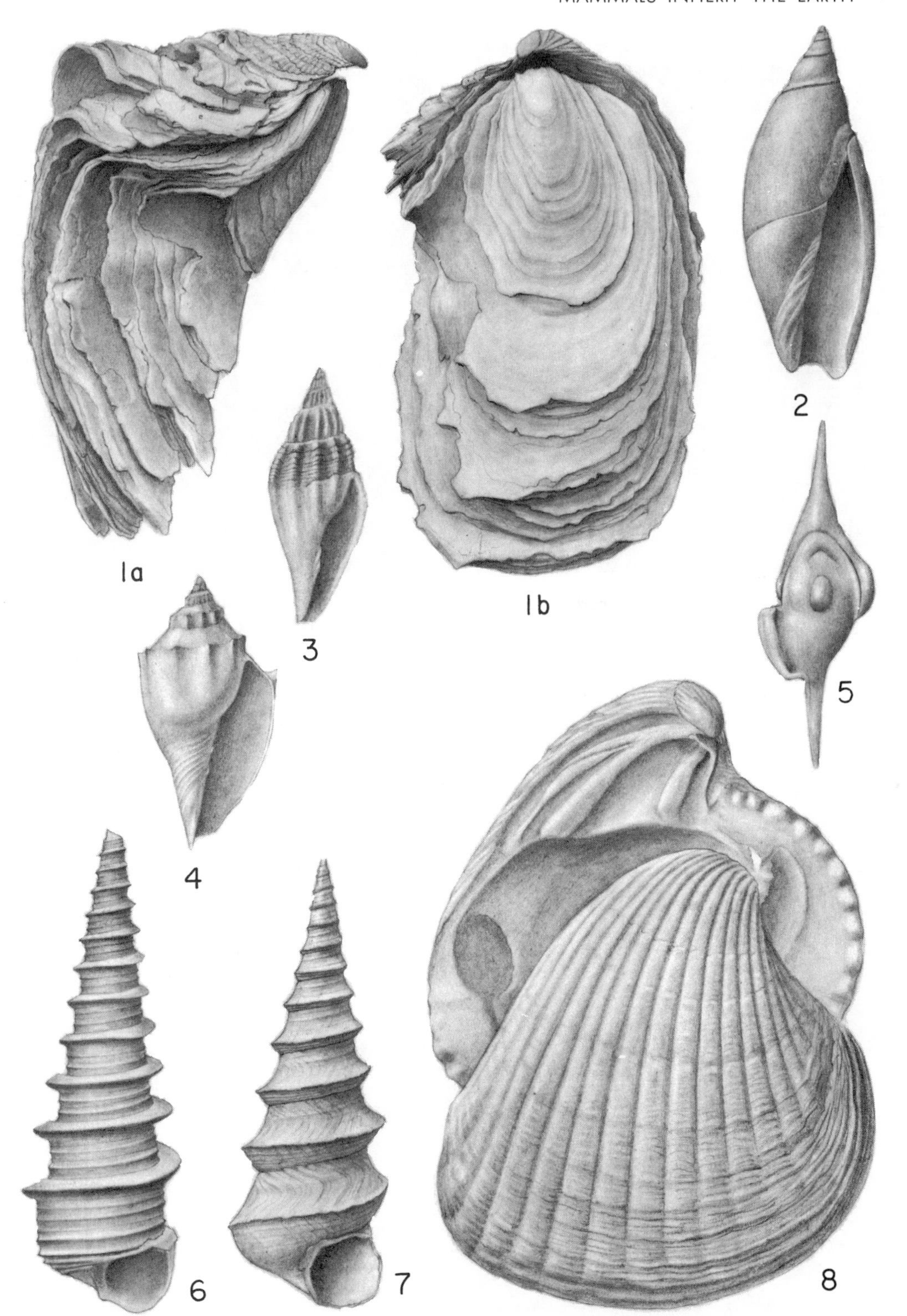

Plate 18. Eocene Mollusks.

Figures 1*a*, 1*b*, *Ostraea sellaeformis*; 2, *Oliva alabamiensis*; 3, *Plejona rugata*; 4, *Volutilithes sayana*; 5, *Calyptrophorus trinodiferus*; 6, *Turritella praecincta*; 7, *Turritella mortoni*; 8, *Venericardia planicosta*.

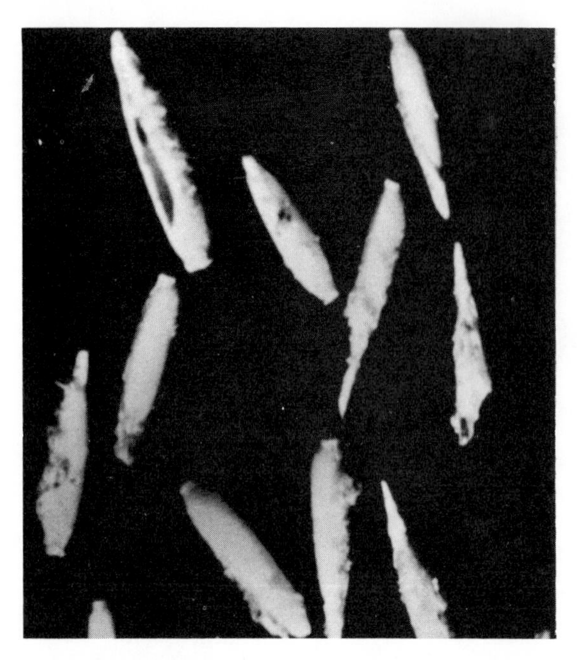

Figure 376. Seeds of grasses and other herbs. Left, the spear grass, *Stipidium,* from the Valentine formation (Pliocene); right, the borage herb, *Biorbia,* from the Ash Hollow formation (Pliocene). (Maxim K. Elias.)

Figure 377. A chunk of nummulitic limestone from the Pyramid of Gizah, Egypt. Herodotus, about 450 B.C., alluded to this stone as an instance of petrified animals. (Eocene.) Natural size. (Yale Peabody Museum.)

Plains region in beds ranging from Mid-Miocene to late Pliocene date (Fig. 376). Careful search in the underlying early Miocene and Oligocene deposits of the same region has thus far been in vain.

Other herbaceous plants are still imperfectly known, but roses with characteristic leaves and thorns have been found in the Oligocene, and unmistakable leaves and seeds of the grape occur in Eocene and later rocks of both Europe and America. Petrified grapevine is known from the Miocene beds of Nevada.

Modernization of the Invertebrates. The invertebrate animals (Plates 18, 19, 20) like the forest plants, had practically accomplished their present evolution before Cenozoic time. A few of the modern species were already living in the Eocene Epoch, and many more were extant in the Miocene.

Special note should be made, however, of the **nummulites,** a family of very large Foraminifera having discus-shaped, or coin-shaped, multichambered shells (Fig. 377). They were extraordinarily abundant in the seas of the Mediterranean region during Eocene and Oligocene time, and their shells contributed largely to the **nummulite limestones** that are widely distributed in southern Europe, northern Africa, and the Himalayan region, where the Eocene is still commonly spoken of as the "nummulitic period." Such shells are less common in the American Eocene but do appear abundantly in the upper Eocene and Oligocene of Florida and the Caribbean region.

Decline of the Reptiles. With the extinctions at the close of the Mesozoic, the reptile dynasty collapsed. Turtles, crocodiles, and lizards lived on about as they are today, except that large land turtles and alligators were more widely distributed during the warmer times. Fossil turtles are abundant in the badlands of Oligocene and Miocene age. Enormous species, large enough to stand waist-high to a man, were common in Florida in Pleistocene time. As noted before, alligators occur frequently in the Eocene and Oligocene deposits as far north as Wyoming and the Dakotas. Snakes are first recorded in the Late Cretaceous and therefore existed throughout the Cenozoic, but, because of their retiring habits and their delicate skeletons, they are always rare fossils.

Figure 378. *Phororhacos,* a giant flightless bird from the Miocene beds of Patagonia. (Reconstruction by Charles R. Knight. From F. A. Lucas, *Animals of the Past.* American Museum of Natural History.)

An Eocene species related to the modern boa constrictor and estimated to be 35 feet long is known from Patagonia.

Birds. Modern types of birds, all toothless, appeared before the close of the Cretaceous, and in the Eocene most of the present orders were represented.[6] Such, for example, were the eagles, vultures, pelicans, quail, and various shore birds. All these stocks persisted through the Cenozoic, though fossil remains are, in general, rare because the bird skeleton is fragile.

Nearly all the continents at one time or another during the Cenozoic had large, flightless birds. One of these (*Diatryma*), known from the early Eocene beds of Wyoming (Fig. 341), stood nearly 7 feet high and had a very stout neck and a head al-

Plate 19. Miocene Pelecypods.

Figures 1–4, *Glans decemcostata;* 5, *Pecten poulsoni* [Oligocene]; 6, *Chlamys decemnaria;* 7, *Lyropecten ernestsmith;* 8, 9, *Venus berryi;* 10, *Glycymeris americana.* (From Gardner, U.S. Geological Survey.)

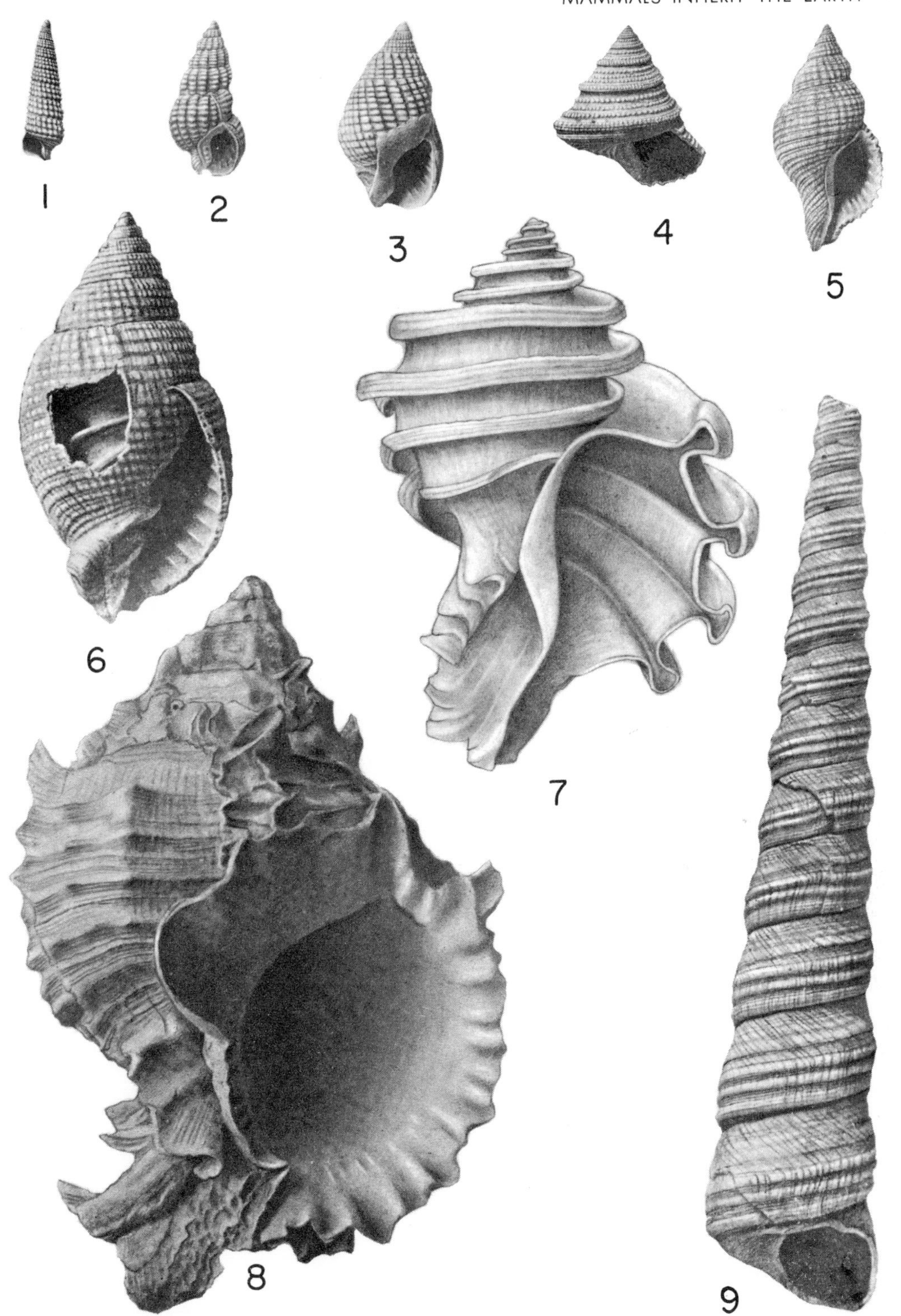

Plate 20. Miocene Gastropods

Figure 1, *Triphora bartschi;* 2, *Uzita neogenensis;* 3, *Illyanassa grandifera;* 4, *Calliostoma mitchelli;* 5, *Urosalpinx trossula;* 6, *Cancellaria rotunda;* 7, *Ecphora quadricostatus;* 8, *Murex pomum;* 9, *Turritella pilsbryi.* (All except 7 after Gardner, U.S. Geological Survey.)

most as large as that of the horse. Another (*Phororhacos*), found in the Miocene of the Argentinian pampas, stood 7 to 8 feet high and had a very massive skull 23 inches long with a strongly hooked beak (Fig. 378). It was undoubtedly the greatest of all birds of prey. The largest bird, however, was an ostrichlike form, *Dinornis*, that lived into historic time in New Zealand and was exterminated by the Maoris only a few centuries ago. This enormous bird stood about 10 feet high and was therefore more than 2 feet taller than the greatest living ostrich. Still another giant (*Aepyornis*) of Madagascar laid the largest known eggs, which normally measured 13 inches long and 9 inches across. Discovery of the eggs of this bird by early navigators inspired the thrilling tales of the roc told by Sinbad the Sailor in the *Arabian Nights*.

REFERENCES

1. Hürtzeler, J., 1958, Oreopithecus bambolii Gervais. *Naturf. Gesellsch. Basel, Verh.*, vol. 69, no. 1, pp. 1–48.

2. Clark, Sir Wilfred E., 1955, *The Fossil Evidence for Human Evolution.* University of Chicago Press, Chicago, pp. 1–181.

3. Simpson, G. G., 1940, Mammals and land bridges. *Washington Acad. Sci., Jour.*, vol. 30, pp. 137–163.

4. Tolmachoff, I. P., 1929, Carcasses of the mammoth and rhinoceros found in the frozen ground of Siberia. *American Philosophical Society, Trans.*, vol. 23, Part 1, Art. 1, pp. 11–74.

5. Elias, Maxim, 1942, Tertiary prairie grasses and other herbs from the High Plains. *Geol. Soc. Amer., Special Paper 41*, pp. 1–176.

6. Howard, Hildegarde, 1950, Fossil evidences of avian evolution. *Ibis*, vol. 92, 1–21.

Romer, Alfred S., 1945, *Vertebrate Paleontology*, 2nd ed. Univ. of Chicago Press, pp. 1–687. This fine volume has been an invaluable source of information concerning the fossil vertebrates from fishes to man.

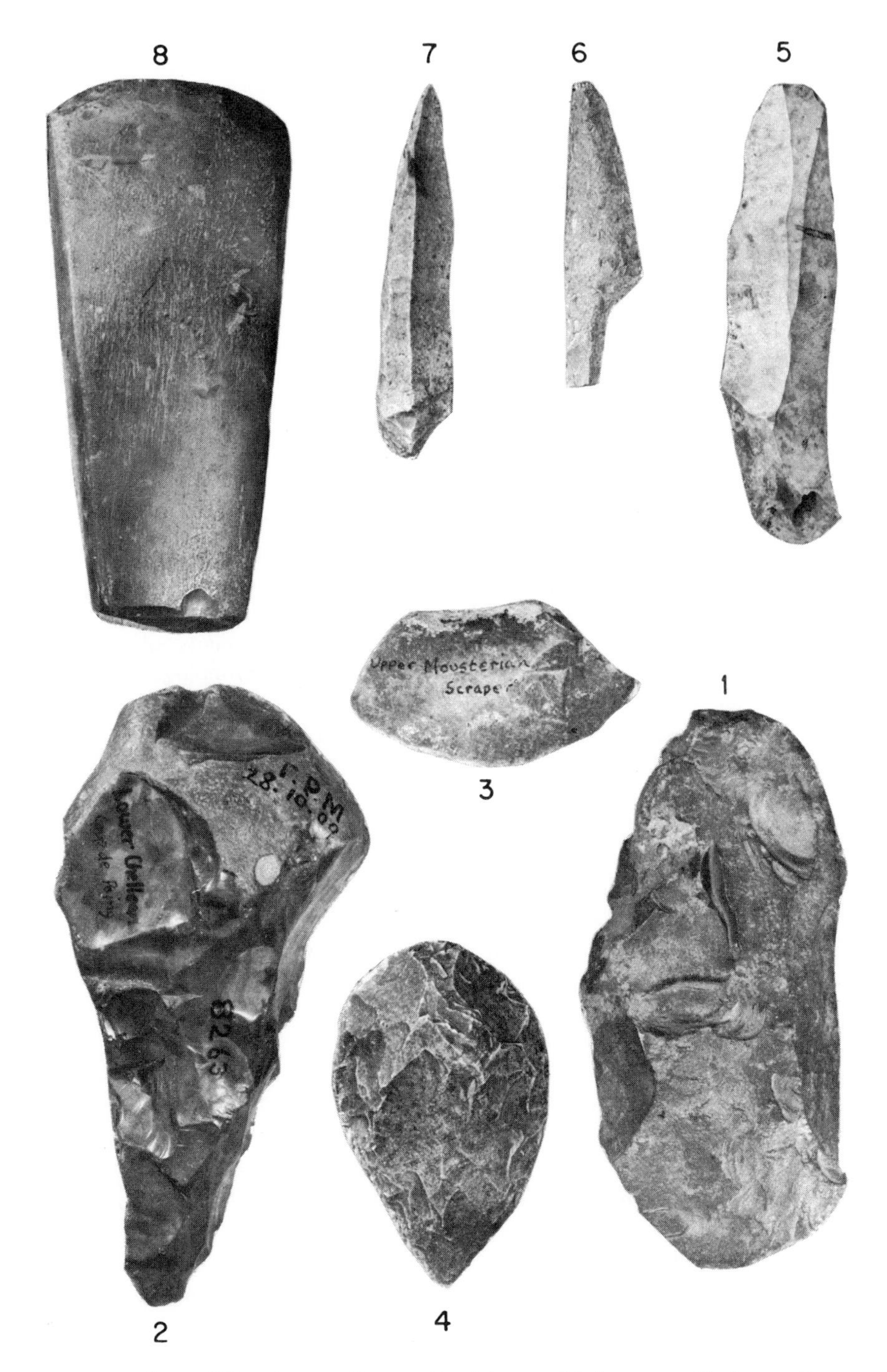

Figure 379. Stone artifacts. No. 1 is an eolith from a pre-Chellean culture; nos. 2 to 7 are paleoliths, 2 is Chellean, 3 and 4 Mousterian, 5 and 6 from Solutrean, and 7 Aurignacean. No. 8 is from the neolitic culture of Denmark.

Chapter **20.** *The Coming of Man*

PREHISTORIC DOCUMENTS

Artifacts. STONE IMPLEMENTS SHAPED BY PREhistoric man are widespread and locally abundant in western Europe. During and after the Renaissance they were commonly collected as curios and became the subject of strange superstition. In 1655, for example, Olaf Worm, a Danish student of such objects, wrote that "they are commonly supposed to fall with the lightning from the sky," though "opinions differ as to their origin, since some believe they are not thunderbolts but petrified iron implements, seeing they resemble the latter in shape so closely." And as late as 1802, Thorlacius, writing of stone artifacts discovered in burial mounds, concluded that "the objects found in the mounds are nothing else than symbols of the weapons employed by the Gods of Thunder in chasing and destroying evil spirits and dangerous giants. They could not be ordinary tools and weapons as these have been made of metal since the earliest times."

It now seems almost incredible that beliefs so fantastic could have persisted in Europe for three hundred years after the American pioneers were in contact with the Indians, who were using such artifacts. It must be remembered, however, that European thought at that time was completely dominated by the belief that man was created only about 6,000 years ago and that the whole of human history was recorded in the Scriptures. This left no place for prehistoric man in Europe, and there was a tendency to regard the American Indians and other primitive peoples as degenerates who had wandered far from the center of civilization and had lost the art of working metal. Occasional thinkers, far ahead of their time, had, indeed, realized the true meaning of archeological remains since before the beginning of the Christian Era, but it was not until within the last century that these objects were generally accepted as evidence of prehistoric races. Even then, no one considered the possibility that they might represent the work of extinct *species* of man until after Darwin's *Origin of Species* had paved the way for a belief in the gradual evolution of man from the lower animals.

The appreciation of the true meaning of stone artifacts was first developed in Scandinavia shortly after 1830. It began with the creation by the Danish Government of a scientific commission to study the refuse heaps and shell mounds that had already attracted attention in the region. As a result of this project, extensive collections were assembled at the Royal Museum in Copenhagen and were studied with respect to their stratigraphic occurrence in the mounds. On this basis, Thomsen, the director of the Museum, in 1837 proposed a chronology of human culture divided into the **Stone Age**, the **Bronze Age**, and the **Iron Age.**

Man undoubtedly advanced through this sequence of cultures on the way to civilization, but in western Europe the making of bronze and the smelting of iron had been mastered while aborigines in many parts of the world were still using crude stone implements. Thus the Iron Age in Europe was contemporaneous with the Stone Age in many other parts of the world. Thomsen's chronology is therefore applicable only locally.

The first tools used by man were doubtless those accidentally shaped by nature to fit his hand, such as sharp-edged chips of flint that he could use to scrape skins or to fashion wooden tools. Such stones, which he picked up and used without modification (Fig. 379, 1), are known as **eoliths** (Gr. *eos*, dawn + *lithos*, stone). Showing evidence of wear but not of conscious shaping, they represent the lowest stage of human culture and are found in deposits as old as the late Pliocene.

Eventually man learned to flake off pieces of stone and to shape them, by chipping, into scrapers, hand axes, spear heads, and other useful tools. This was an art slowly acquired through countless generations of trial and experiment by primitive peoples whose lives often depended on the quality of their weapons. Such artifacts, shaped by chipping alone (Fig. 379, 2–7), are known as **paleoliths** (Gr. *palaios*, ancient + *lithos*, stone), and cultures represented by such implements characterized the **Paleolithic Age,** which endured in Eurasia until a few thousand years ago.

The American Indians and other primitive peoples in Africa, Australia, and the Pacific Islands never progressed beyond the paleolithic stage of culture; but in Europe some of the prehistoric people went a step further when they learned to shape and sharpen stone implements by grinding and polishing them against natural abrasive stones (Fig. 379, 8). Such objects, known as **neoliths** (Gr. *neos*,, recent + *lithos*, stone), are found only

Figure 380. Rock shelter at Les Eyzies, Dordogne, France. The re-entrant along the middle of the cliff was occupied by Paleolithic man. (G. G. MacCurdy.)

in deposits younger than the last glacial drift in Europe and mark the highest type of Stone Age culture, attained shortly before the discovery of the use of copper.

Cultures. The assemblage of material objects used by a people reflect and represent its culture. For primitive people such objects include weapons, utensils made of stone or pottery, and clothing and adornment such as amulets or beads.

During the Paleolithic Age the character and variety, and the functions, of the stone implements changed from time to time as new techniques were discovered for shaping flint objects and as climatic fluctuations induced changes in living habits and dress. Thus, it has been possible to recognize in the burial mounds and the refuse heaps of Europe a series of distinct **cultures,** the chief of which are indicated in Table III.

The sequence of cultures is most clearly recorded in the stratified deposits that accumulated about camp sites that were repeatedly occupied, especially the limestone caverns along the river bluffs that were a favorite home of primitive man since they offered protection against inclement weather, wild beasts, and warlike neighbors (Figs. 380 and 381).

The sequence in time of these cultures has been determined in numerous places by simple stratigraphic principles, as illustrated in Figure 382. Here at Laussel, France, a fine rock shelter was used repeatedly by Paleolithic man, who discarded the refuse from his camp onto the slope below, where it accumulated layer upon layer. The sediment that accumulated while the shelter was occupied includes discarded or broken artifacts as well as the bones of animals on which he fed. Layers of sediment formed when the shelter was abandoned are barren. Careful excavation here has revealed five layers of culture separated by barren layers. Of course the order of superposition shows their sequence in time, the Acheulian being the oldest and Solutrean the youngest. In similar stratified refuse heaps before other shelters or caves, the sequence is always the same, though in some, for example the Cave of the Kids (Fig. 381), more subdivisions are recognizable.

Finally, when objects distinctive of a particular

Figure 381. Cave of the Kids in the Valley of Caves (Wady el Mughara) in Palestine. Before this group of caves there is stratified refuse about 70 feet thick, including a succession of eleven prehistoric cultures ranging from the pre-Achulian to the Bronze Age. (G. G. MacCurdy.)

culture are found in stratified deposits associated with one of the drift sheets, or in interglacial deposits, it is possible to correlate the human history with the glacial history of Europe as shown in Table III. Thus it is known that the Abbevillian culture belongs to the first interglacial age, the Acheulian spans the time from early in the second interglacial to near the end of the third interglacial age, and that Mousterian, Auriguacian, and Magdalenian cultures are related to the last ice age.

The time relation of these last three to the advance and retreat of the ice is indicated by the mammal bones associated with cultural objects in the refuse heaps and burial mounds, for they record the chief animals of the chase upon which these peoples were feeding. It is well known, for example, that as the ice advanced over northern Europe an arctic fauna spread southward and the reindeer became the chief source of food, but during the last interglacial period, as in postglacial time, the reindeer retreated to the far north and wild horses became the chief object of food. A refuse heap near one of the Solutrean camp sites, for example, has been estimated to include the remains of some 70,000 wild horses.

Finally, for these later cultures less than 50,000 years old, radiocarbon dating based on charcoal from the ancient campsites, or bones or wooden artifacts, gives us an absolute chronology in years.

Early Flint Workers of England. The most ancient relics of mankind are found in England. Near the city of Ipswich, about 65 miles northeast of London, the upper Pliocene beds include seven layers that have yielded abundant eoliths, now accepted by archeologists as the implements of primitive man. About the turn of this century there was found among these stone implements a stiletto made of deer horn that must have been shaped by human hands. Here, in the coastal margin of England, the beds carrying flint implements are overlain by a thin marine deposit with late Pliocene fossils, thus proving that tool-using humans were living in western Europe a little before the beginning of the Pleistocene Epoch which is very tentatively dated as approximately a million years ago.

Slightly younger deposits (early Pleistocene) of similar nature are found at Foxhall, a few miles northeast of Ipswich, and there the flints are associated with charred wood, suggesting that the ancient flint workers had already discovered the use of fire. At Cromer, still farther northeast of London, there is another bed (the Cromer Forest bed) of early Pleistocene age, from which large but crudely chipped flint implements have been recovered. In none of these localities have any skeletal remains been found, but the crude implements indicate clearly the presence of man in England at the close of the Pliocene and early in Pleistocene time.

Human Fossils. Prehistoric human remains are, for obvious reasons, among the rarest of fossils. With his superior intelligence, man generally avoided such common catastrophes as miring and drowning. Of course this did not reduce the number who died, but it lessened the chances for burial where preservation would be likely. Furthermore, funeral rites, observed by man since very remote times, commonly resulted in destruction of the remains, whether the funerals involved cremation, elevation on scaffolds, or burial in shallow graves, since the graves were generally placed on elevated mounds where both weathering and erosion are active.

A fortunate exception was provided by the cave dwellers, who took refuge in caverns or overhanging shelters along the river bluffs of Europe and parts of Asia during the late Pleistocene, finding there a shelter from the inclement weather and a refuge from the powerful carnivores of the time (Fig. 380). These peoples commonly buried their dead in the caverns where they also would be safe from the ravages of wild beasts—and, fortunately for us, they surrounded them with food and weapons intended for use in the future life. Such cave burials therefore give us not only the physical characters but also the culture of the individual preserved. Thus we find a tie-up between the human fossils, which are rare, and the definite cultures of stone implements, which are widely scattered and almost indestructible. Such burials also commonly include two or more individuals, thus giving us a record of both sexes and of the young as well as the old.

THE FOSSIL RECORD OF MAN

Although artifacts prove that man was present in Europe throughout the Pleistocene Epoch, the earliest skeletal remains have been found in other regions which now deserve our attention.

Australopithecus, a Human Precursor

This extinct genus of homanoid (manlike) primates was briefly discussed in Chapter 18 (p. 425). It inhabited the open veldt in the Transvaal region of South Africa early in Pleistocene time, and is now known from at least 25 skulls and numerous skeletal bones including the pelvis and fragments of limb bones.[1] These were found in a series of limestone caves where they are associated with extinct mammals. The name *Australopithecus* (L. *australo*, southern + *pithecus*, ape) was given soon

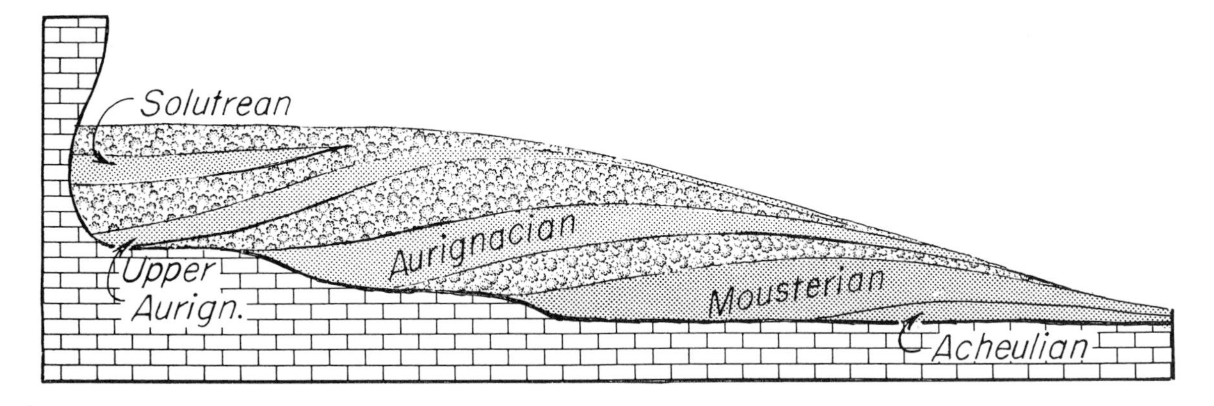

Figure 382. Diagrammatic section of the stratified deposits before the rock shelter of Laussel, France, showing a succession of five distinct cultures. The layers bearing artifacts are stippled, and the cultures are named. (Adapted from G. G. MacCurdy, *Human Origins*, D. Appleton and Company, New York.)

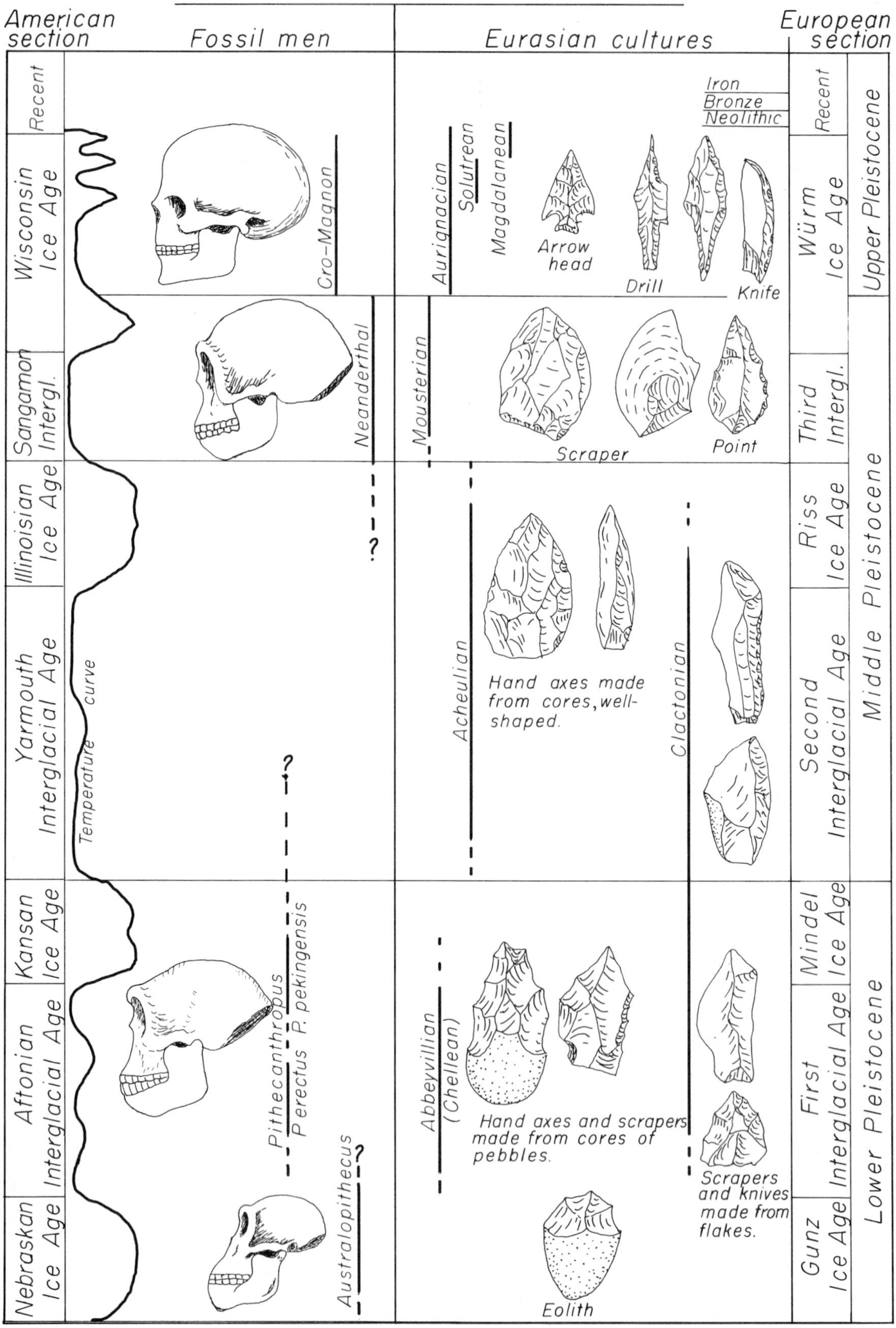

American section

Fossil men

Eurasian cultures

European section

Recent

Wisconsin Ice Age

Sangamon Intergl.

Illinoisian Ice Age

Yarmouth Interglacial Age

Kansan Ice Age

Aftonian Interglacial Age

Nebraskan Ice Age

Temperature curve

Cro-Magnon

Neanderthal

Pithecanthropus P. erectus P. pekingensis

Australopithecus

Aurignacian

Solutrean

Magdalanean

Iron

Bronze

Neolithic

Arrow head

Drill

Knife

Mousterian

Scraper

Point

Acheulian

Hand axes made from cores, well-shaped.

Clactonian

Abbevillian (Chellean)

Hand axes and scrapers made from cores of pebbles.

Scrapers and knives made from flakes.

Eolith

Recent

Würm Ice Age

Third Intergl.

Riss Ice Age

Second Interglacial Age

Mindel Ice Age

First Interglacial Age

Gunz Ice Age

Upper Pleistocene

Middle Pleistocene

Lower Pleistocene

Table III. Sequence of human fossils and of Eurasian cultures during the Pleistocene Epoch. Adapted in part from K. P. Oakley: Man, The Tool-maker. *British Museum of Natural History*, 1952.

after the first discovery when the animal was assumed to be more closely related to the living great apes than to man. The brain, indeed, was less than half the size of that in man and the appearence of the skull is decidedly apelike (Fig. 369, p. 426) but as Le Gros Clark has clearly reasoned, if man and the apes descended from an ultimate ancestor, the divergence of the two lines arose from a basic difference in habits, the apes remaining in the forest and retaining a largely quadrupedal posture, whereas the ancestors of man forsook the forest for life in the open and developed an upright carriage. The rapid increase in the brain came later. Now that a large amount of skeletal material is available for study, it is certain that *Australopithecus* walked upright, and the associated fossils prove that while he was living the region was a treeless veldt much as it is today. Furthermore, his teeth are distinctly homanid rather than apelike (Fig. 370, p. 427). In the apes the canines are enlarged so as to rise well above the general toothline and to interlock when the jaws are closed, there is a gap (diastema) between the canines and the first premolars, and the cheek teeth are in subparallel rows. In contrast, the human canines scarcely rise above the rest, there is no diastema, and the teeth form an evenly curved arcade. In all these features *Australopithecus* is unequivocally in the human line.

No stone implements have been found with these skeletons but Professor Dart, who discovered the first specimen and has given the entire problem long study, believes there is clear evidence that *Australopithecus* used certain bones of the associated animals as tools and weapons.[2]

The precise geological age of these fossils is difficult to establish. Although they are associated with abundant remains of other mammals, the region is so far from the glaciated regions that the fauna is entirely distinct from that of Europe. It is now believed that the age is early Pleistocene.

As Professor Le Gros Clark has concluded,[1]

while they are certainly hominids in the taxonomic sense, the terms "man" and "human" can hardly be applied to them, for there is no certain evidence that they possessed any of the special attributes which are commonly associated with human beings. They are to be regarded, rather, as representative of the prehuman phase of the hominid sequence of evolution. In their morphology they appear to conform very closely to the theoretical postulates for the immediate evolutionary precursor of the *Pithecanthropus* phase of hominid evolution. . . . it would not necessarily follow that the transition occurred in South Africa. It may have occurred in some other part of the world, and the South African fossils in that case may represent but slightly modified survivors of the ancestral stock, which persisted to a much later time in the Transvaal.

Pithecanthropus

Pithecanthropus erectus. The most discussed of all human fossils was discovered in 1891 by Eugene Dubois, a Dutch army surgeon stationed on the island of Java. He had opened a quarry for vertebrate fossils in a 3-foot bed of gravel exposed in the bank of Solo River, and there he came upon several human bones—a skull cap, a left thigh bone, fragments of nasal bones, and three teeth. Although each bone was isolated, and the thigh bone was found almost 50 feet from the skull, Dubois assumed that they belonged to one species if not to one individual, and recent application of the fluorine test confirms his inference that they are at least of the same age.

The skull cap was remarkably thick, the brow ridges very massive, and the forehead low and receding. The brain of this skull, estimated to have had a volume of 900 cubic centimeters, is intermediate in size between that of the largest apes (about 600 cubic centimeters) and the average for the lowest types of living men (about 1,240 cubic centimeters). Moreover, the scars of attachment for the great neck muscles at the base of the skull clearly imply that the head was carried forward, as in the apes, instead of being well balanced on the neck, as in modern man.

Soon after discovery, this find was hailed as a "missing link" between the apes and man and was given the name *Pithecanthropus erectus* (Gr. *pithecos*, an ape + *anthropos*, a man). Almost at once it became a subject of controversy. Skeptics argued that it was an abnormal individual, perhaps an idiot; but statisticians pointed out the extreme improbability of an abnormal individual being the sole survivor of a population to be preserved and discovered. All uncertainty was cleared up by the extensive and careful restudy of the area by Koenigswald[3] between the years 1935 and 1940, which brought to light three additional skulls. The last and most important of these (Fig. 383) includes the upper jaw, part of the lower jaw,

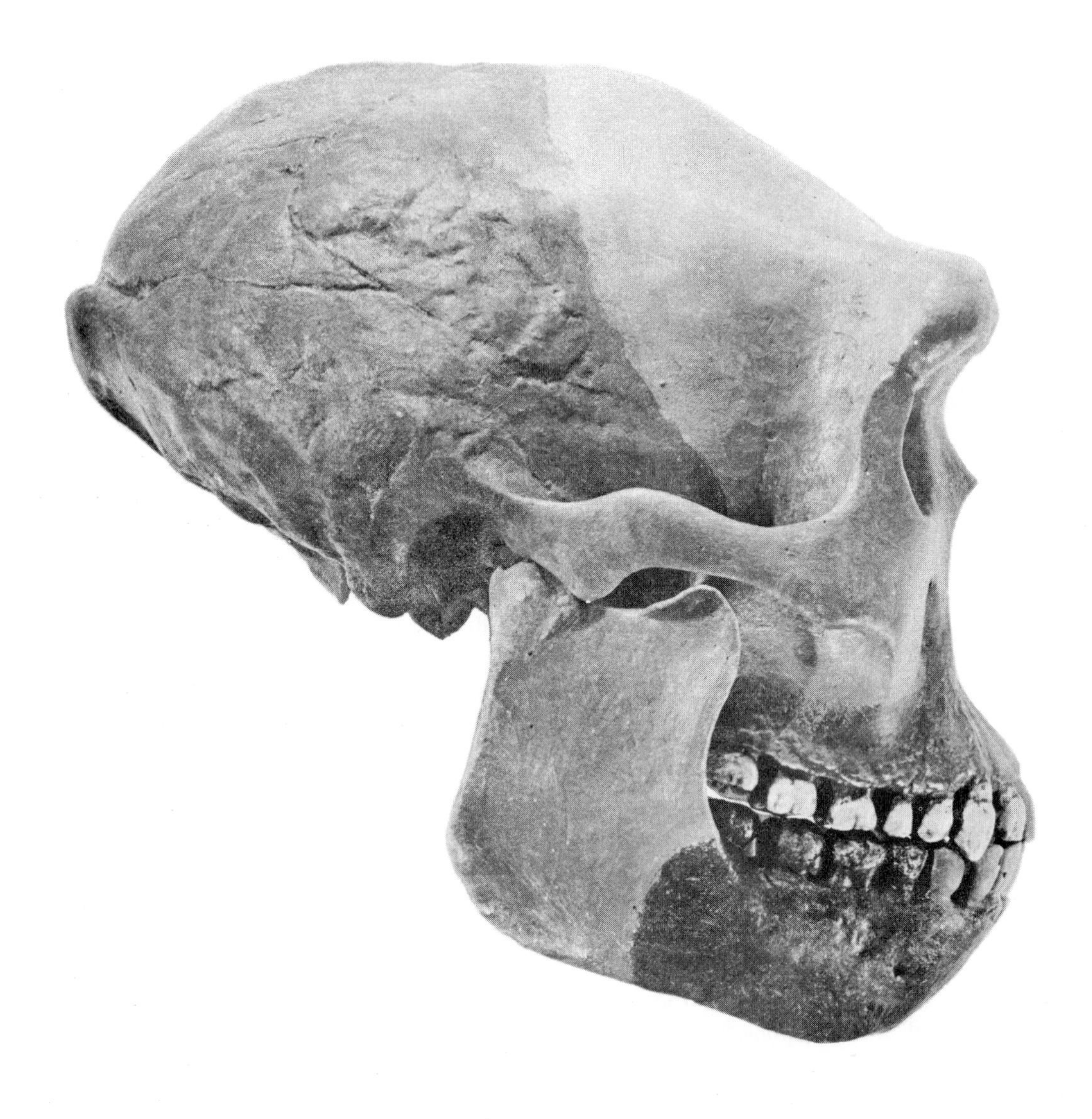

Figure 383. *Pithecanthropus erectus.* Skull No. IV, found by von Koenigswald in 1939, as restored by Franz Weidenreich. The darker parts are actual bone; the lighter parts are restored by comparison with other skulls of the same species.

and several teeth, along with the posterior and basal part of the braincase. It is somewhat larger and more massive than the original skull and is believed to be that of a male, whereas the original was female. These skulls fully confirm the interpretation previously made of the brain size and the shape of the head and face of *Pithecanthropus*, and prove beyond possible doubt that this is a well-defined but primitive human type.

The small brain, low forehead, heavy brow

ridges, protruding mouth, and receding chin give the skull a striking resemblance to that of a great ape, as shown in Figure 384; yet the brain is far larger than that of any great ape, the toothline is even, the canine teeth are relatively small, and the dentition is in all respects human rather than simian. There is no longer any doubt that *Pithecanthropus* was human.

The geologic age of *Pithecanthropus erectus* has been a subject of controversy. The remains are too old to date by radiocarbon, and since they occur in the tropics far from the glaciated regions it is difficult to associate them with a definite glacial or interglacial epoch. Because of the primitive features of the skull it was at first suspected that the date was late Pliocene or Early Pleistocene; but the large fauna of other mammals found in the same bed indicate clearly a Pleistocene age. Because of the great distance from the glaciated regions, it is difficult to correlate these tropical faunas precisely with the sequence in Europe. No artifacts have been found with *Pithecanthropus erectus*, but those found in an overlying layer, like those found with *P. pekingensis*, are of Abbevillian (Chellean) type, and this suggests a date preceding the second interglacial age (Table III).

Six faunal zones are now known in the Pleistocene deposits of Java, and all the remains of *Pithecanthropus* are from a single one of these, the so-called Trinil horizon. Other human remains of more modern type are found in some of the higher zones.

Pithecanthropus pekingensis (Peking Man). A series of discoveries in 1928 and 1929 near Peking, China, brought to light another species of *Pithecanthropus* that is commonly known as Peking Man. The remains were found amid cave deposits of Chicken Bone Hill (Chou Kou Tien) about 30 miles south of Peking.[4] At the time of habitation, the site was a spacious limestone cavern, but it has since been filled with debris fallen from the walls or washed in from above and cemented in part by travertine.

Once the great significance of this primitive human race was perceived, systematic exploration of the deposits was undertaken with the joint support of the Geological Survey of China and the Rockefeller Foundation, and for more than a decade, 50 to 100 technicians and laborers worked continuously at the excavation. As a result, about 40 individuals were recovered, including men and women and children. In addition, a large fauna of contemporary mammals was found, many of which represent the prey that Peking man brought home from the chase. About seven-tenths of these are deer, suggesting that this was the chief animal hunted.

The human remains are nearly all skulls and lower jaws (Fig. 385), though a few limb bones

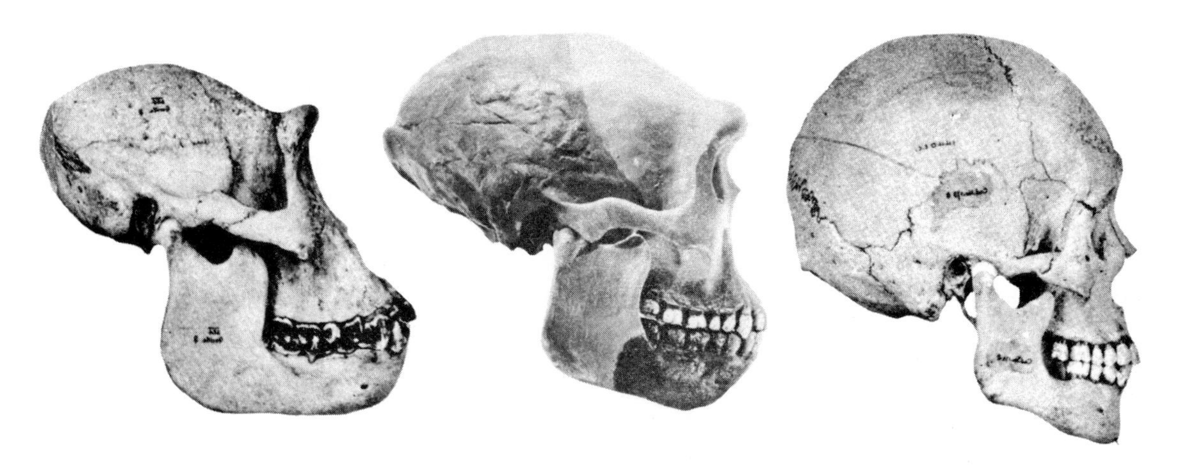

Figure 384. Skulls of modern gorilla (left), *Pithecanthropus* (center), and modern man (right). The apelike character of *Pithecanthropus* may be seen in the low forehead, heavy brow ridges, protruding jaws, and chinless profile. (After F. Weidenreich in *Natural History*)

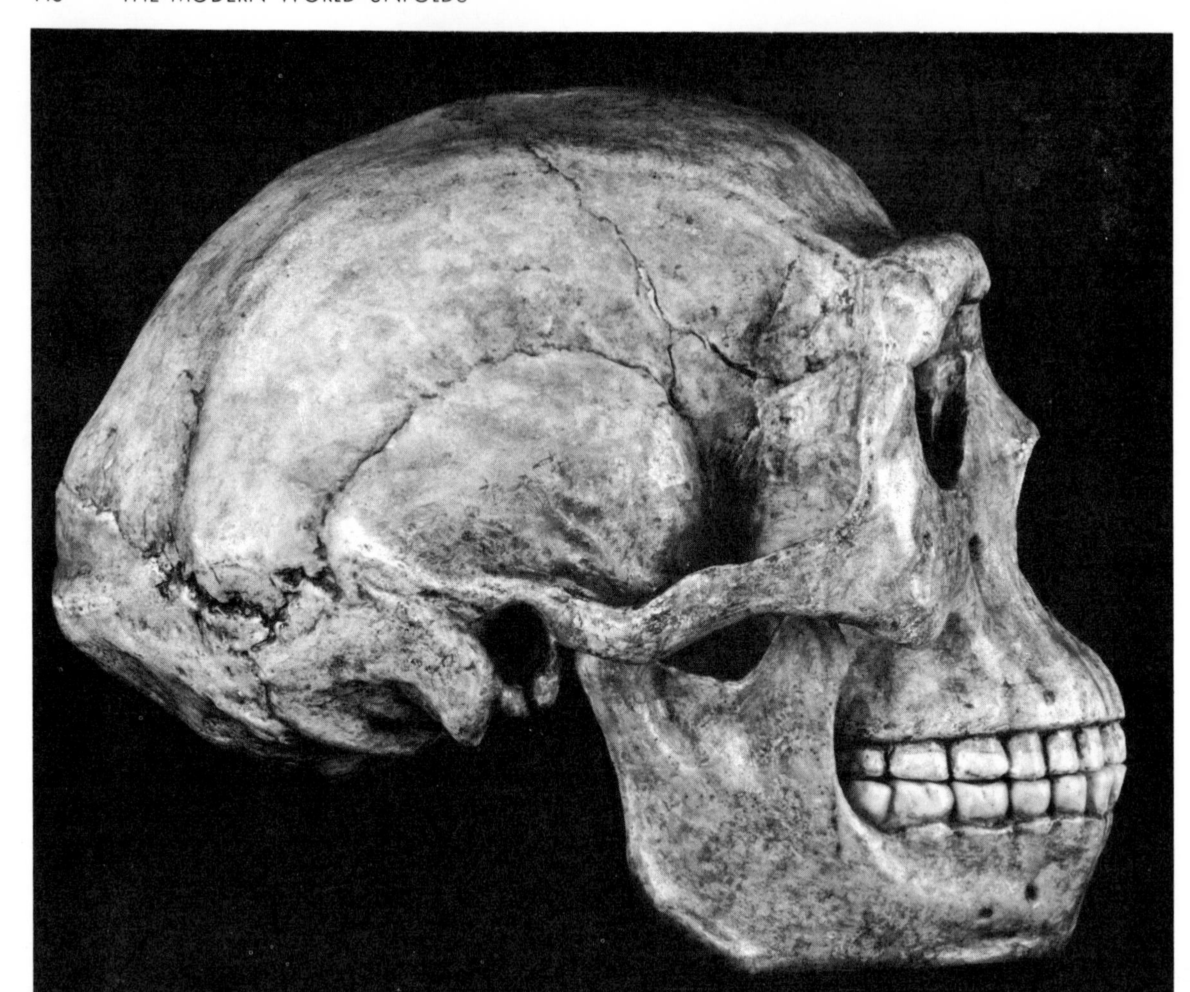

Figure 385. *Pithecanthropus pekingensis.* Model of a skull of Peking Man by Franz Weidenreich. Note the prognathous jaws, and receding chin, the heavy brow ridges, the low forehead. About ¾ natural size.

have been found. The absence or rarity of other skeletal parts, as well as evidences that the base of each skull had its base broken away in a definite manner, suggests strongly that the heads had been severed from the bodies and that the brains had been eaten. Professor A. C. Blanc[5] of the University of Rome has advanced this interpretation, citing the observations of Wirz[5] on the Marind Anim tribe of New Guinea. This tribe opens the base of the skull in exactly this manner in order to extract the brain which is then baked in a pie with sago and eaten as part of a ceremonial rite concerned with the naming of a child. The child is then given the name of the one whose brain has been eaten, the skull being dried and painted and preserved as a sacred household object during the life of the child.

It is a tragedy that during World War II all the hard-won remains of Peking Man disappeared. It is believed that they were packed by the Japanese for shipment to their homeland and were lost in transit. Fortunately, however, they had been critically studied and well described and illustrated by Davidson Black and Franz Weidenreich, and excellent casts of the most important skulls are still extant.

Associated with the skeletons have been found charred animal bones and layers with charcoal debris, ranging through a thickness of 20 feet of deposits. It is therefore clear that these people used fire. With them have also been found more than 2,000 crude artifacts of the Chellean cultural type, made from greenstones and vein quartz. These stone implements include choppers, scrapers, gravers, and awls. Some of them were evidently used also for fashioning weapons from animal bones, such as the daggers made from deer antlers. In other words, Peking Man was already human, and was able to organize his life so as to select intelligently the materials useful for fuel, weapons, and tools, besides being a successful hunter of animals.

The associated mammals indicate that Peking Man was approximately contemporaneous with *Pithecanthropus erectus* of Java. Indeed, there is some uncertainty whether the two are specifically distinct.

Neanderthal Man

Best known of all the extinct species of man is *Homo neanderthalensis*, who inhabited the caverns of western Europe during the last interglacial age and part of the last glacial age. The original discovery of this race was made in the Neander Valley near Düsseldorf, Germany, whence the name. Although found the previous year, this remarkable skeleton was first described in 1858, the year before the publication of Darwin's *Origin of Species*. Its striking characteristics and the timeliness of the discovery led to an immediate appreciation of the significance of the Neanderthals as a species far more apelike than any living men.

Since 1858, several entire skeletons have been recovered, and incomplete remains of many men, women, and children of the Neanderthal race have been found in the caves and rock shelters of Belgium, France, Italy, Spain, Croatia, Iraq, Crimea, and Palestine. Their stone implements (the Mousterian culture), moreover, are found scattered throughout western Europe and farther eastward in Asia Minor, North Africa, Syria, northern Arabia, and Iraq. Among the striking Neanderthaloid discoveries of the last few years may be mentioned the skeleton at Broken Hill, Rhodesia; that near Galilee in Palestine; and others at the Cave of the Kids near Mount Carmel, Palestine. From these abundant remains it is possible to present an adequate picture of the racial characteristics and the culture of these interesting people.

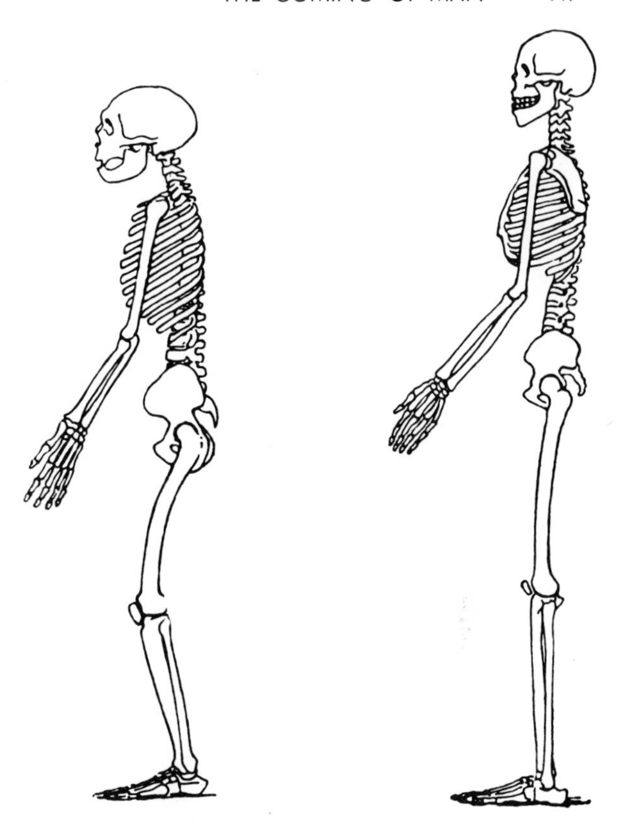

Figure 386. Skeleton of Neanderthal man (left) and of a modern Australian, showing contrast in posture. (After Boule from Woodward, British Museum, *Guide to Fossil Man*.)

The Neanderthals (Fig. 387) were stocky and short of stature, rarely exceeding 5 feet 4 inches. Although they stood upright, their carriage was more like that of a great ape than is that of living man, because the spine lacked the fourth or cervical curvature and the thigh bones were sigmoidally curved in compensation. The head accordingly was carried far forward, and the body had a slouched appearance (Figs. 386, 387). Both hands and feet were large, and the great toe was offset against the rest, as in the great apes.

The head differed from that of modern man in the very low forehead, heavy brow ridges, and receding chin (Figs. 388 and 389*B*). The face was undoubtedly coarse-featured and brutal. Nevertheless the brain was approximately equal in size to that of modern man (1,400 to 1,600 cubic centimeters), the brain case being low at the front but large in the back and lower part. It has been inferred from the proportions of the brain that the

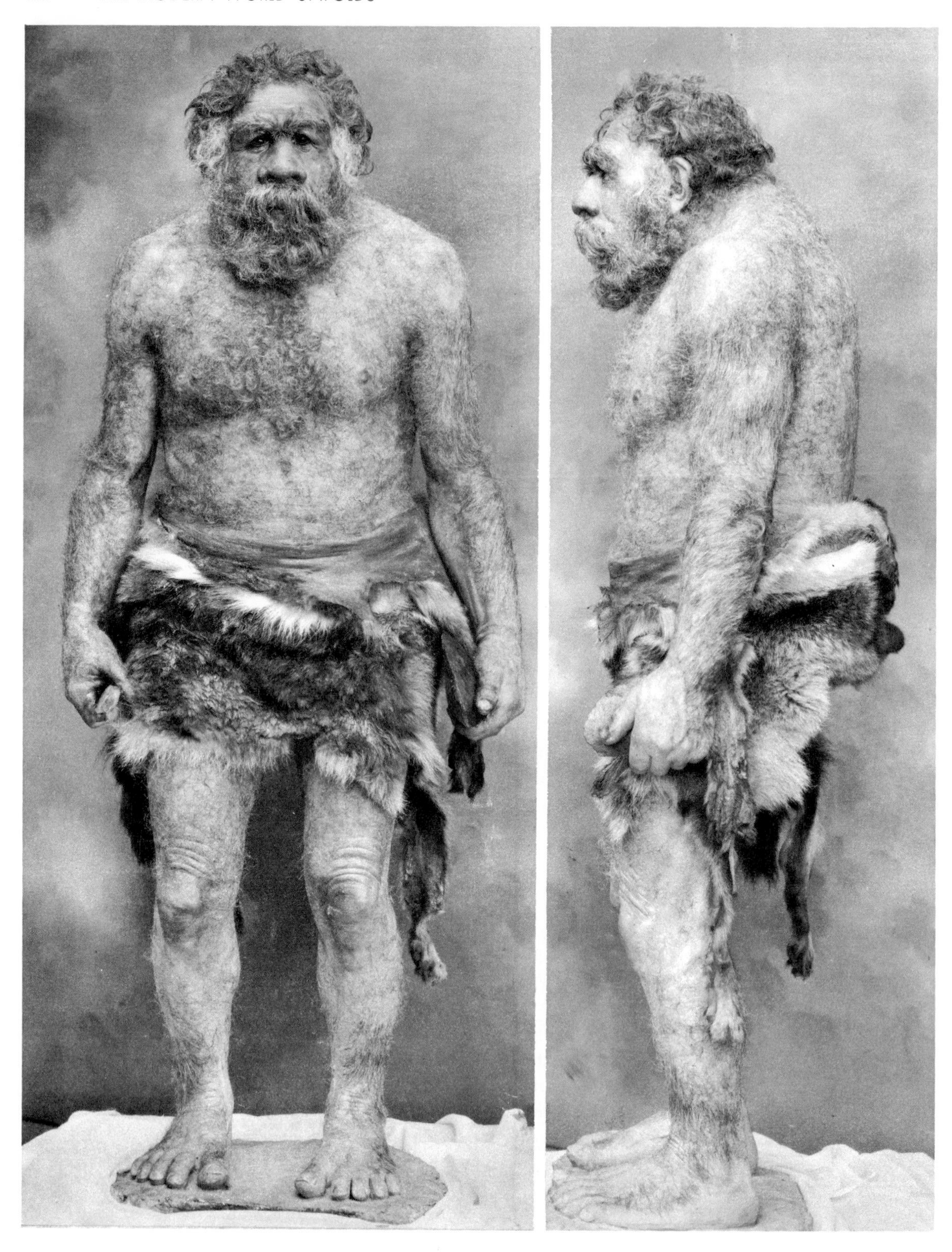

Figure 387. Old Man Neanderthal. Front and side views of a restoration by Blaschke. Note the slouched posture and compare with Figure 386. (Chicago Natural History Museum.)

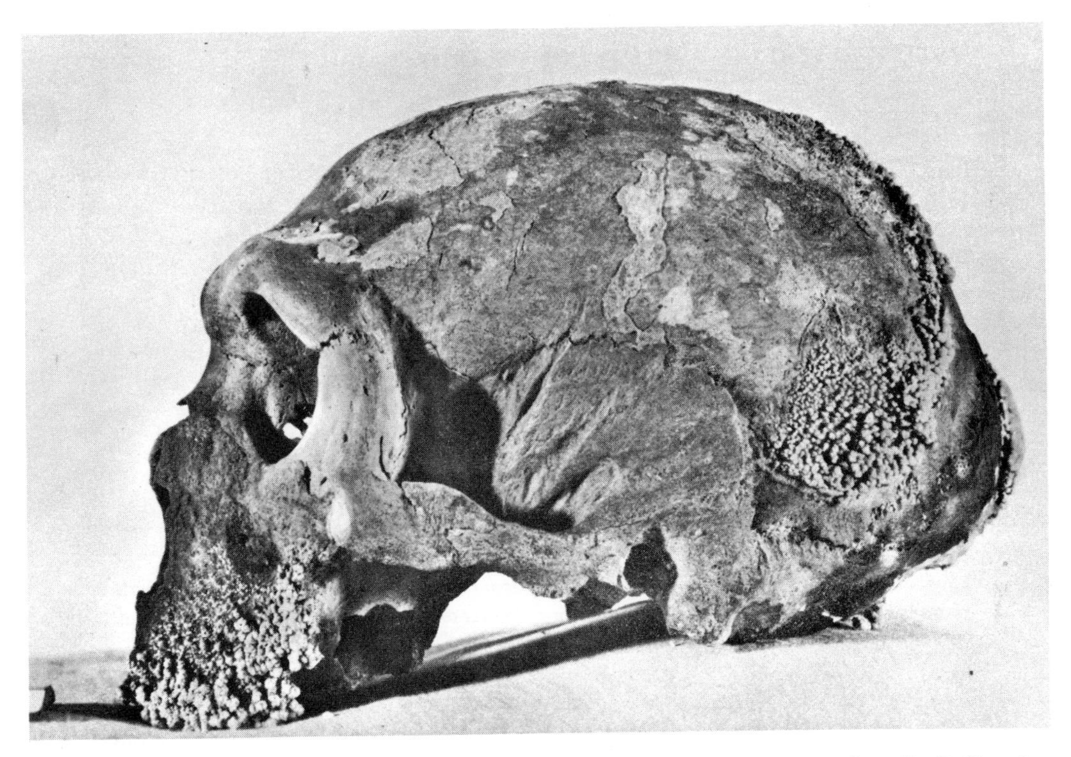

Figure 388. Neanderthal skull from the grotto at Monte Circeo, south of Anzio, Italy. (A. C. Blanc.)

species was deficient in the higher qualities of reasoning and association, and probably less capable than modern man in social organization. It must be remembered, however, that Neanderthal man dominated all Europe during the last interglacial age and the early part of the last glacial age, a period estimated to exceed 100,000 years.

The Neanderthals made fairly good stone implements, and they also knew how to kindle a fire, for hearths have been found in their cave abodes. In at least two instances the skeletons have been found in their original burial places, where they had been laid away with implements, paints, and food, indicating that the race held a belief in immortality, and buried the dead with ceremonial rites.

Among the stone implements of these people, the hand ax, scraper, and point are most characteristic. Flint-tipped spears were used, but there is no evidence that Neanderthal man used the bow and arrow. In view of his relatively feeble weapons, it is remarkable that he was a successful hunter of big game, including the bison, cave bear, horse, reindeer, and mammoth, all of which inhabited Europe during his reign.

Recent excavation in a cave in Shanidar Valley in the Zagros Mountains of northern Iraq[6] has revealed four stratigraphic levels bearing archeological remains, and in the next-to-the-lowest of these, two Neanderthal skeletons were found along with artifacts of the Mousterian culture and hearths where fires had been tended. This layer is estimated to be between 45,000 and 60,000 years old.

The fine skull shown in Figure 388 was found in the inner recesses of a former sea-cave, now uplifted, at Monte Circeo on the coast south of Anzio, Italy.[7] The circumstances here prove that the cave was occupied late in the last interglacial age. The skull was surrounded by a ring of stones indicating some sort of burial ceremony, and the base had been broken away as were those of Peking Man, indicating that the brain had been eaten.

The Neanderthaloids resemble *Pithecanthropus* in their prognathous jaws, receding chin, massive brow ridges and low forehead, in all of which they stand in contrast to modern man (Fig. 389). They show a distinct advance over *Pithecanthropus*, however, in having a larger brain, about equal in

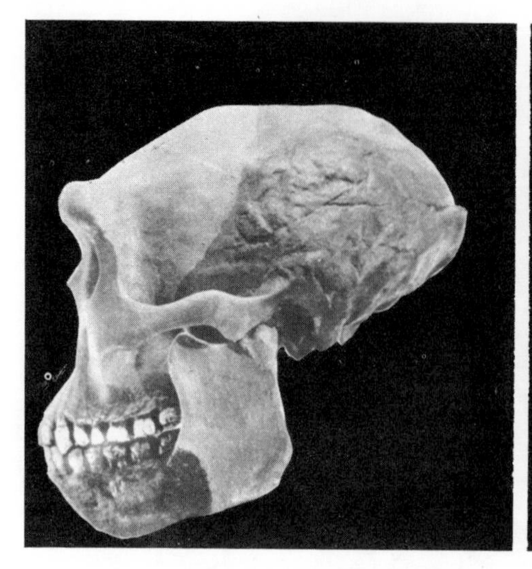 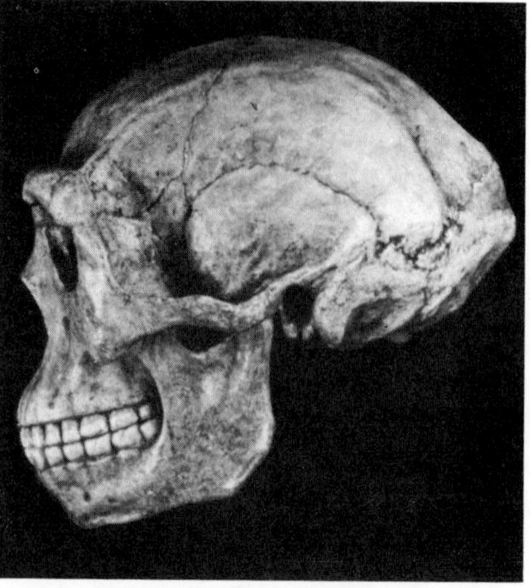

Figure 389A. Skulls of *Pithecanthropus erectus* (left) and *Pithecanthropus pekingensis* for comparison with those of *Homo neanderthalensis* and *Homo sapiens*. (From models by Franz Weidenreich, American Museum of Natural History.)

volume to that of modern man, though differing in shape.

In one important respect the Neanderthal people differ from both *Pithecanthropus* and modern man, namely in the curvature of the thigh bone that gave them a slouched stance. It is now suspected, therefore, that they represent a specialized sideline in which the curved thigh bones, the very massive brow ridges, and thick skull bones became accentuated, whereas some of the less specialized remains currently attributed to *Homo neanderthalensis* are in the direct line to modern man and should be regarded as *Homo sapiens*.[8]

Homo sapiens Arrives

The Cro-Magnons. Early in the last glacial age, about 35,000 years ago, modern men appeared in southern Europe and quickly replaced the Neanderthalers. They have been called the Cro-Magnon race for the original discovery of five skeletons at the rock shelter of Cro-Magnon in the French village of Les Eyzies in the Dordogne Valley. They brought with them the distinctive Aurignacean culture.

The original find included the skeleton of a grown man, two young men, a woman, and a child. Numerous other remains have since come to light, so that the race is well known from many skeletons and from associated stone implements and other evidences of culture and art.

Unlike the Neanderthaloids, the Cro-Magnons were tall and straight, with relatively long legs, straight thigh bones, and the complete double curvature of the spine that permitted the balance of the head as in modern man. The chin was prominent, the jaws not protruding, the forehead high, and the brain fully as large as in modern races. In physical development the Cro-Magnons were essentially modern (Fig. 389*B*)).

In mental development, also, they were superior, for they had abundant and well-formed implements. They used bone for awls and ivory for skewers and ornaments; they made spears and bows and arrows; and they dressed themselves in fur. Their bodies they ornamented with sea shells derived from the Mediterranean and Atlantic coasts, with fossil shells from places far inland, with the teeth of mammals and even of human beings. Toward the close of the last ice age they made beads and bracelets and other objects of shell and ivory.

Endowed with more intelligence and better weapons than their predecessors, the Cro-Magnons lived better and enjoyed leisure that enabled them to develop a type of art and culture that has excited the wonder and admiration of all anthropologists. Besides personal adornment and the use of clothing, this artistic development was expressed in picture writing on the walls of their caves, in sculpture on fragments of stone or on bone, and finally in the polychrome paintings left on the walls of certain caverns in southern France and Spain (Fig. 390).

The Cro-Magnons were the last of the Paleolithic peoples in Europe. Their history is recorded in four cultural stages, the Aurignacean, the Solutrean, the Magdalenian, and the Azilian. It is probable that there is no break in the lineage, however, between them, and the people who introduced the Neolitic culture into Europe about 5,500 years ago, and modern man.

A significant recent find was that at Shanidar Cave in Iraq, mentioned on page 451, where the Aurignacian culture is recorded in layer number 3 and material from near its base gives a radiocarbon date of 34,000 years B.P. (before the present[9]). The Magdalenian culture near Hamburg, Germany, gives radiocarbon dates ranging from about 9,300 to 10,500 B.P.[10]

When the remarkable cave art of the Cro-Magnons was discovered it seemed puzzling that the pictures were drawn on the walls of the most remote chambers where they could be seen only by artificial light. It now seems obvious that these chambers were holy places where religious and other ceremonial rites were performed (Fig. 390). Some of the finest paintings are on the walls of the cavern at Lascaux northeast of Les Eyzies where charcoal from a hearth gives a radiocarbon date of about 15,500 B.P.[11]

NEOLITHIC PEOPLES AND THE BEGINNING OF CIVILIZATION

As the last ice sheet disappeared from Europe, the climate moderated and became moister. The reindeer, which had been the chief source of food and clothing for Cro-Magnon man while the ice still occupied northern Europe, now vanished from most of the continent. These changes in climate and food were accompanied by human migrations, as man spread northward in the wake of the vanishing ice. About this time the art of finishing stone implements by grinding and polishing was developed in southern Europe, and a new culture, the Neolithic, spread quickly over the continent. This was accompanied by the development of the art of making pottery, the domestication of animals, and the adoption of habits of communal life. Later on, permanent habitations in the form of stone or wooden huts or tents of skins became general, and agriculture was pursued. In order to secure protection, villages were commonly built on piles over lake shores, swamps, or streams.

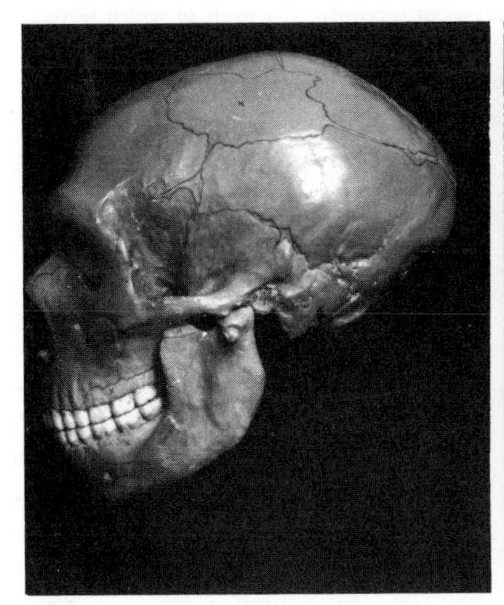

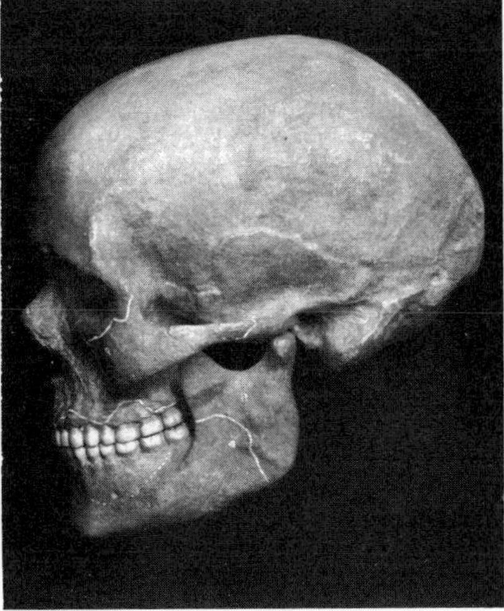

Figure 389B. Skulls of Neanderthal man (left) and Cro-Magnon man (right) (From models by J. H. McGregor, American Museum of Natural History.)

Figure 390. Ceremonial rite by the Cro-Magnons in the recesses of a cavern, the walls of which have been adorned with polychrome paintings. An idealized reconstruction drawn by Rudolph F. Zallinger for Life's *The Epic of Man*, suggesting the initiation of youths into the clan at puberty. (Courtesy of Time, Inc.)

An important factor in the development of communal life was the development of agriculture, and in Europe this centered around the cultivation of the wild einkorn that grows naturally in Armenia, Georgia, and Turkey, and from which some 14 modern species of wheat have been developed.[12]

The oldest known association of einkorn with human culture is at Jarmo in Iraq, where radiocarbon dates the association at 4750 B.C., or 6,700 years ago. It was domesticated at about the same time in the eastern Caucasus, Asia Minor, and Greece. Carbonized grains of einkorn have been found in the neolithic deposits of the Lake Dwellers in central Europe, and a modern type of wheat has been found at Mohenjo-Daro, in the Indus Valley where it is dated at 2500 B.C.[9]

EARLY MAN IN NORTH AMERICA

All the Paleolithic races of men described above lived in the Old World. It is generally accepted that man evolved in that hemisphere, for no remains of the higher primates are known in America. The date of man's first migration to this continent is a problem that has been long under discussion, but one on which numerous recent finds have thrown light. It now appears certain that he arrived before the extinction of several of the characteristic Pleistocene mammals, notably the Columbian elephant, the American mastodon, a large extinct species of bison, a native camel, three species of horse, and the giant ground-sloth. Indeed, it has been suspected that he may have contributed to the extinction of some of these great game animals. All the American human fossils are attributable, nevertheless, to the modern species, *Homo sapiens*.

A notable discovery of human bones was made at Vero, south of Daytona Beach, Florida, in 1916, and at Melbourne, about 40 miles farther south. Numerous fragments of human remains occur at the latter place in a bed of sand that also contains bones of the giant ground-sloth, two extinct species of horse, the mastodon, the Columbian elephant, and a saber-tooth tiger.

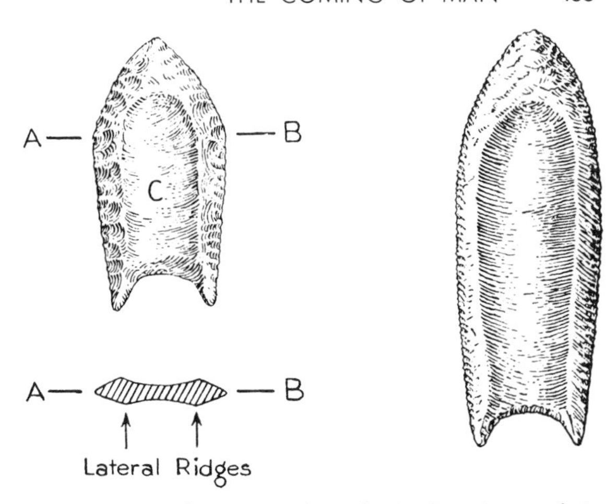

Figure 391. Folsom points from the Lindenmeier ranch in Colorado. The longitudinal fluting (C) of these finely chipped points is distinctive. (After F. Roberts.)

In 1926 stone implements were found near Folsom, New Mexico, associated with an extinct species of bison, *Bison taylori*. Later excavation revealed an arrowhead between two bison ribs, and eventually the remains of 40 to 50 specimens of the extinct bison were found within a small area, representing a kill and barbeque. Among these were 16 arrow points of a distinctive type (Fig. 391) now known as Folsom points. In recent years the Folsom culture has been found to be widely distributed in southwestern United States, and at several places it is associated with extinct animals. A notable example is the Lindenmier site north of Fort Collins, Colorado, where at a depth of 14 to 15 feet below the present surface the Folsom culture is associated with a "bison kill" similar to that at Folsom. Here the remains of an extinct camel were found with the bison. From this ancient camp site some 2,000 stone implements have been recovered, including scrapers, drills, gravers, and blades.[13]

A similar occurrence was found near Plainview, Texas, in 1944, where extensive quarrying in a gravel bed led to the recovery of skeletons of between 50 and 100 bison of an extinct species larger than the modern buffalo.[14] With these were found 19 projectile points and 8 stone scrapers. It is believed that the bison were stampeded into falling from the river bluff. The artifacts resemble those at Folsom. At this quarry the only other animal found was a large wolf, but, near by, the same bed yielded the Columbian elephant and a fossil horse.

Burned bison bone associated with the Folsom culture near Lubbock, Texas, has given radiocarbon dates of about 9,700 to 9,883 years B.C.

Folsom points found in the northern foothills of the Brookes Range in Alaska tend to confirm the generally accepted belief that man reached North America from Asia by way of Bering Strait.

Artifacts have also been found deeply buried in river-terrace gravels at numerous localities in southwestern United States, and in several of these they are associated with remains of extinct mammals.

Terraces along Blanco Creek about 100 miles southeast of San Antonio, Texas, for example, have yielded six sites in which flint artifacts are associated with bones of extinct animals including elephants, mastodons, horses, bison, camels, glyptodons, etc.

The valley about Mexico City has yielded several bits of evidence of early man. A skeleton and associated artifacts were found beneath a lava flow in the suburban village of San Angel, and the same culture was found beneath 10 to 12 feet of sediments northwest of the city. The lava flow is believed to have occurred at least 2,000 years ago, and possibly as much as 10,000 years. Hence these people long preceded the Aztecs, who date from about A.D. 500. In 1946 more remains were found near Tepexpan. Here a human skeleton was discovered in a layer that also yielded several artifacts (three gravers, a scraper, and a bone point), as well as bones of the imperial mammoth, bison, horse, and glyptodont.

These are but samples of a large number of occurrences of either artifacts or human fossils associated with the large extinct mammals that were common in North America during the Pleistocene Epoch.

One of the most remarkable archeological sites in America is Russell Cave, [15] discovered about 1953 and now a national monument presented to the Government by the National Geographic Society in 1958. It is a limestone cavern in a hillside in Jackson County, Alabama, and was repeatedly occupied by prehistoric man since about 10,000 years B.P. Stratified deposits more than 20 feet thick show a succession of cultures that have been dated by radiocarbon. The deepest of these includes a hearth from which charcoal gives a date of 9,020 years, and the youngest is dated as 1650 A.D. Some 2½ tons of artifacts had been recovered from the cave by 1958, along with several skeletons.

REFERENCES

1. Clark, Sir Wilfred E., 1955, *The Fossil Evidence for Human Evolution.* University of Chicago Press, Chicago, pp. 1–181.

2. Dart, Raymond A., 1955, Cultural status of the South African man-apes. *Smithsonian Annual Report for 1955,* pp. 317–338.

3. Von Koenigswald, G. H. R., 1937, A review of the stratigraphy of Java and its relations to early man, pp. 23–32. In: G. G. Maccurdy (ed.), *Early Man,* J. B. Lippincott, Philadelphia.

Clark, Sir Wilfred E., 1955, *The Fossil Evidence for Human Evolution.* University of Chicago Press, Chicago, chapter 3, pp. 81–96.

4. Black, Davidson, Teilhard de Chardin, and W. C. Pei, 1933, Fossil Man in China: The Choukoutien Cave Deposits with a synopsis of our present knowledge of the late Cenozoic in China. *Geol. Surv. China, Mem., Series A,* no. 11, pp. 1–158.

Black, Davidson, 1934, On the Discovery, Morphology and Environment of Sinanthropus pekingensis. *Philos. Trans., Royal Soc. London, Series B.,* vol. 223, pp. 57–120.

5. Blanc, A. C., 1939, L 'Uomo fossile del Monte Circeo i un cranio neanderthalianos nella grotta Guattari a San Felice Circeo, R. C. Accad. Naz. dei Lincei, Vol. 29, Ser. 6, Sem. 1, Fasc. 5, Roma.

Wirz, P., 1925, Die Marind Anim von Holl. Süd - Neu-Guinea, In *Univ. Abh. aus dem Gebiete der Auslandeskunde,* Hamburg, III, p. 59.

6. Anonymous, 1957, Archeological discoveries in Iraq. *Science,* vol. 126, pp. 834–835.

7. Blanc, A. C., 1939, L'uomo fossile de Monte Circeo e la sua posizione cronologica nel quadro del pleistocene laziale, *Soc. Toscana Sci. Nat., Atti,* Pr. verbali, vol. 48, no. 2, pp. 19–20.

Blanc, A. C., et al., 1955, Instituto Italiano di Paleontologia Umana. *Quaternaria,,* vol. 2, pp. 265–316.

8. Clark, Sir Wilfred E., 1955, *The Fossil Evidence for Human Evolution.* Chapter 2: The Antiquity of *Homo sapiens* and the Problems of Neanderthal Man. University of Chicago Press. pp. 48–74.

Weckler, J. E., 1957, Neanderthal Man. *Scientific American,* vol. 197, no. 6, pp. 89–96.

9. Anonymous, 1957, Archeological discoveries in Iraq. *Science,* vol. 126, p. 834.

10. Barensen, G. W., E. S. Deevey and L. J. Gralenski, 1957, Yale natural radiocarbon measurements, III. *Science,* vol. 126, pp. 908–919.

11. Arnold, J. R., and W. F. Libby, 1951, Radiocarbon dates. *Science,* vol. 113, pp. 111–120.

12. Mangelsdorf, Paul C., 1953, Wheat. *Scientific American,* vol. 189, no. 1, pp. 50–59.

13. Miller, Carl F., 1956, Life 8,000 years ago uncovered in an Alabama cave. *National Geographic Magazine,* vol. 110, pp. 542–558.

14. Sellards, E. H., Glen L. Davis and G. E. Mead, 1947, Fossil bison and associated artifacts from Plainview, Texas. *Geol. Soc. Amer., Bull.,* vol. 58, 927–954.

15. Miller, Carl F., 1958, Russell Cave: New light on Stone Age life. *National Geographic Magazine,* vol. 113, pp. 426–437.

EPILOGUE

"It is always necessary to close a lecture on Geology in humility. On the ship Earth *which bears us into immensity toward an end which God alone knows, we are steerage passengers. We are emigrants who know only their own misfortune. The least ignorant among us, the most daring, the most restless, ask ourselves questions; we demand when the voyage of humanity began, how long it will last, how the ship goes, why do its decks and hull vibrate, why do sounds sometimes come up from the hold and go out by the hatchway; we ask what secrets do the depths of the strange vessel conceal and we suffer from never knowing the secrets. . . .*

"You and I are of the group of restless and daring ones who would like to know and who are never satisfied with any response. We hold ourselves together on the prow of the ship, attentive to all the indications that come from the mysterious interior, or the monotonous sea, or the still more monotonous sky. We console each other by speaking of the shore toward which we devoutly believe we sail, where we shall indeed arrive, where we shall go ashore tomorrow, perhaps. This shore not one of us has ever seen, but all would recognize it without hesitation were it to appear on the horizon. For it is the shore of the country of our dreams, where the air is so pure there is no death, the country of our desires, and its name is 'truth.'"

—PIERRE TERMIER.

Appendix A. An Introduction to Animals and Plants

Scientific Names. THE BEGINNER IN NATURAL HISTORY is usually dismayed by the scientific names of unfamiliar types of animals and plants, and is inclined to wonder why common names are not used instead. The answer to this is very simple: a name is common only because it is familiar. Such words as *boa constrictor, gila monster,* and *rhinoceros* are common, but a small child finds them fully as difficult as *Homo sapiens* (man), or *Equus caballus* (the horse). Moreover, only a few thousand kinds of animals are at all commonly known, and the rest, already exceeding 825,000 kinds, can therefore have no really "common" names.

Furthermore, so long as we have a diversity of languages, there can be no really common names of general and world-wide usage. To the Germans, the common name of the horse is *Pferd;* to the French, *cheval;* to the Italians, *cavallo,* etc. Moreover, a common name such as *bear* has many different meanings; to a New Englander it implies one species, to a Montanan another, and to an Alaskan a quite different kind of bear. Therefore, if naturalists of all countries are to share in scientific studies, it is obviously necessary that each species should bear a name that applies to one kind alone and is recognized in all languages. For such names, naturalists have wisely turned to the classical languages, Greek and Latin.

The early naturalists did, indeed, give each kind of animal but a single name. Thus, in the Roman Empire, the cat bore the name *felis,* and the horse was called *equus.* This scheme sufficed so long as only a few hundred kinds of animals were known, and the scholars of the civilized world all lived in a relatively small area about the Mediterranean. But as culture spread during the Middle Ages, and animals from other regions were studied, it became necessary to accompany each name with a short diagnosis or description in order to distinguish it from some similar, previously known kind. Latin scholars at first used the name *felis* for the domestic cat, but they later became acquainted with the great tawny cat of Africa, as well as the spotted cat of the tropics.

When it became necessary to accompany the common name with sufficient adjectives or descriptive phrases to indicate clearly which kind was meant, the great Swedish naturalist, Linnaeus, devised the plan of giving each species a double name, the first representing the group (genus), the second a special or specific name for that particular kind. The latter is generally a descriptive or qualifying adjective standing in place of a descriptive paragraph, and, in harmony with the Latin custom, it follows the word which it modifies. Thus, the house cat became *Felis domestica,* and the great spotted cat, *Felis leopardalis* (Lat. *pardalis,* spotted). The scientific name is, therefore, in reality, a nickname, or an abbreviation of the longer diagnosis that would otherwise be required.

It should be noted that the generic name is capitalized, and that the specific name is not.

Classification of Animals and Plants. In dealing with any large or complex group of objects, some scheme of classification or orderly grouping is required. To appreciate this fact, we need only contemplate an army of individuals without organization, a great library with the books placed at random on the shelves, or a dictionary with the words arranged by chance! Nowhere is the need for organization more keenly felt than in the study of the enormously varied forms of animal and plant life. Here, obviously, the most useful basis of classification is blood kinship, and a **biologic classification** has therefore been adopted which aims to group creatures according to their degree of actual relationship, regardless of superficial resemblances or differences.

In this biologic scheme, the animal and plant kingdoms are divided, first, into **phyla** (Gr. *phylon*, stock or race), each phylum including organisms that are alike in some fundamental anatomical characters. For example, animals with backbones form the phylum **Vertebrata** (Lat. *vertebratus*, having a backbone); those with jointed legs and bodies, such as insects, spiders, and crabs, form the phylum **Arthropoda** (Gr. *arthron*, joint + *pous*, foot).

Each phylum in turn is divisible into **classes**, within which the resemblances are still closer. For example, among the vertebrates the fishes constitute one class, birds another, and mammals a third. Classes are further subdivided into **orders**. Thus, the class Mammalia includes the orders **Carnivora** (flesh-eating types), **Rodentia** (gnawers like rats and squirrels), etc. Orders are divisible into **families**, and these in turn into **genera**, each genus including one or several kinds (**species**) of animals that are very closely related and structurally alike. For example, the cats form the genus *Felis*, and the dogs and wolves the genus *Canis*. The species is the next smallest unit, including individuals very closely alike.

ANIMALS

The following table presents in simple form the major subdivisions of the animal kingdom, groups that are wholly extinct being italicized. See also the *Tree of Life*, Fig. 46, page 67.

A SIMPLE CLASSIFICATION OF THE ANIMAL KINGDOM

Phylum **Protozoa**—single-celled, generally miscroscopic animals. Ex.: amoeba, foraminifera, radiolaria, and many disease germs.
Phylum **Porifera**—sponges.
Phylum **Coelenterata**—coral-like animals, lacking viscera.
  Class **Hydrozoa**—hydroids, *stromatoporoids.*
  Class **Anthozoa**—corals and sea-anemones, *tetracorals,* hexacorals, *honeycomb corals.*
Phylum **Platyhelminthes**—flatworms (never fossil).
Phylum **Nemathelminthes**—threadworms (never fossil).
Phylum **Trochelminthes**—rotifers, all microscopic (never fossil).
Phylum **Brachiopoda**—brachiopods.
Phylum **Bryozoa**—moss animals.
Phylum **Echinodermata**—echinoderms.
  Class **Asteroidea**—starfish.
  Class **Echinoidea**—sea-urchins, heart-urchins, sand dollars.
  Class **Crinoidea**—sea-lilies or feather-stars.
  Class **Blastoidea**—*sea buds* or *blastoids.*
  Class **Cystoidea**—*cystoids.*
Phylum **Mollusca**—mollusks.
  Class **Pelecypoda**—clams, oysters, scallops.
  Class **Gastropoda**—snails, conchs, etc.
  Class **Cephalopoda**—squids, devilfish, nautiloids, *ammonites,* and *belemnites.*
Phylum **Annelida**—segmented worms, earthworms, beach worms, etc.
Phylum **Arthropoda**—invertebrate animals with jointed legs.
  Class **Trilobitoidea**—*trilobites.*
  Class **Crustacea**—lobsters, crabs.
  Class **Myriapoda**—centipedes, millipeds, etc.
  Class **Chelicerata**—spiders, scorpions, eurypterids.
  Class **Insecta**—insects.
Phylum **Vertebrata** (Chordata)—animals with backbones.
  Class **Pisces**—fishes (actually four classes).
  Class **Amphibia**—salamanders, frogs, *labyrinthodonts.*
  Class **Reptilia**—crocodiles, turtles, *dinosaurs, ichthyosaurs, plesiosaurs, mosasaurs, pterosaurs,* snakes.
  Class **Aves**—birds.
  Class **Mammalia**—milk-feeding, warm-blooded animals (including man).

Phylum Protozoa

Single-celled animals constitute the phylum **Protozoa** (Gr. *protos*, first + *zoön*, animal), so called on the assumption that it includes the most primitive types of animal life. Although widely distributed and extremely numerous, protozoans are nearly all microscopic and therefore are seldom seen.

Each protozoan is a tiny droplet of fluid living matter enclosed in a membranous cell wall. Unlike higher animals, it has no special visceral organs for digestion, circulation, reproduction, etc. Food

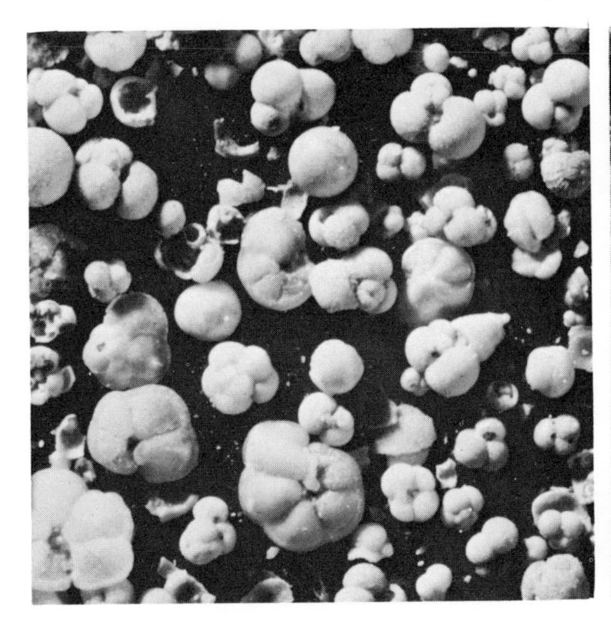

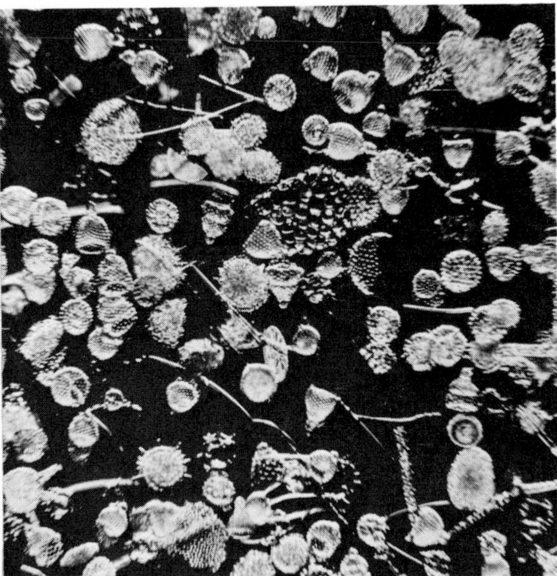

Figure 392. Protozoan Shells. Left, globigerina ooze (×10) dredged from a depth of 2898 feet about 100 miles west of Martinique, West Indies. Right, radiolarian ooze (×35) from the Miocene beds of the island of Barbados, West Indies. (*Yale Peabody Museum.*)

consists of other microscopic creatures, commonly plants, which are swallowed whole. Lacking a mouth, the little animal takes its food through a temporary rupture in its cell wall, and later voids the indigestible residue by the same means. Once in the body, the food particle is attacked by fluids that digest it, and the single-celled animal assimilates this food without the need of a circulatory system. When fully grown, the tiny animal reproduces by simply splitting into two or more young, each of which is like the parent but smaller. Since the parent passes completely into its offspring, **there is no death** in the normal course of events for these simple creatures. Individuals may be killed, of course, by unfavorable environment or by other animals; this, however, may be considered accidental, for death is not the inevitable fate of each individual, as it is with all higher animals.

Although protozoans probably exceed all other types of animal life combined, both in number of individuals and in total bulk, the vast majority are soft-tissued and incapable of fossilization. There are, however, two prolific groups of them that form delicate shells of calcium carbonate or silica, and have left an imposing record. These are the orders Foraminifera and Radiolaria.

The **Foraminifera** (Fig. 392) build tiny chambered shells, commonly of calcium carbonate. They inhabit all the oceans but are rarely found in fresh waters. The majority live on the bottom or cling to seaweeds, but about twenty kinds float near the surface of the open oceans, whence their shells, abandoned at time of reproduction, rain down like a snowfall to cover the sea floor. The commonest of these is *Globigerina*, and the soft, fine-grained, limy deposit made mainly by its shells is known as **globigerina ooze** (Fig. 392). Approximately 50,000,000 square miles of the sea floor are now covered to an unknown depth by these deposits. At various times in the geologic past, foraminiferal shells have accumulated in shallow water to form extensive beds of chalk or limestone. The pyramids of Gizeh, for example, are made of a limestone that is widely spread in the Mediterranean region and is largely made of coin-shaped shells known as **nummulites** (Fig. 377, p. 434). Still older limestones of the late Paleozoic are formed of **fusulines,** a tribe having shells about the size and shape of wheat grains (Fig. 199, p. 238).

The **Radiolaria** (Fig. 392) make their shells of silica. Differing from the capsulelike shell of the foraminifer, these are of a loose, open texture, like

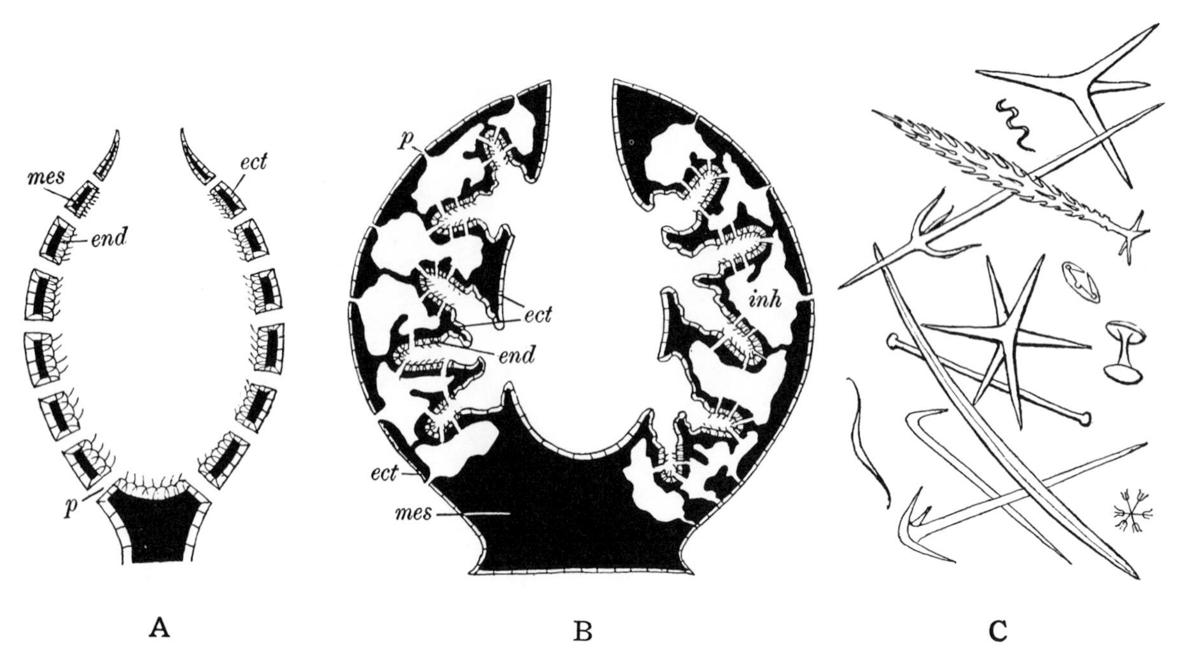

Figure 393. Sponges. *A*, diagrammatic vertical section of a very simple sponge; *B*, similar section of a more complex sponge; *C*, various types of sponge spicules, greatly enlarged. *ect*, ectoderm; *end*, endoderm; *inh*, inhalant canal; *mes*, mesoglea; *p*, wall pore. (From Brooklyn Museum of Natural History.)

a delicate glass sieve. They form deposits of radiolarian ooze on parts of the deep-sea floor.

Phylum Porifera

The Porifera or sponges are multicellular animals in which there is little specialization of tissues. The "bath sponge" is but the silken skeleton of one highly specialized type. The essential features of the group are better displayed by a very simple sponge (Fig. 393*A*). Such an individual has the form of a slender vase; there is nothing to it but a living *wall* surrounding a large hollow space. This wall is made up of three layers like a jelly sandwich, the outer layer being formed of protective cells (ectoderm), the inner layer of feeding cells (endoderm), and the middle layer of a noncellular jelly-like substance (mesoglea). The endodermal cells feed as do protozoans, each capturing and swallowing other microscopic organisms; the ectodermal cells do not take food but absorb what is needed from the near-by endodermal cells. Thus no digestive or circulatory organs are required.

To strengthen this delicate wall, either mineral spicules or threadlike fibers of spongin, an organic substance allied to silk, are formed in the gelatinous layer. These are secreted by specialized cells and are united to form a loose meshwork. In the bath sponge, the spicules are all made of spongin, but in many sponges the spicules are of silica or calcium carbonate (Fig. 393*C*). The mineral spicules are commonly preserved, and are among the oldest records of life on the Earth.

Phylum Coelenterata

The third phylum of animals includes the **hydroids, corals,** and **jellyfish.** These, like the sponge, consist essentially of a body wall, lacking any internal organs, whence the name Coelenterata (Gr. *koilos,* hollow + *enteron,* inside cavity).

Hydroids. *Hydra* is a simple representative of the phylum, and particularly of the class **Hydrozoa.** A vertical section through its slender subcylindrical body (Fig. 394) shows a wall of three layers, as in the sponge. But in three respects it is vastly ahead of the sponge. First, it has muscular tissue that permits change of shape and even locomotion, and makes possible a circlet of muscular tentacles about the mouth with which to capture food; second, in the inner layer are special gland cells that excrete digestive juices into the central cavity; and, third, it bears stinging cells like those of the jellyfish that can paralyze other animals coming into contact with it. The hydroid is thus able to capture, swallow, and digest animals almost as large as itself (Fig. 394).

Hydras live as solitary individuals, but many hydroids reproduce by budding and thus form colonies of individuals organically united (Fig. 394). Many of these secrete a bell-like or vaselike sheath (hydrotheca) about their body as a protection. These sheaths are formed of chitin, a substance similar to fingernails.

Many hydroid secrete calcium carbonate about the base of the colony, forming laminated coral-like structures.

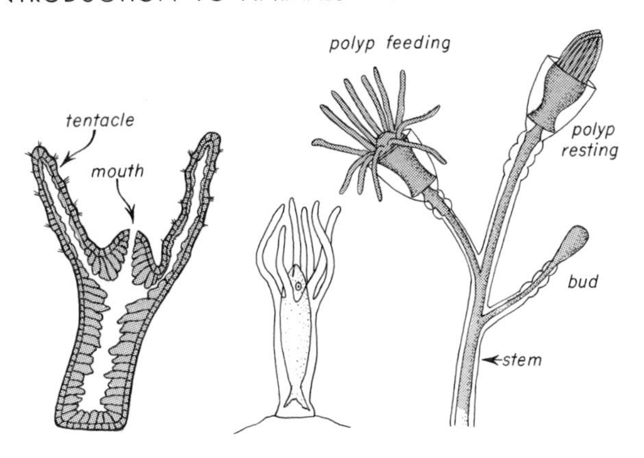

Figure 394. Hydroids. Left, diagrammatic vertical section of *Hydra*, much enlarged; center, *Hydra* devouring a young trout (×2); right, a colonial hydroid, *Obelia*, with two adult individuals and a young bud.

Corals. The corals and sea-anemones form another class of this phylum, the **Anthozoa** (Gr. *anthos*, flower + *zoön*, animal), so named because of their bright colors and flowerlike symmetry (Fig. 395). The coral animal resembles *Hydra* in essentials, but has in addition thin radial partitions (mesenteries) that extend from the wall part way into the central cavity, subdividing it into a series of alcoves.

The coral animal secretes about its side and base an external skeleton of calcium carbonate. The animal is correctly termed a **polyp**, and its skeleton, **coral**.

For some unknown reason the base of the coral polyp is invariably marked by radial infoldings which alternate in position with the internal mesenteries. The skeleton secreted against this base is marked by radial ridges or plates known as **septa**. Coral polyps may live singly, but many kinds reproduce by budding new polyps from the margins of the older, and thus develop colonies in

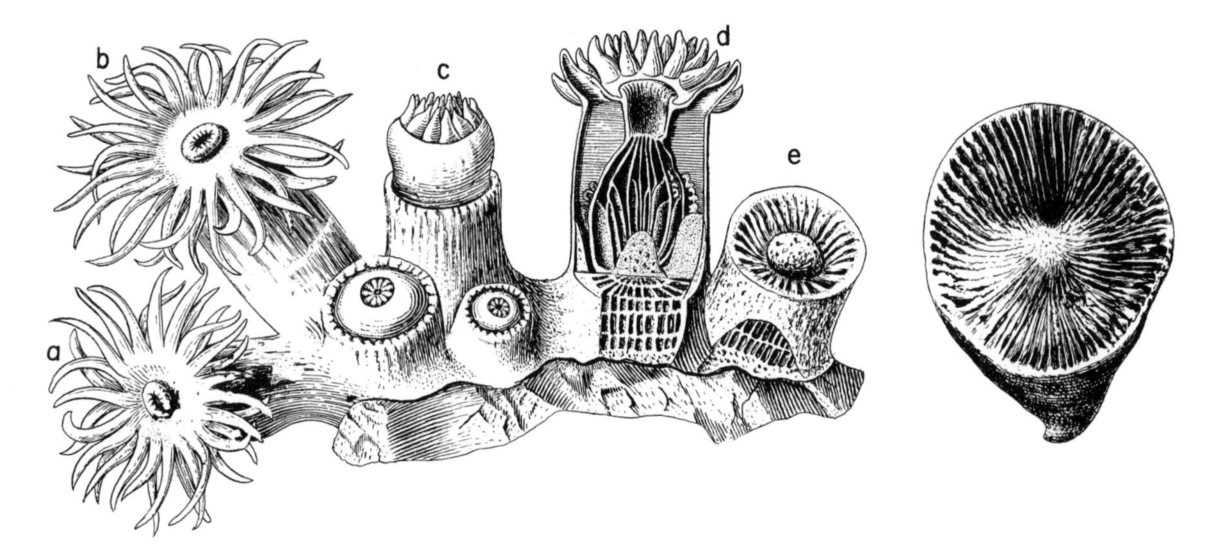

Figure 395. Left, portion of a colony of a modern coral with living polyps (*a–d*) and an exposed coral showing the septa (e); right, a horn coral.

Figure 396. Brachiopods. Left, a shell in position of growth, attached to a point of rock by the pedicle. Center, dorsal view of same, showing the pedicle foramen and the bilateral symmetry (i.e., each side is a mirror reflection of the other). Right, side view showing that the valves are unequal in size and in shape.

which many individuals cooperate to build a complex stony skeleton.

The skeleton of a solitary coral may be cushion-shaped or horn-shaped or subcylindrical, and usually has a cuplike depression at the summit, in which the base of the polyp is housed. In colonial forms the skeleton is commonly branching or massive, with depressions for the bases of the individual polyps. **The radiating septa are absolutely distinctive of the coral skeleton and serve to distinguish it from all other types of shells.**

It is well known that corals make reefs in the sea, but only where it is warm and shallow. Accordingly, the coral reefs in the rocks of past geologic ages are regarded as evidence of mild temperature and of shallow water. Corals have been important agents in rock-formation at various times in the past. Coral reefs now occupy an area of about half a million square miles of the shallow seas, and their limy debris spreads over a vastly greater area.

Nearly all the modern corals belong to the subclass **Hexacoralla**, so named because their septa are introduced in cycles of six or multiples of six. In these the septa are equally spaced, so that they seem to radiate with regular symmetry in all directions from the center. This group has been the dominant one since the beginning of Mesozoic time. The subclass **Tetracoralla** (Fig. 395, left), on the contrary, which was dominant in the Paleozoic era, shows more or less conspicuous bilateral symmetry, with septa introduced in cycles of four.

Phylum Brachiopoda

The brachiopods constitute a phylum of rather small marine animals that invariably bear an external shell of two pieces, known as valves (Fig. 396). Although between 200 and 300 kinds are now living, they are seldom seen on the beach and are hardly known except to specialists; but they are extremely abundant fossils, especially in Paleozoic rocks, and so challenge the interest of geologists.

The body is much more complex than that of the coral, having a digestive system, kidneys, a nervous system, reproductive organs, and well-developed muscles. In life, the animal is attached to the bottom by a fleshy stalk (pedicle) at the posterior end, its mouth facing upward. The two valves of the shell are hinged together at the posterior end of the body and can be opened more or less widely at the front. They are borne on the back and front surfaces of the body (not on the sides), and thus a plane of symmetry passes through the middle of each valve. Special muscles open and close the shell, and a pair of interlocking teeth and sockets at the posterior end forms a hinge. A hole (pedicle foramen) for the passage of the stalk is usually present near the apex of the ventral valve.

Insofar as the brachiopod shell consists of two valves, it resembles the shell of a clam, but the likeness is purely superficial. The structure of the body is unlike that of a clam, and the shell valves are borne in a wholly different position. In the clam, the valves are on the *sides* of the body and are hinged *along the back;* in the brachiopod, they are borne on the *back* and *front* surfaces and are hinged *across the posterior end.* As a result, the symmetry of the shell is quite dissimilar in these two groups, the brachiopod shell being **inequivalved** although each valve is **equilateral,** each half being a mirror reflection of the other, like the left and right sides of a coat. The clam shell is **equivalved,** right and left valves being mirror reflections of one another (except in deformed types like the oyster), but each valve is **inequilateral**, the front and hind ends being normally different in shape.

Brachiopod shells vary greatly in shape (Pl. 4, figs. 10–22, p. 150), some being strongly biconvex, others planoconvex, and others concavoconvex, the space between the valves in the last type being so thin that the animal must have had the proportions of a flatworm. In many brachiopods the hinge is short, and the posterior end of the shell pointed or "beaked" as in Figure 396; in others, it is long and straight, and the shell is "square-shouldered." Some shells are smooth, many are ribbed, and some are spiny. In spite of the diversity of form, **the brachiopod shell is easily recognized by its symmetry.**

Brachiopods are rather small animals, the average length of shell being between 1 and 2 inches. A few attained a diameter of 3 or 4 inches, and the largest that ever lived had a breadth of about 1 foot.

Phylum Bryozoa

The Bryozoa or moss animals form another important phylum little known to the general public, in spite of the fact that living forms are commonly attached to the rocks and seaweeds everywhere along the seacoast (Fig. 397). Anatomically the bryozoan is very simple and in many respects more like a brachiopod than other animals, but, unlike the brachiopod, it is invariably minute and always grows in colonies. The individuals rarely attain a diameter much greater than that of a period on this page, but thousands of them living together may form a colony some inches across. Locally they combine to make reef limestones (Fig. 129, p. 164).

Figure 397. Bryozoa. Left, *Menipea*, a living colony of mosslike form. Right, fossil bryozoans of many kinds weathering from a piece of Lower Devonian limestone. Natural size.

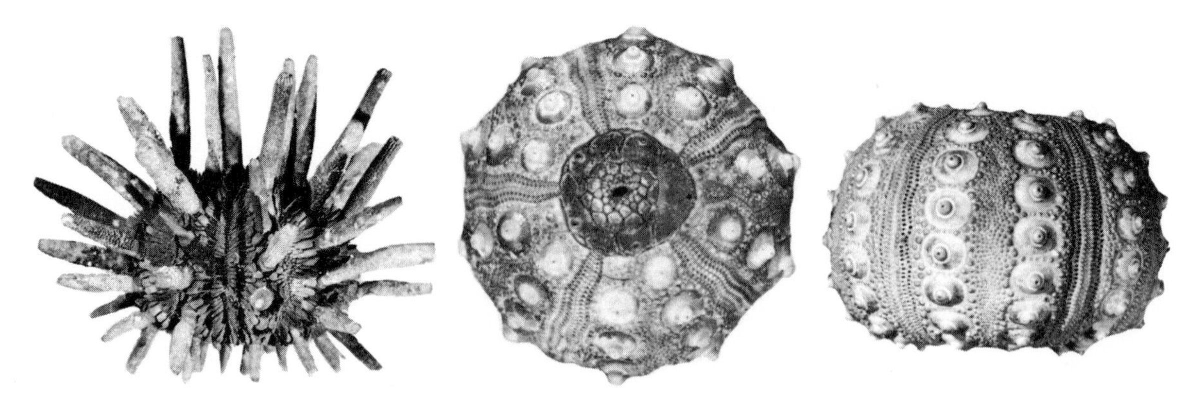

Figure 398. Three views of the echinoid, *Cidaris*. Left, a young individual as it appears alive; center, upper surface of shell with spines removed, showing the five ambulacral areas (with rows of pores) and five interambulacral areas (with large bosses for spine bases); right, side view showing the arrangement of the plates to be in vertical columns. About ½ natural size.

Unlike the brachiopod, the bryozoan forms a simple skeleton in the form of a slender tube or a boxlike cell, with an opening at or near one end through which the front end of the body can be thrust out while feeding. Many bryozoans have only a soft, delicate covering of chitin, but the majority secrete a skeleton of calcium carbonate.

The form of the colonial skeleton varies enormously with different species. It may be branching and mosslike, whence the name (Gr. *bryon*, moss), or stemlike, leaflike, massive, or encrusting. In spite of all this diversity, the bryozoan skeleton is easily recognized because it is made up of minute tubules or cells.

Phylum Echinodermata

The **echinoderms** are peculiarly different from all other animals. This great phylum includes the starfishes, echinoids, crinoids, blastoids, and cystoids. Their bodies are short and commonly globular. Almost all have a radial and five-rayed symmetry. Nearly all develop a shell in the form of limy plates that are secreted in the body wall and fit edge to edge like the pieces in a mosaic. The types enumerated above represent five distinct classes, which will be discussed in order.

Echinoids or Sea-Urchins. A typical echinoid (Fig. 398) has a globular or bun-shaped body bristling with slender, movable spines, whence the name (Gr. *echinos*, hedgehog). The mouth is at the center of the lower side, and the axis of the body is vertical. Stripping away the spines, we find the body wall of the animal to be a rigid, boxlike shell of polygonal plates arranged in twenty vertical columns. Upon these plates are scattered small rounded nubs, each of which was the pivot for a spine.

Radiating from the summit of the shell to the mouth are five paths along which the plates are thickly perforated with small double-barreled pores. These paths are the food grooves, or **ambulacral areas.** In life each pair of pores bears a slender muscular organ known as a **tube-foot.** The tube-feet are part of a remarkable **ambulacral system**, found only among the echinoderms, which serves for feeble locomotion, for the gathering of food, and for respiration. The body cavity is spacious and includes a well-developed digestive system, a nervous system, and reproductive organs.

We have described a typical sea-urchin as a radially symmetrical animal, but there are some specialized types (heart-urchins and sand dollars) in which a secondary bilateral symmetry has modified the primitive, pentameral form. In all echinoids, however, a five-rayed symmetry is clearly evident even though somewhat irregular.

Starfishes. Next of kin to the echinoids, the starfishes are distinguished by their star-shaped form (Fig. 399), the body being depressed and extended at the sides into tapering rays. The skeleton is made of small limy plates, articulated by fleshy tissues so as to permit some flexibility as in a coat of chain-mail.

Starfishes probably have been abundant since early Paleozoic time, but are rarely found as fossils, because their loosely joined plates fall apart with the decay of the flesh, and such small irregular plates are not easily recognized.

Crinoids. The crinoids or sea lilies (Fig. 400) look more plantlike than animallike, for their globular bodies are supported by flexible stalks which anchor them to the sea floor, mouth upward. The animal consists of three chief parts, a **stem**, the **body** proper, and a series of branching **arms**.

In spite of its plantlike appearance, the crinoid is an animal, essentially comparable in its structure to a starfish, though in making this comparison we must turn the starfish with its mouth upward.

The body of the crinoid is covered by a series of limy plates which fit edge to edge like those of the echinoid. These plates are arranged in several horizontal cycles, one above another, beginning at the upper end of the stem. Normally the plates in each cycle number five or some multiple of five, so that five-rayed symmetry is the rule here, as in the sea-urchins and starfish. The stalk is strengthened by the secretion within it of a series of button-shaped limy plates which are superposed like buttons on a string. These "stem joints" are united by muscular tissue, so that the stem has flexibility enough to let the animal swing with the currents. The mouth is at the summit of the body, and from it the food grooves radiate on to the upper sides of the arms. Indeed, the arms are structures developed merely to extend the food grooves.

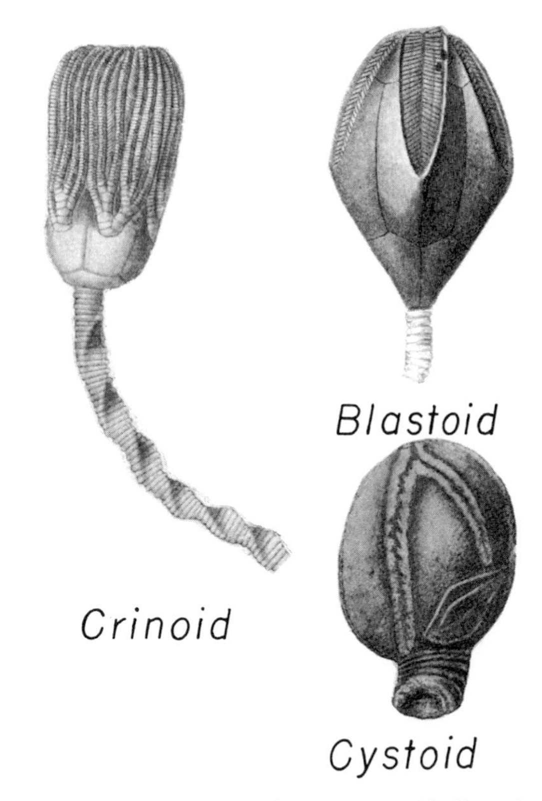

Figure 400. Stalked echinoderms. A crinoid, *Platycrinus*, with part of its stem; a blastoid, *Pentremites*, without its stem; a cystoid, *Sphaerocystites*, with most of its stem missing. Natural size. After Wachsmuth and Springer, Romer, and Schuchert.

Figure 399. A primitive starfish, *Devonaster eucharis*. Artificial cast from a natural mold in Middle Devonian sandstone of New York. Natural size. (*Yale Peabody Museum.*)

The living crinoids are brillantly and beautifully colored with shades of lavender, purple, red, lemon-yellow, or brown, and it is fitting that they should be called sea lilies. They tend to grow in patches on the sea floor and where present are commonly very abundant, so that they present much the appearance of submarine flower beds as they sway gracefully with the bottom currents. Upon the death of the animal its limy plates commonly fall apart. Crinoid remains are among the com-

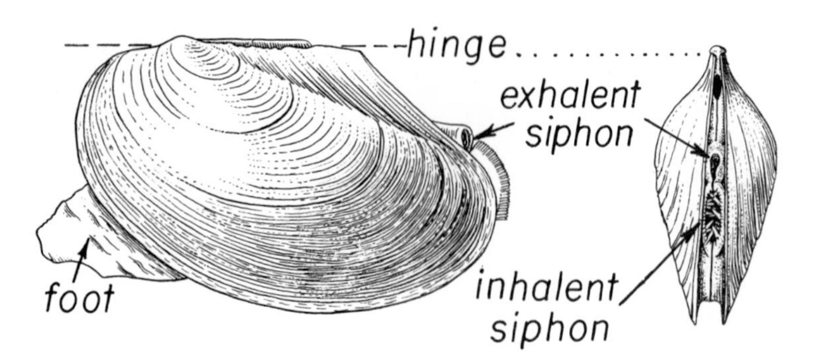

Figure 401. Pelecypod shell. The common river clam, *Anodonta*, seen from the left side and from the posterior end.

monest fossils in some of the Paleozoic formations, and they give distinctive character to "crinoidal limestones," some of which have wide extent.

Blastoids. The blastoids or sea buds (Gr. *blastos,* bud) form another group of stalked echinoderms (Fig. 400). Their bodies are globular or bud-shaped and are encased in a shell of 13 chief plates of which 3 form a basal cycle, while 2 succeeding cycles have 5 plates each. There are no arms, the food grooves lying upon the surface of the body as they do in the echinoids. These food grooves are always simple, 5 in number, and arranged in perfect five-rayed symmetry about the mouth, which is at the summit. The 5 ambulacral areas are submerged a little below the level of the chief body plates in such a fashion as to give the entire body a superficial resemblance to a flower bud in which the sepals are just beginning to part.

Blastoids are all extinct and are known only from Paleozoic rocks. They were very abundant during only one geologic period, namely, the Mississippian.

Cystoids. The cystoids (Gr. *cystis,* bladder) are primitive echinoderms with globular or almond-shaped bodies but differ from both crinoids and blastoids in that their plates are irregularly arranged, so that the body shows no definite symmetry (Fig. 400). They are extremely varied in details. Some had arms, and others had none; many were stalked, but some apparently were attached directly to the sea floor or were free. They were the most primitive echinoderms.

Phylum Mollusca

This great phylum includes the clams, the snails, the devilfish, the squids, the pearly nautilus, and the extinct ammonites. These commonly possess solid, limy, external shells, and they are generally known as "shellfish." The phylum is an enormous one, with probably no fewer than 50,000 species now living.

Pelecypods (Clams). A typical clam has a laterally compressed body encased in a bivalved shell, the two halves of which lie on the sides of the body and are hinged along its back.

The body is generally elongated, and the mouth is at the front end, but there is no distinctly marked head. Lining each valve there is a thin, fleshy extension of the body wall, the mantle, which hangs freely about the body like a loose garment. The most conspicuous organs are the great gills, which hang as a double pair of thin plates between the mantle and the sides of the body.

The shell (Fig. 401) is opened by an elastic ligament at the hingeline, which is placed under tension (or in some cases under compression) when the valves are closed. The shell of most clams is closed by a pair of heavy transverse muscles which run through the animal's body from side to side. Normally one muscle is near the front, and the other near the back end.

The typical clam is free to creep slowly about by thrusting out the ventral edge of its muscular body wall, which serves to draw the animal along. Secondarily, many clams have given up this freedom and lie on one side and adhere to the bottom, as does the oyster, or attach themselves to the rocks by silken threads, as does the blue clam. Still others burrow in the mud or even in hard rock.

The clam shell, like that of all other mollusks, consists of three layers. The outer one is a film of organic material to protect the limy part of the shell from solution. The second layer is of calcite and commonly has a white, porcelain-like appearance, while the inner layer is made of aragonite or mother-of-pearl and has the iridescence of pearl. In fact, the precious pearl is a secretion formed between the mantle and the shell, usually in an attempt by the animal to protect itself against a parasite or other irritant.

Gastropods (Snails). Though fundamentally like the clam in many of its anatomical structures, the snail is in several ways more highly specialized. It has an elongate muscular body with a distinct head bearing a pair of eyes and a pair of tentacles or feelers. Its mouth is provided with a flexible rasping tongue whereby it can shred either plant or animal food; it is therefore not dependent on microscopic objects. As a result its gills are small and plumelike, since they are used only for respiration. Internal organs resemble those of the clam in most respects.

The shell of the snail is coiled spirally and consists of a single valve. As in the clam, the shell is secreted by a mantle, so that the body may be measurably free.

When disturbed, the snail can withdraw completely into its shell, but normally it extends most of its body and creeps about, carrying the shell upon its back (Fig. 402). The ventral surface of the body has developed into a muscular creeping sole, whence the group is known technically as the **Gastropoda** (Gr. *gaster*, stomach + *pous*, foot).

Most commonly the gastropod shell is coiled in a helicoid (corkscrewlike) spiral, but many fossil forms are bilaterally symmetrical like a watch spring. Rapidly expanding shells have few volutions, but slowly expanding ones commonly have high slender spires. The shell may be ornamented with spines, ribs, or nodes.

Cephalopods. The squids and devilfish represent a class of mollusks that has been abundant and important in all the seas since early Paleozoic time. Unlike the sluggish snails and clams, they are active, alert, and aggressive. With their keen eyesight and strong powers of swimming, they alone of all invertebrates are able to compete actively with the vertebrate animals of the seas. The living **giant squid** is the largest invertebrate animal of all time.

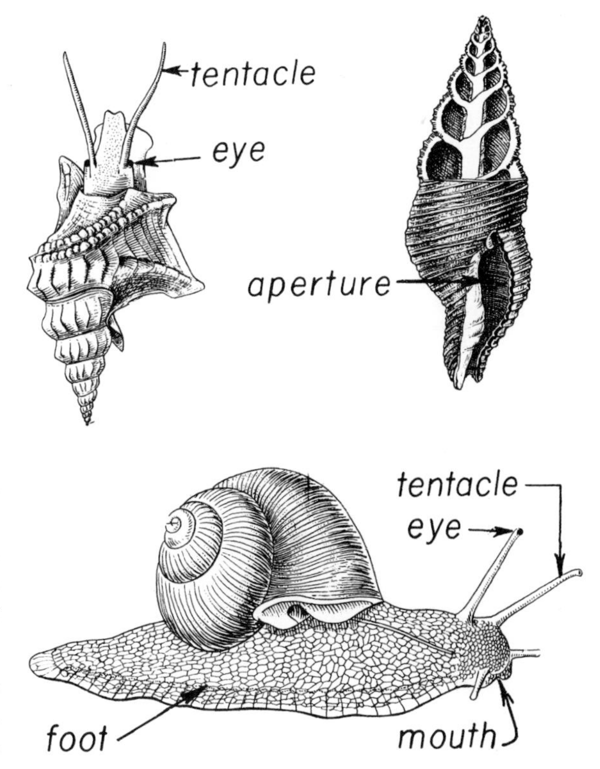

Figure 402. Gastropods. Upper right, empty shell with front side of spire cut away; upper left, another shell with the snail crawling upward on the page, the head, with eyes and tentacles, showing above the shell; below, a common land snail in crawling position with creeping "foot" extended and shell coiled over the back. (After Hatschek and Cori.)

The name cephalopod (Gr. *cephale*, head + *pous*, limb or foot) was suggested by the fact that all members of the class bear a circlet of fleshy limbs about the mouth, which is at the front of the head.

The squid and devilfish are shell-less, but the pearly nautilus (Fig. 403) bears an external chambered shell, as did a host of forms known only as fossils. Here, then, are living examples of the two great subclasses of cephalopods. The first is represented by the squids, whose only shell is vestigial and internal; the second by the nautilus with its external, chambered shell. Obviously the shelled cephalopods are of chief interest to the geologist, since they alone are ordinarily preserved as fossils.

The cephalopod shell has essentially the form of a slender cone, which may be straight or coiled

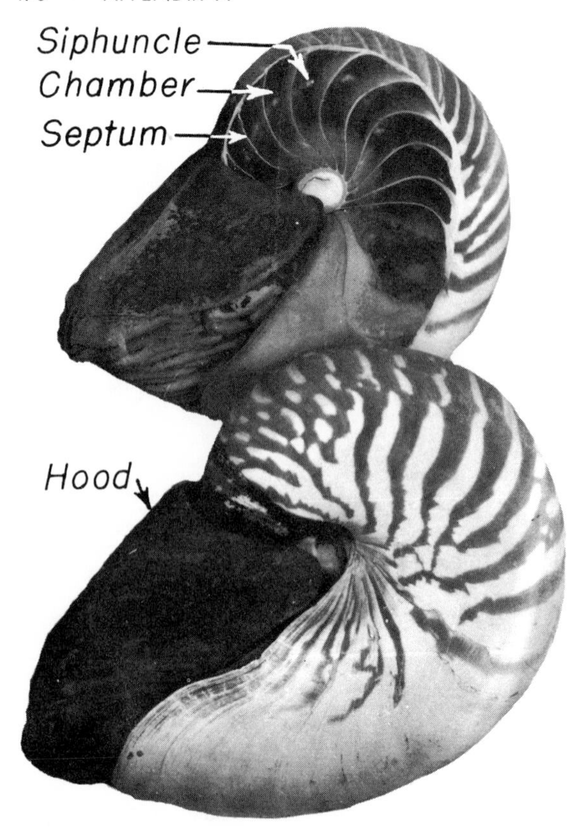

Figure 403. Cephalopods. The pearly nautilus in its shell. The lower shell is intact, but the upper one has the left side cut away to reveal the hollow chambers separated by curved septa and connected by the tubular siphuncle.

(Fig. 116, p. 151). If coiled, it is almost invariably in a flat spiral like a watch spring. The animal's body occupies only the larger end of the shell, the rest having been partitioned off into a series of chambers by transverse plates known as septa. In the living nautilus (and presumably in extinct types) the chambers are filled with gas and thus serve to buoy up the animal and its shell.

The chambers represent successive portions of the shell that were vacated as the growing body moved forward; and the partitions or **septa** are walls secreted against the bluntly rounded posterior end of the body to give it support after the animal has moved forward. These partitions are attached to the inner surface of the shell, and the line of junction is known as a **suture.** The form of the sutures and the course which they take in the shell are of great importance in the classification of the cephalopods. Since the septa are formed within the shell, the **suture is not visible externally, but in fossil forms where the chambers have been solidly filled with mineral matter and the outer shell then dissolved away, the sutures show clearly as sharp lines on the fossil** (Fig. 116). The animal retains connection with the abandoned chambers by a slender tube, the **siphuncle,** which runs back through all the septa. **Septa and a siphuncle are absolutely distinctive features of the cephalopod shell** and serve to distinguish it readily from that of the snail.

Nearly all the primitive cephalopods had straight shells, which, to an animal swimming backward, presented obvious disadvantages. Curved, loosely coiled, and tightly coiled shells were developed in that order, the forms with straight shells eventually became extinct. Besides being compact, the coiled shell brings the supporting gas chambers directly above the center of gravity, so that the animal can float at ease in the water.

Nautiloids. The shelled cephalopods are further divisible into two great subclasses. In the first the septa were simple, saucer-shaped plates secreted against the smoothly rounded posterior end of the animal's body. In these, of course, the sutures run directly around the shell as simple lines without marked flexures (Fig. 116), as in the nautilus (Fig. 403). This order has been named, accordingly, the **Nautiloidea.** The pearly nautilus is the only living representative.

Ammonites. The ammonites, cousins of the nautiloids, also bore chambered shells; but in these the septa were fluted or ruffled near their edges, and as a result the sutures from strongly crenate lines around the shell. In the earliest ammonites the fluting of the septa was very slight, and each suture showed only a few simple bends (Pl. 8, figs. 9, 12), but gradually the fluting became highly complex, and the suture lines accordingly assumed a complicated form (Pl. 14, fig. 11).

Belemnites. The belemnites (Fig. 271, p. 316) were squidlike cephalopods that lived only during the Mesozoic Era. They possessed a conical chambered shell like that of a primitive straight-shelled nautiloid, but it was internal, having been overgrown completely by flesh (Pl. 14, fig. 8, p. 315).

Squids are closely related to the belemnites, but

in the former the shell (also internal) is reduced to a mere vestige (the "pen").

Phylum Arthropoda

The insects represent a phylum of animals characterized by jointed walking legs, whence the name **Arthropoda** (Gr. *arthron,* joint). Other examples are the spiders, scorpions, lobsters, and crabs, and some important fossil groups such as the trilobites and eurypterids. All these have segmented bodies and jointed limbs. Their bodies are protected by a neatly fitting jointed armor made of chitin. In some, like the lobster and crab, this skeleton is strengthened by the addition of calcium carbonate. This is undoubtedly the largest and most diversified phylum in the animal kingdom.

Insecta. The insect possesses an elongate, bilaterally symmetrical body distinctly divided into head, thorax, and abdomen. The sharp constriction separating thorax and abdomen, as in the wasp, has suggested the group name (Lat. *insectus,* cut into). The abdomen is without limbs, but the thorax bears three pairs of walking legs and commonly two pairs (in one order, one pair) of wings. The head bears a pair of compound eyes and a pair of slender feelers or antennae. The mouth is provided with specialized biting or sucking devices. The physical senses are rather highly developed.

Insects are too easily destroyed to be commonly preserved as fossils, but locally they are found as far back as the late Paleozoic (Fig. 195, p. 236).

Crustacea. The lobster and crab represent another great class of the arthropods, but, unlike the insects, these, and nearly all their kin, live in the water and breathe by means of gills. The name **Crustacea** (Lat. *crusta,* crust) refers to their hard, crustlike armor, but it must be confessed that many examples of the class do not have a hard shell.

In most Crustacea each of the segments of both thorax and abdomen bears a pair of jointed appendages (in some forms, part or all of the abdominal segments lack appendages). Commonly those on the thorax are walking legs (as in the lobster), and those on the abdomen are for swimming, but in many of the primitive Crustacea all the limbs are flattened swimming paddles. The gills are generally plumose and are attached to the legs.

Chelicerata. Spiders and scorpions belong to a class of arthropods known as the Chelicerata. The head of a spider is fused to the thorax to form a cephalothorax, which is separated from the abdomen by a deep constriction and bears four pairs of walking legs. The abdomen is not segmented. The head bears several simple eyes but nothing like the compound eyes of the insect. Also it does not bear antennae. The ability to spin a web is a characteristic feature of the spider. Spiders, being soft-bodied, are rarely preserved as fossils, but specimens found in the Lower Devonian rocks of Scotland are among the most ancient records of land animals.

The **eurypterids** or "sea scorpions" (Figs. 134 and 135, p. 167 and 169) were a remarkable race of large aquatic chelicerates closely resembling the scorpions in bodily form. Indeed, they were probably the direct ancestors of the scorpions. The eurypterids were confined to the water, and chiefly marine waters, and their limbs were partially modified into swimming paddles. They were relatively large, the average length being several inches. One form, *Pterygotus,* from the Silurian rocks of New York State, had a length of about 9 feet and ranks as the largest arthropod of all time. The eurypterids are common and striking fossils in certain middle Paleozoic formations, but the race died out before the close of the Peleozoic era.

Trilobita. (Pronounced *trī' lo bī'ta*)), these animals formed a primitive but exceedingly important group of arthropods which is now extinct and is known only as fossils from the Paleozoic rocks. In these the body was depressed and distinctly divisible into head, thorax, and tail (Pl. 1, p. 117). Head and tail were each covered by an unsegmented shield, but the thorax was jointed. The entire body was longitudinally trilobed by reason of a pair of grooves that separated a rounded central axis from the lateral areas. **This trilobation is at once the most distinctive feature of the group** and the one which gave it the name **Trilobita.**

The trilobites usually possessed a pair of compound eyes and a pair of antennae or feelers. Each body segment bore a pair of legs, and these were essentially alike from head to tail. Each leg consisted of two branches, the lower one of which was

Figure 404. A typical reptile, the Florida alligator.

a jointed limb for crawling, while the upper and outer branch was a delicate, featherlike structure, commonly regarded as a gill.

Phylum Vertebrata

The most advanced of all animals are those possessing a vertebral column or backbone. So important is this phylum that it is often contrasted with all the other animals, which are known collectively as **invertebrates.** The vertebrates are characterized by the highly organized character of their nervous system, with the spinal cord running along the dorsal side of the body, and by many other important details, but **the possession of a backbone is the most obvious and distinctive character.** There are eight distinct classes, as follows: **fishes** (four classes), **amphibians, reptiles, birds,** and **mammals.**

Fishes. Fishes are **primitively aquatic, cold-blooded vertebrates that breathe by means of gills.** Most of them possess paired lateral fins as well as a tail fin.

This is an enormous and highly diversified group with a long geologic record and, although commonly treated as a single class, is now subdivided into four distinct classes. Many are scaled, but several of the extinct groups bore an armor of bony plates and some (for example, the catfish) are not protected by either scales or bone. The skeleton is made of bone in the majority of modern fishes, but in most of the early groups it consisted of cartilage, as in modern sharks and sturgeon.

It is important to distinguish between the fishes, which are primitively adapted to life in the water and breathe by means of gills, and, on the other hand, certain fishlike animals that have returned from the land to become secondarily adapted to the water. Among the latter are whales, porpoises, and seals, and certain extinct reptiles (ichthyosaurs, plesiosaurs, and mosasaurs). These secondarily aquatic animals breathe only by means of lungs and must come to the surface for air. They mimic fish but are not closely related to them.

Amphibia. The frogs and salamanders constitute a class of vertebrates that are only partially adapted to life on the land and have many features to remind us of a fishlike ancestry. Indeed, they are certainly the most primitive class of land vertebrates, and they clearly evolved from fishes. The salamander is a typical representative of the class (the frog being a modern and extremely specialized form). Because its members live partly in water and partly on land, the class has received the name Amphibia (Gr. *amphi,* on both sides + *bios,* life). **The metamorphosis from an aquatic youth (tadpole) to a terrestrial adult life distinguishes amphibians from all other land animals.**

Reptiles. The reptiles constitute a very large class of vertebrates and one that for long geologic ages completely dominated the Earth. The group includes the alligators (Fig. 404), crocodiles, lizards, turtles, and snakes, and the extinct dinosaurs and pterosaurs. The crocodile is a very typical reptile.

Reptiles are cold-blooded, egg-laying animals. In shape, many of them closely resemble an amphibian, but they all differ from the amphibians in the way the young develop. The reptile lays its eggs on the land, that is, out of the water. These are provided with stored-up food in the form of yolk, so that the young can develop fully enough to crawl about and care for themselves immediately upon hatching. In other words, the reptiles are completely adapted for terrestrial life.

Although united by such features as their cold blood, their egg-laying habit, and various details of skeletal structure, the many different stocks of reptiles specialized greatly; some returned secondarily to aquatic life, and one group, the extinct pterosaurs, developed wings.

Birds. The birds constitute a very well-defined class of vertebrates characterized by the presence of feathers and warm blood and by the egg-laying habit. In them the front limbs are specialized as wings. The birds diverged from one group of reptiles at about the same time the mammals were developing from another.

Mammals. The mammals are warm-blooded. They bring forth their young alive and nourish them with milk. All of them bear hair, though in some, as the whale and the elephant, the hair is almost lost through specialization. They constitute the dominant group of land animals of the Cenozoic and modern worlds, and some (seals, porpoises, and whales) have secondarily returned to the sea.

One small aberrant group, the monotremes, lays eggs. Two living genera are believed to represent an ancient, primitive stock of the mammals, but no paleontological record of this group is known.

The mammals did not appear on the Earth until Mesozoic time, and there is clear evidence that the ancestral types descended from one of the primitive groups of reptiles.

PLANTS

A SIMPLE CLASSIFICATION OF THE PLANT KINGDOM (AFTER BERRY, 1920)

Phylum **Thallophyta**—bacteria, fungi, seaweeds, etc.
Phylum **Bryophyta**—moss plants.
Phylum **Pteridophyta**—ferns.
Phylum **Arthrophyta**—scouring rushes, *calamites, sphenophylls.*
Phylum **Lepidophyta**—club mosses, "ground pine," *lepidodendrons, sigillarias.*
Phylum **Pteridospermophyta**—*seed ferns.*
Phylum **Cycadophyta**—cycads, *williamsoniellas, cycadeoids.*
Phylum **Coniferophyta** (gymnosperms)—*cordaites,* pines, sequoias, gingkos.
Phylum **Angiospermophyta**—flowering and fruiting plants, hardwood trees, etc.

Phylum Thallophyta

Plants of simple structure, such as bacteria, fungi, and seaweeds, are embraced for convenience, in a single phylum, the Thallophyta (Gr. *thallos,* young shoot + *phyton,* plant), so named because of their soft, nonwoody nature. The **bacteria** are single-celled, microscopic, and soft-tissued. Diatoms are aquatic plants, likewise single-celled and microscopic, which live in vast numbers near the surface of the seas and lakes and form one of the chief sources of food for all the marine animals. They secrete delicate siliceous shells which accumulate over large areas of the modern ocean floor as **diatom ooze.**

Plants probably evolved in the water and developed there for long ages before they could adjust themselves to the conditions upon the land. This is inferred, at least, from the fact that nearly all the thallophytes are still aquatic plants. Some of the seaweeds attain a length of 100 feet, but, regardless of size, these plants have no woody tissue and no circulatory system, for they lack the vascular tissue that serves to conduct the sap in higher plants and at the same time forms woody growth. It is for this reason that they can not successfully leave the water. All those forms that do live on land, such as fungi and lichens, are small, and grow only where there is considerable moisture. All the thallophytes have a simple system of reproduction by means of spores.

Most of the thallophytes are poorly adapted for preservation as fossils. A number of types of the algae, however, cause the precipitation of calcium carbonate, which settles over them to form a limy deposit. Figure 405 shows such a deposit (a "water biscuit") formed by a moldlike colony of microscopic blue-green algae that covered a pebble in a stream bed. The deposit has a finely laminated texture due to the addition of concentric films of the calcium carbonate. Similar limy deposits (Fig. 76, p. 101) occur in rocks of all ages as far back as the Cryptozoic Eon, and include the very earliest direct evidence of life on the Earth.

The calcareous algae play a very important role in the formation of modern "coral reefs," commonly depositing as much as 25 percent of the reef.

Phylum Bryophyta

This small phylum, including the mosses and liverworts, represents the simplest stage of adaptation to land life. Like the thallophytes, these

Figure 405. Calcareous algae. A "water biscuit" from the bed of Little Conestoga Creek, near Philadelphia, Pennsylvania. Left, external view of the colony; right, a median section showing the concentric laminae of algal deposit about an angular pebble. Slightly less than natural size. (*Yale Peabody Museum.*)

plants lack vascular tissue, hence remain very small and thrive only in moist places. Almost nothing is known of them as fossils.

Phylum Pteridophyta

The great tribe of the ferns constitutes the phylum Pteridophyta (Gr. *pteris,* fern). They are the simplest of plants to be well adapted to land life. They have well-developed vascular tissue and are differentiated into roots, stem, and leaves. Whereas many of the ferns are small and herbaceous, the tree ferns of the tropics have woody trunks and commonly reach a height of 20 to 50 feet, bearing a crown of large fronds. Ferns are distinguished above all else by the fact that **they reproduce by means of spores borne on the under sides of the leaves or on slightly modified leaves,** never in cones.

Ferns are among the oldest fossil land plants known, being recorded first in the Lower Devonian rocks. They have been a prolific tribe in all subsequent ages.

Phylum Arthrophyta

The scouring rushes and their kind constitute a well-defined tribe characterized by regularly jointed stems, whence the name (Gr. *arthron,* joint). The existing horsetail or scouring rush (*Equisetum*) grows abundantly in moist places in many parts of the country. In all the arthrophytes the stem has only a thin cylinder of woody tissue around a large center of pith. Reproduction is by means of spores which are borne in **strobili** (cones) at the tops of the stems.

Modern arthrophytes are mostly small, and the race is decadent, having passed its climax in the late Paleozoic, when giant scouring rushes (calamites) grew to the height of trees and had stems as much as 12 inches in diameter (Figs. 192 and 193, pp. 233, 234).

Phylum Lepidophyta

The **scale trees** or lepidophytes (Gr. *lepis,* scale) constitute another well-defined tribe of plants that occupy a humble place in the modern world but were very important in the Paleozoic forests (Figs. 192 and 193, pp. 233, 234). The ground pines or club mosses are modern examples. Like the arthrophytes, these plants bear spores in strobili at or near the tips of the stems.

Many of the Paleozoic species attained the size of forest trees. In these the leaves, when shed, left prominent scars regularly spaced over the bark of the trunk and limbs (Fig. 194, p. 235). The name lepidophyte refers to these characteristic markings.

Phylum Pteridospermophyta

The oldest and most primitive seed-bearing plants were fernlike in everything but their fruit, whence the name (Gr. *pteris*, fern + *sperma*, seed). They are commonly known as **seed ferns.**

The distinction between the spore-bearing and seed-bearing plants is comparable to that between the egg-laying and the viviparous animal, both in its nature and in its significance. The egg is a simple cell, deposited to hatch into an embryo that must look out for itself at a very immature stage of of its development; the spore, likewise, is a single cell cast free to generate and grow as best it can. On the other hand, the viviparous animal retains the egg in the mother's body until it has developed into an embryo of considerable complexity before birth liberates it to shift for itself. Similarly, the seed is an embryo plant formed after the fertilization of the ovum, which is retained and nourished by the mother plant until considerable size has been attained and food is stored up to give the new plant a good start in life. The development of seed is a very considerable specialization. That it was an obvious advantage is suggested by the dominance of seed-bearing plants on the modern lands.

The seed ferns were common from the late Devonian to the end of the Paleozoic, when they died out, probably having given rise meanwhile to other phyla of seed-bearing plants.

Phylum Cycadophyta

The living sago palms or cycads represent an extensive tribe, mostly extinct, which has particular interest as the probable connecting link between

Figure 406. Stems, foliage, and flowers of the cycadeoid, *Williamsonia*. Lower Jurassic of Mexico. Natural size. (*G. R. Wieland.*)

the seed ferns and all higher plants, especially the true flowering plants (angiosperms). It is a great phylum, divisible into two well-marked orders, the one, **Cycadeoidea,** entirely extinct, and the other, **Cycadales,** represented by the modern cycads. The cycads (Fig. 243, p. 286) possess short trunks and large pinnate leaves, and bear seeds in loose cones. The trunk is heavily armored with persistent leaf bases.

The cycadeoids (of Late Paleozoic [?] and Mesozoic age) bore conspicuous flowers. These plants were of two chief types, one stocky, like the modern cycads, and the other slender and branching. The branched cycadeoids are of the greater interest from the evolutionary point of view. They possessed rather slender stems bearing flowers at forks (Fig. 406). It is believed that these plants developed from seed ferns and on the one hand evolved into the thick-bodied cycadeoids and on the other were at least closely allied to the early angiosperms. This group of cycadophytes is abundantly represented in the Triassic and Jurassic and probably was present in the late Paleozoic.

Phylum Coniferophyta

The conifers constitute another great tribe of rather primitive seed plants characterized by the development of cones and, generally, by evergreen foliage. The leaves are as a rule needlelike or straplike and have parallel veins. There are several orders. The pines are typical.

The oldest group of conifers is the **cordaites,** which were common in the forests from Devonian to Permian time. Unlike the later conifers, they had large straplike leaves, and their seeds were loosely arranged in racemes instead of cones.

Other groups, including the pines, araucarians, and gingkos, are known throughout the Mesozoic and later periods.

Phylum Angiospermophyta

The most advanced of all plants are the hardwood trees and the true flowering plants, included in the phylum Angiospermophyta, of which at least 125,000 kinds have been described. They are all, of course, seed-bearing, but show a great advance over the other seed-bearing phyla in that their seeds are protected in a closed capsule or ovary. For this reason they are known as angiosperms (covered seed) in contradistinction to the gymnosperms (naked seed), which include the seed ferns, conifers, and cycads.

The angiosperms are commonly characterized as **the flowering plants,** but this is hardly justified, since even the conifers and cycadophytes have flowers of a sort, and many of the latter had large and complicated flowers probably rivaling in size and brilliance the best of the angiosperms.

The angiosperms are first certainly identified in the Lower Cretaceous rocks, where the characteristic netveined leaves of deciduous trees make their appearance.

Author Index

Subject Index†

*Asterisks refer to illustrations.

†Includes names and ideas that appear in the text, but not formation names shown on the correlation charts or biologic names in the legends of the plates of invertebrate fossils.